BAREFOOT BOOKS

The barefoot child symbolises the human being whose natural integrity and capacity for action are unimpaired. In this spirit, Barefoot Books publishes new and traditional myths, legends and fairy tales whose themes demonstrate the pitfalls and dangers that surround our passage through life; the qualities that are needed to face and overcome these dangers; and the equal importance of action and reflection in doing so. Our intention is to present stories from a wide range of cultures in such a way as to delight and inspire readers of all ages while honouring the tradition from which the story has been inherited.

Barefoot Books Ltd
PO Box 95 Kingswood Bristol BS15 5BH

English consultant: Susan Adler

Illustration design by Marcello Garofolo

Graphic design: Design/Section
Illustration reproduction by Radstock Reproductions
Midsomer Norton, Bath
Printed and bound in Belgium by
Proost International Book Production

This book has been printed on 100% acid-free paper
First published in Great Britain in 1994 by
Barefoot Books Ltd

ISBN 1 898000 16 6

Little Buddha

The Story of Prince Siddhartha

by

Giovanni Mastrangelo

Barefoot Books
Bath

༄། ཨོཾ་ག་ཏེ་ག་ཏེ་པཱ་ར་ག་ཏེ་པཱ་ར་སཾ་ག་ཏེ་བོ་དྷི་སྭཱ་ཧཱ།

The story of Prince Siddhartha begins with a strange dream, the kind that comes along every so often and isn't like dreaming at all. This rare dream came to a queen in the city of Kapilavastu, in India, many many years ago – two thousand five hundred, to be exact. It appeared in the form of a big white elephant. The

elephant went right into the lofty rooms of the palace of Suddhodhana, who was king of the Sakyas. Then – slowly, solemnly, gently – it entered the queen's chamber as she slept.

The next morning, light bursts in through the carved windows of the king's palace and brightens even the saddest corners of the kingdom. Queen Maya is happier than usual. Just look at her. She is still a girl and has eyes like black pearls. Her dark skin is softer than moss, and her hands move among the coloured silks of her clothes like fawns in a wood.

Here comes the king. Suddhodhana is a large, impressive man with a fat moustache and a thick beard.

The queen hugs him, full of excitement, and tells him at once about her dream, still clear and true and alive in her. She tells him all in one breath about the elephant who slowly entered the room without making a sound and, looking into her eyes, gently brushed its trunk along her side.

Maya remembers a game she played with the elephant, like a whirling dance. She tells the king about the joy that has stayed with her even after she has woken up, even now that the light has already spread across the world, drawing a veil over everyone's dreams.

'This dream,' says Suddhodhana, with the confidence of someone accustomed to being king, 'is as clear as a message. The gods are granting us an heir, a great prince who will reign over the land, a wise man, a son at last.' And believe me, the king was telling the truth, because all good men in those days knew how to interpret signs and omens. They read dreams the same way we now read newspapers and they listened carefully to the magic thoughts that visit all of us from time to time.

Have you ever wondered what India is like? Imagine green valleys and enormous trees laden with red and purple flowers, and the scent of spices wafting through the villages, the shrill music of the snake-charmers. Ancient rivers rush through mysterious jungles. Imagine all those different colours and smells!

The Indian countryside opens up in front of you, full of marvels and mysteries. Look at the palace of a mighty Maharajah – an Indian prince – and at the jungle that shakes as a herd of wild elephants pounds through it. A tiger slinks silently away, its prey between its jaws.

And now imagine a grove of enchanted trees close to a gurgling stream. You are in the Lumbini wood, and Queen Maya has just arrived.

Nine months have already passed since her prophetic dream, and Maya is on a journey with her devoted hand-maidens. She has stopped at Lumbini just to rest a little.

In those days, when a baby was about to come into the world, its mother would leave her husband for a while and move back into her parents' house. Instead of hospitals they had grandmothers and housekeepers and doting aunts and handmaidens who knew how to make a house fit to welcome a baby.

And yet Prince Siddhartha did not come into the world in his grandparents' palace, but quite unexpectedly in the charming little wood at Lumbini!

Maya steps down from her carriage, then heads into the forest, struggling slightly because of her large belly. Only the cries of tropical birds and the velvet sounds of the

Indian forest can be heard. The light bounces off the moist leaves, shimmering in the half light of the dense vegetation.

A tall tree slowly bends a branch over her head as if to bow, and Maya grows calm, feeling all the living things of the earth protecting her – even the trees. She raises her arms to the sky, singing softly, and gently takes hold of a friendly branch.

The baby is born right here in the heart of the woods,

while his mother sings a lullaby, cradled by the trees and the wind. The first cry of that great son mingles with her quiet song.

I should tell you now that Siddhartha wasn't a baby like any other. In that ancient language his name meant 'he who brings good'.

As soon as he was born, as the handmaidens were washing him with care, he suddenly stood up and started to walk – seven pretty steps – under the gaze of his mother. She smiled with surprise. At every step a lotus flower bloomed in his footprint.

He stood still and, looking at his mother with watchful eyes, called these words out loud and clear:

'I have been born to reach Enlightenment
And free all creatures from pain.
This is my last rebirth.'

Now, let me ask you something: do you understand what he really meant?

As the days pass, excitement grows in the air at Kapilavastu. Everyone wants to see this baby prince who already walks and talks like a wise man.

'It's a miracle, it's a miracle!' the people cry.

All sorts of men and women pour into the Court from town and countryside: the great and the small, the proud and the humble, nobles and peasants, even thieves and holy men, and of course the high priests of India, the Brahmans.

In the throne room, crammed with people, Suddhodhana holds the newborn Siddhartha in his arms. Queen Maya stands at his side.

In the midst of this gathering, an old man dressed in rags, with long white hair, suddenly appears. He is Asita, a hermit, a great soothsayer, a holy man, a man of wisdom, who lives in silence in a lonely mountain cave.

As a sign of respect, King Suddhodhana holds out the child to him. At a single glance the old saint sees signs – invisible to anyone else – that predict the child's future. He sees the mark of a wheel on the soles of the little feet and the blond tuft of hair between his dark eyebrows. He sees the child's hands webbed like the foot of a heron that can fly above the world, and the crown coming out of the top of his head. And those long soft ears of his.

What a strange baby. He looks like an alien, and yet he's so beautiful. To Asita he shines like the sun.

Suddenly two tears stream down the wise man's face.

'What do you see, Asita?' Maya asks, alarmed. 'Why are you weeping?'

'I weep for my old age, my queen,' says the old man, holding little Siddhartha in his arms. 'When your son is a man, I shall no longer be alive to hear his words, which will be those of a great teacher of wisdom. I weep for myself and my old age.'

'Won't my son be a great king for his people?' asks the king, worried. 'Won't he sit upon the throne of his ancestors before becoming a teacher of wisdom?'

'Your son will be the true master of himself and will show the world the way to escape from Pain and Death!' replies Asita.

'First of all, he must become the pride of his father and the king of his land,' proclaims Suddhodhana, 'ruling his kingdom with justice. Later, when he is nearing old age, he can teach wisdom to others if he wishes, and retire to an existence of solitude and prayer. Like you, Asita, who are holy and pure and full of the wisdom which only comes late in life.'

'Be that as it may, Suddhodhana,' says the holy man, 'but remember: people's desires do not always match with the perfect timetable of Destiny.' And with that, Asita caresses the child and leaves for the mountains, to live in silence among the clouds and the snow, which in the Himalayas is so much whiter and deeper than anywhere else.

Maya listened carefully to Asita's words and her eyes grew sad as he left the throne room.

'But why is the queen sad all of a sudden?' you will ask.

I don't know quite how to answer that question, but I do know that the very next day Maya fell seriously ill – a strange illness that the Court doctors could not cure, and shortly afterwards the young queen died in her bed.

Sooner or later everyone dies, but all the fine things you have done in your life stay on for ever. Thoughts stay alive too, shining and spinning around with the stars and the planets.

Everyone's life comes back again and again, travelling inside the air and through time into people's dreams and memories.

Siddhartha was only a few weeks old when Prajapati, Queen Maya's sister, took the place of his real mother, loving him as tenderly as if he were her own son.

What a grand life he led, this young prince! A life of pomp and splendour, and lights and games in the palace. And not just one palace either. The king built *three* magnificent palaces for him.

One palace was for the springtime, when everything is born and comes to life. Another was for the summer, which is hot and scented like fruit trees. And the third palace was for the rainy season. In these three palaces, Siddhartha grew up and prepared to become a man and a great king.

In the palace of the rainy seasons the best teachers educated him. In the spring palace there were hundreds of horses and many athletes to show him how to harden his body. And in the summer palace – the most splendid of all three – the young prince spent his days listening to music

and poems, and playing games with his friends in the laughing gardens.

Even when he was little, Siddhartha showed unusual qualities for a prince. Although he lived in luxury, he would often put aside his toys to sit quietly and watch the thoughts passing through his head.

'And how could he see the thoughts inside his own head?' you will ask.

Well, I'll tell you. He *meditated*.

Every day he used to sit cross-legged in meditation with his eyes closed, following the coloured drawings that sparkled, like fireworks, in his head. He would sit still and quiet, watching dreams of adventure unfold in front of him as if they were stories told by a silent voice. This same voice is hidden deep inside each one of us.

That's how meditation starts. If you try, right now, to close your eyes and look inside yourself, you'll begin to

see the mysterious and enticing world that Siddhartha was exploring.

Prince Siddhartha's days at Court passed quickly. He spent hours riding his magnificent stallion, Kanthaka the king of all horses, in the woods of the spring palace grounds with his bow over his shoulder, racing after leaping deer. Not once did a single arrow of Siddhartha's strike a deer or a fox or a bird, since the prince loved animals and preferred to be their friend rather than wound them or kill them.

Now, the young prince had a cousin called Devadatta who didn't feel at all the same way about hunting. And not only hunting!

Siddhartha and Devadatta were the same age. But, whereas Siddhartha stopped to think before every action and carefully followed what his heart told him, his cousin

was a bully who acted on impulse, and never thought for a single moment about the well-being of the creatures around him.

One spring day, while Siddhartha was playing in the palace gardens, a wounded swan fell to the ground. Siddhartha pulled out the arrow that had pierced its wing, then carefully cleaned the wound.

'Give me that swan!' His cousin Devadatta shouted at

him as he ran up, still holding his bow. 'I saw it first and I hit it. It's mine! Give it back to me!'

Siddhartha protected the swan from his cousin's fury as it shrank, frightened, into his arms.

An argument broke out between the two cousins: It belongs to me! No it's mine! I'm the one who hit it! And so on and so on until they decided to ask the king who should keep the bird.

'I saw the swan fly out of a bush in the hunting reserve,' Devadatta repeated before the king and the Court judges, 'so I fired off my arrow and hit it. The bird flew for a little longer, then fell behind the trees. A few moments later, when I got off my horse to fetch it, I found Siddhartha holding it. I am the hunter, not him, and that swan is mine.'

'So it was Devadatta who saw the swan first!' exclaimed the chief judge. 'And you, Siddhartha,' he added, 'what do you have to say?'

Then Siddhartha stood up and said: 'Tell me, wise judges of the king, to whom does the life of a living creature belong? To the one who has taken it, as Devadatta tried to do with the life of the swan? Or to the one who gave it back as I did?'

On hearing him, the judges no longer had any doubt.

They proclaimed that the swan belonged to Siddhartha and entrusted it to him so he could take care of it. When the swan's wound healed, the prince took it back to the

gardens, set it free, and watched it fly slowly away, through the trees and into the sky.

In the years that followed, Suddhodhana's kingdom prospered. His people lived in peace and the land was generous. The harvest grew richer every season and the markets of the city glittered with rare and precious goods.

The king was kind and just, and everyone loved him as a father. Only one thing troubled his heart: Asita's prophecy. Suddhodhana feared that as soon as his son grew up, he would leave the palace to go and live in the forest. For even today the Indian forests shelter men, and holy men like Asita, who want to seek Enlightenment. They look for happiness in meditation and solitude rather than in the pleasures of daily life. They leave their jobs and families to go and live in the forest. Some of them stay there for ever, sitting in meditation under enormous trees. They gaze at visions of immense and silent skies, of immaculate mountain peaks, of tranquil and scented seas. Ordinary people call them 'ascetics'.

'And how did these ascetics get food and drink and defend themselves from wild animals?' I can hear you ask. Be patient, for in this story we'll have plenty of time to talk about these men and their adventures.

For the moment, let's go back to the spring palace grounds in Kapilavastu.

Siddhartha is now a young man and excels at everything he does. He has become a great athlete, a first-rate horseman and wrestler. He is better than anyone else at archery and can run faster than a torpedo. Everyone, men and women, see him as a champion, a magnificent prince who one day will reign over the kingdom with courage and honesty.

For Suddhodhana's subjects, the name of Siddhartha is as sweet as honey.

His rival, Devadatta, tries on every occasion to outdo his cousin, but in every contest of skill, and at schoolwork and in every other way, Siddhartha proves to be the winner.

༄། ཨོཾ་ག་ཏེ་ག་ཏེ་པཱ་ར་ག་ཏེ་པཱ་ར་སཾ་ག་ཏེ་བོ་དྷི་སྭཱ་ཧཱ།

Do you wonder why everything young Siddhartha does turns out so well?

I think meditation teaches him how to concentrate on the right thoughts. When he shoots an arrow or when he studies or even when he is simply strolling in the garden, he never lets himself be tricked by those whims or fears that come creeping into our minds from time to time.

It's the same for every boy and girl.

Playing football, for instance, or at school, or when it's time to say good night and go to bed, we let a thousand ideas and a thousand voices pop up like a mushroom in our heads. 'Is this right? Is this wrong?' some voices ask. 'And what will the other children think about me?' other voices whisper. 'Now I'll show him!' Or: 'I'm not at all sleepy, I don't want to go to bed yet . . .' So many different feelings take hold of our minds that we often get distracted and sometimes we get ourselves into deep trouble.

Siddhartha's secret was that he never listened to his whims and fears. By meditating, he learned to ignore these sneaking thoughts the moment they appeared; he stayed calm and alert at all times and every single thing he did turned out just right.

His father, the king, was very pleased with him, but in his heart he feared that Siddhartha wanted to follow

Asita's example, for the hermit's words still troubled him: '. . . He shall be the true master of himself and will show the world the way to escape from Pain and Death!'

The more the king thought about the hermit's prophecy, the less he wanted Siddhartha, as he grew, to be aware of the inevitable sadness of life, or of death which comes to us all, humans and animals alike.

Driven by this secret worry, the king ordered his

guards not to let the prince out of the palace. He wanted to be sure that everywhere Siddhartha looked, he saw only joy, youth and beauty.

Old people were banned from the Court, and so were the sick or the sad. Only the prettiest girls and the most handsome athletes filled the prince's days, and every evening the palace rooms were lit up with laughter, parties and songs.

The king even ordered that all the flowers in the gardens were to be cut before they withered and immediately replaced with new ones, so that Siddhartha's thoughts could not dwell for an instant on things which are born to grow old and inevitably die.

So it was that Siddhartha grew up as a prisoner in paradise, until one day Suddhodhana decided the moment had come for his son to marry.

The king threw an enormous party in the summer palace. It lasted for a whole week: there were banquets, music, dancing girls covered in jewels, dazzling lights, poets and minstrels, acrobats and snake-charmers. A procession of young princesses came to Kapilavastu from all over India, and even as far away as Tibet, to be chosen as the bride of the legendary young prince.

Siddhartha saw them one by one and, as was the custom, he gave each a princely gift.

Last of all, Yashodara came forward.

She was indeed a beautiful girl, with delicate cheeks and an Indian angel's black hair and wide, wide, wonderful eyes. Siddhartha fell in love with her at first sight, enchanted by those great calm eyes.

He did not give her precious stones, or silks or glittering golden jewels. For Yashodara alone, he took a garland of fragrant flowers from around his neck and, offering it to her, chose her as his bride.

Shortly afterwards, Suddhodhana himself married the young couple, as is the tradition in India.

The king was very happy with this marriage because

he was sure that soon Yashodara would have a child and that Siddhartha's attachment and love for his new family would prevent Asita's prophecy from ever coming true.

And for a while it seemed that the king was right.

From the first day of their marriage, the newly-weds were so happy that the idea of leaving the palace to see the world outside the walls didn't even cross their minds. They spent their days amid hanging gardens and fountains without noticing time slipping by and flying away. The months passed with horseback riding in the palace grounds, enormous fun at Court games and amusements, swimming in the summer palace's marble pools, spending whole nights talking about the stars and the moon, which in India lights up the forests, full of rustling sounds.

Siddhartha lived in the most complete happiness, and the following spring, Yashodara gave birth to a son.

Siddhartha named him Rahula, and his happiness became even greater.

Everyone in Kapilavastu was happy for the birth of another heir to the throne of the Sakyas and Suddhodhana was no longer worried about Asita's prophecy. Life at Court unfolded in happy hours for everyone.

One summer's evening, Siddhartha is lying on the cushions and silk rugs spread out on the highest terrace of the whole palace, the one that looks out on the cool wind and on the evening star.

Yashodara is at his side with her arms around him,

and they gaze out together at the falling night. A young handmaiden plays the lute in the moonlight, and sings a song that comes from somewhere else.

'Nothing is better, nothing is best;
Take heed of this and you'll get the rest.
Who is longing for damask and wisdom,
Words, horses and beauty?
Who wants to see Kapilavastu tonight?
Where the girls give amber for love
And the swan croons to the moon.
Nothing is better, nothing is best;
Take heed of this and you'll get the rest.'

Siddhartha is enchanted by the beauty of the melody, and for the first time the prince wonders about life in Kapilavastu. He doesn't even know what it is like! He has never seen anything of what lies outside the palace's golden walls.

'Do beauty and happiness really exist outside the palace?' Siddhartha asks the singer. 'And tell me, you who sing about gardens far from my eyes, what is life like in these places?'

And with her songs she showed him houses and streets, parks, people and things.

The very next day Siddhartha asked his father to let him visit the city.

'Why this sudden curiosity?' asked the king, sternly. 'Don't you already have everything you need to be happy here in the palace?'

Then Siddhartha, with the calm of someone who knows his request is reasonable, said these words to his father: 'How can I reign one day in your place if I've never seen the city where my people live? And how will my people be able to love me if they've never seen my face?'

This was enough to convince his father, who was a good king and couldn't say no to a just request.

In a few days Suddhodhana had organised everything, giving orders left and right. The streets of Kapilavastu were to be splendid, with showers of petals raining down from the windows. He wanted music and young people and excited children everywhere. But above all, the king ordered that old people were to be kept away from the streets and the squares, and with them the poor and all the beggars of the city. The sick were to stay hidden in their houses and no sad faces were to appear on the balconies to celebrate Siddhartha's visit, so that the prince

would not have so much as a glimpse of the suffering and sadness of life.

On the morning set for his visit, Siddhartha, dressed in gold and silk, comes out in his chariot on to the streets of Kapilavastu.

'Siddhartha is like the sun!' whisper the women as he goes by.

'What wise eyes our future king has,' say the men enthusiastically.

'He glitters! He glitters! Siddhartha glitters like gold!' exclaim the little children, clapping their hands in delight.

'And look at Kanthaka, the champion, who draws the golden chariot with his head held haughty and high. What a splendid horse! What a grand prince!' shout the bigger boys, who know his fame as an athlete and dream of becoming like him.

Siddhartha, smiling down from his chariot at that colourful and noisy young crowd, looks in wonder at shops, houses and trees. Wherever he turns his eye, he sees wealth, gaiety and joy.

'It's like the song I heard the other night!' says Siddhartha happily to Channa, his faithful charioteer.'The outside world is even more exciting than my palaces!'

But all of a sudden, a man appears at a street corner, bent over a stick, shuffling his feet. He looks up at the royal chariot and his watery eyes meet the bright gaze of the prince. Then he disappears into a doorway.

'Channa, who is that man with white hair and wrinkles on his face?' asks Siddhartha, with the astonishment of someone who has never seen an old person before.

I'm sure you're wondering how an old man managed

to walk undisturbed among the festive crowd that morning, after the king had ordered that old people were to be kept off the streets.

It's hard to say. Either the old man was running late and by mistake found himself in the street at the wrong time, or he appeared to Siddhartha by a powerful spell, as if Destiny hadn't at all forgotten about Asita's prophecy.

'The man you just saw, my prince, is just an old man,' replied Channa.

'An old man . . . ? He must belong to a race I've never heard of.'

'It is not a particular race, my prince. All men and women become like that. We are all growing a little older all the time.'

'Will this misfortune come to me too?' asked Siddhartha, frightened.

'To you and to Princess Yashodara, to your father, to Rahula, to the birds, to the trees and even to Kanthaka the king of all horses. Everything under the sun is growing old as we speak.'

The smiling faces moved like a rippling river in the street, and the cries of the people covered Siddhartha's words as he spoke: 'How can these men and women, and the children too, be completely happy knowing that they must grow old and that sooner or later they will be tired and slow, with weak and pale eyes, like that old man I just saw. Why? Channa? Why do we have to grow old?'

But not a single word came out of the charioteer's mouth in reply.

Why do we grow old? Can you answer that?

Siddhartha, shaken by what he had just seen, decided to cut short his visit to the city and told Channa to turn the chariot around and head back to the palace, where he went to sit on the Terrace of the Wind to meditate.

There he is, watching the thoughts that pass through his head. The watery eyes of the old man appear again and again in his mind. And a voice repeats again and again: Old Age . . . Old Age . . .

A few days later, Siddhartha asked to go back to the streets of Kapilavastu. Suddhodhana consented, hoping that a new visit to the city would distract his son from his sad thoughts.

Once more, the king had the streets of the city prepared. He ordered the soldiers to follow his instructions very carefully this time; the prince was not to be troubled again.

Imagine once again the gold and silks, the showers of petals that colour the streets, the people packed along the

roadsides acclaiming their prince, the women smiling from the balconies, the cries, the festive sounds, the scent of flowers.

Here comes the golden chariot again, pulled by Kanthaka, with Channa escorting the prince.

'Nothing is better, nothing is best;
Take heed of this and you'll get the rest . . .'

The words of the song echo in Siddhartha's ears when, all of a sudden, the prince sees a woman trembling with fever mingled in among the happy crowd. She coughs, leaning on a tall youth who helps her stay on her feet.

'What's wrong with that woman?' asks Siddhartha, astonished.

How on earth did a sick woman manage to get by the

king's guards unseen? How is it that no one noticed her, in spite of the king's strict orders?

No, my friends, it could not be another blunder or a slip-up. The real cause for the sick woman's appearance is Destiny.

Destiny controls everything that happens in the world, mysteriously guiding our lives. It is an invisible power that takes us by the hand, sending us signs and omens, showing us visions, thoughts and shining ideas that sometimes take on the shape of people, plants and animals.

'Why does that women have yellow, sweaty skin?' asks Siddhartha again.

'She has been struck by an illness.'

'Illness? You mean to say that she was struck by an arrow by accident? Or that she fell from her horse jumping a hedge?'

'Illness, my prince, does not come about by accident but grows inside us, making our throat swell, or our temperature rise, or our skin get blotchy. All men, women and animals, fall ill at least once in their lives.'

'Tell me, Channa, do kings fall ill too?'

'Kings and beggars, thieves and soldiers, priests and merchants, horses, athletes, children . . .'

The smiling faces moved like a rippling river in the

street, and the cries of the people covered Siddhartha's words as he spoke: 'And how can these men and women, and the children too, be completely happy knowing that suffering lies in wait for them and that illness can burst out suddenly, making their lives miserable and sad, like that woman who can't stop coughing?'

Siddhartha, having discovered the existence of illness, asked Channa to turn the chariot around and go straight back to the palace.

'Old Age and Illness,' the voices of his thoughts repeat as he sits in meditation on the Terrace of the Wind. 'Is this the fate of every living creature?'

Once again King Suddhodhana was very concerned about his son. He didn't know what to do to tear Siddhartha away from the sad thoughts that had taken hold of him since his visits to the city. He tried parties and banquets, races, dancers, poets, archery tournaments, entertainment of every kind. Now, you tell me, what else could he have done?

A few days later, Siddhartha told him he wanted to go back to the city again.

This time Suddhodhana personally inspected the streets of Kapilavastu, making sure they were splendid and perfect. But this time, too, something went wrong with his plans.

Siddhartha spotted a strange procession hurrying across a square as he passed in his chariot.

'What are those people doing, Channa?' Do you see them over there all in a row, crying, behind that man

sleeping on a wooden litter? 'Who are they? Where are they going?'

You've probably already realised that the prince had come across a funeral. The man he thought was sleeping, followed by weeping people, was in fact dead.

Siddhartha didn't know that Death existed. But who of us, in the end, really knows Death? They've only told us that it will happen one day, and that every human being, sooner or later, must die. That's all we know.

Siddhartha, who at the palace had never heard anyone say a single word about Death, suddenly discovered its existence and learned that in India the people's corpses had to be burned. This new knowledge upset him even more than when he learned about old age and illness.

'Turn the chariot around, Channa.' Siddhartha's voice trembled with fright.

Now he is quite certain that his greatest enemy is Death, which is there for everyone, with no exceptions. Women and children, horses, trees, fish in the sea, insects and snakes; poor people, rich people, fat, happy, good or bad. There is no difference. We all have to die.

'First of all, what is Death?' wondered Siddhartha, 'How and where can I meet Death so as to defeat it while I am still young, before it decides to come and get me?'

Now, you should know that when a young hero finally discovers who he must fight, his next step is to meet the Enemy face to face. For Siddhartha this wasn't an easy problem to solve. You can't find Death the same way you find a fire-breathing dragon or a cruel pirate or an emperor who sows terror throughout the galaxy!

But then you should also know that when a young hero has decided to fight his battle, Destiny takes him on its back and helps him to find the right Path to follow. A true hero – always remember this – is never alone.

Returning to the palace, the golden chariot passed by a dense forest. On the side of the road, Siddhartha saw a beggar, sitting in tranquil meditation under a tree dotted with yellow flowers.

'Stop the chariot, Channa,' said the prince, and he approached the beggar to ask him who he was, and why he was wearing rags, and why he wasn't with everybody else in the streets of Kapilavastu.

'I am an ascetic and I live at the edge of the forest. I am not concerned with what happens in the city,' replied the man with a voice that seemed to come from far away. 'Now tell me, young prince, how can I celebrate together with the others, indulging in life's pleasures, if I know for sure that I too must grow old, and then, like the rest of mankind, die? It is not pleasure I seek, or wealth, or fame. I seek Enlightenment.'

'Enlightenment . . . ?' Siddhartha looked at him in surprise.

'This,' continued the ascetic, pointing his finger to the middle of his glowing forehead, 'this is my battlefield.'

'It is as clear as the sun: illness, old age and death are born inside every person! And it is inside myself,' exclaimed Siddhartha, touching his forehead like the ascetic, 'that I shall go and look for Death to challenge it and defeat it for once and for all.'

The very next day, Siddhartha went to his father and

told him that he wanted to go into the forest to live among the ascetics, until he met Death and fought it.

Suddhodhana wouldn't hear of it.

'What do you care about Death . . . ?' he said. 'You're still too young . . . Don't you think about your son, Rahula . . . ? The kingdom needs you . . . And what about Yashodara . . . ? And I who raised you . . . ? Why do you want to abandon a happy life for an uncertain future?'

And in the days that followed he doubled the parties, the Court games, the presents. He ordered the guards not to let his son out of the palace walls again.

But, once more, Siddhartha was helped by events that were only apparently mysterious.

Night has fallen and music rings out in the palace, while dancers entertain the many guests. The shimmering light of a thousand candles is reflected on the mirrors and on the tinkling earrings of the girls.

Siddhartha wanders restlessly through the rooms of the party and sees only smiles and delights, when suddenly, a small cloud glides down from the Terrace of the Wind and enters the palace, like a sleep-inducing gas or mysterious magic. The prince is amazed to see that when people are grazed by this blue mist, they suddenly slump to the floor.

One after another, all the guests fall asleep, in the strangest poses. A man yawns like a lion, dribbling his wine, then blissfully closes his eyes. A large red patch spreads on his white shirt. Dancers freeze half way through a pirouette or a graceful leap, falling back on to the embroidered cushions in the funniest positions. One of them falls asleep on the spot, hugging a drum, another lies with her mouth open, snoring like a caterpillar, while another is sprawled, dreaming, on the rug, her earrings twisted up under her nose like a golden moustache.

Siddhartha, who has not been touched by the magic cloud, observes the sleeping men and women all over the floor, pondering how little difference there is between a

dead person and someone who has suddenly fallen asleep.

He crosses the silent rooms and enters the chamber where Yashodara and Rahula are sleeping in each other's arms.

'How can I leave them?' he wonders, weeping with love. But then, struck once again by how much Sleep resembles Death, Siddhartha makes up his mind.

The journey he is about to undertake will not be useful to him alone. Death is the enemy of us all, Yashodara and Rahula and everyone else.

And if our hero, in fact, were to find a sure path for escaping the suffering Death has always inflicted on the world, wouldn't we be happy to take it, even now, two thousand five hundred years later?

Siddhartha tore his loving eyes off his son and swiftly crossed the sleeping rooms of the palace.

When he reached the stables, he managed to wake up his faithful charioteer with some difficulty.

'Channa, Channa, get Kanthaka the king of all horses ready. I am leaving tonight to conquer Death, which hides inside us and dominates the world of the living.'

Channa, still groggy from his deep sleep, obeyed his beloved master, grumbling a little.

'The king's elephants will start to trumpet if they hear suspicious noises.'

'Don't worry, Channa. Nothing can disturb the elephants in their mysterious sleep tonight.'

'The guards won't let us pass.'

'The guards, my dear Channa, are sleeping like logs,' said Siddhartha. 'Destiny is taking care of everything tonight!'

The enormous bronze gates of the palace opened by themselves, while the king's elephants slept quietly in the stables, leaning on their huge sides. The guards, in their copper armour, snored loudly with their faces all scrunched up.

Outside the palace walls, the city of Kapilavastu lies in darkness. Kanthaka gallops swiftly through streets and countryside wrapped in dreams. Siddhartha rides and Channa runs faster than a leopard behind him, clutching

the tail of the king of all horses. They are going so fast that neither feet nor hooves seem to touch the ground.

All night long, Siddhartha travelled with Channa and Kanthaka, and when the first ray of sun peeked over the horizon, they found themselves at the edge of a forest near Bhargava, where there was a retreat for ascetics from all over India.

In this sacred place, the deer and the birds did not flee at the sight of humans, and snakes and wild animals never attacked anyone. The dense forest opened here and there in small clearings.

Siddhartha got off Kanthaka, certain he had come to the right place to begin his fight. He drew out his sword and cut his long, flowing hair. Then he spoke to Channa:

'Channa, my friend, take this gem. It is as pure as my love for you,' he said, plucking a gleaming emerald from his royal diadem. 'You have been faithful to me and I wouldn't be here without your help. Now go back to

Kapilavastu with Kanthaka and tell my father that I didn't leave because I was discontented. Tell my wife and my son that I shall love them always.'

Channa, still panting, was leaning against a tree, but his exhaustion was nothing in comparison with the sorrow he felt at parting with his master and friend. He cried like a fountain, and so did Kanthaka, who shed tears as big as glasses of water.

'Don't cry,' Siddhartha said to his friends. 'This is why I am leaving in search of Enlightenment. I want to defeat the sorrow that troubles all creatures when they have to leave the ones they love. Please explain this to my father too.'

Shortly after Channa and Kanthaka had left, Siddhartha met an old man dressed in an ochre-coloured robe. The prince, still wearing his palace finery, suggested they swap clothes. Naturally the poor man was happy to accept.

'Bless you, young prince,' said the old man, decked out in gold and silk, with Siddhartha's diadem slipping sideways over his eye. 'This forest is as dark and mysterious as the hidden Mind of man. I hope you'll find what you are looking for. . .' With that, the beggar vanished like a thunderbolt into the heart of the forest.

After this bizarre encounter, Siddhartha, dressed as an ascetic, entered the forest, as lonely as a child at night. He walked and walked, without ever feeling tired, while the animals peered and the trees rustled. Then, just before nightfall, he came to a clearing as big as a town square.

There he found a large group of men getting ready for the night in complete silence.

They were ascetics, monks and beggars, with long hair and the rumpled clothing of folk who sleep in the open, night after night. When these men saw Siddhartha emerge from the heart of the forest, lit by the red glow of sunset, they saw him as a vision of Destiny.

'Here is a young man with royal bearing,' the ascetics thought to themselves. 'He wears his monk's robe as if it were the tunic of a prince and his eyes are full of hope and courage. Who on earth can this new man be?'

And Siddhartha went straight to them and said: 'I have left my old life behind me. From now on, I shall live here in the forest until I have found a way to defeat Death. This is the Path I want to find. Do you know it?'

Then a man came forward, with such big eyes that if you looked into them carefully you could see his thoughts like running rivers.

His name was Arada, and he was a famous master of wisdom. Many ascetics followed his teachings and listened to all his advice: what to do; how to meditate, and when; and, above all, why.

'People's lives,' said Arada to Siddhartha, tearing a handful of grass from the meadow, 'are like leaves of grass: every time you tear them out, they sprout up all over again. Every time someone dies, he is reborn again. It is not the body that comes back: the legs, the chest, the eyes and all the rest become still and hard and after three days they stink. But when someone dies, that person's mind automatically goes into another existence and so continues like this, for ever, just like someone who has to move out of his house because it is too old and it is falling down around him.' With that, Arada opened his hand and let go of the severed leaves of grass. Already they were withering.

'And tell me, what has happened now to the life of that grass you tore up?' asked Siddhartha intently.

'It's already down there, regrowing under the earth again,' replied Arada with a smile, pointing to the ground.

'And where do people's lives regrow?'

'In most cases inside other humans. If we behave well, respecting the laws of the earth and the sky, our next existence will be even happier. But if we are wicked, if, for example, we kill other creatures for any reason, or if we are violent and hurt other living beings, then in our next existence our minds will be reborn into a sad life, full of suffering. Someone who has been especially wicked in this life can even come back as an animal. We have to be kind to others if we want to be happy in our next life.' Arada raised his arm, brushed his hand against Siddhartha's forehead and went on to say, 'Children are born and born again for ever, Siddhartha. You too are much much older than you think, because you have already existed thousands and thousands of times inside other bodies. It's the same for all creatures in the world: deer, birds, fish, cats, ants, plants and all the rest.'

'And why, if I've already lived, can't I remember my past lives?' asked Siddhartha, amazed, and the sage Arada replied with a booming laugh that bounced off the tree trunks, giving the impression that the whole forest was laughing.

'You must be patient,' Arada said. 'Only after great effort, when your mind is still and calm and when you are able to meditate without being disturbed by so much as the smallest thought crossing your mind, when you can't even be distracted by a feather tickling your nose, then and only then will you be able to remember your past lives. This is Enlightenment. In that moment you will understand that only your body is going to die. Your Mind will simply move to another house. That is the only way I know to conquer Death. But be careful, Siddhartha. Very few have ever managed to follow that Path.'

The night passed and Siddhartha didn't feel tired. Instead of sleeping, he asked one question after another, and the ascetic answered all of them patiently.

The next day Siddhartha stayed in meditation for a long time under a tree, and Arada's words came back to his mind, loud and clear.

'The Path that was shown to me last night,' he reflects calmly, 'will never bring me to meet Death and challenge it.' The hours pass and Siddhartha is still sitting perfectly still under the same tree. He stands up only when evening comes, and the ascetics gather in the clearing.

'Arada, I thank you from the bottom of my heart for the teachings you gave me last night,' said Siddhartha in front of everyone, 'but yours is not the Path I am seeking. I did not give up my existence as a prince only to find a better one in my next life. I left my son and Yashodara and my father to find a way that will serve everybody, a way that directly conquers Death, and which doesn't put off the final battle for ever.'

His words moved all present. 'What a strong man this is!' they thought as he set off barefoot into the darkness. 'He wants to fight single-handed the same battle that even the wisest ascetics of the earth have already lost thousands and thousands of times.'

And Siddhartha went off alone, followed only by the mysterious sounds of the night, while in the sky dark clouds gathered and covered the moon. In the heart of the forest, he began to meditate again, paying no attention to the thunder and lightning.

While Siddhartha is sitting in the rain with his eyes closed, five strange characters silently approach him. They are drenched to the bone, dressed in rags, with hair down to their shoulders and the thin faces of men who haven't eaten a square meal for a long time.

One of them has his right fist tightly closed. The fingernails, which have never been cut, grow right through the flesh, poking out of the back of the hand. Another one walks on all fours like a dog, and his knees have become as hard as the soles of shoes. Another, with his wrists tied behind his back, slithers on the ground like a snake. The fourth holds his arms up above his head, with the palms of his hands pressed together as if he were praying. He stays in that position, even at night, when he lies down to sleep. The fifth drags an enormous load of heavy stones on his back and every step is a superhuman effort.

To see them standing there you can't help thinking: poor things! What terrible punishment have these five creatures been condemned to?

Partly to rest, partly to find out more about this new ascetic sitting alone in the night to meditate, the five characters gather around him, silently waiting for him to open his eyes.

A whole night goes by and Siddhartha doesn't budge an inch. When morning comes, he opens his eyes.

'We are ascetics,' said the one carrying the load of stones on his shoulders, 'and we seek to conquer Death, which sooner or later comes for us all.'

'This is the very Path I am looking for,' replied Siddhartha, suddenly very interested. 'What courage you have, my friends, facing Death in the state you are in. I want to fight at your side. But tell me, who inflicted these horrible tortures on you? Why such cruelty?'

The five men exchanged rapid glances.

'No one inflicted this punishment on us,' said the fifth ascetic, leaning on his load of stones. 'We ourselves chose them.'

'You yourselves . . . ?'

'Death is the greatest of all pains. We look for Pain on purpose so we can fight it. After having conquered it, and after having learned to bear the greatest suffering, we will be ready to face Death too.'

'Death creates Pain . . .' repeated Siddhartha to

himself, understanding the simple reasoning of the five ascetics. 'So if first I overcome Pain, then I'll be able to face the final battle with Death . . .'

From that day on, and for many years to follow, Siddhartha wandered about the forest with the five warrior-ascetics. He chose Hunger as his special enemy.

Fruit, berries, roots. Every day he ate less than the day before, until he ate only one single pomegranate seed

every morning. Then he meditated, staying perfectly still for the whole day.

He sat there with his eyes closed, fighting hunger-pangs in his mind, like an armed knight fighting off hungry dragons who are attacking him from every side.

You know what happens when you're very hungry, don't you? It's not only the stomach that cries out! You get weak and sad and nervous. You may even burst into tears. The hungrier you are, the more you suffer, and the struggle grows increasingly harsh.

Then Siddhartha cut out the pomegranate seed and decided to eat only two sesame seeds a week.

Hunger became more ferocious, and at every new attack Siddhartha warded off the blow, brilliantly passing every test, accepting every challenge that Pain threw his way.

As the years passed, he grew very weak and he had difficulty in making even the smallest movement. He spent all day and most of the night sitting still, breathing ever so slowly.

Even today, in a museum in Lahore, in Pakistan, you can see a famous bronze statue of Siddhartha meditating during those years when Hunger was his enemy.

His bones stick out through the skin, his face is sunken, his eyes closed.

In his mind are visions of battles, of retreats, of swords unsheathed against Pain and its armies. There are visions of fires, of small victories, of bloody conflicts.

On the outside, his body is weak and dried up, and yet if you look at him carefully, even in the bronze statue in the museum, you can see signs of the heroic adventures Siddhartha was going through inside himself.

His five companions, impressed by the great strength

of will that Siddhartha showed in his battle against Hunger, tried increasingly to imitate his courage, following him wherever he went.

Siddhartha was twenty-nine when he left his existence as a prince and now, after six years in the forest, he was thirty-five.

From the fifth year on, the five ascetics had to carry Siddhartha around the forest, so weak had he become.

It was they who brought him his sesame seeds and a bowl of water every so often. They were the ones who pulled off the twigs and the worms and the snails that strolled undisturbed through his long hair.

One day they stopped on the bank of a small river at the edge of the forest. Siddhartha sat down under a big

banyan tree with the help of his five friends. He closed his eyes and in silence resumed his endless battle.

༄། ཨོཾ་ག་ཏེ་ག་ཏེ་པཱ་ར་ག་ཏེ་པཱ་ར་སཾ་ག་ཏེ་བོ་དྷི་སྭཱ་ཧཱ།

Meanwhile, on the opposite bank of the river, a fisherman was teaching a young boy how to play the lute. 'If you tighten the strings too much,' the voice said, 'they will snap, and if you leave them too slack they won't play, but if they are tuned to the right point, then, and only then, does the music start . . .' And the fisherman played a melody that mingled with the bubbling sound of the river.

Siddhartha, with his eyes closed, felt those sounds entering deeply into him and his fight against Pain suddenly ceased.

Weakness, hunger-pangs and all those desperate and terrible thoughts that torment every hungry man stopped as if a sudden truce had been called on the battlefield and thousands of soldiers had lowered their bloodied swords and spears at the same time. In a twinkling, Siddhartha's mind was free from all thoughts and a vast calm came over him.

'If you tighten the strings too much, they will snap, and if you leave them too slack, they won't play . . .' echoes the voice of the shepherd across the river. Siddhartha opens his eyes with the look of someone who has been struck by a clever idea.

The countryside in front of his eyes is radiant and the river flows peacefully by. It is springtime, and a woman passes by holding a bowl of rice.

This woman was Nandabala, the daughter of a shepherd who lived nearby in a poor hut. She had never been to school and, having never travelled, knew nothing about the rest of India.

Nandabala was taking a bowl of rice as an offering to

the spirits of the forest. When she saw Siddhartha, all skin and bones under the banyan tree, she stopped to take a better look at him. His eyes were open and, in spite of his tormented body, they revealed a great calm.

'This must be the Prince of the Spirits of the Forest in person!' thought Nandabala, struck by his eyes. 'I'd better give him my offering,' and she held out the bowl of rice with a little curtsey.

When you have been eating two sesame seeds a week for years, a simple bowl of rice suddenly becomes a banquet for fifty people.

Siddhartha ate with his hands very very slowly. He felt a bit stronger, and a new idea began to form in his mind.

'For twenty-nine years I lived in the splendour of my palaces, never seeing sadness or even knowing of the existence of Death. Then for six years, I fought Pain as a warrior-ascetic, seeking it in Hunger and in the hardship of suffering. First I lived in pleasure, then in pain, but I still have not succeeded in meeting Death face to face.'

When he had finished the bowl of rice, he tried to stand up. He slowly made his way down to the river and, entering the water, thought out loud: 'If you tighten the strings too much, they will snap, and if you leave them too slack, they won't play . . . It is in the Middle Way, the one that lies half way between pain and pleasure, that I will find the path that leads to the final battle . . .'Just then, a white swan let out a cry as it landed on a stone sticking out of the water in the middle of the river.

Then Siddhartha set Nandabala's wooden bowl down to float on the water. As if speaking to the stream, he said: 'May this bowl go against the current if I reach Enlightenment.'

Miraculously the bowl span around and, instead of being carried away by the river like all the other things floating in it, it began slowly to make its way upstream.

The five ascetics, who were gathering roots for their supper on the other bank, had seen Siddhartha take the bowl of rice from Nandabala's hands.

'Siddhartha has lost his battle. Hunger has won,' said the first, raising his right hand pierced through by his fingernails.

'Let's go away. Siddhartha is no longer one of us,' the second ascetic barked in disappointment.

'Look! He is even bathing!' said the one with his arms stuck in the air, shocked.

And three of them ran away up the hill, while the fourth slithered behind them, and the fifth followed, struggling under his burden of stones.

Siddhartha saw them go as he came out of the water and tried to call them back, but they were so taken up with their suffering that they didn't even hear him.

Then he returned to the banyan tree that was as large and majestic as a knight's castle. This tree became known as the Tree of Enlightenment, and even today in India, in a place called Bogdhaya, you can still see an enormous tree that descends directly from the first roots of that ancient banyan.

Siddhartha sits down, closes his eyes and steps inside himself. He finds the hunger-pangs sleeping like dogs in

the sun. The armies of Pain have disappeared. Peace reigns over the battlefield. And even those brave thoughts that had defended his mind from enemy attacks for six years are still and motionless like wooden puppets. And his warrior's pride has vanished together with the hope of victory, since there is no longer an enemy to fight.

But this truce is only temporary: Mara the Mighty is preparing for the final battle.

Mara is General of Generals, the absolute Master of Evil. He is the one who secretly feeds everyone's fear of Death, using every means: trickery, ambush, betrayal.

He is inside each one of us, yet it is almost impossible for us to see him because his appearance changes continuously and his voice, hidden, often filters in among our thoughts. Mara can take the shape of any person or thing. He has entire armies under his command.

'Siddhartha has found the Middle Way,' said Mara to his sons and daughters. 'Look how calm he is. He has already taken the Path that leads people to defeat Death. If he were to succeed while he is still alive, then others could learn as well. We can't let that happen.'

Then he ordered his two sons, Pride and Power, to enter into action. These two appeared, flying like two winged spirits in Siddhartha's limpid mind, and said these flattering words: 'You who have fought Pain for six years and who are the son of a king, you who have the wisdom of an ascetic and the strength of a warrior, stand up, Siddhartha, stand up and command. The whole world will fall at your feet.'

Behind Pride and Power came their sisters, Passion and Desire. They were dressed in red and they moved rhythmically, as alluring as two beautiful panthers, ready to snatch Siddhartha's attention at the first opportunity.

But Siddhartha stayed as firm as a rocky mountain.

Then Mara told his daughter Vanity to complete her brothers' and sisters' work. Vanity was a ravishing beauty. It was enough just to look into her eyes to believe everything she said.

'Few men in the world would have been able to do what you have done,' she said softly. 'No one is nobler than you, splendid prince. The whole world will be grateful to you for what you have done. You have shown people that Pain is not invincible. Stand up, and thousands

of them will come to listen to your teachings, Master of Masters. Stand up now. You have reached your goal.'

Siddhartha hears all these words inside him. Vanity has a sweet, thin voice. Pride speaks with the confidence of a king, while Power sounds like thunder.

But Siddhartha's mind does not move forward in time to dream about his future glory. His attention stays where it is, fixed in the present, without running after promises and flattery.

Now Fear, Mara's oldest daughter, flies in, wicked-eyed, dressed in black, clutching in her terrible claws a bottomless jug from which water gushes like a waterfall. A puddle forms, as big as a small dark lake.

'Open your eyes!' a horrible voice from inside the puddle suddenly orders. It is Mara himself.

'Open your eyes, Siddhartha! You have come to a point in your Path where everything your mind sees becomes real in the world of the living. You are approaching Death, Siddhartha; open your eyes!'

And Siddhartha opens his eyes and on the meadow in front of him he sees that same puddle of threatening water whose voice he has just heard in his mind. Now everything is happening for real.

The river and the meadow grow dark, and grey clouds fill the sky.

'Attack, my faithful ones. Attack!' thunders Mara's voice. 'If his mind did not give in to flattery and pleasure, Fear will remind him that all humans must be afraid of Death instead of rebelling against their destiny. Attack!'

Mara's soldiers appear by the hundreds, armed with swords and pointed spears, marching down the hill in formation. Siddhartha sees fires, catapults, cruel faces thirsting for revenge, and thousands of archers. He hears the threatening sound of drums that mark the beat of their crashing footsteps. The armies of Evil advance on the Tree of Enlightenment, determined to destroy all hope of salvation.

Even the earth trembles.

Siddhartha sees everything and does not bat an eyelid. He sees the fury of Pain and the river that flows calmly and the trampled grass and the tree he is sitting under and Mara's dark puddle and the springtime blooming, yellow

and white, on the branches.

Siddhartha sees everything, the good and the evil of life at the same time, but he holds firm on the Middle Way, without worrying about what could soon happen to him, seeking no refuge in the pleasures that Mara shows him to avoid the frontal attacks of Fear.

The puddle ripples slightly, and while the archers take aim against him, visions of the past float on the surface. His father, King Suddhodhana, appears, begging him to return to Kapilavastu, and then Kanthaka, whom no one has ridden since the day he left. Here's Rahula sleeping in his cradle and Yashodara combing her hair and sighing with love for him.

'Stand up Siddhartha, stand up now, if you want to save your life. . .' a thousand voices shout.

His mother, Maya, appears on the water too, as in a mirror that reflects the happiest memories of his life.

Then Siddhartha sees the arrows aimed at him break away from the bows and a swarm of spears darkens the sky. He stays perfectly still and makes no attempt to protect his face with his hands.

Incredible! The spears and arrows, a moment before hitting him, transform into rose petals and spray him with the smell of springtime.

Mara is worried. He stirs and the puddle swirls again.

'Look at me, look into my eyes!' he roars, and Siddhartha sees his mother's face turn into that of a monster. It has swollen lips and sharp teeth. Its eyes are blood-red and the explosions that come out of its mouth fill the air with the smell of dying flowers.

'This is Mara the Mighty calling you. You cannot resist me any longer, because I am everywhere, both inside you and outside you. You cannot defeat me.' And as he speaks, his image changes again one more time and Siddhartha sees Siddhartha's face reflected in the water.

The earth trembles again.

Siddhartha looks up from his reflection and sees the meadow and the ancient trees and the birds. He sees the

river flowing and a lotus flower carried along by the stream. Everything shines and there is the scent of flowers.

For the first time he fully grasps the beauty of the Earth. Now he loves everything he sees as he had once loved himself.

Now he can see his past lives all at once, as if time no longer existed.

A deer springs out of a bush. Siddhartha was a deer once. A fish darts out of the river and splashes back in. Siddhartha knows he was a fish many lives ago. A shepherd crosses the meadow and Siddhartha sees all his past existences as a man. He realises at last that he has lived thousands and thousands of times before. He has been a king, a soldier, a beggar, a bricklayer, a sailor, a groom, an astronomer, a poet, a nurse, a singer too, and even an acrobat. Sometimes, passing from one life to the next, he was killed. At other times, he didn't even have the time to realise that he was about to die. At other times again, he simply went to sleep.

Now he sees everything once more, and in an instant he is no longer just Siddhartha. Now he is a fish and a deer and a flower. And a man and a bird. He is every creature of the earth at the same time. This is the state of any enlightened mind. It shines for ever.

Siddhartha slowly moves his hand for the first time since he has been sitting under the tree. Solemnly, he touches the Earth that has seen him reborn into thousands of different bodies.

Then he looks back into the puddle. His reflection is no longer there. The only thing mirrored in it now is the clear sky, embracing all that exists in the universe.

Mara has vanished and with him Siddhartha. The fear of Death has disappeared too.

The man who walks away from the Tree of Enlightenment has become a Buddha – that is to say, an Enlightened One – and when the time comes for his body to die, his calm and shining Mind will no longer need to find another body, because now it is everywhere, wherever there is a speck of life. For ever.

'There is a little Buddha hidden inside each one of us.'

Even today, after two thousand five hundred years have gone by, all Buddhas of all times are everywhere. For ever, inside and outside us, they smile.

THE HEART SUTRA

The running head used in this book is the opening mantra of the Heart Sutra, written in Tibetan script. The mantra reads:

oṃ gate gate pāragate pārasaṃgate bodhi svāhā

oṃ - gone, gone, gone beyond, gone altogether beyond. Enlightenment! - svāhā

'Oṃ' is the sound of universal consciousness; 'svāhā' is an exclamation of joy.

The Heart Sutra is one of the most popular sutras in the Buddhist tradition and is often used as a basis for meditation. For a full explanation of its significance, readers are recommended:
The Heart of Understanding by Thich Nhat Hanh (Parallax Press, 1987);
Buddhist Wisdom by Edward Conze (Unwin Hyman - revised edition - 1988);
and *Entering the Stream* (Rider, 1994).

Aidan Roantree

Effective Maths

Leaving Certificate Maths – Higher Level

2

CJFallon
ESTABLISHED 1895

Published by

CJ Fallon
Ground Floor – Block B
Liffey Valley Office Campus
Dublin 22

ISBN 978-0-7144-1952-7

First Edition February 2014
This Reprint May 2023

The paper stock used in this publication comes from managed forests. This means that at least one tree is planted for every tree felled. The inks used for printing are environmentally friendly and vegetable based.

Preface

This book, ***Effective Maths 2***, covers the second half of the new syllabus for Leaving Cert Higher Level Maths. The first book, ***Effective Maths 1***, began the coverage of this new syllabus. The syllabus has been changing incrementally for a number of years. These books reflect and take on board the final changes to the syllabus, and so will be valid for many years.

These books are designed to reflect the content and ambitions of the new course, as intended by the NCCA, who are responsible for the implementation of the new Project Maths course.

The objectives of the new course call for the learning of maths through investigation and discovery, including the use of technology and group work. It is intended that these books be supplemented, wherever possible, by this work. To this end, some interactive modules will be available on the CJ Fallon website (www.cjfallon.ie), and will be added to over time.

However, the length of the new course at Higher Level means that most classes will focus on learning the required material, and ***Effective Maths*** aims to facilitate that in the best possible way.

Of course, the use of technology and group work are only a means and not an end. The real aim of the new course is that students **understand** the material they are being asked to learn and are able to apply their understanding to practical situations.

This book places at its core an effective understanding of the mathematical concepts on the course. For this reason, all of the key concepts are fully explained and placed in context. Some teachers may feel that such explanations are superfluous, but research has shown that many teachers and most students appreciate such explanations.

The chapters of the books are arranged in a sequence such that material required to understand a new concept has been covered in earlier chapters. For example, sequences and series is covered before financial maths, as many questions in this topic require concepts from sequences and series. Also, many of the topics in Book 2 require ideas from the topics in Book 1, such as calculus requiring algebra and trigonometry. Nevertheless, teachers can feel free to alter the order of chapters as they see fit.

It is my wish that these books are found to be useful and informative by all students and teachers using them. In particular, I hope that they will engender in many students a deep liking for maths and an appreciation of its contribution to civilisation and society.

Finally, I would like to thank Pat Doyle for his many helpful suggestions and comments in the preparation of these books.

Aidan Roantree
Dublin, 2014.

Contents

Arrangements and Combinations 21

Combinatorics is the branch of maths that involves counting, specifically in our case, counting the number of possible outcomes when some kind of experiment is performed. One example is counting the number of possible ways of choosing a Lotto panel of 6 numbers from the whole numbers from 1 to 42.

Combinatorial problems occur in many different areas of maths, e.g. in algebra and geometry, but especially in probability theory, as we will see in the following chapters. Many famous mathematicians, including Pascal, Newton, Bernoulli and Euler made important contributions to the field of combinatorics. Currently, the field is of enormous importance in computer science, where calculating the fewest number of operations required to perform a task is critical, in that using more efficient algorithms can significantly reduce costs.

Our exposure to combinatorics is limited to arrangements (permutations), where order is important, and combinations (selections, choices) where order is not important.

21.1 Experiments

An **experiment** consists of taking some kind of measurement. The possibilities when the experiment is performed are called **outcomes**.

An experiment must be well-defined. Asking someone to pick a nice colour is not a well-defined experiment because it is not clear what exactly a 'nice' colour is. On the other hand, picking a classmate at random and asking them for their birth-month is a valid experiment because the possible outcomes are clear.

The number of possible outcomes for an experiment may be either finite or infinite. Examples are:

1. **Finite.** Throw a die. There are 6 possible outcomes: 1, 2, 3, 4, 5 and 6.
2. **Infinite.** Measure the height of a classmate. In theory, the outcome could be any real number from 0 upwards.

In some cases, the number of possible outcomes may be finite, but too many to be listed, e.g. picking an even whole number between 1 and 1,000,000 inclusive.

Exercises 21.1

1. Which of the following are valid experiments? Explain your reasoning.
   (i) Asking someone how they feel.
   (ii) Asking someone to pick from a list of ten options which best describes how they feel.
2. Which of the following are valid experiments? Explain your reasoning.
   (i) Measuring the rainfall, in mm, at a certain spot over a 24 hour period.
   (ii) Asking a student for their attitude to bullying in school.

3. A bag contains 20 discs, numbered from 1 to 20 inclusively.
   (i) If one disc is chosen at random, and its number noted, is this a valid experiment? How many possible outcomes are there?
   (ii) Five different discs are chosen at random. Is measuring the product of the numbers on the five discs an experiment? Is listing all possible outcomes a practical proposition?
4. One person is chosen at random and asked to state the day of the week on which they were born.
   (i) Is this a valid experiment?
   (ii) List the possible outcomes.
   (iii) How many possible outcomes are there?
5. From a standard pack of cards, a single card is drawn at random. The card drawn is noted.
   (i) Is this a valid experiment? How many possible outcomes are there?
   (ii) If the card drawn is a red card, how many possible outcomes are there?
   (iii) If the card drawn is not a diamond, how many possible outcomes are there?

21.2 Fundamental Principles of Counting

In many practical cases, an experiment consists of a number of stages, all of which must be carried out before the experiment is completed. Often in these cases, it is not practical to list all the possible outcomes and so count them. Instead, we need rules and formulae.

Fundamental Principle of Counting

Suppose to obtain an outcome for an experiment we have to perform one stage **and** another stage. Suppose the number of outcomes for the first stage is x and the number of outcomes for the second stage is y. Then the total number of outcomes for the experiment is

$$x \times y.$$

i.e. **and** means we **multiply**.

The Fundamental Principle of Counting, sometimes called the First Fundamental Principle of Counting, can be extended to an experiment consisting of any number of stages. Very simply, each time we come across the word **and**, we **multiply** the numbers.

Example 1

In a restaurant, Susan wants to pick 1 starter from 5 possible starters, 1 main course from 12 possible main courses and 1 dessert from 6 possible desserts. In how many ways can she pick her meal?

Solution

*(To complete her experiment of picking a meal, Susan has to pick one starter **and** one main course **and** one dessert. So we will multiply the numbers. She has 5 ways of picking a starter, 12 ways of picking a main course and 6 ways of picking a dessert. We can lay out the calculation as shown overleaf.)*

The number of possible meals Susan can pick is:

Starter	and	Main	and	Dessert	
5	×	12	×	6	= 360

Thus, there are 360 possible meals Susan could pick.

In other cases, an experiment may be performed in one way or in another, e.g. pick a digit from 1 to 9 or pick a letter. Again, in simple cases the outcomes can be listed and counted, but as the numbers get larger we need a formula.

If an experiment may be performed in one way **or** in another way, then we **add** the numbers of outcomes for each way to get the total number of possible outcomes for the whole experiment. This is called the Second Fundamental Principle of Counting.

Second Fundamental Principle of Counting

Suppose an experiment can be performed in one way **or** in another way, but not both. Suppose x is the number of outcomes for the first way and y is the number of outcomes for the second way. Then the total number of outcomes for the experiment is

$$x + y$$

i.e. **or** means we **add**.

Note 1: Like the First Fundamental Principle of Counting, the Second Fundamental Principle of Counting can be extended to any number of different ways. Once again, each time we come across the word 'or', we add. In more involved questions, combinations of 'and' and 'or' are often needed.

Example 2

A security code for a door consists of two letters followed by two digits from 0 to 9.

For example, BX04 and GG55 are possible codes.

(i) Mary chooses her own code. If there are no restrictions, in how many ways can she form her code?

(ii) Joe wants his code to contain the letter 'J' and to have no repeated letters or digits. In how many ways can he form his code?

Solution

(To form a code we have to do four things: pick a first letter ***and*** *a second letter* ***and*** *a first digit* ***and*** *a second digit.)*

(i) *(There are 26 letters in the alphabet. Because repetitions are allowed, the number of ways of picking the second letter is also 26. Likewise, there are 10 digits and because repetitions are allowed, the number of ways of picking the second digit is also 10.)*

The number of codes Mary can form is:

1st letter	and	2nd letter	and	1st digit	and	2nd digit	
26	×	26	×	10	×	10	= 67600

(ii) *(Joe can have 'J' either as the first letter or as the second letter. Because of the word 'or', we add the numbers, by the Second Fundamental Principle of Counting. If 'J' is the first letter, then he can pick the second letter in 25 ways, and if 'J' is the second letter, then he can pick the pick the first letter in 25 ways. Also, the first digit can be picked in 10 ways and the second in 9 ways.)*

'J' first: $1 \times 25 \times 10 \times 9 = 2250$

'J' second: $25 \times 1 \times 10 \times 9 = 2250$

('J' first) or ('J' second): $2250 + 2250 = 4500$.

Exercises 21.2

The menu of the little restaurant 'The Hungry Orc' is shown below. It consists of options for each of three courses: starters, main courses and desserts. Each menu item is also represented by a single letter, for convenience.

Starters		Main Courses		Desserts	
Mushroom Soup	(M)	Lemon Sole	(L)	Banoffi	(B)
Caesar Salad	(C)	Peking Duck	(P)	Gateau Diane	(G)
Steamed Mussels	(S)	Rack of Lamb	(R)	Assorted Ice Cream	(A)
		Fillet Beef	(F)		
		Vegetarian Stir Fry	(V)		

1. Siobhan wants to pick a starter and a main course. How many possible outcomes are there?

2. Barry only wants a main course and a dessert. He also does not like fish, and so he won't pick the lemon sole. How many possible outcomes are there?

3. Caoimhe intends to take all three courses, i.e. a starter, a main course and a dessert.
(i) How many possible outcomes are there?
(ii) If she decides against rack of lamb and banoffi, how many possible outcomes are there?

4. Colm only wants two courses, i.e. two of starter, main course and dessert.
(i) How many possible outcomes are there?
(ii) Colm decides that he wants either Caesar salad or lemon sole, but not both. How many possible outcomes are there?

5. Tim and Serena dine at The Hungry Orc one evening.
(i) If they both have three course meals, in how many ways can the two of them together choose their meals?
(ii) If they agree not to make the same choice for any course, how many different meals are possible?

6. Charlie and Ger dine at The Hungry Orc one evening. They each have three courses.
(i) If Charlie picks either the mushroom soup or the rack of lamb, but not both, in how many ways can he pick his meal?
(ii) Ger wants to try at least one of the Peking duck and the gateau Diane. In how many ways can she choose her meal?

7. How many four digit numbers greater than 4000 can be made from the digits 1, 2, 3, 4, 5,
(i) if no digit may be used more than once?
(ii) if repetitions are allowed?

8. A code consists of picking one of the letters A, B, C and one of the digits 1, 2, 3, 4, 5, e.g. one code is B4.
   (i) How many codes are possible?
   (ii) How many codes contain an even digit?

9. A code consists of a letter followed by three digits, e.g. T044.
   (i) How many codes are possible?
   (ii) If it is known that the second digit is 2, how many codes are possible?
   (iii) If it is known that the last digit is odd, how many codes are possible?

10. A code consists of two letters (A–Z) followed by two digits (0–9).
   (i) How many possible codes are there, if repetitions are not allowed?
   (ii) How many of these codes contain the letter X, if repetitions are allowed?

11. Sean writes down a code number, which is to be a whole number between 10 and 1000 inclusive.
   (i) How many two digit codes have different digits?
   (ii) How many three digit codes have different digits?

12. A password for a mobile phone consists of five digits, from 0 to 9 inclusive. Eithne chooses her own password.
   (i) How many passwords are possible?
   (ii) If she wants her password to begin with a 4 and end with an odd number, how many passwords are now possible?

21.3 Arrangements (Permutations)

Suppose we have three different books, which we will call A, B and C. We want to arrange all of these books in order on a shelf. One possible arrangement is BAC, which stands for B first, then A and then C. The full list of possible arrangements is

ABC	BAC	CAB
ACB	BCA	CBA

Thus, the total number of possible arrangements of 3 different objects is 6.

For a small number of objects like this, we can easily list the possible outcomes and count them. But when the number of objects grows, to even 8 or 10, it is not practical to list all possible arrangements. So we need a formula.

Using the First Fundamental Principle of Counting, we can consider the process of arranging n different objects to be an experiment with n stages: pick a first object **and** pick a second object **and** so on to picking the last object. There are n ways of picking the first, $n - 1$ ways of picking the second, and so on to 1 way of picking the last.

1st	and	2nd	and		and	last
n	$\times$	$n - 1$	$\times$	....	$\times$	1

This expression, $n \times (n-1) \times (n-2) \times .... \times 1$, is a very important one in mathematics, and is called ***n* factorial**, and written $n!$. For example, $6! = 6 \times 5 \times 4 \times 3 \times 2 \times 1 = 720$.

All modern scientific calculators have the factorial function, either as *x!* or *n!*.

We now have a formula for the number of **arrangements** (also called **permutations**) of all of a number of different objects.

Arrangements (Permutations) of all of *n* different objects

The number of arrangements of all of n different objects is

$$n! = n(n-1)(n-2)\ldots 1,$$

where $n \in \mathbb{N}$ and $0! = 1$.

Suppose we are asked to arrange all of a number of different objects, but there are restrictions imposed. Then it is important that we look at the restrictions first. These questions all use the Fundamental Principles of Counting to deal with 'and' and 'or'.

Example 1

(i) How many arrangements are possible of all of the letters of the word SUNDAY?

(ii) How many of these arrangements start with the letter S?

(iii) How many of these arrangements start with S and end with Y?

Solution

(i) *(Here we are just asked to arrange all six letters with no restrictions.)*

Number of arrangements = $6! = 720$

(ii) *(Here we have a restriction: the S must be first. So we say that we place S first* ***and*** *then arrange the other five letters.)*

(S first) **and** (arrange all other five letters)
Number of arrangements = $(1) \times (5!) = 120$

(iii) *(There are two restrictions here: S must be first and Y must be last. We will put these letters in their positions and then arrange the other four letters.)*

(S first) **and** (Y last) **and** (arrange the other four letters)
Number of arrangements = $(1) \times (1) \times (4!)$
$= 24.$

In some arrangements questions, certain objects must be side by side.

Example 2

(i) How many arrangements are possible of all of the letters of the word UKRAINE?

(ii) In how many of these arrangements do all four vowels appear side by side?

Solution

(i) *(We are simply arranging all seven letters, with no restrictions.)*

Number of arrangements = $7! = 5040$

(ii) *(The four vowels are U, A, I, E. If two or more objects must appear side by side, we start by considering them as one unit,* ***and*** *then arrange them among themselves.)*

[Arrange UAIE, K, R, N] **and** [Arrange U, A, I, E]

Number of arrangements = $(4!) \times (4!)$
$= 24 \times 24$
$= 576$

In some cases, we are only asked to arrange **some** of a number of different objects. Again, for small numbers, we can list the possible outcomes and count them, or we can use the First Fundamental Principle of Counting. But for larger numbers neither is practical: we would like a formula.

In general, suppose we want to arrange r out of n different objects, where $r < n$. The number of ways this can be done is written

^nP_r or 'nPr' (on a calculator),

and is given by the following formula.

Arrangements (Permutations) of *r* of *n* different objects

The number of arrangements of r out of n different objects is

$$^nP_r = \frac{n!}{(n-r)!} = n(n-1)....(n-r+1)$$

where $n \in \mathbb{N}$ and $r < n$.

The formula is fine in theory, but most calculations can be done by using the 'nPr' function on your calculator.

Example 3

Seven cards are marked one each with the digits 1, 2, 3, 4, 5, 6 and 7.

(i) How many four digit natural numbers can be formed from four of these cards?

(ii) How many of these four digit numbers are odd?

Solution

(i) *(We are being asked to arrange four out of seven different objects.)*

Number of four-digit natural numbers

$= {}^7P_4$

$= 840$

(ii) *(To get an odd number, the last digit must be 1, 3, 5 or 7. We pick this digit first. Then we have to arrange three from the remaining six digits to fill the first three places. We then use the First Fundamental Principle of Counting to multiply the numbers.)*

[Pick last digit] and [Arrange 3 from 6 for the first three places]
Number of odd four-digit numbers

$= (4) \times ({}^6P_3)$

$= 4 \times 120$

$= 480$

Alternatively, using the First Fundamental Principle of Counting from the beginning:
[Pick last] and [Pick 1st] and [Pick 2nd] and [Pick 3rd]
Number of odd four-digit numbers

$= 4 \times 6 \times 5 \times 4 = 480.$

Exercises 21.3

1. (i) How many arrangements are possible of all the letters of the word TUESDAY?
   (ii) How many of these arrangements begin with the letter T?

2. (i) How many arrangements are possible of all the letters of the word WORLDS?
   (ii) How many of these arrangements end with the letter S?

3. There are 5 horses, A, B, C, D and E in a race. All horses finish the race and there are no dead heats.
   (i) In how many different orders can all the horses finish the race?
   (ii) If A is disqualified and placed last, in how many ways can all the horses finish?

4. (i) How many arrangements are possible of all of the letters of the word PORTUGAL?
   (ii) How many of these arrangements start with the letter P?
   (iii) How many of these arrangements start with the letter P and end with the letter L?

5. (i) How many different five digit natural numbers greater than 50000 can be formed from the digits 2, 4, 5, 6, 8, if each digit can be used only once in any given number?
   (ii) How many of these numbers are odd?

6. (i) How many arrangements are possible of all of the letters of the word POLAND?
   (ii) How many of these arrangements have vowels in the first two positions?

7. All the letters of the word TRIBUNE are to be arranged in order.
   (i) How many arrangements are possible?
   (ii) How many arrangements have the T and the R side by side?

8. Eight people, including Stephen, Louise and Mark, sit in a row.
   (i) How many arrangements of all eight people are possible?
   (ii) In how many of these arrangements are Stephen, Louise and Mark sitting next to each other?

9. Dermot wants to choose a six-letter password for a web-site. He decides to use the letters of his name, with none repeated.
   (i) How many different passwords can Dermot pick?
   (ii) His surname begins with R. He decides that he wants his password to contain DR, side by side in that order. How many different passwords can he pick?
   (iii) Then he decides just to have D and R side by side in either order. How many different passwords can he now pick?

10. A five digit code, with all different digits, is to be formed from the digits 1, 2, 3, 4, 5.
    (i) How many codes are possible?
    (ii) How many of these codes have the even digits side by side?
    (iii) How many of these codes have the odd digits side by side?

11. In how many ways can the letters of the word METCALF be arranged if M is at the beginning and the A and the E are side by side?

12. Find the number of possible arrangements of all of the letters of the word CHEMISTRY. How many of these arrangements
    (i) start with M?
    (ii) have the two vowels side by side?
    (iii) have the three letters T, R and Y side by side?

13. Five men and five women are to be arranged in a line.
    (i) In how many ways can all ten be arranged if there are no restrictions?
    (ii) If the men are to occupy the odd-numbered positions (i.e. first, third, etc), in how many ways can all ten be arranged?

14. A four digit code, with all different digits, is to be picked from the digits 0 to 9 inclusive. How many codes are possible?

15. There are 40 horses running in the Grand National one year, for which there are prizes for the first four horses to finish. Assuming no dead heats, in how many ways can the prizes from first to fourth be awarded?

16. How many whole numbers between 5000 and 9000 can be formed from the digits 1, 2, 3, 4, 5, 6, 8, 9, if no digit may be used more than once?

21.4 Combinations (Choices or Selections)

Suppose we have 4 music CDs, which we will call A, B, C, D. We want to bring 2 of them to a party. In how many ways can we choose the 2 to bring with us?

The possible choices are: AB AC AD BC BD CD. Thus, there are 6 possible **choices** or **combinations** or **selections**.

The key difference between a choice and an arrangement is that with a choice, order is not important. For example, AB and BA represent the same choice, even though they would be different arrangements.

Once again, listing the possible outcomes is fine if the numbers are small. But when they become larger, e.g. choosing 6 numbers from 42 for a Lotto panel, it is essential to have a formula. But first we need some notation. The number of ways of choosing 2 objects from 4 different objects is written $\binom{4}{2}$ or ${}^4C_2$ (which is the old-fashioned notation). Both are read as '4 C 2' or '4 choose 2'.

In general, the number of combinations (choices) of r objects out of n different objects is written $\binom{n}{r}$, where $n, r \in \mathbb{N} \cup \{0\}$ and $r \leq n$. The following formula shows how $\binom{n}{r}$s can be calculated.

Combinations (choices) of *r* of *n* different objects

The number of combinations of r out of n different objects is

$$\binom{n}{r} = \frac{n!}{r!(n-r)!} \qquad \textbf{Definition 1}$$

$$= \frac{n(n-1)....(n-r+1)}{r!} \qquad \textbf{Definition 2}$$

where $n, r \in \mathbb{N} \cup \{0\}$ and $r \leq n$.

It can be shown that the two definitions are equivalent (the same). Definition 1 is used for theoretical purposes, while Definition 2 is used in practical situations.

All good scientific calculators have an 'nCr' function. In most cases, it is sufficient to use this function on your calculator to find the answers to questions. To answer the above question, we would press:

4	nCr	2	=

and the calculator would return the answer 6.

In practical questions involving combinations, we have to focus on how many objects are being chosen from and how many are being chosen. If certain objects must be chosen, or must not be chosen, that will affect one or both of n and r.

Example 1

(i) In how many ways can 4 different cards be chosen from a standard pack of 52 cards?

(ii) How many of these choices contain the king of diamonds?

Solution

(i) *(There are 52 cards and we are choosing 4.)*

Number of choices = $\binom{52}{4}$ = 270 725

(ii) *(If the king of diamonds must be one of the cards chosen, then we really only have to choose 3 cards from the remaining 51.)*

Number of choices = $\binom{51}{3}$ = 20 825.

Example 2

In how many ways can we choose 3 or 4 or 5 cards from a standard pack of 52 cards?

Solution

(There are 52 cards, and we have to choose 3 ***or*** *4* ***or*** *5 cards. We will need to use the Second Fundamental Principle of Counting:* ***or*** *means we* ***add****.)*

[Choose 3 from 52] or [Choose 4 from 52] or [Choose 5 from 52]

$$\text{Number of choices} = \binom{52}{3} + \binom{52}{4} + \binom{52}{5}$$
$$= 22100 + 270725 + 2598960$$
$$= 2891785.$$

Example 3

(i) How many choices of four letters are possible from the letters of the word MINERALS?

(ii) How many choices of four letters contain two vowels and two consonants?

(iii) How many choices of four letters contain at least one vowel?

Solution

(i) *(We have to choose 4 letters from the 8 letters of the word MINERALS.)*

Number of choices = $\binom{8}{4}$ = 70

(ii) *(Because the question refers to two types of object, vowels and consonants, we have to divide all letters into two groups. There are 3 vowels: I, E, A and 5 consonants: M, N, R, L, S. So we have to choose 2 vowels* ***and*** *2 consonants. We will use the First Fundamental Principle of Counting to find the total number of choices:* ***and*** *means we* ***multiply****.)*

[Choose 2 from 3 vowels] and [Choose 2 from 5 consonants]

$$\text{Number of choices} = \binom{3}{2} \times \binom{5}{2}$$
$$= 3 \times 10 = 30$$

(iii) *(If a choice has to contain at least one vowel, then it can contain one, two or three vowels. We could calculate each of these and then add, by the Second Fundamental Principle of Counting. However, a faster way is to calculate the opposite and subtract from the total, which we already know is 70. The opposite of at least one vowel is no vowels. To pick no vowels, we must pick all 4 letters from the 5 consonants.)*

We want: pick 4 letters including at least one vowel
Opposite: pick 4 letters with no vowels, i.e. pick 4 from 5 consonants

Number of choices for opposite $= \binom{5}{4} = 5$

Number of choices for what we want = 70 – 5 = 65.

Combinations satisfy some interesting properties, which we will make use of later.

Properties of Combinations

1. $\binom{n}{0} = 1$ and $\binom{n}{n} = 1$

2. $\binom{n}{r} = \binom{n}{n-r}$.

In the last section, we defined 0! = 1. This was to allow for the use of one formula for all expressions of the form $\binom{n}{r}$. Then, to show the above properties:

1. Using Definition 1,

$$\binom{n}{0} = \frac{n!}{0!n!} = \frac{n!}{n!} = 1$$

and $\binom{n}{n} = \dfrac{n!}{n!0!} = \dfrac{n!}{n!} = 1.$

2. Using Definition 1,

$$\binom{n}{n-r} = \frac{n!}{(n-r)![n-(n-r)]!}$$

$$= \frac{n!}{(n-r)!r!}$$

$$= \binom{n}{r}$$

Thus, for example, $\binom{18}{0} = 1$, $\binom{14}{14} = 0$ and $\binom{20}{18} = \binom{20}{20-18} = \binom{20}{2}$.

If the n in $\binom{n}{r}$ is unknown, then we cannot use a calculator. Instead we use Definition 2.

According to Definition 2:

(i) $\binom{n}{1} = \frac{n}{1} = n,$

(ii) $\binom{n}{2} = \frac{n(n-1)}{2 \times 1} = \frac{n(n-1)}{2}$, and so on.

Example 4

Determine the value of $n \in \mathbb{N}$ if $\binom{n}{2} = 78$.

Solution

$$\binom{n}{2} = 78$$

$$\frac{n(n-1)}{2} = 78$$

$$n^2 - n = 156$$

$$n^2 - n - 156 = 0$$

$$(n - 13)(n + 12) = 0$$

$$n - 13 = 0 \quad \text{or} \quad n + 12 = 0$$

$$n = 13 \quad \text{or} \quad n = -12$$

As $n \in \mathbb{N}$, the answer is $n = 13$.

Exercises 21.4

Evaluate each of the following.

1. $\binom{13}{5}$ **2.** $\binom{11}{8}$ **3.** $\binom{17}{2}$ **4.** $\binom{8}{7}$ **5.** $\binom{15}{5}$ **6.** $\binom{23}{3}$

7. In how many ways can seven books be chosen from a group of ten different books?

8. In how many ways can five different cards be chosen from a standard pack of 52 cards?

9. How many different straight lines can be formed by joining any two of eight points, no three of which lie in a straight line?

10. In how many ways can four different flags be chosen from nine differently coloured flags? If one of the flags is blue, in how many ways can this flag be among those chosen?

11. Anne completes a Lotto panel by choosing six numbers from the numbers from 1 to 42 inclusive.
- **(i)** In how many ways can Anne complete the panel?
- **(ii)** Her birthday is April 23rd. So she always picks 4 and 23 as two of her numbers. In how many ways can she now complete the panel?

12. Six points lie on the circumference of a circle. How many different triangles can be drawn having some of these points as vertices?

13. In how many ways can a party of 6 children be chosen from a group of 14 children, which includes Jane and Mark, if
- **(i)** any child may be selected?
- **(ii)** Mark must be selected?
- **(iii)** Jane must not be selected?
- **(iv)** Jane and Mark must either both be selected or both not selected?

14. Four different digits are to be chosen from the digits 1 to 9 inclusive.
- **(i)** If there are no restrictions, how many choices are possible?
- **(ii)** How many of these choices contain two even digits and two odd digits?
- **(iii)** How many choices of four digits contain at least three odd digits?
- **(iv)** How many choices of four digits contain at least one even digit?

15. A group of eight pupils is to be divided into a group of five and a group of three. In how many ways can this be done?

16. How many different groups of six can be selected from five boys and seven girls? How many of these groups consist of three boys and three girls?

17. A committee of five is to be selected from four students and five teachers.
(i) How many different committees of five are possible?
(ii) How many of these possible committees have three students and two teachers?

18. A student has to choose eight out of ten questions on an examination paper.
(i) How many choices are possible if any eight questions can be chosen?
(ii) How many choices are possible if exactly two out of the first three questions must be attempted?
(iii) How many choices are possible if at least two out of the first three questions must be attempted?

19. A man is dealt five cards from an ordinary pack of playing cards.
(i) In how many ways will the cards contain exactly two kings?
(ii) In how many ways will the cards contain at least one king?
(iii) In how many ways will the cards contain three of one kind and two of another kind, e.g. three jacks and two aces?

20. A club has only 8 women and 6 men as members. A team of 3 is to be chosen to represent the club. In how many ways can this be done if
(i) there are no restrictions?
(ii) the club captain must be on the team?
(iii) there must be at least one woman on the team?
(iv) there must be more women than men on the team?

21. Find the value of the natural number n if $\binom{n}{2} = 91$.

22. Find the value of the natural number n if $\binom{n}{2} = 136$.

23. Find the value of the natural number n if $\binom{n+1}{2} = 190$.

Revision Exercises 21

1. Katie must choose five subjects from nine available subjects.
The nine subjects include French and German.
(i) How many different combinations of five subjects are possible?
(ii) How many different combinations are possible if Katie wishes to study German but not French?

2. Six people, including Mary and John, sit in a row.
(i) How many different arrangements of the six people are possible?
(ii) In how many of these arrangements are Mary and John next to each other?

3. **(i)** How many different selections of four letters can be made from the letters of the word FLORIDA?
(ii) How many of these selections contain at least one vowel?

4. The password for a mobile phone consists of five digits.
(i) How many passwords are possible?
(ii) How many of these passwords start with a 2 and finish with an odd digit?

5. How many three-digit numbers can be formed from the digits 1, 2, 3, 4, 5 if
(i) the three digits are all different?
(ii) the three digits are all the same?

6. **(i)** How many different groups of four can be selected from five boys and six girls?
(ii) How many of these groups consist of two boys and two girls?

7. A committee of five is to be selected from six students and three teachers.
(i) How many different committees are possible?
(ii) How many of these possible committees have three students and two teachers?

8. At the Olympic Games, eight lanes are marked on the running track.
Each runner is allocated to a different lane. Find the number of ways in which the runners in a heat can be allocated to these lanes when there are
(i) eight runners in the heat.
(ii) five runners in the heat and any five lanes may be used.

9. How many arrangements of the letters SWARMED are possible if the A and the R must be separated by at least one letter?

10. How many natural numbers, with different digits, can be formed with the digits 1, 2, 3, 4? How many can be formed if 0 is substituted for 1?

11. **(i)** How many integers between 100 and 1000 have different digits?
(ii) How many integers between 100 and 10000 have different digits?

12. How many different arrangements of 5 letters can be formed from 7 different consonants and 4 different vowels if no 2 consonants or vowels can come together, and no repetitions are allowed?

13. How many five letter selections of the letters of the word REGIONAL consisting of three consonants and two vowels can be formed if no letter is repeated? In how many ways can these five be arranged?

14. Find the number of ways in which 8 different books can be distributed to 2 people, A and B, if each is to receive at least 2 books.

22 Introduction to Probability

The idea of chance is well known to all. We often ask questions such as 'what is the chance of next week-end being fine?'. The idea of probability is to put the concept of chance on a firm mathematical footing.

This is important if we want to compare probabilities, i.e. to see which of many possible outcomes is most likely. In finance, probability is used to assess risk, e.g. the risk of a company experiencing a downtown in trade or, in actuarial work, the probability of a person surviving to a certain age.

In medieval times, the idea of probability was treated intuitively, e.g. the probability of a ship sinking while undertaking a certain voyage. The mathematical treatment of probability started with a series of correspondence between two great French mathematicians, Pierre de Fermat and Blaise Pascal. This correspondence was devoted to how to divide the stake in an unfinished game of chance. Later, other mathematicians such as Bernoulli and De Moivre established a more solid mathematical basis for probability, as we begin to see in this chapter.

22.1 Concept of Probability

The concept of **chance** applies to any real life situation in which there is uncertainty. For example, we could talk about the chance of lightning striking your school this month or of there being a white Christmas in Cork this year. In each case, we are talking about an event that may or may not happen. Each of the above examples is difficult to predict accurately.

Probability is the mathematical treatment of the idea of chance. We take the ideas of 'highly unlikely' and 'very likely' for example, and convert them into numerical form. With this as our aim, there is the need for clear definitions and concepts, along with rules and formulae for the purpose of calculation.

Examples where we talk about probability include the following:

(i) getting a diamond when a card is selected at random from a standard pack of cards,

(ii) getting a total of 10 when two different numbers are chosen at random from the numbers 1, 2, 3, 4, 5, 6, 7, 8, 9,

(iii) getting all heads when a fair coin is tossed four times.

As we will see, probability is measured on a scale from 0 to 1. A probability of 0 represents something that can't happen, e.g. that Tokyo will win the All-Ireland hurling championship. A probability of 1 represents something that must happen, e.g. that you will die.

Then, the nearer a probability is to 0, the less likely it is to happen, e.g. the probability of winning the National Lottery is very small. The nearer a probability is to 1, the more likely it is to happen, e.g. the probability of it raining somewhere in Ireland in April next year would be very close to 1.

A probability of 0·5, or $\frac{1}{2}$ or 50%, represents something that is equally likely to occur and not to occur, e.g. getting a head when a fair coin is tossed. Probabilities greater than 0·5 are more likely to occur than not to occur, while probabilities less than 0·5 are more likely not to occur than to occur. The following probability line illustrates these.

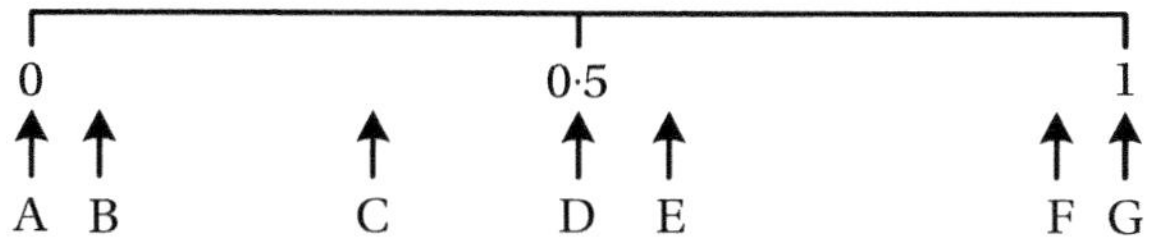

You should try answering the following questions yourself, with reference to the events A to G whose probabilities are shown.

1. Name an event that is extremely likely, but not certain, to occur.
2. Name an event which is impossible, i.e. can't occur.
3. Name an event which is equally likely to occur and not to occur.
4. Name three events that are more likely to occur than C.
5. Name an event that is not impossible, but is less likely to occur than C.

The mathematical treatment of probability needs us to understand a number of important concepts, and to learn some notation.

1. Experiment

Examples of **experiments** are: pick a card, choose two numbers, toss a fair coin four times, etc. It is important to be able to identify an experiment and realise that it is independent of any particular outcome that we want to happen. Carrying out the experiment once is often referred to as a **trial**.

Many experiments are referred to as **random** experiments. To be random, there should be no way of knowing the outcome of a trial until after it has been conducted. On the other hand, if a person is chosen **at random** from the members of a club, it implies that each club member has an equal chance of being chosen.

2. Outcomes (Sample Points)

When an experiment is performed, each possible outcome is referred to as a **sample point**. For example, if a die is thrown, the possible outcomes, and sample points, are the numbers 1, 2, 3, 4, 5 and 6. In a simple case like this, the possible outcomes may be easily counted. We say that we have a finite number of discrete outcomes. Later, we will consider experiments where the sample points are all values in an interval, e.g. a person's height.

3. Sample Space (S)

The set of all possible outcomes is called the **sample space** (or **outcome space**) and is denoted by the letter S. For example, if a single number is picked at random from the whole numbers from 1 to 10 inclusive, the sample space is $S = \{1, 2, 3, 4, 5, 6, 7, 8, 9, 10\}$.

The sample space, S, has to be seen in the light of what we want to happen. For example, suppose we have the experiment of throwing two dice.

(i) Suppose we want to find the probability of getting a '1' on the first die and an even number on the second. Then the sample space is $\{(1,1), (1,2), (1,3), ..., (6,5), (6,6)\}$. There are 36 possible sample points, and each of these is an **elementary outcome** because it cannot be broken down into a number of cases. Each of these elementary outcomes is equally likely.

(ii) Now suppose we are interested in the probability of getting a total of 9 when the numbers on the two dice are added. Then the sample space should be considered to be all possible totals when two dice are thrown, i.e. $\{2, 3, ..., 11, 12\}$. These sample points (outcomes) are not elementary outcomes because most can be broken down into a number of elementary outcomes. Nor are they equally likely: we are more likely to get a total of 7 than a total of 12.

Unless we are given a specific task, we take the default sample space to consist of all elementary outcomes.

4. Event (E)

An **event** is something that may, or may not, happen when an experiment is conducted. The symbol for an event is E. It is very important to be able to distinguish between an experiment and an event. An experiment is what must happen, e.g. picking a card from a standard pack of cards, we can get any of

52 different cards. An event is what we want to happen, e.g. getting a diamond. For this event, there are 13 possible outcomes, or sample points.

5. **Experimental Probability**

Suppose we want to find the probability of getting a head when a fair coin is tossed. The sample space, S, for this experiment is $S = \{\text{head, tail}\}$. The event, E, is $E = \{\text{head}\}$.

We can take the fair coin and toss it as many times as we like. From the results of these trials, we can estimate the probability of getting a head, written $P(E)$ or $P(\text{head})$. This type of probability is called **experimental probability**, and it provides an estimate of the true, or theoretical, probability.

For example, suppose we toss the coin 100 times and get a head 46 times and a tail 54 times.

Then $$P(E) = \frac{\text{number of times a head occurs}}{\text{number of trials}} = \frac{46}{100} = \frac{23}{50}.$$

This method of calculating probability is called **relative frequency**. Note that if *you* toss a coin 100 times, your experience will most likely be different. However, the greater the number of trials involved, the closer the experimental probability will be to the theoretical probability.

Definition of Experimental Probability

Suppose S is the sample space for an experiment, and E is an event. Then the definition of the (experimental) probability of E, $P(E)$, is the relative frequency of E, i.e.

$$P(E) = \frac{\text{number of times } E \text{ occurs}}{\text{total number of trials}}.$$

6. **Theoretical Probability**

Suppose we toss a coin many, many times. If the event, E, is getting a head, then as the number of trials increases, common sense tells us that the value of the experimental probability, $P(E)$, will get closer and closer to $\frac{1}{2}$. If it were possible to repeat the experiment an infinite number of times, then the value of the **long run relative frequency**

$$P(E) = \frac{\text{number of times a head occurs}}{\text{number of trials}}$$

would be exactly $\frac{1}{2}$.

This is called the **theoretical probability**, or simply the **probability** of the event E. It is important to remember that experimental probability, i.e. probability taken from experimental data, only provides an estimate of the true probability of an event.

Definition of Probability (Theoretical Probability)

Suppose S is the sample space for an experiment, and E is an event. Then the definition of the (theoretical) probability of E, $P(E)$, is the value of the ***long run relative frequency*** of E, i.e.

$$P(E) = \frac{\text{number of times } E \text{ occurs}}{\text{total number of trials}},$$

as the total number of trials becomes very large.

From the definition, we can say that $0 \leq P(E) \leq 1$, as the number of times E occurs can neither be negative nor greater than the total number of trials.

7. Expected Number in Repeated Trials

Suppose the probability of an event E occurring in a single trial is p, i.e. $P(E) = p$. Then, if n trials are performed, the expected number of times that E will occur is $n \times p$.

For example, the probability of getting a head when a coin is tossed is $\frac{1}{2}$. Thus, the expected number of heads when a coin is tossed 1000 times is

$$1000 \times \frac{1}{2} = 500.$$

Example 1

A small restaurant records the main course choices of its customers over a period of time. The results are given in the table below.

Choice	Beef	Chicken	Fish	Vegetarian	Lamb
Number	22	54	76	10	38

(i) How many main course choices were recorded?

(ii) What is the probability that a new customer will choose lamb as her main course? Is this experimental probability or theoretical probability?

(iii) The restaurant has bookings for 40 people one evening. How many lamb courses can it expect to serve that evening, rounding up to the nearest whole number?

Solution

(i) The number of choices is $22 + 54 + 76 + 10 + 38 = 200$.

(ii) Based on the figures available, the probability that a new customer will choose lamb is $\frac{38}{200} = \frac{19}{100} = 0{\cdot}19 = 19\%$.

As the calculation is based on experimental data, this is an example of experimental probability.

(iii) The expected number of customers who will choose lamb for their main course is

$$n \times p = 40 \times 0{\cdot}19 = 7{\cdot}6 = 8,$$

rounding up to the nearest whole number.

Exercises 22.1

1. A card is picked at random from a pack of cards. We want to find the probability of getting a diamond.
   (i) Describe the sample space in terms of elementary outcomes.
   (ii) List the outcomes in the event.
   (iii) If instead the sample space was $S = \{\text{club, diamond, heart, spade}\}$, are all sample points equally likely? Discuss.
   (iv) With this sample space, list the outcome in the event.

2. We have a die which may or may not be fair. We want to find the probability of getting an even number when the die is thrown. The die is thrown 120 times and the results are given in the table below.

Number	1	2	3	4	5	6
Frequency	17	28	22	11	16	26

(i) Describe the experiment. List the outcomes in the sample space.
(ii) Describe the event. List the outcomes in the event.
(iii) Use the data in the table to estimate the probability of getting an even number when the die is thrown.
(iv) This die is now thrown a further 600 times. Based on the data above, what is the expected number of times a '2' will be obtained in these 600 throws?

3. A restaurant menu contains 5 main courses, which we will call A, B, C, D, E. In order to streamline their ordering of ingredients, the manager decides to find the probability of a customer ordering each of the main courses. Over a period of time, she decides to record the number of customers who choose each of the main courses. The results are given in the following table.

Main course	A	B	C	D	E
Frequency	51	72	23	45	59

(i) How many customer choices were recorded?
(ii) Use the data in the table to calculate the experimental probability that a customer will pick main course B.
(iii) Main courses A, C and D require carrots. Estimate the probability that a customer will have carrots in their main course.
(iv) If on a given evening, the restaurant serves 75 customers, estimate the expected number of customers who will be served carrots.
(v) Choices B and D are vegetarian. Estimate the probability of a customer choosing a vegetarian option.

4. A bag contains five discs numbered 1, 2, 3, 4, 5. Fifty students choose two of these discs at random, and the sum of the two numbers chosen is recorded. The results are given in the table below.

Total	3	4	5	6	7	8	9
Frequency	4	3	12	9	15	2	5

(i) From the table, what are the elements of the sample space? Are these elementary outcomes? Explain.
(ii) Are the outcomes in the sample space equally likely? Explain.
(iii) Use the data to estimate the probability that the sum of the numbers drawn is an even number.

5. Four cards are chosen from a standard pack of cards. We want to find the probability of getting exactly three '7's.
(i) Viewing the sample space as the number of '7's we can get, list the outcomes in the sample space.
(ii) Are these outcomes equally likely? Explain.

6. A fair die is thrown four times, and on each occasion a number less than 3 is the result. Is the probability of getting a number less than 3 on the next throw different from the probability of getting a number less than 3 on the first throw?

7. The probability of an archer hitting the bulls-eye with a single arrow is 0·35. If he shoots 60 arrows, what is the expected number of bulls-eyes he will get?

8. Data shows that the probability of a cyclist having a puncture while cycling 1 km is 0·00035. Over a year, a dedicated cyclist cycles 10000 km. What is the expected number of punctures he will have in that year? Is it possible for him to have exactly this number of punctures?

22.2 Probability for Equally Likely Outcomes

In this section, we consider calculating probabilities (theoretical probabilities) in cases where the sample points are all equally likely.

Some examples are as follows.

(i) Pick a card at random from a standard pack of cards. The equally likely outcomes are the 52 cards.

(ii) A student is picked at random from those in your class. The equally likely outcomes are all the students in your class.

(iii) Two different digits are chosen at random from the digits from 1 to 9 inclusive. Each possible choice of two digits, e.g. 3 and 7, is equally likely.

In practice, we can use the following procedure to calculate the probability of an event.

1. Identify the experiment, and determine n, the number of possible outcomes for the experiment. This number may be written $n = \#(S)$, where $\#(S)$ stands for the number of elements in the sample space, S.

2. Identify the event, E, and determine r, the number of outcomes in the event. This number can be written $r = \#(E)$, and is often referred to as the 'number of favourable outcomes.'

Then we can use the following formula.

Probability for Equally Likely Outcomes

Suppose S is the sample space for an experiment, and $\#(S) = n$. Suppose E is an event, and $\#(E) = r$. If all sample points are equally likely, then $P(E)$, the probability of E, is given by

$$P(E) = \frac{r}{n} = \frac{\#(E)}{\#(S)} = \frac{\text{number of favourable outcomes}}{\text{total number of possible outcomes}}.$$

In some probability questions, it will be necessary to use the results from arrangements and combinations to calculate n or r or both. It may also be necessary to use the Fundamental Principles of Counting.

Example 1

A bag contains twenty discs marked with the whole numbers from 1 to 20 inclusive.

(i) If one disc is picked at random from the bag, find the probability that the number on the disc is divisible by 3.

(ii) If two discs are picked at random from the bag, what is the probability of getting one even numbered disc and one odd numbered disc?

Solution

(i) (*We must identify the experiment and sample space. Then we calculate n. Moving on to the event, we calculate r. At that stage we can write down the probability.*)

Experiment: Pick a disc. (*S is the numbers from 1 to 20.*)

$n = \#(S) = 20$

Event: Pick a disc which is divisible by 3: 3, 6, 9, 12, 15, 18.

$r = \#(E) = 6$

Then $P(E) = \frac{r}{n} = \frac{6}{20} = \frac{3}{10}.$

(ii) (*The experiment here is different: choose any 2 from 20 different numbers. It is not practical to list the outcomes in S, but we can count them using the 'nCr' formula from Chapter 21. The event, E, is more complicated. We want to choose 1 from 10 even numbers* ***and*** *1 from 10 odd numbers. We can then use the Fundamental Principle of Counting to calculate r.*)

Experiment: Choose 2 from 20 numbers.

$n = \#(S) = \binom{20}{2} = 190$

Event: (Choose 1 from 10 even) and (Choose 1 from 10 odd)

$r = \binom{10}{1} \times \binom{10}{1} = 10 \times 10 = 100$

Then $P(E) = \frac{r}{n} = \frac{100}{190} = \frac{10}{19}.$

Example 2

A bag contains 4 red, 3 blue and 5 white markers. Three markers are drawn at random from those in the bag. Brian bets that all three markers will be of different colours while Katie bets that all three markers will be of the same colour. Determine who has the greater probability of winning.

Solution

(*First, we must identify the experiment and count the number of outcomes in the sample space. The experiment is to choose* ***any*** *3 from all 12 markers.*)

Experiment: Choose 3 from 12 markers

$n = \#(S) = \binom{12}{3} = 220$

Brian:

(*The event, E, is getting one marker of each colour, i.e. one red* ***and*** *one blue* ***and*** *one white. The Fundamental Principle of Counting may be used to find r.*)

Event, E: Choose (1 from 4 red) **and** (1 from 3 blue) **and** (1 from 5 white)

$r = \#(E)$

$= \binom{4}{1} \times \binom{3}{1} \times \binom{5}{1} = 4 \times 3 \times 5 = 60$

Then $P(E) = \frac{r}{n} = \frac{60}{220} = \frac{3}{11}.$

Katie:

(*The event, E, is getting three markers the same colour. We can break this down to either 3 red or 3 blue or 3 white. The Second Fundamental Principle of Counting can then be used to calculate r.*)

Event, E: Choose (3 from 4 red) **or** (3 from 3 blue) **or** (3 from 5 white)

$$r = \#(E)$$

$$= \binom{4}{3} + \binom{3}{3} + \binom{5}{3} = 4 + 1 + 10 = 15$$

Then $P(E) = \frac{r}{n} = \frac{15}{220} = \frac{3}{44}$.

Thus, Brian has a greater probability of winning.

If an experiment consists of two stages, with a small number of possible outcomes for each stage, then these outcomes can be shown in what is called a **two way table**. Then the outcomes that belong to an event can be highlighted and counted. A good example of this is when two dice are thrown. A two-way table is especially useful for two stage experiments where the event is particularly involved.

Example 3

Two dice are thrown. What is the probability that we get a total which is a prime number?

Solution

(*When two dice are thrown, we can get any number from 1 to 6 on the first die, and any number from 1 to 6 on the second die. These can be laid out in the form of a table, as shown below. The outcomes belonging to the event can then be indicated by dots or other marks.*)

Experiment: Throw two dice.

If we use the notation (3,5) to stand for getting a 3 on the first die and a 5 on the second, then

$$S = \{(1,1), (1,2), \dots, (6,5), (6,6)\}. \text{ Thus}$$

$$n = \#(S) = 6 \times 6 = 36$$

Event, E: Get a prime total, i.e. a total of 2, 3, 5, 7 or 11. The table below shows which outcomes give a prime total.

2nd Die						
6	●				●	
5		●				●
4	●		●			
3		●		●		
2	●		●		●	
1	●	●		●		●
	1	2	3	4	5	6

1st Die

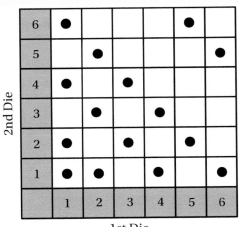

From the table,

$$r = \#(E) = 15$$

Then $P(E) = \frac{r}{n} = \frac{15}{36} = \frac{5}{12}$.

Exercises 22.2

1. A class consists of 10 boys and 12 girls. One student is chosen at random as the class representative. We want to find the probability that it is a boy.
   (i) What is the experiment? Describe the elementary outcomes in the sample space, S. What is $\#(S)$?
   (ii) Describe the event E and the outcomes in the event. What is $\#(E)$?
   (iii) Calculate the probability of getting a boy when one student is chosen at random from a class of 10 boys and 12 girls.

2. A bag contains 5 green markers and 7 red markers. One of these markers is picked at random from the bag. We want to find the probability that it is a green marker.
   (i) What is the experiment? Describe the elementary outcomes in the sample space, S. What is $\#(S)$?
   (ii) Describe the event E and the outcomes in the event. What is $\#(E)$?
   (iii) Calculate the probability of getting a green marker when one marker is picked at random from a bag containing 5 green and 7 red markers.

3. A fair die is thrown once. We want to find the probability of getting a '3' or a '4'.
   (i) What is the experiment? List the outcomes in the sample space, S. How many outcomes are there in the sample space?
   (ii) Are all these outcomes equally likely? Discuss.
   (iii) What is the event, E? How many outcomes are there in the event, i.e. what is the number of favourable outcomes?
   (iv) Calculate the probability of getting a '3' or a '4' when a fair die is thrown once.

4. Two different numbers are chosen at random from the whole numbers from 1 to 10 inclusive.
   (i) How many choices are possible?
   (ii) List the choices that give a total of 5 when the two numbers are added.
   (iii) What is the probability that we get a total of 5 when two different numbers are chosen from the whole numbers from 1 to 10 inclusive?

5. A shelf contains ten different books, which includes the books A, B and C. Three books are chosen at random from the shelf.
   (i) In how many ways can these three books be chosen?
   (ii) In how many ways can the three books be chosen if the choice contains exactly one of A, B and C?
   (iii) Find the probability that if three books are chosen at random from the shelf, then exactly one of the books A, B and C will be chosen.

6. A bag contains three red markers and five blue markers. The red markers are numbered 1, 2 and 3, while the blue markers are numbered 4, 5, 6, 7 and 8. A single marker is drawn at random from the bag. Find the probability that
   (i) it is a red marker.
   (ii) the number on the marker drawn is not a 2 or a 4.
   (iii) the marker is either red or shows an even number.

7. Two people are picked at random from 5 men and 7 women. Find the probability of getting
   (i) one man and one woman.
   (ii) two women.

8. Four people are selected at random from a group of 6 Irish, 5 Welsh and 9 English people. Find the probability that all those selected are of the same nationality.

9. A group of students consists of 5 girls and 8 boys. One of the girls is called Mary and one of the boys is called John. If two people are chosen at random from the group, find the probability that neither Mary nor John is chosen.

10. A person chooses 3 balls at random from a bag containing 8 black, 6 white and 4 red balls. Find the probability that one of each colour is chosen.

11. All the letters of the word TODAY are arranged at random.
- **(i)** In how many ways may this be done?
- **(ii)** In how many ways can the letters be arranged if the O and the A must be side by side?
- **(iii)** Find the probability that if all the letters of the word TODAY are arranged at random, the O and the A will be side by side.

12. Two dice are thrown.
- **(i)** What is the probability of getting two identical numbers or a total of five?
- **(ii)** What is the probability that the product of the two numbers is at least twice their sum?

13. Two dice are thrown. What is the probability of getting
- **(i)** a total of two or a total of six?
- **(ii)** a total greater than nine or a total which is prime?

22.3 Set Theory and the Axioms of Probability

In the last section, we met the formula $P(E) = \frac{\#(E)}{\#(S)} = \frac{r}{n}$, for calculating probabilities.

However, ***this formula is only valid if each of the outcomes in the sample space is equally likely***, which is not always the case. To develop a more general mathematical theory of probability, we will use the concepts and results from set theory.

The usual representation of the sample space, S, is as a universal set, and an event, E, is shown as a subset of S, as seen opposite.

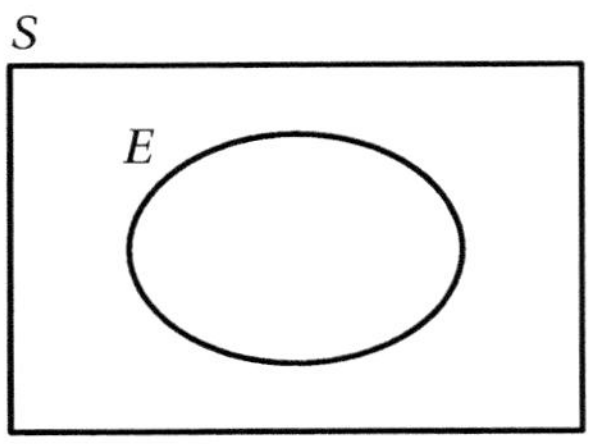

From the set theory point of view, there are some ideas we need to understand. When talking about more than one event, we will call them A, B, etc.

1. **Null Set, $\varnothing$.**
   The null set is the event that contains no elements, or outcomes.

2. **Intersection is the same as 'and'.**
   Suppose A and B are two events, which are represented by two sets on a Venn diagram. The intersection of the two sets, $A \cap B$, represents those outcomes that belong to both events. We call this the event that both A **and** B occur. This is shown opposite.

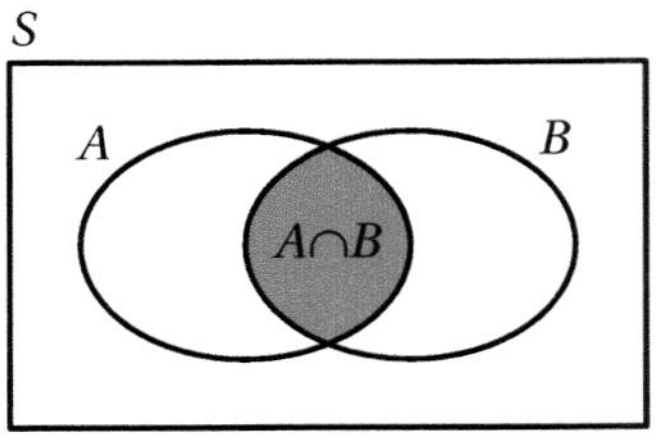

3. **Union is the same as 'or'.**
   Suppose A and B are two events. Then the event that either A or B, or both, occur, i.e. the event A **or** B, is represented by the **union** of the two sets, A and B, which is shown opposite.

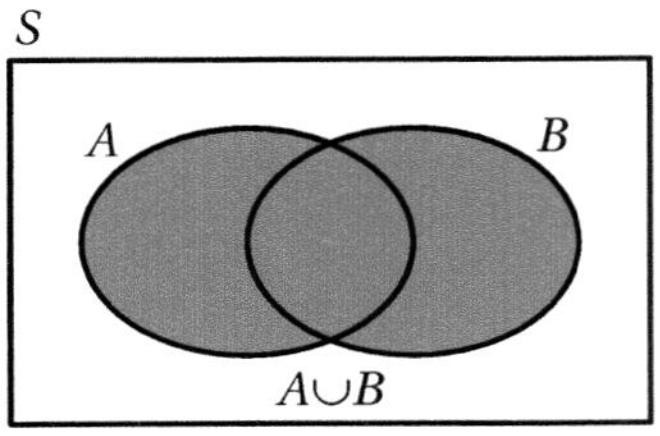

4. **Disjoint is the same as 'mutually exclusive'.**
Two events, A and B, are said to be **mutually exclusive** if they have no outcomes in common, i.e. it is not possible for both events to occur in a single trial. In terms of set theory, we call the sets A and B **disjoint**. This means that the intersection of the two sets is the null set, i.e. $A \cap B = \varnothing$. This is shown opposite on a Venn diagram.

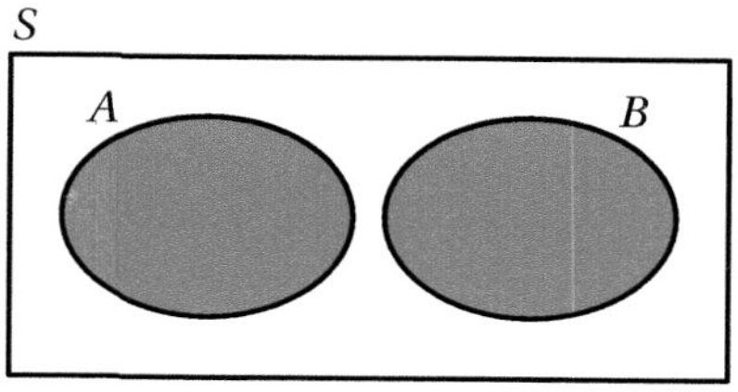

If the sets are shown overlapping, then the region of overlap is empty.

The mathematical treatment of general probability (not necessarily equally likely outcomes) is based on a number of ***axioms***, which are starting assumptions, taken to be obvious. These may then be used to develop rules, results, formulae, etc.

Axioms of Probability

To each event, E, of a sample space S of an experiment, we associate a number, $P(E)$, which is the probability of E. Probability satisfies the following axioms, where $\varnothing$ is the null set.

Axiom 1: $0 \le P(E) \le 1$.

Axiom 2: **(i)** $P(S) = 1$
(ii) $P(\varnothing) = 0$.

Axiom 3: If A and B are mutually exclusive events, then
$P(A \cup B) = P(A) + P(B)$.

Axiom 1 generalises what we met for equally likely events in the last section. The probability of any event cannot be negative and cannot be greater than 1.

The sample space, S, covers all possible outcomes for an experiment, and so must happen when a trial is conducted. Axiom 2 says that if some event must happen, then its probability is 1. Also, the null set, $\varnothing$, cannot happen (because we must get some outcome when a trial is conducted), and so its probability is 0.

Axiom 3 states that if two events are mutually exclusive, then the probability of one event or the other happening can be found by adding their individual probabilities. This axiom can be extended to any number of mutually exclusive events, i.e.

$$P(A \cup B \cup C....) = P(A) + P(B) + P(C) + ...$$

Example 1

For an experiment, A, B and C are three events such that $P(A) = \frac{2}{3}$, $P(B) = \frac{1}{5}$ and $P(C) = \frac{3}{7}$.

(i) If A and B are mutually exclusive, calculate $P(A \cup B)$.

(ii) By calculating $P(A) + P(C)$, explain why A and C are not mutually exclusive.

Solution

(i) (*As A and B are mutually exclusive, we can use Axiom 3.*)

$$P(A \cup B) = P(A) + P(B)$$
$$= \frac{2}{3} + \frac{1}{5} = \frac{13}{15}.$$

(ii) (*The following is a further example of what is known as* ***proof by contradiction.***)

Suppose A and C are mutually exclusive. Then we can use Axiom 3 to calculate the probability of the event $A \cup C$.

$$P(A \cup C) = P(A) + P(C)$$
$$= \frac{2}{3} + \frac{3}{7} = \frac{23}{21}$$

But, by Axiom 1, the probability of any event cannot be greater than 1, and so this cannot be true. Hence, A and C are not mutually exclusive.

Example 2

A single card is drawn at random from a pack of cards.

(i) Are the events of getting a '4' and getting a king mutually exclusive? Discuss.

(ii) Calculate the probability of getting a '4' or a king.

Solution

(i) Getting a '4' and getting a king are mutually exclusive as it is not possible for a single card drawn from a pack of cards to be simultaneously a '4' and a 'king'.

(ii) Let A be the event that we get a '4', and let B be the event that we get a king.

Then

$$P(A) = \frac{4}{52} = \frac{1}{13} \quad \text{and} \quad P(B) = \frac{4}{52} = \frac{1}{13}.$$

Thus $P(\text{'4' or king}) = P(A \cup B)$

$$= P(A) + P(B)$$
$$= \frac{1}{13} + \frac{1}{13} = \frac{2}{13}.$$

Exercises 22.3

1. E is an event for an experiment. Which are possible values of $P(E)$, the probability of E?

(i) $\frac{4}{5}$, **(ii)** $\frac{11}{9}$, **(iii)** $\frac{-1}{6}$, **(iv)** 0, **(v)** $\frac{118}{123}$.

2. The probabilities of three events, A, B and C are $\frac{114}{139}$, $\frac{41}{50}$ and $\frac{53}{66}$, respectively.

(i) Which of the three events is most likely to occur when the experiment is performed?

(ii) Is it possible for any two of the three events to be mutually exclusive? Explain.

3. A and B are two mutually exclusive events for an experiment. $P(A) = \frac{13}{25}$ and $P(B) = \frac{2}{7}$. Calculate $P(A \cup B)$.

4. E and F are two events for an experiment. $P(E) = \frac{3}{5}$ and $P(F) = \frac{2}{7}$.

(i) If $P(E \cup F) = \frac{29}{35}$, are E and F mutually exclusive? Explain.

(ii) If E and F are mutually exclusive, calculate $P(E \cup F)$.

5. A and B are two events for an experiment. $P(A) = \frac{4}{9}$ and $P(A \cup B) = \frac{38}{45}$.
   If A and B are mutually exclusive, calculate $P(B)$.

6. E and F are two events for an experiment and $P(E) = \frac{5}{9}$. If E and F are mutually exclusive, find the greatest possible value of $P(F)$.

7. A single disc is picked at random from a bag containing 20 discs, numbered from 1 to 20 inclusive. A is the event that the number on the disc picked is divisible by 5, and B is the event that the number on the disc picked is divisible by 7.
   (i) Are A and B mutually exclusive? Explain.
   (ii) Find the probability that the number on the disc picked is divisible by 5 or by 7.

8. A coin is tossed four times. A is the event that we get 4 heads, and B is the event that we get 2 heads and 2 tails.
   (i) Are A and B mutually exclusive? Explain.
   (ii) Find the probability that we get 4 heads or 2 heads and 2 tails.

9. Two different numbers are chosen from the digits 1, 2, 3, 4, 5. A is the event that the sum of the two chosen numbers is even, and B is the event that the sum of the two numbers chosen is odd.
   (i) Calculate $P(A)$.
   (ii) Calculate $P(B)$.
   (iii) Are A and B mutually exclusive? Explain.
   (iv) Calculate $P(A \cup B)$. Explain your answer.
   (v) If C is the event that one of the chosen numbers is 2, are A and C mutually exclusive? Explain.

10. An EU committee consists of 5 French, 3 Polish and 4 Italian members. Three of these people are to be selected at random. A is the event that all three are of the same nationality, and B is the event that one of each nationality is picked.
   (i) Calculate $P(A)$.
   (ii) Calculate $P(B)$.
   (iii) Are A and B mutually exclusive?
   (iv) Calculate the probability that the three people chosen are either of the same nationality or one of each of the three nationalities.

22.4 Success and Failure

From the theory of sets, the **complement** of E, written E' or E^c, is the set of elements belonging to S which do not belong to E. This region can be indicated on a Venn diagram, as shown opposite.

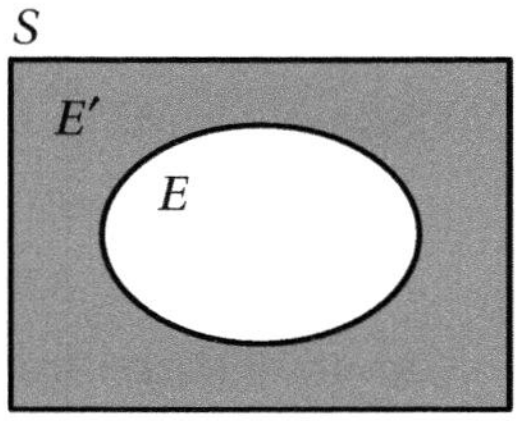

For example, if $S = \{1, 2, 3, 4, 5, 6\}$ and $E = \{1, 2\}$, then $E' = \{3, 4, 5, 6\}$.

The idea of the complement can often be used with great effect in probability questions. Sometimes it can be very tedious to calculate directly the probability of a specified event, E. In many such cases, it can be much easier to calculate the ***opposite*** of E, i.e. that E does not happen. In terms of sets, this is just the complement of E, i.e. E'.

From the diagram above, we can see that E and E' are disjoint sets (mutually exclusive events) and their union is the whole sample space, S. Thus,

$S = E \cup E'$
$P(S) = P(E \cup E')$
$1 = P(E) + P(E')$ ... by Axioms 2(i), 3
$P(E) = 1 - P(E')$.

Thus, the probability of the event E can be found by subtracting the probability of its complement, E' (which means that E does not happen), from 1. E', the complement of E, can also be defined by $E' = S \setminus E$, read as 'S not E' or 'S less E'.

The usual approach to this in probability is to use the following terminology.
Success: This is the event E, that we want to find the probability of.
Failure: This is the event E', meaning the opposite of E, or alternatively, that E does not happen.

Thus, we have the following formula.

Probability of Success and Failure

If **success** is the event E, and **failure** is the event E', which is that E does not happen, then

$$P(\text{success}) = 1 - P(\text{failure}).$$

Naturally, to take advantage of what can often be a very useful shortcut, it is very important to be able to identify the opposite of an event specified in a question. It is equally important to be able to decide if it is easier to calculate the probability of E directly, or to use this formula. Some indicators that we should consider using the success formula are phrases such as 'at least', 'at most', 'more than', and so on.

Example 1

A multinational company, with operations in France, Italy and Ireland has a board of directors which consists of 7 French, 6 Italian and 5 Irish directors. A group of three directors is to be chosen at random to attend a conference. What is the probability that there is at least one Irish director in the group selected?

Solution

(*The phrase 'at least' means that we should consider using success and failure. If failure is easier to calculate than success, then we will use this approach. In this question, success would be getting 1 or 2 or 3 Irish directors. Failure, the opposite, would be getting no Irish directors. This is much easier to calculate the probability of.*)

Experiment: Choose 3 from 7 + 6 + 5 = 18 directors

$$n = \#(S) = \binom{18}{3} = 816$$

Success: Choose 1 or 2 or 3 Irish directors

Failure: Choose 0 Irish directors

= Choose 3 from 7 + 6 = 13 other directors

$$r = \binom{13}{3} = 286$$

Then $P(\text{failure}) = \dfrac{286}{816} = \dfrac{143}{408}$

and $P(\text{success}) = 1 - P(\text{failure})$

$$= 1 - \frac{143}{408} = \frac{265}{408}.$$

Exercises 22.4

1. A pair of dice are rolled. What is the probability of getting one or more '6'?
2. Four children are chosen at random from 8 boys and 8 girls. What is the probability of getting at most 3 boys?
3. Two dice are thrown and the numbers obtained are added. What is the probability of getting a total more than 4?
4. Four letters are chosen at random from the letters of the word MISBEHAVIOUR. What is the probability of getting at least one vowel?
5. A fair coin is tossed three times.
   (i) Find the probability of getting at least one head.
   (ii) Find the probability of getting at most one head.
6. Three people are chosen at random from 5 men and 9 women.
   (i) Find the probability of getting at least one man.
   (ii) Find the probability of getting at most one man.
7. Six people are chosen at random and asked to name their birth-months. Assuming that each month is equally likely, find the probability of at least two of the people having the same birth-month.
8. There are thirty days in June. Five students have their birthdays in June. The birthdays are independent of each other and all dates are equally likely. What is the probability that at least two of the students have the same birthday?

Revision Exercises 22

1. Four cards are selected from a standard pack of 52 cards. Find the probability that
   (i) the four cards selected are the four kings.
   (ii) two of the cards are clubs and the other two are diamonds.
2. Nine cards are numbered from 1 to 9 inclusive. Three cards are drawn at random from the nine cards.
   (i) Find the probability that the card numbered 8 is not drawn.
   (ii) Find the probability that all three cards drawn have odd numbers.
   (iii) Find the probability that at least one even numbered card is drawn.
3. There are sixteen discs in a board-game: five blue, three green, six red and two yellow. Four discs are chosen at random. What is the probability that
   (i) the four discs are blue?
   (ii) all four discs are different in colour?
   (iii) two of the discs are blue and two are not blue?
   (iv) at least one of the discs is blue?
4. Ten discs, each marked with a different whole number from 1 to 10, are placed in a box. Three of the discs are drawn at random from the box.
   (i) What is the probability that the disc with the number 7 is drawn?
   (ii) What is the probability that the three numbers on the discs drawn are odd?
   (iii) What is the probability that at least one of the numbers drawn is odd?
5. Three cards are chosen from a standard pack of 52 cards. Find the probability that
   (i) the three cards are diamonds.
   (ii) two cards are black and one is a diamond.
   (iii) at least one of the cards is a diamond.

6. Seven cards are numbered with the whole numbers from 1 to 7 inclusive. Two cards are chosen at random from the seven cards.
   E is the event that both numbers are even.
   F is the event that the sum of the two numbers chosen is odd.
   (i) Are E and F mutually exclusive? Explain.
   (ii) Calculate $P(E)$.
   (iii) Calculate $P(F)$.
   (iv) Calculate $P(E \cup F)$.

7. A and B are two events for an experiment. If $P(A) = \frac{5}{7}$ and $P(B) = \frac{4}{9}$, are A and B mutually exclusive events? Explain.

8. A and B are two events for an experiment. $P(A) = \frac{3}{8}$ and $P(B) = \frac{15}{32}$.
   (i) Do we know if A and B are mutually exclusive events? Explain.
   (ii) Can we calculate, from the information given, $P(A \cup B)$? Explain.

9. Two beads are selected from a box containing three black, three red and three yellow beads. Find the probability that
   (i) both discs are yellow.
   (ii) neither of the two discs is yellow.
   (iii) at least one of the discs is yellow.

10. A group of eight is to be chosen at random from eight men and six women. What is the probability that
    (i) the group contains the same number of men and women?
    (ii) the group contains at least one woman?
    (iii) the group contains at least seven men?

11. **(i)** In how many ways can all the letters of the word FRIDAY be arranged?
    (ii) In how many of these arrangements are the two vowels side by side?
    (iii) Find the probability that if the letters of the word FRIDAY are arranged at random, the two vowels will be side by side.

12. **(i)** In how many different ways can eight people be seated in a row?
    (ii) Three girls and five boys sit in a row, arranged at random.
    Find the probability that the three girls are seated together.

13. A bag contains four white marbles and n red marbles. Two marbles are selected at random from the bag.
    (i) If the probability that both are red is $\frac{1}{3}$, find the value of n.
    (ii) The marbles are returned to the bag and three marbles are drawn at random.
    What is the probability that two of these are red?

14. A box contains four silver coins, two gold coins and x copper coins. Two coins are picked at random from the box. If it is known that the probability of picking two copper coins is $\frac{4}{13}$, find the value of x.

15. A bag contains discs of three different colours.
    There are 5 red discs, 1 white disc and x black discs.
    Three discs are picked together at random.
    (i) Write down an expression in x for the probability that the three discs are all different in colour.
    (ii) If the probability that the three discs are all different in colour is equal to the probability that they are all black, find the value of x.

Rules of Probability

23

As the mathematical approach to probability becomes more involved, we build on the axioms of probability first seen in the last chapter. These introduced us to the concept of mutually exclusive events, i.e. events which cannot happen simultaneously.

Expanding on this, we meet first the General Addition Rule, which is required for events which are not mutually exclusive. After this, the next logical concept is that of conditional probability, i.e. the probability of one event occurring knowing that another event has occurred. An understanding of conditional probability is important to properly comprehend the next important concept, namely that of independent events. This in turn leads to the Multiplication Rule and the need to replace it with the General Multiplication Rule when events are not independent.

Finally, we examine Bernoulli trials, named after the famous Swiss mathematician, Jacques Bernoulli. These are independent and identical trials where we are interested in calculating the probability of the number and location of successes and failures.

23.1 General Addition Rule

In the last chapter, Axiom 3 of Probability said that if A and B are two mutually exclusive events for an experiment, then $P(A \cup B) = P(A) + P(B)$. However, if A and B are not mutually exclusive, then we cannot just add $P(A)$ and $P(B)$ to calculate $P(A \cup B)$, because the answer will be too large.

To derive a formula for $P(A \cup B)$ when the events A and B are not mutually exclusive, let $x = P(A \backslash B)$, $y = P(A \cap B)$ and $z = P(B \backslash A)$, where $A \backslash B$ (A less B or A not B) stands for the part of the event A which does not also belong to the event B.

As the events $A \backslash B$, $A \cap B$ and $B \backslash A$ are mutually exclusive, $P(A) = x + y$ and $P(B) = y + z$.

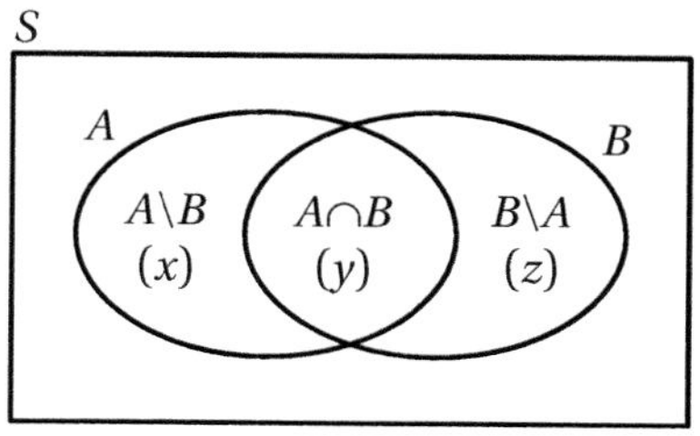

Then

$$\begin{aligned} P(A \cup B) &= x + y + z \\ &= (x + y) + (y + z) - y \\ &= P(A) + P(B) - P(A \cap B) \end{aligned}$$

If you think about it, this makes sense. When the events are not mutually exclusive, $P(A) + P(B)$ counts the probability of the intersection twice. Because we must not count each probability more than once, we have to subtract the probability of the intersection. This is the General Addition Rule.

General Addition Rule

If A and B are two events of an experiment, i.e. A and B are both subsets of the sample space, S, then

$$P(A \cup B) = P(A) + P(B) - P(A \cap B),$$

or $\quad P(A \text{ or } B) = P(A) + P(B) - P(A \text{ and } B)$.

You should note that if A and B are mutually exclusive, then $P(A \cap B) = 0$, and so the General Addition Rule simplifies to Axiom 3: $P(A \cup B) = P(A) + P(B)$. Thus, there is no conflict.

Example 1

Two cards are chosen at random from a standard pack of 52 cards. What is the probability that we get either two hearts or exactly one king?

Solution

(*Getting two hearts and exactly one king are not mutually exclusive. The two cards could be the king of hearts and the 4 of hearts. Then we have the option of trying to list and count all the outcomes in the event. This would be too tedious, so we will use the General Addition Rule.*)

Let A be the event of getting two hearts and let B be the event of getting exactly one king. We want to find the probability of A or B, i.e. $P(A \cup B)$.

Experiment: Choose 2 from 52 cards.

$$n = \binom{52}{2} = 1326$$

A: Choose 2 from 13 hearts.

$$r = \binom{13}{2} = 78$$

Then $P(A) = \frac{78}{1326} = \frac{1}{17}$

B: Get exactly one king.

Choose (1 from 4 kings) and (1 from 48 other cards).

$$r = \binom{4}{1} \times \binom{48}{1} = 192$$

Then $P(B) = \frac{192}{1326} = \frac{32}{221}$

$A \cap B$: Choose 2 hearts to include exactly one king.

Choose (king of hearts) and (1 from 12 other hearts).

$$r = 1 \times \binom{12}{1} = 12$$

Then $P(A \cap B) = \frac{12}{1326} = \frac{2}{221}$

Using the General Addition Rule,

$$P(A \cup B) = P(A) + P(B) - P(A \cap B)$$
$$= \frac{1}{17} + \frac{32}{221} - \frac{2}{221} = \frac{43}{221}.$$

Example 2

E and F are two events of an experiment. The probability of $(E \cup F)'$ is 0·39.

(i) What is $P(E \cup F)$, i.e. the probability of $E \cup F$? Explain.

(ii) If $P(E) = 0{\cdot}45$ and $P(F) = 0{\cdot}36$, find $P(E \cap F)$, i.e. the probability that both E and F occur.

Solution

(i) As $S = (E \cup F) \cup (E \cup F)'$, and these sets are disjoint, by Axiom 3,

$$P(S) = P(E \cup F) + P((E \cup F)')$$
$$1 = P(E \cup F) + 0{\cdot}39 \qquad \text{... by Axiom 2}$$
$$P(E \cup F) = 1 - 0{\cdot}39$$
$$P(E \cup F) = 0{\cdot}61.$$

(ii) By the General Addition Rule,

$P(E \cup F) = P(E) + P(F) - P(E \cap F)$

$0{\cdot}61 = 0{\cdot}45 + 0{\cdot}36 - P(E \cap F)$

$P(E \cap F) + 0{\cdot}61 = 0{\cdot}81$

$P(E \cap F) = 0{\cdot}2.$

or (by Venn diagram)

Let $x = P(E \cap F)$.
Then $P(E \backslash F) = 0{\cdot}45 - x$
and $P(F \backslash E) = 0{\cdot}36 - x$.
Thus,
$P(S) = 1$
$(0{\cdot}45 - x) + x + (0{\cdot}36 - x) + 0{\cdot}39 = 1$
$1{\cdot}2 - x = 1$
$x = 0{\cdot}2$, as before.

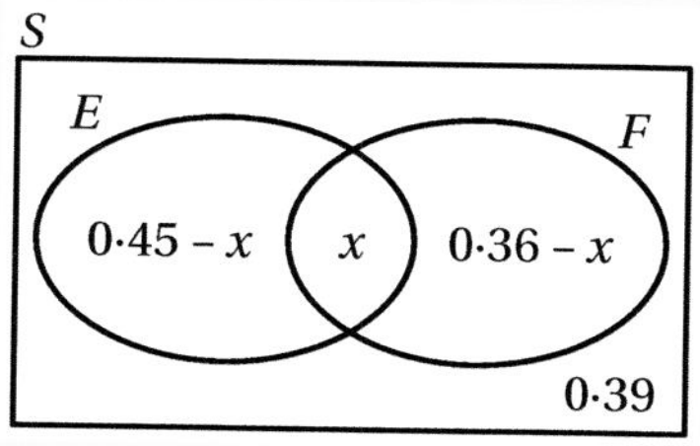

Exercises 23.1

1. A and B are two events of an experiment. If $P(A) = 0{\cdot}55$, $P(B) = 0{\cdot}34$ and $P(A \cap B) = 0{\cdot}21$, calculate $P(A \cup B)$.

2. E and F are two events of an experiment. If $P(E) = \frac{13}{36}$, $P(F) = \frac{3}{4}$ and $P(E \cap F) = \frac{7}{36}$, write $P(E \cup F)$ as a fraction.

3. For two events, E and F, of an experiment, $P(E \cup F) = \frac{9}{10}$, $P(F) = \frac{2}{5}$ and $P(E \cap F) = \frac{1}{4}$. Find $P(E)$, as a fraction.

4. For two events A and B, $P(A) = 0{\cdot}54$, $P(B) = 0{\cdot}29$ and $P(A \cup B) = 0{\cdot}59$. Calculate $P(A \cap B)$, $P(A \backslash B)$ and $P(B \backslash A)$.

5. A and B are two events of an experiment. $P((A \cup B)') = 0{\cdot}39$, $P(A \cap B) = 0{\cdot}1$ and $P(B \backslash A) = 2P(A \backslash B)$. Find $P(B)$.

6. A and B are two events of an experiment. $P(A \cup B) = 0{\cdot}7$, $P(B) = 4P(A)$ and $P(A \backslash B) = 2P(A \cap B)$. Calculate $P(B \backslash A)$.

7. E and F are two events of an experiment. $P(E) = 0{\cdot}39$ and $P(F) = 0{\cdot}53$.
   (i) What is the smallest possible value of $P(E \cup F)$?
   What can we say about E and F in this case?
   (ii) If $P(E \cap F) = 0{\cdot}11$, calculate $P(E \cup F)$ and $P(F \backslash E)$.

8. A single card is drawn at random from a standard pack of cards. Let A be the event that it is a red card, and B be the event that it is a '6'.
   (i) Calculate $P(A)$ and $P(B)$.
   (ii) Describe $A \cap B$ and calculate $P(A \cap B)$.
   (iii) If a single card is chosen at random from a pack of cards, what is the probability that it is either a red card or a '6'?

9. Two dice are thrown. Let E be the event that the dice show identical numbers, and let F be the event that the numbers on the dice have a total of eight.
   (i) Calculate $P(E)$.
   (ii) Calculate $P(F)$.
   (iii) Describe $E \cap F$ and calculate $P(E \cap F)$.
   (iv) If two dice are thrown, what is the probability that the two numbers obtained are either identical or have a total of eight?

10. There are four main courses on a restaurant menu one evening and the main courses chosen by the men and women diners that evening are recorded in the table below.

Main course	beef	pork	fish	nut
Men	15	7	4	2
Women	6	10	8	4

Three of the diners are selected at random for a survey. A is the event that the chosen diners are all women. B is the event that all three chosen diners took pork as their main course.

(i) Calculate $P(A)$.
(ii) Calculate $P(B)$.
(iii) Describe $A \cap B$ and calculate $P(A \cap B)$.
(iv) Calculate $P(A \cup B)$.

11. In a group, 6 of 10 men wear glasses and 5 of 12 women wear glasses. If two people are chosen at random from the group, what is the probability that they are either both men or both wear glasses?

23.2 Conditional Probability

The probability of an event may change if we know that another event has occurred. For example, suppose that a fair die is thrown and we know that an even number has appeared. What is the probability that the number obtained is less than 4?

If we let A be the event that we know has occurred, i.e. that an even number has appeared, and B be the event that the number obtained is less than 4, then we want to find the probability of B **given** A. This can be written
$P(B|A) = P(\text{less than } 4|\text{even number appeared})$.

This kind of probability is called **conditional probability**, i.e. the probability of B occurring conditional on the fact that A has occurred.

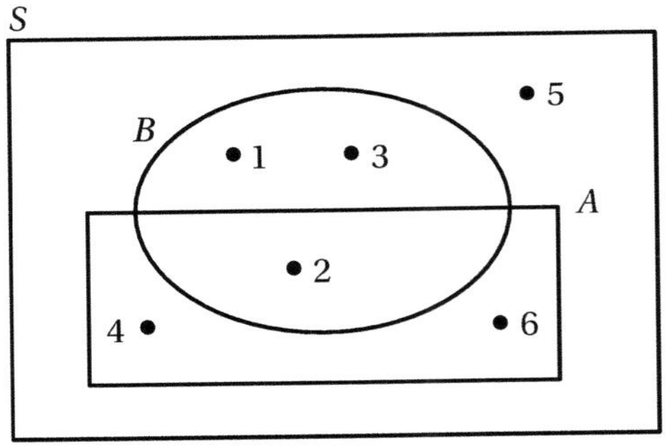

To evaluate this, notice that as A has happened, it becomes the sample space. Thus, $S = A = \{2, 4, 6\}$ and $n = \#(A) = 3$. Also, the event, $B|A$, is restricted to that part of the sample space which is less than 4, i.e. $A \cap B = \{2\}$. Thus, $r = \#(A \cap B) = 1$.

Then $$P(B|A) = \frac{\#(A \cap B)}{\#(A)} = \frac{r}{n} = \frac{1}{3}.$$

To relate this probability to the unconditional probabilities of A and B, notice that the number of outcomes in the original sample space is 6. If we divide above and below by this, we get

$$P(B|A) = \frac{1}{3} = \frac{\frac{1}{6}}{\frac{3}{6}} = \frac{P(A \cap B)}{P(A)}.$$

This result is generally true and gives us the formula for conditional probability.

Definition of Conditional Probability

If A and B are two events, then $P(B|A)$ stands for the probability of B, given that A has occurred. This is given by:

$$P(B|A) = \frac{P(A \cap B)}{P(A)} = \frac{P(A \text{ and } B)}{P(A)}.$$

In a sample space for which each outcome is equally likely, we also have:

$$P(B|A) = \frac{\#(A \cap B)}{\#(A)}.$$

In practice, to tackle questions involving conditional probability:

(i) identify what we know has happened (we will call it A), and calculate $P(A)$, or $\#(A)$ if the sample space contains only equally likely outcomes,

(ii) identify what we now want to find the probability of (we will call it B),

(iii) identify the event $A \cap B$, i.e. that both A and B occur, and calculate $P(A \cap B)$, or $\#(A \cap B)$ if the sample space contains only equally likely outcomes,

(iv) use the definition, $P(B|A) = \frac{P(A \cap B)}{P(A)}$, or $P(B|A) = \frac{\#(A \cap B)}{\#(A)}$ for equally likely outcomes, to calculate the conditional probability.

Example 1

In a certain college, 25% of students failed maths, 15% of students failed chemistry and 10% of students failed both maths and chemistry. A student is selected at random.

(i) Find $P(M)$, the probability that the student failed maths.

(ii) Find $P(C|M)$, the probability that the student failed chemistry given that he/she failed maths.

Solution

(i) (*If we imagine that the number of students in the college is 100, then 25 of these failed maths. Thus, the probability of picking a student who failed maths is* $\frac{25}{100}$ *or 0·25.*)

$P(M) = 0{\cdot}25.$

(ii) (*Next up is to identify C, which is those students who failed chemistry, and then* $M \cap C$, *which is those who failed both maths and chemistry. We are told that 10% of students failed both.*)

$P(M \cap C) = 10\% = 0{\cdot}1.$

Then, by the definition of conditional probability,

$$P(C|M) = \frac{P(M \cap C)}{P(M)}$$
$$= \frac{0{\cdot}1}{0{\cdot}25} = \frac{2}{5}.$$

Example 2

Three cards are chosen at random from a standard pack of 52 cards. What is the probability that all three cards chosen are clubs, given that exactly two of the chosen cards are known to be picture cards (jack, queen or king)?

Solution

(Let A be the event we are told has happened and let B be the event that we want to find the probability of. Because all choices of three cards are equally likely, we only need to count outcomes.)

A: Exactly two of the cards are picture cards.
Choose (2 from 12 picture cards) and (1 from 40 other cards).

$$\#(A) = \binom{12}{2} \times \binom{40}{1} = 66 \times 40 = 2640$$

B: All clubs.

$A \cap B$: Exactly 2 are picture cards and all are clubs.
Choose (2 from 3 club picture cards) and (1 from 10 other clubs).

$$\#(A \cap B) = \binom{3}{2} \times \binom{10}{1} = 3 \times 10 = 30$$

Then

$$P(B|A) = \frac{\#(A \cap B)}{\#(A)} = \frac{30}{2640} = \frac{1}{88}.$$

In the calculation of

$$P(B|A) = \frac{P(A \cap B)}{P(A)},$$

there can be difficulty in the calculation of $P(A)$, especially if A can occur in a number of mutually exclusive ways. The following example shows how we can deal with such questions.

Example 3

Kevin has reached the final of a TV game show, where he has a chance of winning €100,000. The first thing he has to do is spin a wheel. This will determine which of three boxes, X, Y, Z, he will open. The wheel is arranged so that the probabilities of it choosing boxes X, Y, Z are respectively 0·2, 0·3 and 0·5.

Kevin then has to choose a card at random from the box determined by the wheel. Each box has a number of winning cards and a number of losing cards: box X has 1 winning and 3 losing cards, box Y has 3 winning and 1 losing cards and box Z has 2 winning and 3 losing cards.

Given that Kevin wins the €100,000 prize, what is the probability that he chose box X?

Solution

Let A be the event that Kevin wins the €100,000 prize, and B be the event that he chose box X.
We need to calculate

$$P(B|A) = \frac{P(B \cap A)}{P(A)} \qquad \text{... as } P(B \cap A) = P(A \cap B)$$

or $$P(\text{box X}|\text{wins}) = \frac{P(\text{box X and wins})}{P(\text{wins})}$$

(*Calculating* $P(A) = P(\textit{wins})$ *is involved because Kevin could win having chosen box X* ***or*** *box Y* ***or*** *box Z, which are mutually exclusive.*)

$$P(\text{wins}) = P(\text{box X and wins}) + P(\text{box Y and wins}) + P(\text{box Z and wins})$$

(*From the given information, we know that* $P(\text{box X}) = 0{\cdot}2$ *and* $P(\text{wins}|\text{box X}) = \frac{1}{1+3} = \frac{1}{4} = 0{\cdot}25$, *as there is 1 winning card out of 4 in box X.*
We can use the fact that

$$P(\text{wins} \mid \text{box X}) = \frac{P(\text{box X and wins})}{P(\text{box X})}$$

to find $P(\text{box X and wins}) = P(\text{box X}).P(\text{wins}|\text{box X})$.)

$P(\text{box X and wins}) = P(\text{box X}).P(\text{wins}|\text{box X}) = (0{\cdot}2)(0{\cdot}25) = 0{\cdot}05$

Likewise:

$P(\text{box Y and wins}) = P(\text{box Y}){\cdot}P(\text{wins}|\text{box Y}) = (0{\cdot}3)(0{\cdot}75) = 0{\cdot}225$ and

$P(\text{box Z and wins}) = P(\text{box Z}){\cdot}P(\text{wins}|\text{box Z}) = (0{\cdot}5)(0{\cdot}4) = 0{\cdot}2$

Thus,

$$\begin{aligned} P(\text{wins}) &= P(\text{box X and wins}) + P(\text{box Y and wins}) + P(\text{box Z and wins}) \\ &= 0{\cdot}05 + 0{\cdot}225 + 0{\cdot}2 \\ &= 0{\cdot}475 \end{aligned}$$

and so

$$\begin{aligned} P(\text{box X}|\text{wins}) &= \frac{P(\text{box X and wins})}{P(\text{wins})} \\ &= \frac{0{\cdot}05}{0{\cdot}475} \\ &= \frac{2}{19}. \end{aligned}$$

In practice, the calculation of $P(\text{wins})$ can be laid out in the form of a **tree diagram**. On such a diagram, the mutually exclusive events are shown as different branches, and as we progress along each branch, we multiply the probabilities. This is shown on the next page, where W stands for winning and N stands for not winning. We don't have to calculate any probabilities we are not interested in.

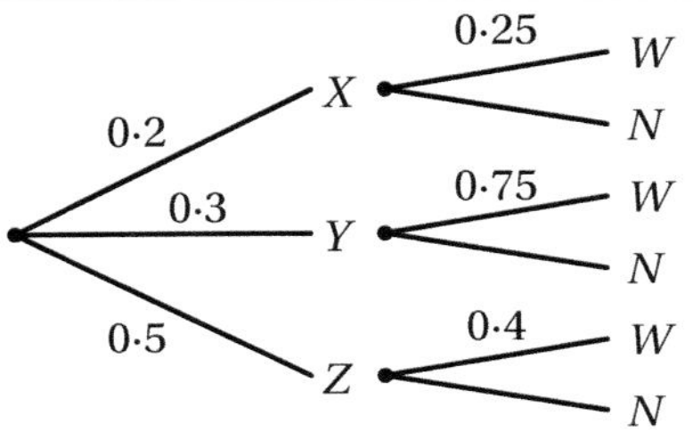

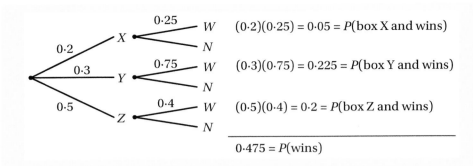

$(0{\cdot}2)(0{\cdot}25) = 0{\cdot}05 = P(\text{box X and wins})$

$(0{\cdot}3)(0{\cdot}75) = 0{\cdot}225 = P(\text{box Y and wins})$

$(0{\cdot}5)(0{\cdot}4) = 0{\cdot}2 = P(\text{box Z and wins})$

$0{\cdot}475 = P(\text{wins})$

Note that the probability 0·25 on the top branch is the probability of W given that X has already occurred.

Thus $P(\text{box X}|\text{wins}) = \dfrac{P(\text{box X and wins})}{P(\text{wins})} = \dfrac{0{\cdot}05}{0{\cdot}475} = \dfrac{2}{19}$, as before.

Misuses of Conditional Probability: The Prosecutor's Fallacy

$P(B|A)$and $P(A|B)$ are not necessarily the same. From the definition,

$$P(B|A) = \frac{P(A \cap B)}{P(A)}$$

while $$P(A|B) = \frac{P(A \cap B)}{P(B)}.$$

So, unless $P(A) = P(B)$, $P(B|A)$ and $P(A|B)$ will not be the same.

Confusing $P(B|A)$ and $P(A|B)$, whether accidentally or deliberately, is very common in statistical arguments. An example of the misuse of conditional probability is the so-called 'prosecutor's fallacy'. Here is a classic case.

In a murder trial, fibres from a very rare jacket (only 10 were sold in a city of 1 million people) are found on the victim. Mr Smith, who lives near the murder scene, owns such a jacket.

The prosecutor argues that, given that Mr Smith is innocent, the probability that he owns such a jacket, denoted by $P(J|I)$ where 'J' stands for owning such a jacket and 'I' stands for being innocent, is

$$P(J|I) = \frac{\#(J \cap I)}{\#(I)} = \frac{9}{999999} = 0{\cdot}000009$$

which is so small that the jury must convict.

However, what is known is that Mr Smith owns such a jacket and we want to find the probability that he is innocent. Thus the probability the prosecutor should be talking about is $P(I|J)$. The calculation for this is as follows.

$$P(I|J) = \frac{\#(I \cap J)}{\#(J)} = \frac{9}{10} = 0{\cdot}9$$

So the true probability that Mr Smith is innocent is 90%. You would hope that the defence counsel is aware of the maths and explains it to the jury.

Exercises 23.2

1. A coin is tossed three times. If both heads and tails appear, find the probability that exactly one tail appears.

2. A pair of dice is thrown. If the numbers appearing are different, what is the probability that the sum of the numbers on the dice is even?

3. A student takes two tests, A and B. The probability of passing in test A is $\frac{1}{2}$ and the probability of passing in test B is $\frac{3}{4}$. The probability of passing in both tests is $\frac{1}{3}$.
   If the student passes in test A, what is the probability that she also passes in test B?

4. In a class of all girls, 40% of the girls have brown hair, 25% have brown eyes and 15% have both brown hair and brown eyes. A girl is selected at random from the class.
   (i) If she has brown hair, what is the probability that she also has brown eyes?
   (ii) If she has brown eyes, what is the probability that she also has brown hair?

5. Two different numbers are chosen from the whole numbers from 1 to 9 inclusive.
   (i) If one of the two numbers is '5', what is the probability that the sum of the two numbers chosen is even?
   (ii) If the sum of the two chosen numbers is even, what is the probability that one of the numbers is '5'?

6. Three people are picked at random from 5 men, which includes Peter, and 8 women.
   If Peter is among those chosen, what is the probability that at least one woman is among those chosen?

7. Let A and B be events such that $P(A) = \frac{1}{3}$, $P(B) = \frac{1}{4}$ and $P(A \cup B) = \frac{1}{2}$. Find
   (i) $P(A \cap B)$, **(ii)** $P(B|A)$, **(iii)** $P(A|B)$.

8. E and F are events such that $P(E|F) = \frac{1}{2}$, $P(F|E) = \frac{1}{3}$ and $P(E \cap F) = \frac{1}{7}$.
   Find $P(E \cup F)$.

9. A test for a particular disease gives a 90% positive result for those who have the disease, and give a negative result for the remaining 10%. For those who do not have the disease, the test gives a positive result in 1% of cases and a negative result in the remaining 99% of cases. From a large population, in which only 0·2% have the disease, a person is selected at random and tested. If the test gives a positive result, what is the probability that the person selected actually has the disease?

10. Box A contains 3 red and 5 white marbles; box B contains 2 red and 1 white marbles; box C contains 2 red and 3 white marbles. A box is selected at random and a marble is selected at random from that box. If the marble is red, what is the probability that it came from box A?

11. Three machines A, B and C produce respectively 50%, 30% and 20% of the total number of items of a factory. The percentages of defective items output by these machines are respectively 3%, 4% and 5%. If an item is selected at random and found to be defective, find the probability that it was produced by machine A.

12. In a certain college, 4% of the men and 1% of the women are taller than 1·8 m. Also, 60% of the students are women. If a student is selected at random and is found to be taller than 1·8 m, what is the probability that the student is a woman?

13. In a certain school, 25% of the boys and 40% of the girls study Higher Level maths. 60% of the students in the school are boys. If a student is picked at random and is found to study Higher Level maths, what is the probability that the student is a girl?

14. A factory has three machines X, Y and Z producing respectively 50%, 30% and 20% of all the components it makes. From established data, 4%, 6% and 3% respectively of the components produced by these machines are defective.
    If a single component is selected and found to be defective, calculate the probability that it was produced by machine X.

23.3 Independent Events

Two events, E and F, are said to be **independent** if the occurrence of one event has no bearing on whether or not the other occurs. For example, in tossing a coin twice, the outcome of the first toss has no bearing on what we get on the second toss. On the other hand, suppose a die is rolled twice. Then the events of getting an even number on the first roll and of getting a total of 10 on the two throws are not independent. Knowing that the first roll gives an even number makes the probability of getting a total of 10 greater.

If E and F are independent events, then $P(F|E) = P(F)$, i.e. the probability of F is the same, whether or not E has occurred. By the same token, if E and F are independent, then $P(E|F) = P(E)$. If one of these conditions is true, then the other is automatically true. In some instances, $P(F|E) = P(F)$ or $P(E|F) = P(E)$ is used as the definition of an independent event.

But a more common definition of independent events does not involve conditional probability, although it is derived from it. If E and F are independent events, then

$$P(F \mid E) = \frac{P(E \cap F)}{P(E)}$$

$$P(E \cap F) = P(E).P(F \mid E)$$

$$P(E \cap F) = P(E).P(F) \qquad \text{... as } P(F \mid E) = P(F)$$

This is the most common definition of independent events.

Definition of Independent Events

E and F are independent events if

$$P(E \cap F) = P(E).P(F)$$

or $\quad P(E \text{ and } F) = P(E).P(F)$

For events that involve the entire experiment, and not just a stage, it can often be quite difficult to tell intuitively whether or not they are independent. This is why we need to use the definition.

Example 1

A blue die and a white die are thrown. E is the event that the number on the blue die is 3 greater than that on the white. F is the event that the total of the numbers on the two dice is 7.

(i) Find $P(E)$, $P(F)$ and $P(E \cap F)$.

(ii) Investigate if E and F are independent.

Solution

(i) (*The sample space for the event is the outcomes when two dice are thrown. These outcomes can be listed in the form (3,4), standing for a 3 on the blue die and a 4 on the white. The number of outcomes in the sample space is $6 \times 6 = 36$.*)

$S = \{(1,1), \ldots, (6,6)\}$ and $\#(S) = 36$.

E: The number on the blue die is 3 greater than that on the white.

$E = \{(4,1), (5,2), (6,3)\}$ and $\#(E) = 3$.

$$P(E) = \frac{\#(E)}{\#(S)} = \frac{3}{36} = \frac{1}{12}$$

F: The total of the numbers on the two dice is 7.

$F = \{(1,6), (2,5), (3,4), (4,3), (5,2), (6,1)\}$ and $\#(F) = 6$.

$$P(F) = \frac{\#(F)}{\#(S)} = \frac{6}{36} = \frac{1}{6}$$

$E \cap F$: The number on the blue die is 3 greater than the number on the white and the total of the two numbers is 7.

$E \cap F = \{(5,2)\}$ and $\#(E \cap F) = 1$.

$$P(E \cap F) = \frac{\#(E \cap F)}{\#(S)} = \frac{1}{36}$$

(ii) *(To see if the events are independent, we will check if the definition $P(E \cap F) = P(E).P(F)$ is true.)*

$$P(E).P(F) = \frac{1}{12} \cdot \frac{1}{6} = \frac{1}{72} \neq P(E \cap F)$$

Thus, the events E and F are not independent.

In general, two events E and F are independent if any one of the following three conditions is met:

(i) $P(E|F) = P(E)$,

(ii) $P(F|E) = P(F)$,

(iii) $P(E \cap F) = P(E).P(F)$.

Exercises 23.3

1. Two coins are tossed. The possible outcomes can be listed in the form HT, standing for a head on the first coin and a tail on the second.
- **(i)** If E is the event of getting a head on the first coin, find $P(E)$.
- **(ii)** If F is the event of getting a head on the second coin, find $P(F)$.
- **(iii)** Find $P(E \cap F)$ and $P(F|E)$. Hence, investigate if E and F are independent.
- **(iv)** Show that $P(E \cap F) = P(E).P(F)$.

2. A family has three children. A is the event that the family has at most one boy. B is the event that the family has children of both sexes. Assume that each child is equally likely to be a boy or a girl.
- **(i)** Calculate $P(A)$ and $P(B)$.
- **(ii)** By calculating $P(A \cap B)$, investigate if A and B are independent.

3. Three cards are selected at random from a standard pack of 52 cards. E is the event that we get three kings and F is the event that we get exactly one heart.
- **(i)** Calculate $P(E)$ and $P(F)$.
- **(ii)** By calculating $P(E \cap F)$, investigate if E and F are independent.

4. Let A and B be events such that $P(A) = \frac{1}{4}$, $P(A \cup B) = \frac{1}{3}$ and $P(B) = p$. Find the value of p if A and B are independent.

5. Let A and B be independent events with $P(A) = \frac{1}{2}$ and $P(A \cup B) = \frac{2}{3}$. Find $P(B|A)$.

6. Show that if $P(E|F) = P(E)$, then $P(F|E) = P(F)$, assuming that neither is zero.

7. A group of 7 women and 5 men go hill-walking. 4 of the women and 2 of the men are from Cork and the rest are from Kerry. Two of the group are chosen at random.
Let E be the event that the two chosen are from Cork and let F be the event that the two chosen are both women.
Investigate if E and F are independent.

8. A committee consists of a certain number of men and women from Ireland, England and Scotland, as shown in the table below.

	Ireland	England	Scotland
Men	5	3	1
Women	7	2	4

Three people are chosen at random from all the committee members.
E is the event that they are all from Ireland. F is the event that they are all women.
(i) By finding $P(E)$, $P(F)$ and $P(E \cap F)$, investigate if E and F are independent.
(ii) Verify the answer from part (i) by investigating if $P(F|E) = P(F)$.

23.4 Multiplication Rule

From the definition of conditional probability, $P(F|E) = \dfrac{P(E \cap F)}{P(E)}$, we get the so-called General Multiplication Rule, which applies to all events.

General Multiplication Rule
If E and F are events, then
$$P(E \cap F) = P(E).P(F|E)$$
or $P(E \text{ and } F) = P(E).P(F|E)$

If E and F are independent events, this becomes the same as the definition of independent events.

Multiplication Rule for Independent Events
If E and F are independent events, then
$$P(E \cap F) = P(E).P(F)$$
or $P(E \text{ and } F) = P(E).P(F)$

The Multiplication Rule (either form) can be extended to three or more events. It is primarily used for calculating probabilities when there are a number of consecutive stages, or sequential stages, e.g. choosing one number after choosing another.

Suppose two cards are drawn in succession, without replacement, from a standard pack of cards. What is the probability that we get a king followed by a queen?

1. **Theory**
As the probability of the second card being a queen depends on what the first card is, we can use the General Multiplication Rule to calculate
$$P(\text{1st king and 2nd queen}) = P(\text{1st king}).P(\text{2nd queen}|\text{1st king})$$
$$= \frac{4}{52} \cdot \frac{4}{51} = \frac{4}{663}.$$

2. Practice

If we understand that P(2nd queen) actually stands for P(2nd queen | 1st king), we can use the Multiplication Rule for Independent Events to get

$$P(\text{1st king and 2nd queen}) = P(\text{1st king}).P(\text{2nd queen})$$
$$= \frac{4}{52}\cdot\frac{4}{51} = \frac{4}{663}.$$

Example 1

A box contains 5 red, 7 yellow and 4 blue discs. Discs are drawn successively from the box and not replaced.

(i) What is the probability that the first three discs are yellow, blue, yellow, in that order?

(ii) What is the probability that the first blue disc is the fourth disc drawn from the box?

Solution

(i) *(Clearly the probabilities of the outcomes for the second and subsequent discs are dependent on what went before. But if we understand that 'P(2nd blue)' stands for the probability that the second disc drawn is blue, after the first is yellow, then we can use the Multiplication Law for Independent Events. Likewise with P(3rd yellow).)*

$$P(\text{1st yellow and 2nd blue and 3rd yellow})$$
$$= P(\text{1st yellow}).P(\text{2nd blue}).P(\text{3rd yellow})$$
$$= \frac{7}{16}\cdot\frac{4}{15}\cdot\frac{6}{14} = \frac{1}{20}.$$

(ii) *(If the first blue disc is the fourth drawn, then the first three discs must be 'non blue', i.e. red or yellow.)*

$$P(\text{fourth disc drawn is first blue})$$
$$= P(\text{1st non blue}).P(\text{2nd non blue}).P(\text{3rd non blue}).P(\text{4th blue})$$
$$= \frac{12}{16}\cdot\frac{11}{15}\cdot\frac{10}{14}\cdot\frac{4}{13} = \frac{11}{91}.$$

Example 2

Box A contains 3 white and 2 black discs. Box B contains 5 white and 7 black discs. A disc is removed at random from box A. Its colour is noted and then it is placed in box B. A disc is now removed at random from box B and its colour noted. Find the probability that of the two discs removed, one is white and the other black.

Solution

(For what we want, we can either get 'white then black' or 'black then white'. These are mutually exclusive, with different probabilities. So we will find the probability of each and then add. If the first disc is white, then box B will contain 6 white and 7 black discs. On the other hand, if the first disc is black, then box B will contain 5 white and 8 black discs.).

$$P(\text{white then black}) = P(\text{white}).P(\text{black})$$
$$= \frac{3}{5}\cdot\frac{7}{13} = \frac{21}{65}$$

and $$P(\text{black then white}) = P(\text{black}).P(\text{white})$$
$$= \frac{2}{5}\cdot\frac{5}{13} = \frac{10}{65} = \frac{2}{13}$$

Thus $P(\text{white and black}) = P(\text{white then black}) + P(\text{black then white})$
$$= \frac{21}{65} + \frac{10}{65} = \frac{31}{65}.$$

(Alternatively, we can lay this calculation out in the form of a tree diagram. There are two branches that give us what we want; their probabilities can be found by multiplying from left to right, according to the Multiplication Law.)

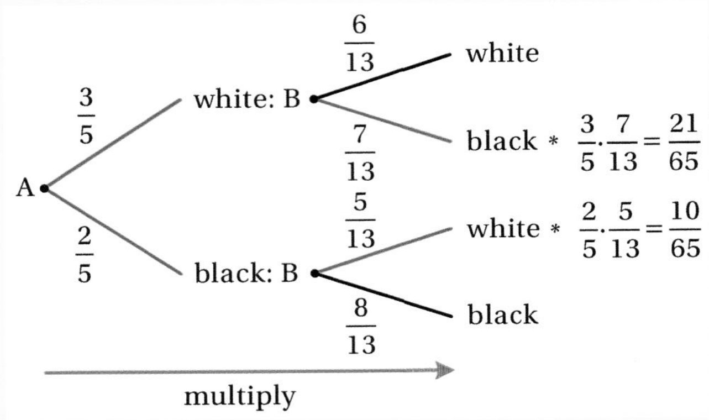

(From the tree, we can always leave out the branches we are not interested in.)

Thus $P(\text{white and black}) = \frac{21}{65} + \frac{10}{65} = \frac{31}{65},$ as before.

A tree-diagram approach is only suitable for questions in which
(i) there are two or three stages (one or two 'ands'), and
(ii) there are a small number of possible outcomes at each stage.

Suppose three cards are drawn in succession, without replacement, from a pack of cards, and we want to find the probability of getting a king, a queen and a jack, in any order. First of all,

$$P(\text{king and queen and jack}) = \frac{4}{52} \cdot \frac{4}{51} \cdot \frac{4}{50} = \frac{8}{16575}$$

and $$P(\text{king and jack and queen}) = \frac{4}{52} \cdot \frac{4}{51} \cdot \frac{4}{50} = \frac{8}{16575}, \quad \text{etc.}$$

Thus, the probability of getting these three cards in any order is the same.

So in practice, we calculate the probability of one particular order, and multiply by the number of ways the cards can be obtained, which is called the **multiplier**. Here the multiplier is 3! = 6, as this is the number of ways of arranging 3 different objects. If some of the objects are the same, then we have to use combinations.

Example 3

Five different cards are selected at random from a standard pack of cards. What is the probability that we get three aces and two kings?

Solution

(We start by finding the probability of ace, ace, ace, king, king, in that order.)

$$P(\text{ace, ace, ace, king, king}) = \frac{4}{52} \cdot \frac{3}{51} \cdot \frac{2}{50} \cdot \frac{4}{49} \cdot \frac{3}{48} = \frac{1}{1082900}$$

(The number of possible orders is the same as the number of ways of choosing 2 out of 5 places for the kings. The aces then automatically fill the remaining places.)

Number of possible orders $= \binom{5}{2} = 10$ (this is the multiplier)

Thus,

$$P(\text{3 aces and 2 kings}) = 10 \times \frac{1}{1082900} = \frac{1}{108290}.$$

or

Experiment: Choose 5 from 52 cards

$$n = \binom{52}{5} = 2598960$$

E: Choose (3 from 4 aces) and (2 from 4 kings)

$$r = \binom{4}{3} \times \binom{4}{2} = 4 \times 6 = 24$$

$$P(E) = \frac{24}{2598960} = \frac{1}{108290}, \quad \text{as before.}$$

Exercises 23.4

1. Two cards are drawn at random, without replacement, from a pack of cards. What is the probability of getting:
   (i) two hearts?
   (ii) a heart followed by a spade?
   (iii) two '10's?
   (iv) a '10' followed by a '9'?

2. Box A contains 5 red marbles and 3 white marbles. Box B contains 2 red marbles and 6 white marbles. If a marble is drawn at random from each box, what is the probability that
   (i) they are both red?
   (ii) they are both of the same colour?
   (iii) at least one of the marbles is red?

3. A bag contains 8 white, 6 black and 4 red discs. Discs are selected at random from the bag and not replaced.
   (i) What is the probability that the first three discs out are white, red and black, in that order?
   (ii) What is the probability that the first white disc is the third disc drawn out of the bag?
   (iii) What is the probability that there is at least one black disc in the first four discs drawn out of the bag?

4. A box contains 5 circuit boards of which 2 are known to be defective. A women tests the boards until the 2 defective boards are found. Having being tested, a board is removed from the box and will not be tested again. She chooses the next board to test at random from those that remain in the box.
   (i) What is the probability that the process ends after her second test?
   (ii) What is the probability that the process ends after her third test?

5. In a game, cards are dealt successively, without replacement, from a standard pack of cards until a queen is obtained.
   (i) What is the probability that the game ends on the fourth card?
   (ii) What is the probability that at least three cards are dealt?

6. A class has 10 boys and 5 girls. Three students are selected, at random and in order, from the class. Find the probability that
   (i) the first two are boys and the third is a girl.
   (ii) the first and third are boys and the second is a girl.
   (iii) the first and third are of the same sex, and the second is of the opposite sex.

7. Box A contains nine cards, numbered 1 to 9 inclusive. Box B contains five cards numbered 1 to 5 inclusive. A box is chosen at random and a card is picked at random from that box. If the card shows an even number, another card is drawn from the same box. On the other hand, if the card shows an odd number, a card is drawn from the other box.
   (i) What is the probability that both cards show even numbers?
   (ii) What is the probability that both cards show odd numbers?

8. A box contains 7 red balls and 4 blue balls. A ball is removed at random from the box and not replaced. A second ball is then removed at random from the box. What is the probability that the second ball is red?

9. When two people are chosen at random from a group of 4 men and 8 women, what is the probability that we get one man and one woman?

10. Two discs are drawn, in succession and without replacement, from a bag containing 6 blue and 8 yellow discs. Find the probability
    (i) that both discs are blue.
    (ii) that one disc is blue and the other is yellow.

11. A committee contains 4 Irish, 7 French and 5 German representatives. Three of these are chosen at random to form a sub-committee. Find the probability
    (i) that all three are French.
    (ii) that all three are of the same nationality.
    (iii) that two French and one German representatives are chosen.
    (iv) that all three chosen are of different nationalities.

12. Three different cards are selected at random from a standard pack of cards. What is the probability of getting
    (i) a heart, a diamond and a spade?
    (ii) two hearts and a diamond?

13. Four different cards are selected at random from a standard pack of cards. What is the probability of getting two hearts and two spades?

14. Four letters are chosen at random from the letters of the word TAILORED. What is the probability of getting
    (i) a 'T' and three vowels?
    (ii) two vowels and two consonants?

23.5 Repeated Bernoulli Trials

Suppose an experiment consists of a number of repeated identical trials. For example, an experiment might consist of tossing a fair coin six times. Each toss of the coin is called a trial, and these trials are both identical and independent. The outcome of any individual toss has no bearing on any toss that may follow.

Repeated identical trials are called **Bernoulli trials**, after Jacques Bernoulli (1654–1705), one of a large family of Swiss mathematicians, if they satisfy the conditions outlined in the following definition.

Jacques Bernoulli

Bernoulli Trials

A number of repeated trials are called Bernoulli trials if:

1. they are independent,
2. they are identical, and
3. each trial has only two possible outcomes, which may be termed 'success' and 'failure'.

For example, repeatedly tossing a coin and being interested in the number of heads are Bernoulli trials. We would call getting a head in a single trial a 'success', and then getting a tail is a 'failure'.

Other examples of Bernoulli trials are:

(i) was a new-born baby a girl?
(ii) did a voter vote for a particular candidate?
(iii) did a shopper buy a particular product?

In each case, there is a clear idea of success (yes) and failure (no), and the trials may be repeated, with each trial having no bearing on any other.

Many trials appear to have more than two possible outcomes, but by an appropriate grouping of the possible outcomes, we may consider that there are only two, which we then call success and failure.

For example, suppose a die is thrown repeatedly and we are interested in the number of times we get a '5' or a '6'. Then we call success = $\{5, 6\}$, and failure = $\{1, 2, 3, 4\}$.

For a single Bernoulli trial, it is usual to let $p = P(\text{success})$ and $q = P(\text{failure})$. Because we must get either success or failure, $p + q = 1$. Thus, $q = 1 - p$.

There are a number of types of question on Bernoulli trials.

Type 1: First Success (or First Failure)

Suppose we have a number of identical Bernoulli trials, each with probability of success p and probability of failure q. What is the probability that the first success occurs in the fourth trial?

If the first success (s) is in the fourth trial, then the first three trials must all end in failure (f). Because the trials are independent, we can use the Multiplication Rule:

$$\begin{aligned} P(\text{1st success in 4th trial}) &= P((\text{1st f}) \text{ and } (\text{2nd f}) \text{ and } (\text{3rd f}) \text{ and } (\text{4th s})) \\ &= q \times q \times q \times p \\ &= q^3 p \end{aligned}$$

In general, the probability of getting the first success in the nth trial is $q^{n-1}p$. Likewise, the probability of the first failure occurring in the nth trial is $p^{n-1}q$.

Repeated Bernoulli Trials: First Success and First Failure

Suppose a single Bernoulli trial has probability of success p and probability of failure q. Then

(i) the probability of the first success occurring in the nth trial is $q^{n-1}p$
(ii) the probability of the first failure occurring in the nth trial is $p^{n-1}q$.

Example 1

For a single trial, p, the probability of success is 0·4.

(i) Find q, the probability of failure in a single trial.

(ii) If the trials are repeated, find the probability that the first success occurs in the fourth trial.

(iii) If the trials are repeated, find the probability that the first failure occurs in the third trial.

Solution

(i) *(Use P(failure) = 1 – P(success).)*

$$q = 1 - p = 1 - 0{\cdot}4 = 0{\cdot}6$$

(ii) *(If the first success is in the fourth trial, then the first three trials must all result in failure.)*

$$\begin{aligned} P(\text{1st success in 4th trial}) &= q \times q \times q \times p \\ &= q^3 p \\ &= (0{\cdot}6)^3(0{\cdot}4) = 0{\cdot}0864 \end{aligned}$$

(iii) *(If the first failure occurs in the third trial, then the first two trials must result in success.)*

$$\begin{aligned} P(\text{1st failure in 3rd trial}) &= p \times p \times q \\ &= p^2 q \\ &= (0{\cdot}4)^2(0{\cdot}6) = 0{\cdot}096. \end{aligned}$$

Type 2: Exact Number of Successes (Binomial Distribution)

Suppose a single Bernoulli trial has probability of success p and probability of failure q. If this trial is repeated six times, what is the probability of getting exactly two successes?

If there are two successes (s), then there must be four failures (f) in the six trials. One way this could occur is (s and s and f and f and f and f). The probability of this occurring is

$$p \times p \times q \times q \times q \times q = p^2q^4.$$

But this is not the only way we could get two successes and four failures, and each way has the same probability. So we need to find the multiplier. This is the number of ways of choosing 2 out of 6 positions to put the successes in, the failures automatically occupying the other positions. From combinations, the multiplier is $\binom{6}{2}$.

If we let the random variable X stand for the number of successes, then we can write what we want as $P(X = 2)$. Thus,

$$P(X = 2) = \binom{6}{2} p^2 q^{6-2} = \binom{6}{2} p^2 q^4.$$

In general, if the random variable X stands for the number of successes in n Bernoulli trials, for which the probabilities of success and failure in a single trial are p and $q = 1 - p$, respectively, then the possible values of X are 0, 1, 2, ... , n, i.e. $X \in \{0, 1, 2, \ldots, n\}$. The probability that $X = r$, i.e. that we have r successes in the n trials, is given by

$$P(X = r) = \binom{n}{r} p^r q^{n-r}.$$

The distribution of X, along with the associated probabilities, $P(X = r)$, for $0 \le r \le n$, is called a **binomial distribution**, as each probability is a term in the binomial expansion of $(q + p)^n$.

Binomial Distribution: *r* Successes in *n* Trials

Suppose a single Bernoulli trial has probability of success p and probability of failure q. Then the probability of exactly r successes in n trials is given by

$$P(X=r)=\binom{n}{r}p^rq^{n-r}.$$

It is important to realise that the formula for $P(X=r)$ says nothing about the order of the successes and the failures.

Example 2

A die is thrown eight times. What is the probability that we get at most two '6's?

Solution

(The Bernoulli trial is throwing the die. For this, success is getting a '6', and $p=\frac{1}{6}$*. Failure is not getting a '6', and* $q=1-\frac{1}{6}=\frac{5}{6}$*. Let X be the number of '6's we get in eight trials. If we have to get at most two '6's, then X = 0 or X = 1 or X = 2. We will calculate the probability of each of these and then add, as these events are mutually exclusive.)*

For a single trial, success is getting a '6', and failure is not getting a '6'.

Thus, $p=\frac{1}{6}$ and $q=1-\frac{1}{6}=\frac{5}{6}$.

For the experiment, $n=8$. Let X be the number of successes. We want $P(X\leq 2)$.
$P(X\leq 2)=P(X=0)+P(X=1)+P(X=2)$.

$$P(X=0)=\binom{8}{0}\left(\frac{1}{6}\right)^0\left(\frac{5}{6}\right)^8=\frac{390625}{1679616}=0{\cdot}23257$$

$$P(X=1)=\binom{8}{1}\left(\frac{1}{6}\right)^1\left(\frac{5}{6}\right)^7=\frac{625000}{1679616}=0{\cdot}37211$$

$$P(X=2)=\binom{8}{2}\left(\frac{1}{6}\right)^2\left(\frac{5}{6}\right)^6=\frac{437500}{1679616}=0{\cdot}26048$$

Thus, $P(X\leq 2)=0{\cdot}23257+0{\cdot}37211+0{\cdot}26048=0{\cdot}86516$.

Type 3: *k*th Success in *n*th Trial

Suppose a single Bernoulli trial has probability of success p and probability of failure q. What is the probability that the fifth success occurs in the eighth trial?

To obtain the fifth success in the eighth trial, the first seven trials must result in exactly four successes **and** the eighth trial must result in success.

As these are independent,

P(fifth success in eighth trial)

= P((four successes in seven trials) and (success in eighth trial))

= P(four successes in seven trials).P(success in eighth trial)

$$=\left[\binom{7}{4}p^4q^3\right].p$$

$$=\binom{7}{4}p^5q^3$$

Example 3

A fair die is thrown repeatedly. What is the probability that the third '6' occurs on the eighth throw? Give your answer correct to three decimal places.

Solution

(*We start by considering an individual trial: throwing a die. Success is getting a '6', while failure is not getting a '6'.*)

Trial:	Success:	getting a '6'	$p = \frac{1}{6}$
	Failure:	not getting a '6'	$q = \frac{5}{6}$

Then

$$P(\text{3rd success in 8th trial}) = P((\text{2 successes in 7 trials}) \text{ and } (\text{success in 8th trial}))$$

$$= \left[\binom{7}{2}p^2q^5\right].p$$

$$= \binom{7}{2}p^3q^5$$

$$= \binom{7}{2}\left(\frac{1}{6}\right)^3\left(\frac{5}{6}\right)^5$$

$$= \frac{21875}{559872}$$

$$= 0{\cdot}039.$$

Exercises 23.5

1. A fair coin is tossed repeatedly. Find the probability that the first tail appears on
   (i) the second toss.
   (ii) the fifth toss.
   (iii) the tenth toss.

2. A coin is biased so that the probability of heads is 0·6 and the probability of tails is 0·4. The coin is tossed repeatedly. Find the probability that the first head appears on
   (i) the first toss.
   (ii) the second toss.
   (iii) the ninth toss.

3. A fair die is thrown repeatedly. A success is getting a '5' or a '6'. Find the probability of getting the first success on the
   (i) third throw.
   (ii) fifth throw.
   (iii) eighth throw.

4. A fair die is thrown repeatedly. Find the probability that the first even number appears on
   (i) the second throw.
   (ii) the fourth throw.
   (iii) the sixth throw.

5. A four-sided die is equally likely to show the numbers 1, 2, 3, 4 when thrown. Find the probability that the first '3' appears on
   (i) the second throw.
   (ii) the fifth throw.
   (iii) the seventh throw.

6. A fair coin is tossed six times.
   (i) Find the probability of getting head, head, head, head, tail, tail, in that order.
   (ii) Find the probability of getting exactly four heads.
   (iii) Find the probability of getting at least four heads.

7. A fair die is thrown five times.
   (i) Find the probability that a '4' appears exactly once.
   (ii) Find the probability that a '4' does not appear at all.
   (iii) Find the probability that a '4' appears at least four times.

8. A coin is biased so that it is twice as likely to show heads as tails. The coin is tossed eight times.
   (i) Find the probability of getting exactly four heads.
   (ii) Find the probability of getting at least six heads.
   (iii) Find the probability of getting at least six tails.

9. A die is loaded so that '5' and '6' are both twice as likely to occur as the other numbers. This die is thrown six times.
   (i) Find the probability that we get a '5' exactly twice.
   (ii) Find the probability that we get a '5' three or four times.

10. A fair eight-sided die is rolled six times. For a particular game, success is getting a '6', a '7' or an '8'. Find the probability of getting
    (i) exactly three successes.
    (ii) exactly four successes.
    (iii) at least three successes.

11. A fair coin is tossed repeatedly.
    What is the probability of getting the fourth head on the sixth toss?

12. A game involves a person throwing a fair die repeatedly until two '6's are obtained.
    The game ends when the second '6' is thrown. Find the probability that the die is thrown five times.

13. A coin is biased so that a tail is three times as likely to occur as a head. This coin is tossed repeatedly.
    What is the probability that the seventh head appears on the tenth toss?

14. A die is loaded so that the probability of a '6' appearing is twice that of any other number appearing.
    What is the probability of the third '6' appearing on the eighth throw of the die?

15. A fair coin is tossed repeatedly. Find the probability that
    (i) the fourth head occurs on the seventh or eighth toss.
    (ii) the fourth and fifth heads occur on the eighth and ninth tosses.

Revision Exercises 23

1. A single card is selected at random from a standard pack of cards. A is the event that the card is a king, and B is the event that the card is not a heart.
   (i) Find $P(A)$, $P(B)$ and $P(A \cap B)$.
   (ii) Are A and B mutually exclusive? Explain.
   (iii) Are A and B independent? Explain.
   (iv) Calculate $P(A \cup B)$.

2. One box of chocolates contains five hard centres and three soft centres. Another box of chocolates contains eight hard centres and seven soft centres. A box is chosen at random and a chocolate is taken at random from the box. If this chocolate is soft-centred, find the probability that it came from the first box.

3. The probability that an archer hits the bull's-eye with any one shot is $\frac{1}{5}$. Find the probability that he hits the bull's-eye
(i) with his second shot.
(ii) exactly once in his first three shots.
(iii) at least once in his first four shots.

4. Two numbers are selected at random from the whole numbers from 1 to 9 inclusive. If the sum of the two chosen numbers is even, find the probability that both numbers are odd.

5. Let A and B be events such that $P(A) = \frac{3}{8}$, $P(B) = \frac{5}{8}$ and $P(A \cup B) = \frac{3}{4}$. Find
(i) $P(A|B)$.
(ii) $P(B|A)$.
Explain why $P(A|B) \neq P(B|A)$.

6. Two fair dice are thrown. What is the probability of a total greater than 7 if at least one of the dice shows a '5'?

7. Three cards are selected at random from a standard pack of cards. What is the probability that the cards chosen are either all clubs or contain at least one king?

8. Anne and Brendan play a game in which they take it in turns throwing a die.
The first person to throw a six wins. Anne has the first throw.
(i) Find the probability that Anne wins on her second throw.
(ii) Find the probability that Anne wins on her first, second or third throw.

9. Five unbiased coins are tossed.
(i) Find the probability of getting three heads and two tails.
(ii) The five coins are tossed eight times. Find the probability of getting three heads and two tails exactly four times. Give your answer correct to three decimal places.

10. A bag contains the following cardboard shapes: 10 red squares, 15 green squares, 8 red triangles and 12 green triangles. One of the shapes is drawn at random from the bag.
E is the event that a square is drawn.
F is the event that a green shape is drawn.
(i) Find $P(E \cap F)$.
(ii) Find $P(E \cup F)$.
(iii) State whether E and F are independent events, giving a reason for your answer.
(iv) State whether E and F are mutually exclusive events, giving a reason for your answer.

11. Whenever Anne's mobile phone rings, the probability that she answers the call is $\frac{3}{4}$.
A friend phones Anne six times.
(i) What is the probability that she misses all the calls?
(ii) What is the probability that she misses the first two calls and answers the others?
(iii) What is the probability that she answers exactly one of the calls?
(iv) What is the probability that she answers at least two of the calls?

12. Four students work separately on a mathematical problem. The probabilities that the four students have of solving the problem are as follows: $\frac{3}{4}, \frac{1}{2}, \frac{4}{7}, \frac{2}{3}$.
Show that the probability that the problem will be solved by at least one of the four students is $\frac{55}{56}$.

13. Three cards are drawn, one after the other, from a pack of 52 playing cards. Find the probability that the first is a king, the second is an ace, and the third neither an ace nor a king.

14. A die is loaded so that the probability of getting a '3' in a single throw is $\frac{2}{7}$. If the die is thrown repeatedly, find the probability that the second '3' occurs on the fifth throw.

15. Find the probability of guessing correctly at least six out of 10 answers on a true/false multiple choice test.

16. Records show that, on average, 7 out of 10 people recover from a particular disease after receiving a certain treatment. Of five people who have the disease and are treated, find the probability that

(i) the first three treated will recover, and the other two will not.
(ii) exactly three of the five people treated recover.
(iii) more than three of the five people will recover.

17. A box contains nine cards, each one having a different whole number from 1 to 9 written on it. A card is selected at random from the box, the number on it noted and the card replaced in the box. This is repeated three times.

(i) Find the probability that all three numbers are odd.
(ii) Find the probability that exactly two of the numbers are odd.
(iii) If it is known that the first number is odd, find the probability that the sum of the three numbers is even.

18. A class contains 10 boys and 20 girls. Half the boys and half the girls have blue eyes.
If a student is chosen at random from the class, find the probability that it is a boy or that the student has blue eyes.

19. A and B are events, and A' is the complement of A.
$P(A \cup B) = \frac{3}{4}$, $P(A') = \frac{2}{3}$ and $P(A \cap B) = \frac{1}{4}$.

(i) Calculate $P(A)$.
(ii) Calculate $P(B)$.
(iii) Are A and B independent? Give a reason for your answer.
(iv) Calculate $P(A \cap B')$.

20. The probabilities of events are sometimes expressed as 'odds', e.g. in betting. In practice, odds tend to be given in the form known as 'odds against'. For example, if the odds for a particular horse winning a race are '4 to 1', this means that there are 4 chances against the horse winning the race, to 1 chance for it winning the race. There are $4 + 1 = 5$ chances in total. Thus, the probability of the horse winning the race is $\frac{1}{5}$.
Two horses, A and B, run in the same race, for which there is only one winner.

(i) If the odds of horse A winning the race are '9 to 4', find the probability of A winning the race.
(ii) If the odds of horse B winning the race are '7 to 2', find the probability of B winning the race.
(iii) Calculate the probability that the race is won by either A or B.

Expected Value and Games

24

This chapter moves the study of probability to a new level with the introduction of the idea of a random variable. For much of further work with probability, it is necessary to be able to consider the outcome of an experiment as a single number. For example, a die may be thrown 10 times and the outcomes can be listed in terms of a sequence of numbers. A random variable takes this experiment and assigns numbers to outcomes, according to some rule, e.g. the random variable X may represent the number of '4's obtained, or the number of even numbers obtained.

This chapter is concerned with the expected value of a random variable, e.g. the expected number of '4's when a die is thrown 10 times. An analysis of the expected value is very useful in game theory, and especially in deciding if games are fair or favourable to a particular player. A game with no financial element is fair if each player has an equal chance of winning. For games with a financial element, it is only advisable to play if the likelihood of winning is greater than that of losing. In spite of this, people still play games of chance, e.g. the Lotto, where logic dictates that they shouldn't, because of the attraction of winning a very large prize.

24.1 Expected Value of a Random Variable

When an experiment is conducted, the possible outcomes need not be numbers. For example, if a coin is tossed three times, then the possible outcomes are {TTT, TTH, THT, THH, HTT, HTH, HHT, HHH}, where 'T' stands for tail and 'H' stands for head.

For some of the applications of probability, we need the outcomes of an experiment to be treated as numbers. This is the job of a **random variable**, usually written as a capital letter, e.g. X or Y. For the example of the coin being tossed three times, we could let the random variable X stand for the number of heads obtained. Then $X = \{0, 1, 2, 3\}$. X here is a discrete random variable, as the elements of X can be listed as separate numbers. In other cases, a random variable can be continuous, e.g. the weights of new-born babies.

It is important to realise that while each of the elementary outcomes in {TTT, ..., HHH} is equally likely, the possible values of the random variable X are not. To each value of X we can assign its probability by what is called a **probability function**. This can be written in the form $P(X = 2)$, or more simply as $P(2)$ when X is understood, to stand for the probability of getting 2 heads.

A random variable and its probability function can be laid out in the form of a table, as shown below. We are free to list elementary outcomes, or have calculations, in the column on the left of this probability table.

S	$x \in X$	$P(x)$
TTT	0	$\frac{1}{8}$
TTH, THT, HTT	1	$\frac{3}{8}$
THH, HTH, HHT	2	$\frac{3}{8}$
HHH	3	$\frac{1}{8}$

You should note that if we add up all the probabilities, we always get a total of 1. This is from Axiom 2(i) of probability: $P(S) = 1$. Thus, for the example above,

$$P(0) + P(1) + P(2) + P(3) = 1,$$

which can be abbreviated to

$$\sum_{x \in X} P(x) = 1,$$

where the symbol on the left can be read as 'sigma P of x for all x an element of X'. This so-called sigma notation can be used any time we are summing a number of similar quantities.

The probability table can also be laid out in a form that is similar to a frequency table which you would have met at Junior Cert.

x	0	1	2	3
P(x)	$\frac{1}{8}$	$\frac{3}{8}$	$\frac{3}{8}$	$\frac{1}{8}$

You will notice that the lower row contains fractions (or decimals) instead of frequencies (whole numbers). Nevertheless, we can still calculate the mean, μ, of this data in the usual way. For a probability distribution, the mean is often referred to as the **expected value** or as the **expectation**, which for the random variable X, is written $E(X)$. Then

$$\mu = E(X) = \frac{0\left(\frac{1}{8}\right) + 1\left(\frac{3}{8}\right) + 2\left(\frac{3}{8}\right) + 3\left(\frac{1}{8}\right)}{\frac{1}{8} + \frac{3}{8} + \frac{3}{8} + \frac{1}{8}} = \frac{\frac{12}{8}}{1} = \frac{3}{2}.$$

You should understand clearly what this does and does not represent. The expected value, $E(X)$, is not the most likely outcome for the experiment. In fact, it may not even be one of the possible outcomes. For this example, having $E(X) = \frac{3}{2}$ says that if three fair coins are tossed many, many times, then the average of the number of heads we get will get closer and closer to $\frac{3}{2}$.

In general, for the probability distribution of the random variable, X, given by the probability table:

Outcome	x_1	x_2	......	x_n
Probability	$P(x_1)$	$P(x_2)$	......	$P(x_n)$

,

we have the expected value given by

$$\mu = E(X) = \frac{x_1P(x_1) + x_2P(x_2) + \ldots\ldots + x_nP(x_n)}{P(x_1) + P(x_2) + \ldots\ldots + P(x_n)}$$

$$= x_1P(x_1) + x_2P(x_2) + \ldots\ldots + x_nP(x_n) \qquad \text{... as } P(x_1) + \ldots + P(x_n) = 1$$

$$= \sum_{x \in X} xP(x),$$

using sigma notation. When X is clearly understood, this last expression can be further abbreviated to $\sum xP(x)$, which stands for the sum of all terms of the form $xP(x)$.

Expected Value (of a Random Variable)

Suppose X is a discrete random variable for an experiment, and $X = \{x_1, x_2, \ldots\ldots, x_n\}$. Let $P(x_1) = P(X = x_1)$, etc. Then the expected value of X, written $E(X)$ or μ, is given by

$$E(X) = x_1P(x_1) + x_2P(x_2) + \ldots + x_nP(x_n)$$
$$= \sum xP(x).$$

In practice, the calculation of the expected value can be laid out by extending the probability table to include a column called '$xP(x)$', as seen below in Example 1.

Example 1

Paul selects two cards, at random and without replacement, from a pack of cards.

What is the expected number of hearts that he gets?

Solution

(To choose 2 from 52 cards, the number of ways is $\binom{52}{2} = 1326$. *This is far too many elementary outcomes to be listed individually.*

Because the question is concerned with the number of hearts Paul gets, we should let the random variable X represent the number of hearts. We will need to calculate the probability of getting each possible value of X. This can be done by relative frequency or by the Multiplication Rule, which we will use here.)

Let the random variable X be the number of hearts obtained. Then $X = \{0, 1, 2\}$.

We can now construct the following extended probability table.

Calculations	$x \in X$	$P(x)$	$xP(x)$
$\frac{39}{52} \cdot \frac{38}{51}$	0	$\frac{19}{34}$	0
$2 \times \frac{13}{52} \cdot \frac{39}{51}$	1	$\frac{13}{34}$	$\frac{13}{34}$
$\frac{13}{52} \cdot \frac{12}{51}$	2	$\frac{1}{17}$	$\frac{2}{17}$
		Total	$\frac{1}{2}$

Thus, $E(X) = \sum xP(x)$

$$= 0 + \frac{13}{34} + \frac{2}{17} = \frac{1}{2}.$$

It is possible to have different random variables associated with a given experiment. For example, for the coin being tossed three times, we might consider the random variable Y to stand for the number of identical outcomes. Then $Y = \{2,3\}$.

Exercises 24.1

1. The probability table for a random variable X is given below.

$x \in X$	0	1	2	3	4	5
$P(x)$	$\frac{1}{5}$	$\frac{1}{10}$	$\frac{3}{20}$	$\frac{3}{10}$	$\frac{1}{5}$	$\frac{1}{20}$

Calculate $E(X)$, the expected value of X.

2. The probability table for a random variable X is given below.

$x \in X$	0	1	2	3	4	5
$P(x)$	$\frac{1}{5}$	$\frac{1}{15}$	$\frac{2}{15}$	$\frac{4}{15}$	$\frac{1}{5}$	$\frac{2}{15}$

Calculate $E(X)$, the expected value of X.

3. A die is loaded so that the even numbers are twice as likely to occur as the odd numbers.
- **(i)** Calculate the probability of getting a '1' and the probability of getting a '2'.
- **(ii)** If the random variable X represents the number obtained when the die is thrown, calculate $E(X)$, the expected value of X.

4. Among the 25 students in a class, 4 students have no siblings, 7 have one sibling, 9 have two siblings, 3 have three siblings and 2 have four siblings. Let X represents the number of siblings of a student picked at random from the class.
- **(i)** List the possible values of X.
- **(ii)** Calculate $E(X)$, the expected value of X.
- **(iii)** Is it possible for any student to have this number of siblings? Explain.

5. A single card is selected at random from a standard pack of cards. If the value of an ace is 1, and the value of each picture card is 10, let the random variable X represent the value of the card obtained.
- **(i)** List the possible values of X.
- **(ii)** Construct a probability table for X.
- **(iii)** Calculate $E(X)$.

6. Five fair coins are tossed. Let the random variable X represent the number of tails obtained.
- **(i)** Construct a probability table for X.
- **(ii)** Calculate $E(X)$, the expected value of X.

7. An archer has a probability of 0·35 of hitting the bull's-eye with a single shot. If he fires five arrows at the target, what is the expected number of bull's-eyes that he gets?

8. Four cards are selected at random, and without replacement, from a standard pack of cards. Let the random variable X represent the number of red cards obtained.
- **(i)** List the possible values of X.
- **(ii)** Calculate $E(X)$.

9. The probability distribution of a random variable X is given in the table below.

x	0	1	2	3
$P(x)$	$\frac{1}{4}$	$\frac{2}{7}$	$\frac{1}{3}$	k

- **(i)** Find the value of the constant k.
- **(ii)** Calculate $E(X)$.

10. The probability distribution of the random variable X is given in the table below.

x	0	1	2	3	4
$P(x)$	k	$\frac{1}{12}$	$\frac{5}{12}$	$\frac{1}{3}$	m

$E(X)$, the expected value of X, is $\frac{9}{4}$.
Calculate the values of the constants k and m.

24.2 Games of Chance

Many aspects of real life, for example, children's and adult games, betting, insurance, international trade deals, involve probability to a greater or lesser degree. We don't have to consider all of these, but we will consider some games of pure chance. There are different types of game of pure chance.

1. Games of Pure Chance: No Money Involved

The most straightforward scenario is a game of pure chance, where contestants are vying for the honour of winning. If there can only be one winner, then the game is 'fair' only if each player has an equal chance of winning. One obvious example is if the game is symmetric, i.e. if swapping the players around makes no difference to their chances of winning.

To decide if a game is fair, we should calculate the probability of each player winning. If a game turns out not to be fair, then we can often suggest a change to make it fair.

Example 1

Two archers, Hugh and Mary, have a probability of 0·4 of hitting the bull's-eye, shown as the yellow region opposite, when they shoot at a target. They decide to play a game. In this game, they take turns to shoot at the target. The first person to hit the bull's-eye wins. They have a maximum of three shots each and if neither has won by then, the game is declared a draw. Mary goes first.

(i) Determine the probability that Mary wins the game.
(ii) Determine the probability that Hugh wins the game.
(iii) Explain why this is not a fair game. Who does the game favour?
(iv) Suggest a way to make the game fair.

Solution

(i) (*Mary wins the game if she wins on her first, her second or her third shot. But for Mary to win on her second shot, both herself and Hugh must have missed with their first shots. Likewise, for Mary to win on her third shot, both of them must have missed with each of their first two shots.*)

$$P(\text{Mary wins}) = P(\text{Mary 1st}) + P(\text{Mary 2nd}) + P(\text{Mary 3rd})$$
$$= (0{\cdot}4) + (0{\cdot}6)(0{\cdot}6)(0{\cdot}4) + (0{\cdot}6)(0{\cdot}6)(0{\cdot}6)(0{\cdot}6)(0{\cdot}4)$$
$$= 0{\cdot}59584$$

(ii) (*Because there is the possibility of a draw, we cannot find the probability of Hugh winning by just subtracting the probability of Mary winning from 1. For Hugh to win, he must win on his first, second or third shot. For Hugh to win on his first shot, Mary must have missed her first shot. For him to win on his second shot, there must have been three misses before. Again, for him to win on his third shot, the first five shots must have been missed.*)

$$P(\text{Hugh wins}) = P(\text{Hugh 1st}) + P(\text{Hugh 2nd}) + P(\text{Hugh 3rd})$$
$$= (0{\cdot}6)(0{\cdot}4) + (0{\cdot}6)^3(0{\cdot}4) + (0{\cdot}6)^5(0{\cdot}4)$$
$$= 0{\cdot}357504$$

(iii) Because $P(\text{Mary wins}) > P(\text{Hugh wins})$, the game is not fair, as it favours Mary over Hugh.

(iv) The advantage lies with the person who goes first. So, if the game started with the toss of a coin to see who goes first, then it would be fair. In this case, each would have a probability of $\frac{1}{2}(0{\cdot}59584 + 0{\cdot}357504) = 0{\cdot}476672$ of winning.

2. Games of Pure Chance: Money Involved

Money can be involved in games of pure chance in a number of ways. First, the game might have an entry fee, e.g. buying a ticket in a raffle. Or there might be no entry fee, but the possibility that a player suffers a loss might exist. Of course, there must also be possible winnings, or any rational player would not see the point in playing the game.

To decide if such a game is worth playing, we can let the random variable X represent the possible net positions of the player after playing the game. This should take into account any entry fee, possible losses and possible winnings. Then we can calculate $E(X)$, the expected value of X.

The value of $E(X)$ will determine the type of game, from the point of view of the player.

(i) If $E(X) < 0$, then the game is **unfavourable** to the player.

(ii) If $E(X) > 0$, then the game is **favourable** to the player.

(iii) If $E(X) = 0$, then the game is **fair.**

If a player plays the same game n times, then the expected winnings are $n \times E(X)$. Of course, if $E(X)$ is negative, then this amount will be negative, and so can be translated into expected losses.

If a game which involves an entry fee proves to be unfavourable to a player, then we could work out what entry fee would make the game fair. The player could then offer to pay no more than that to play the game. Alternatively, some of the possible winning or losing amounts could be changed to make the game fair.

In a different, but related, type of game, two players are playing against each other for money. Assuming that the game is a zero-sum game (which means that whatever money one player wins, the other player must lose), then if the game is favourable to one player, it must be unfavourable to the other.

Example 2

At a games arcade, you have to pay €2 to play a game of chance. In this game, two dice are thrown. If the total of the numbers on the two dice is 2, 3, 4, 10, 11 or 12, you double your money, i.e. you get €4 back. If the total is 5 or 9, your stake, €2, is returned to you. However, if the total is 6, 7 or 8 you lose your stake.

(i) What should the random variable, X, be for analysing this game? What are the possible values of X?

(ii) Determine if this game is favourable or unfavourable to a player.

(iii) Calculate the entry fee that would make this a fair game, assuming that you win €2 for a total of 2, 3, 4, 10, 11 or 12, your entry fee (stake) is returned for a total of 5 or 9, and that you lose for other totals.

Solution

(i) The random variable, X, should be your financial state after playing the game. The possible values of X are +2, 0 and −2.

(ii) When two dice are thrown, the number of possible outcomes is $6 \times 6 = 36$. The possible totals are shown in the table below.

Total	Outcomes	No.
2	(1, 1)	1
3	(1, 2) (2, 1)	2
4	(1, 3), (2, 2), (3, 1)	3
5	(1, 4), (2, 3), (3, 2), (4, 1)	4
6	(1, 5), (2, 4), (3, 3), (4, 2), (5, 1)	5
7	(1, 6), (2, 5), (3, 4), (4, 3), (5, 2), (6, 1)	6
8	(2, 6), (3, 5), (4, 4), (5, 3), (6, 2)	5
9	(3, 6), (4, 5), (5, 4), (6, 3)	4
10	(4, 6), (5, 5), (6, 4)	3
11	(5, 6), (6, 5)	2
12	(6, 6)	1

(*We can now form the probability table for X, and extend it to calculate E(X).*)

Totals	Calculation of $P(x)$	$x \in X$	$P(x)$	$xP(x)$
2, 3, 4, 10, 11, 12	$\frac{1+2+3+3+2+1}{36}$	$+2$	$\frac{12}{36}=\frac{1}{3}$	$\frac{2}{3}$
5, 9	$\frac{4+4}{36}$	0	$\frac{8}{36}=\frac{2}{9}$	0
6, 7, 8	$\frac{5+6+5}{36}$	-2	$\frac{16}{36}=\frac{4}{9}$	$-\frac{8}{9}$
			Total	$-\frac{2}{9}$

As $E(X) = \sum xP(x) = €\left(-\frac{2}{9}\right) = -€0{\cdot}22$
is negative, the game is unfavourable to the player.

(iii) Let the entry fee be €y. Then the elements of X are +2, 0 and $-y$.

$x \in X$	$P(x)$	$x\,P(x)$
+2	$\frac{1}{3}$	$\frac{2}{3}$
0	$\frac{2}{9}$	0
$-y$	$\frac{4}{9}$	$\frac{-4y}{9}$
	Total	$\frac{2}{3}-\frac{4y}{9}$

For a fair game: $E(X) = 0$

$$\frac{2}{3}-\frac{4y}{9}=0$$
$$\frac{2}{3}=\frac{4y}{9}$$
$$4y = 6$$
$$y = 1{\cdot}5$$

Thus, a fair entry fee for the game would be €1·50.

3. Decision to Play

In deciding whether or not to play a game, the expected value should not be the only consideration. Consider the following examples.

In one game, you have the choice of winning €1 or tossing a coin. If the coin turns up heads, you win €3, if it turns up tails, you don't win anything. What choice should you make: take the guaranteed €1 or toss the coin? If you toss the coin your expected value is

$E(X) = (€3)(0{\cdot}5) + (€0)(0{\cdot}5) = €1{\cdot}50.$

As this is greater than €1, you should probably toss the coin, and most people would. Losing €1 would not be the end of the world.

In another game, you have the choice of winning €1 million or tossing a coin. If the coin turns up heads, you win €3 million; if it turns up tails, you don't win anything. If you toss the coin, your expected value is €1·5 million, and so, in theory, you should toss the coin. But very few would, because the guaranteed €1 million is a life-changing amount, and most people would be quite happy to settle for that. You will see this logic in practice in game shows such as 'Deal or No Deal'.

Exercises 24.2

1. James and Susan play a game, which consists of each tossing a coin. If one is heads and the other tails, James wins. If both coins show the same, Susan wins.
(i) Determine the probability that James wins.
(ii) Determine the probability that Susan wins.
(iii) Is this a fair game? Give a reason.

2. A bag contains four cards, numbered 1, 2, 3 and 4 respectively.
Ciara and Anne play a game. In this game, Ciara draw a card at random from the bag and does not return it. Anne then draws one of the remaining cards at random.
Ciara wins if both cards are odd, or both are even. Anne wins if one is odd and the other even.
(i) Determine the probability that Ciara wins.
(ii) Determine the probability that Anne wins.
(iii) Is this a fair game? Give a reason.

3. Colm and David play a game. Two dice are thrown. Colm wins if the difference between the two numbers obtained is 2 or more. David wins if the numbers are the same or if the difference between the numbers is 1. Is this game fair? Give a reason.

4. Aoife and Sean play a game. In this game, seven different cards are selected at random from a pack of cards. Aoife wins if there are no kings among those cards chosen. Sean wins if at least one king is chosen.
(i) Determine the probability that Aoife wins.
(ii) Deduce the probability that Sean wins.
(iii) Is this a fair game? If not, who does the game favour?
(iv) If eight cards had been selected instead of seven, would the game be fair, or who would it favour?

5. Jack and Caoimhe throw a die. If the outcome is 1, 3 or 5, Jack gives Caoimhe €2, €3 or €4 respectively. If the outcome is 2, 4 or 6, Caoimhe gives Jack €6, €1 or €1 respectively.
(i) Calculate the expected value for Jack playing the game once.
(ii) Calculate the expected value for Caoimhe playing the game once.
(iii) Is the game fair? Give a reason.

6. Kevin and Conor play a game. Two dice are thrown. If the numbers shown are equal, Kevin gives Conor €9, and if they are not the same, Conor gives Kevin €2.
(i) By calculating expected values, show that this is not a fair game.
(ii) If they play this game 60 times, how much would you expect Kevin to be up or down?
(iii) How much should Kevin give Conor for two equal numbers to make the game fair?

7. Aisling and Sorcha play a game. Each writes down two different numbers, from the numbers 1, 2, 3, 4, 5. If they have no numbers in common, Aisling gives Sorcha €3, but if they have at least one number in common, Sorcha gives Aisling €1.
(i) By calculating expected values, show that this is not a fair game.
(ii) If they play this game 100 times, how much would you expect Aisling to be up or down?
(iii) How much should Aisling give Sorcha, if they have no numbers in common, to make the game fair?

8. Peter and Louise play a game. A coin is tossed four times. If the result is 0, 2 or 4 heads, Peter gives Louise €3, €6 or €3 respectively. If the result is 1 or 3 heads, Louise gives Peter €5.
(i) By calculating expected values, show that this is not a fair game.
(ii) If this game is repeated 120 times, by how much would you expect Peter to be up or down?
(iii) Suggest a different system of payouts that would make the game fair.

9. A game consists of throwing a die. You win the number thrown, in euro. What would be a fair entry fee for this game?

10. A player throws a fair die. If he throws a prime number (2, 3 or 5), he wins that number of euro. If he throws a non-prime number (1, 4 or 6) he loses that number of euro. By calculating the expected value, determine if this is a fair game.

11. The two sides of a fair coin are inscribed with the numbers 1 and 2 respectively. In a game, this coin is tossed and a fair die is thrown. The entry fee for this game is €1.
If the two numbers obtained are the same, you win €4, including the entry fee.
If the difference in the numbers obtained is 4 or more, you win €2, including the entry fee.
Otherwise, you lose.
(i) If X is the random variable representing your financial position after you play the game once, state the possible values of X.
(ii) By calculating the expected value, determine if this is a fair game.

12. A bag contains four red cards numbered 1, 2, 3 and 4, and two blue cards, numbered 5 and 6. A game, with an entry fee of €1, consists of choosing two different cards at random from the bag. If the outcome is two red cards or two odd numbers, you lose.
Otherwise, you win €2, including your entry fee.
(i) Calculate the probability of getting two red cards or two odd numbers.
(ii) By calculating the expected value, determine if this is a fair game.

13. It costs €3 to play a 'spin-and-win' game. You win the amount shown when the wheel stops. The sectors are equal in size and each is equally likely. The arrow points to one sector only when it stops. The winning amounts indicated include the entry fee.
Let X be the random variable which represents your net financial position after playing the game.
(i) List the possible values of X.
(ii) Construct a table showing the probability distribution of X.
(iii) Calculate $E(X)$, the expected value of X.
(iv) Is this game fair? Give a reason.
(v) If the game is not fair, what entry fee would make it fair?

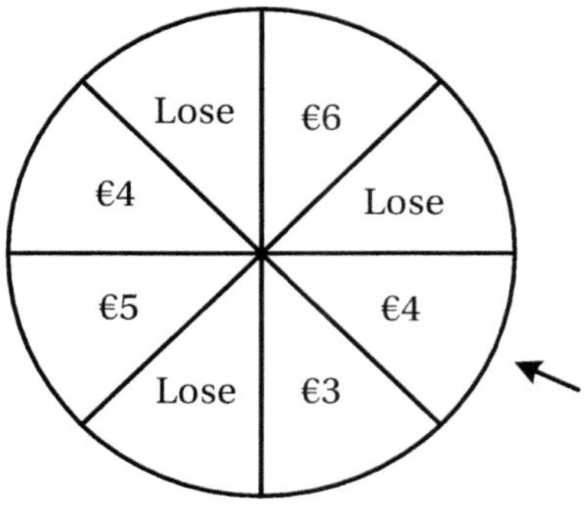

14. It costs €1 to play a game which involves throwing two dice. If the sum of the numbers on the two dice is prime (2, 3, 5, 7 or 11) then you win €1, i.e. you get €2 back.
Otherwise, you lose.
(i) By calculating the expected value, determine if this is a fair game.
(ii) If it is not a fair game, determine what entry fee would make it fair, assuming that you still win €1 for a prime total.

15. There are 10,000 tickets in a lottery draw. Each ticket costs €1. There are three prizes, one of €5000, one of €2000 and one of €1000. When the draw takes place, all 10,000 tickets are placed in a drum, and the prizes are drawn in order. A ticket which wins one prize is not eligible to win any subsequent prize.
Suppose you buy one ticket in this draw.
(i) Let the random variable X be your expected financial position after the draw takes place. What are the possible values of X?
(ii) By calculating $E(X)$, the expected value of X, explain why it does not make economic sense to buy a ticket in this draw.
(iii) Suggest reasons why you might nevertheless decide to buy a ticket in this draw.

16. A large financial company has many thousands of computers used by its employees. From experience, the company estimates that, after each computer is out of warranty, there is an 8% chance, per year, of an individual computer requiring maintenance or repair costing an average of €200. There is also a 6% chance, per year, that an individual computer will need to be replaced at a cost of €1500.
A computer maintenance firm offers the financial company to repair or replace any defective machine out of warranty, at an annual cost of €150 per machine.
(i) By calculating the expected annual cost of each machine out of warranty, show that it does not make strict economic sense to go for the offer made by the computer maintenance firm.
(ii) Suggest why it might still be a good idea for the financial company to agree to the deal.

Revision Exercises 24

1. The pupils in a class are surveyed about the number of siblings they have. The results are given in the table below.

No. of siblings	0	1	2	3	4	5
No. of pupils	3	8	10	2	1	1

If a single pupil is picked at random, what is the expected number of siblings that the pupil has?

2. Two different numbers are chosen at random from the whole numbers from 1 to 7 inclusive. If X is the random variable representing their sum, calculate $E(X)$.

3. A fair coin is tossed until a head or five tails occurs. Find the expected number of tosses of the coin.

4. A biased coin is such that, on a single toss, the probability of a head is $\frac{1}{3}$ and the probability of a tail is $\frac{2}{3}$. This coin is tossed until a head or four tails occurs. Find the expected number of tosses of the coin.

5. A bag contains 50 envelopes of which 10 contain €10 each, 10 contain €5 and the others contain nothing. If you are allowed to choose one envelope at random, what is your expected value?

6. Box A contains 9 envelopes with €10 in each and 1 envelope with €5. Box B contains 5 envelopes with €10 in each and 5 envelopes with €5 in each.
You are allowed to pick a box at random and then pick an envelope from that box. What is your expected value?

7. Bag A contains 1 red and 1 yellow ball. Bag B contains 6 red and 4 yellow balls.
A ball is drawn from bag A (colour unknown) and placed in bag B. Two balls are then selected at random, without replacement, from bag B. What is the expected number of red balls?

8. A bag contains four coins, three of which are fair, and the other having two heads.
A coin is selected at random from the bag and tossed three times. What is the expected number of heads?

9. At golf, the probabilities of Alan defeating Brian, Ciaran and David are $\frac{2}{5}, \frac{5}{6}$ and $\frac{7}{10}$, respectively. The probability of Ciaran defeating David is $\frac{3}{8}$. To win a tournament, Alan must defeat Brian and the winner of the match between Ciaran and David. If the prize for winning the tournament is €1000, what is Alan's expected value?

10. In a game, a player tosses three fair coins. She wins €5 if 3 heads occur, €3 if exactly 2 heads occur and €1 if only one head occurs. On the other hand, she loses €15 if 3 tails occur.
(i) Calculate the expectation of the player.
(ii) The rules are changed so that she loses €20 if 3 tails occur. Calculate the new expectation of the player.

11. In a game, a player tosses three fair coins. He wins €8 if 3 heads occur, €3 if exactly 2 heads occur and €1 if only one head occurs. If the game is to be fair, how much should he lose if no heads occur?

12. A player chooses two different cards from a pack of cards. She wins €40 if the two cards are diamonds, and €5 if just one of the cards is a diamond. She gets nothing if there are no diamonds. If this game is fair, what should be her entry fee for playing the game?

13. A player tosses two fair coins. He wins €1 if one head appears and €2 if two heads appear. If no heads appear, he loses €5.
(i) Determine the expectation of the player.
(ii) Is the game favourable to the player? Give a reason.

14. Six greyhounds who have never raced before take part in a race. For an entry fee of €1, you can bet on choosing the first three, in any order, past the post. For example, if you choose A, B and C, and they finish in the order B, A, C, you win. There are no dead heats. If you are correct, you win €15. Determine if this is a fair game for the player.

15. A game starts by tossing a fair coin. If the outcome is a head, then a fair die is thrown twice. If the outcome is a tail, then two different numbers are selected at random from the numbers 1, 2, 3, 4, 5. The entry fee for this game is €1, and if the outcome is two even numbers, then the player wins €4. Determine if this is a fair game for the player.

16. Tim and Sarah play a game which involves rolling two dice. Tim wins if the sum of the numbers showing on the dice is even, and Sarah wins if the sum is odd.

(i) Determine the probability that Tim wins the game.

(ii) Determine the probability that Sarah wins the game.

(iii) Is this game fair? Explain.

Introduction to Differentiation

25

Differentiation, or differential calculus, is one branch of what is known as calculus. The other branch is integration, or integral calculus, which we will study later. Differentiation, which is involved with the concept of the rate of change, is of crucial importance in the future development of maths and its applications. It has been highly significant in areas as diverse as physics, engineering, statistics, rates of chemical reaction, financial transactions and operations research, as well as being of enormous use in many different fields within mathematics.

Differentiation was proposed in the late 1600s, and from the beginning its importance and its possibilities were obvious. Consequently, the field grew rapidly with many of the great minds from then until now making significant advances.

In this introductory chapter, we meet some necessary preliminary ideas, such as that of a limit, before moving onto the fundamental concept in differentiation, namely the derivative, which is the instrument used to measure the rate of change.

25.1 Limits of Functions

Consider the function

$$f: x \to x^2,$$

whose rule may be written

$$f(x) = x^2.$$

Suppose we let x get closer to the number 3. We don't have to be too exact about this: just imagine that x is a number slightly above 3, e.g. 3·000001, or a number slightly below 3, e.g. 2·999999, and that from there x gets progressively closer to 3.

What happens to $f(x) = x^2$ as this happens to x? Common sense indicates that $f(x) = x^2$ will get closer to $3^2 = 9$ as x gets closer, and closer, to 3.

The number that $f(x) = x^2$ gets closer to as x gets closer to 3 is called the **limit** of $f(x)$ as x **tends** to 3, written

$$\lim_{x \to 3} f(x) = \lim_{x \to 3} x^2.$$

From our discussion above, the value of this limit is 9.

Thus, we can write

$$\lim_{x \to 3} x^2 = 9.$$

In general, the symbol $\lim_{x \to a} f(x)$ stands for what $f(x)$ gets closer to (approaches) as x approaches a.

Definition of a Limit

$$\lim_{x \to a} f(x) = L$$

means that L is what $f(x)$ approaches as x approaches a.

There are different ways of calculating limits. We should start by using Rule 1.

Rule 1

To evaluate $\lim_{x \to a} f(x)$,

we start by evaluating $f(a)$.

Depending on what we obtain for $f(a)$, we may be able to write down the limit immediately. Some cases where this is possible are:

$f(a)$	$\lim_{x \to a} f(x) =$
$k \in \mathbb{R}$	k
$\frac{k}{0}, k \in \mathbb{R}, k \neq 0$	doesn't exist
$\frac{\infty}{k}, k \in \mathbb{R}$	doesn't exist
$\frac{k}{\infty}$	0

The forms $k, \frac{k}{0}, \frac{\infty}{k}, \frac{\infty}{k}$ are called **determinate forms**, as they allow us to determine whether or not the limit exists and if it does what it is.

The forms $\frac{k}{0}$ and $\frac{\infty}{k}$ result in a number that is infinitely large. In these cases we can say that $f(x)$ approaches ∞ or $-\infty$ as x approaches a, which can be very useful information for constructing the graph $y = f(x)$. Whether $f(x)$ approaches ∞ or $-\infty$ will depend on the sign of k, and in the case of $\frac{k}{0}$, how the bottom line approaches 0. However, it should still be remembered that strictly the limit does not exist in either of these cases.

Example 1

Evaluate each of the following limits, if it exists:

(i) $\lim_{x \to 4} \frac{x^2 + 3}{x - 3}$ **(ii)** $\lim_{x \to 3} \frac{2x - 1}{x^2 + x - 12}$

Solution

(i) *($f(x)\big|_{x=4}$ means we try to evaluate $f(x)$ when $x = 4$.)*

$$\lim_{x \to 4} \frac{x^2 + 3}{x - 3} = \left.\frac{x^2 + 3}{x - 3}\right|_{x=4}$$

$$= \frac{(4)^2 + 3}{(4) - 3} = \frac{19}{1} = 19$$

(ii) $$\lim_{x \to 3} \frac{2x - 1}{x^2 + x - 12} = \left.\frac{2x - 1}{x^2 + x - 12}\right|_{x=3}$$

$$= \frac{2(3) - 1}{(3)^2 + (3) - 12}$$

$$= \frac{5}{0}$$

Thus the limit does not exist.

In practice, we will find that many limits are not initially determinate. When this happens, we need another rule to evaluate the limit.

Rule 2

If $f(a)$ is **indeterminate**, i.e. of the form $\frac{0}{0}$ or $\frac{\infty}{\infty}$, then to evaluate $\lim_{x\to a} f(x)$, we can cancel a common factor from the numerator and the denominator. Then try Rule 1 again.

For example, suppose we want to evaluate $\lim_{x\to 2} \frac{x^2-4}{x-2}$.

(i) Try Rule 1.

$$\left.\frac{x^2-4}{x-2}\right|_{x=2} = \frac{(2)^2-4}{(2)-2} = \frac{0}{0},$$

which is indeterminate. Hence, Rule 1 did not work.

(ii) By Rule 2, find a common factor of the top and the bottom, and cancel this.

$$\lim_{x\to 2}\frac{x^2-4}{x-2} = \lim_{x\to 2}\frac{\cancel{(x-2)}(x+2)}{\cancel{x-2}}$$

$$= \lim_{x\to 2}(x+2)$$

(iii) Now we can try Rule 1 again.

$$\lim_{x\to 2}\frac{x^2-4}{x-2} = (x+2)|_{x=2}$$

$$= (2)+2 = 4.$$

We can interpret the limit we have just calculated in terms of functions and their curves.

1. The function

$$f: x \to \frac{x^2-4}{x-2}$$

is defined for all $x \in \mathbb{R}$ except $x = 2$. For all $x \neq 2$,

$$f(x) = \frac{x^2-4}{x-2}$$

can be simplified to $f(x) = x + 2$.

2. The curve $y = \frac{x^2-4}{x-2}$ can be drawn for all $x \neq 2$, where there is a 'gap' in the curve. For all other values of x, the curve can be simplified to $y = x + 2$, which is a line.

3. As $\lim_{x\to 2}\frac{x^2-4}{x-2} = 4$, this tells us that even though the function $f(x) = \frac{x^2-4}{x-2}$ is not defined at $x = 2$, that $f(x)$, i.e. the y coordinates of points on the curve, gets close to 4 as x gets close to 2.

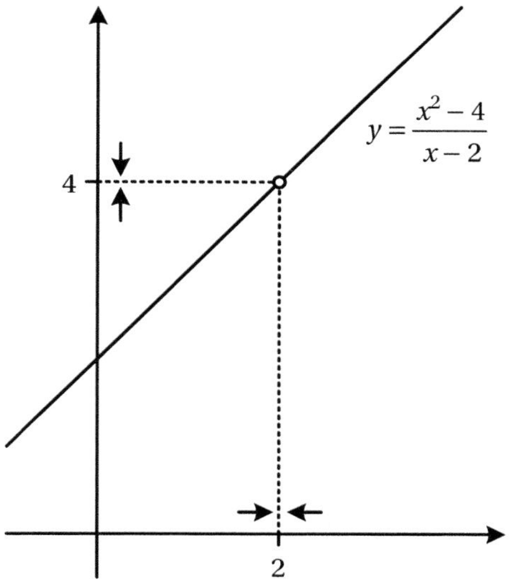

This example illustrates the idea that the theory of limits can be used to deal with awkward situations where functions are not defined, as well as normal situations where functions are defined. Before limits, the best we could say about $f(x) = \frac{x^2-4}{x-2}$ at $x = 2$ is that it is not defined.

Example 2

Evaluate $\lim\limits_{x\to2}\frac{x^2+x-6}{x^2-x-2}$.

Solution

$$\lim_{x\to2}\frac{x^2+x-6}{x^2-x-2}=\frac{(2)^2+(2)-6}{(2)^2-(2)-2}=\frac{0}{0}\quad\text{(indeterminate)}$$

(As this is indeterminate, we will find and cancel a common factor.)

$$\lim_{x\to2}\frac{x^2+x-6}{x^2-x-2}=\lim_{x\to2}\frac{\cancel{(x-2)}(x+3)}{\cancel{(x-2)}(x+1)}$$

$$=\lim_{x\to2}\frac{x+3}{x+1}\qquad\text{... now we can use Rule 1}$$

$$=\frac{(2)+3}{(2)+1}$$

$$=\frac{5}{3}$$

Limits which contain surds can often be calculated by multiplying above and below by the surd conjugate. The purpose of this is to make visible the common factor on the top and the bottom, which we then cancel.

Example 3

Evaluate $\lim\limits_{x\to5}\frac{x-5}{\sqrt{2x-1}-3}$.

Solution

(Check: $\left.\frac{x-5}{\sqrt{2x-1}-3}\right|_{x=5}=\frac{5-5}{\sqrt{9}-3}=\frac{0}{0}$, *which is indeterminate.)*

$$\lim_{x\to5}\frac{x-5}{\sqrt{2x-1}-3}=\lim_{x\to5}\frac{x-5}{\sqrt{2x-1}-3}\times\frac{\sqrt{2x-1}+3}{\sqrt{2x-1}+3}$$

$$=\lim_{x\to5}\frac{(x-5)\left(\sqrt{2x-1}+3\right)}{(2x-1)-(3)^2}$$

$$=\lim_{x\to5}\frac{(x-5)\left(\sqrt{2x-1}+3\right)}{2x-10}$$

$$=\lim_{x\to5}\frac{\cancel{(x-5)}\left(\sqrt{2x-1}+3\right)}{2\cancel{(x-5)}}$$

$$=\frac{\sqrt{2(5)-1}+3}{2}\qquad\text{... by Rule 1}$$

$$=\frac{6}{2}=3.$$

Exercises 25.1

Evaluate the following limits, where they exist.

1. $\lim_{x \to 3} \frac{x^2 + 3x}{x - 1}$

2. $\lim_{x \to 4} \frac{x^2 - 1}{x + 3}$

3. $\lim_{x \to 2} \frac{x^3 - 3x^2 + 10}{2x - 1}$

4. $\lim_{x \to 5} \frac{4x^2 - 1}{x - 2}$

5. $\lim_{x \to 2} \frac{x^2 + 1}{x - 2}$

6. $\lim_{x \to 3} \frac{x^2 + 2x - 1}{x^2 + x - 12}$

7. $\lim_{x \to 5} \frac{2x + 1}{x^2 - 4x - 5}$

8. $\lim_{x \to 2} \frac{x^2 + 3x}{x^2 - 8x + 12}$

9. $\lim_{x \to 5} \frac{x - 5}{x^2 - 25}$

10. $\lim_{x \to 3} \frac{x^2 + x - 12}{x^2 - 4x + 3}$

11. $\lim_{x \to 1} \frac{x^2 - 7x + 6}{x^2 - 3x + 2}$

12. $\lim_{x \to 2} \frac{x^3 - 8}{x^2 - 4}$

13. $\lim_{x \to 4} \frac{\sqrt{x} - 2}{x - 4}$

14. $\lim_{x \to 1} \frac{\sqrt{x} - 1}{x - 1}$

15. $\lim_{x \to 0} \frac{\sqrt{1 + x} - 1}{x}$

16. $\lim_{x \to 6} \frac{\sqrt{x + 3} - 3}{x - 6}.$

25.2 Trigonometric Limits

With trig limits which are initially indeterminate, we can sometimes use trig identities to rewrite the top or the bottom, or both, so that the common factor to be cancelled appears.

For example, to calculate $\lim_{x \to \frac{\pi}{2}} \frac{\cos x}{\sin 2x}$, which you can verify is initially indeterminate, we can use the trig identity $\sin 2A = 2 \sin A \cos A$. Thus,

$$\begin{aligned}
\lim_{x \to \frac{\pi}{2}} \frac{\cos x}{\sin 2x} &= \lim_{x \to \frac{\pi}{2}} \frac{\cancel{\cos x}}{2 \sin x \cancel{\cos x}} \\
&= \lim_{x \to \frac{\pi}{2}} \frac{1}{2 \sin x} \\
&= \frac{1}{2 \sin \frac{\pi}{2}} \\
&= \frac{1}{2}.
\end{aligned}$$

For other trig limits, when $x \to 0$, which are initially indeterminate, we can make use of the following Special Trig Limit.

Special Trig Limit

If x is measured in radians, then

$$\lim_{x \to 0} \frac{\sin x}{x} = 1 \quad \text{and} \quad \lim_{x \to 0} \frac{x}{\sin x} = 1$$

Although an analytic proof of this limit exists (which we do not have to look at), we can verify this limit practically by taking values of x (in radians) very close to 0, and evaluating the fraction $\frac{\sin x}{x}$, or the fraction $\frac{x}{\sin x}$. The closer the value of x is to 0, the closer the fraction is to 1. It is important to note that the angle *must* be measured in radians.

The Special Trig Limit is only valid if the angle is the same as what is on the other side of the line. For example,

$$\lim_{\theta \to 0} \frac{\sin 4\theta}{4\theta} = 1, \quad \lim_{x \to 0} \frac{\sin 2x}{2x} = 1, \quad \lim_{x \to 0} \frac{7x}{\sin 7x} = 1.$$

Example 1

Evaluate $\lim_{x \to 0} \frac{\sin 5x}{4x}$.

Solution

(To arrange to have 5x *below the sin* 5x*, we shift the* 4 *to one side and multiply above and below by* 5.*)*

$$\begin{aligned} \lim_{x \to 0} \frac{\sin 5x}{4x} &= \lim_{x \to 0} \frac{\sin 5x}{5x} \cdot \frac{5}{4} \\ &= (1) \cdot \frac{5}{4} \\ &= \frac{5}{4}. \end{aligned}$$

If a trig limit contains a cosine, note that as $\cos 0 = 1$, $\lim_{x \to 0} \cos ax = 1$, where a is a constant. Also, if a trig limit contains a tan, write the tan as sine divided by cosine.

Example 2

Evaluate $\lim_{x \to 0} \frac{3 \sin 2x}{5x \cos 3x}$.

Solution

(Start by separating the terms that do not give 0 when x = 0, i.e. the 3, the 5 and the cos 3x, from those that do give 0, i.e. the sin 2x and the x. Convert the sin term into a Special Limit.)

$$\begin{aligned} \lim_{x \to 0} \frac{3 \sin 2x}{5x \cos 3x} &= \lim_{x \to 0} \frac{3}{5 \cos 3x} \cdot \frac{\sin 2x}{x} \\ &= \lim_{x \to 0} \frac{3}{5 \cos 3x} \cdot \frac{\sin 2x}{2x} \cdot \frac{2}{1} \\ &= \left(\frac{3}{5}\right)(1)(2) \\ &= \frac{6}{5}. \end{aligned}$$

Exercises 25.2

Evaluate the following limits.

1. $\lim_{x\to 0}\frac{\sin 2x}{3\sin x}$

2. $\lim_{x\to 0}\frac{1-\cos x}{\sin^2 x}$

3. $\lim_{\theta\to 0}\frac{\sin 2\theta}{\theta}$

4. $\lim_{x\to 0}\frac{\sin 10x}{x}$

5. $\lim_{x\to 0}\frac{\sin 6x}{5x}$

6. $\lim_{h\to 0}\frac{\sin\left(\frac{1}{2}h\right)}{h}$

7. $\lim_{x\to 0}\frac{\sin 7x}{3x}$

8. $\lim_{x\to 0}\frac{\sin 3x}{x\cos x}$

9. $\lim_{x\to 0}\frac{2x\cos 2x}{\sin 5x}$

10. $\lim_{x\to 0}\frac{\sin 4x\sin 3x}{2x^2}$

11. $\lim_{x\to 0}\frac{\sin^2 2x}{3x^2}$

12. $\lim_{x\to 0}\frac{5x}{\sin 3x\cos x}$

13. $\lim_{x\to 0}\frac{\tan x}{x}$

14. $\lim_{x\to 0}\frac{\tan 2x}{x}$

15. Express $\sin 7x-\sin 3x$ as a product and hence evaluate

$$\lim_{x\to 0}\frac{3x}{\sin 7x-\sin 3x}.$$

16. Express $\cos 2x-\cos 6x$ as a product and hence evaluate

$$\lim_{x\to 0}\frac{5x^2}{\cos 2x-\cos 6x}.$$

25.3 One-Sided Limits and Continuous Functions

The limit $\lim_{x\to a} f(x)$ is not defined if its value depends on whether x tends to a from the left or from the right.

The limit of $f(x)$ as x approaches a from the left is written $\lim_{x\to a-} f(x)$ and the limit of $f(x)$ as x approaches a from the right is written $\lim_{x\to a+} f(x)$. Together, these are called **one-sided limits**. The limit $\lim_{x\to a} f(x)$ only exists if both one-sided limits exist and are equal.

The diagram opposite shows the graph of the single function $y=f(x)$.

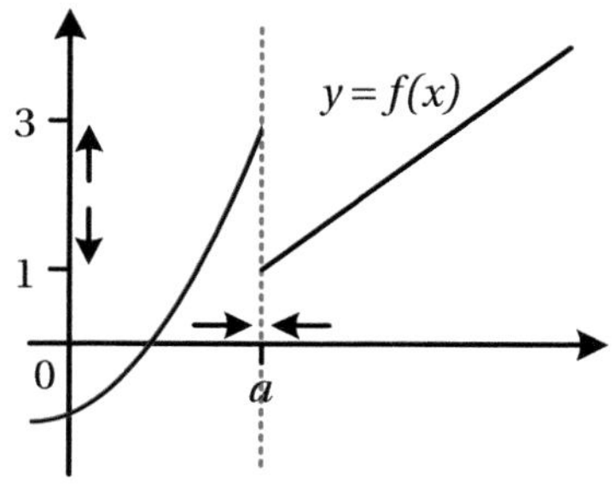

From the diagram, we can see that the limit of $f(x)$, as x approaches a from the left, exists and is equal to 3. Thus we write

$$\lim_{x\to a-} f(x)=3.$$

Likewise, the limit of $f(x)$, as x approaches a from the right, exists and is equal to 1. Thus

$$\lim_{x\to a+} f(x)=1.$$

As $\lim_{x\to a-} f(x)\neq\lim_{x\to a+} f(x)$, i.e. the left hand limit is not equal to the right hand limit, $\lim_{x\to a} f(x)$ does not exist.

Existence of a Limit

The limit $\lim_{x \to a} f(x)$ exists if and only if the one-sided limits

$$\lim_{x \to a-} f(x) \quad \text{and} \quad \lim_{x \to a+} f(x)$$

exist and are equal.

If asked to calculate $\lim_{x \to a} f(x)$, we only have to check the one-sided limits if

(i) we are asked to, or
(ii) we suspect that the one-sided limits are different, or
(iii) $f(x)$ is a piece-wise defined function, with different rules for x on each side of a.

The following example shows how we deal with a piece-wise defined function, which is a function given by different rules on different parts of its domain.

Example 1

The function $f: \mathbb{R} \to \mathbb{R}$ is defined as follows:

$$f: x \to \begin{cases} x^2 + 3 & \text{if } x \leq 1 \\ 5 - x & \text{if } x > 1 \end{cases}.$$

Determine if $\lim_{x \to 1} f(x)$ exists, and if it does, find this limit.

Solution

For $x \leq 1, f(x) = x^2 + 3$. Thus,

$$\lim_{x \to 1-} f(x) = \lim_{x \to 1} (x^2 + 3)$$
$$= (1)^2 + 3 = 4$$

For $x > 1, f(x) = 5 - x$. Thus,

$$\lim_{x \to 1+} f(x) = \lim_{x \to 1} (5 - x)$$
$$= 5 - (1) = 4$$

As $\lim_{x \to 1-} f(x) = \lim_{x \to 1+} f(x)$, $\lim_{x \to 1} f(x)$ exists and is equal to 4. The diagram below shows the situation.

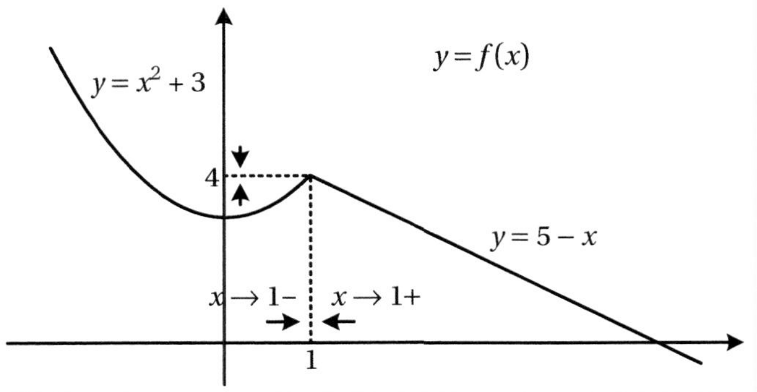

In ordinary language, a function is **continuous** at a particular point if its curve does not have a break at this point, not even a single point gap. More precisely, we have the following definition of when a function is continuous at a point.

Definition of Continuity

The function $f: x \to f(x)$ is continuous at $x = a$ if

(i) $f(a)$ is defined, and

(ii) $\lim\limits_{x \to a} f(x)$ exists, and

(iii) $\lim\limits_{x \to a} f(x) = f(a)$.

If even one of the conditions listed in the definition is not satisfied, then the function is not continuous at $x = a$. If a function is continuous at every point in an interval, then we say that the function is continuous on that interval.

Example 2

The function f is defined by

$$f: x \to \frac{2x+3}{x-2}.$$

Explain why f is not continuous at $x = 2$.

Solution

$$f(x) = \frac{2x+3}{x-2}.$$

Then

$$f(2) = \frac{2(2)+3}{(2)-2} = \frac{7}{0}$$

which is not defined. This breaks condition (i) in the definition.

Thus, f is not continuous at $x = 2$. We may also say that the question of continuity does not arise at $x = 2$ as 2 does not belong to the domain of f.

Example 3

The function $f: \mathbb{R} \to \mathbb{R}$ is defined as follows:

$$f: x \to \begin{cases} x^2 - 1 & \text{if } x \le 3 \\ 2x + 1 & \text{if } x > 3 \end{cases}$$

Explain why f is not continuous at $x = 3$.

Solution

(When $x = 3$, $f(x)$ is given by $f(x) = x^2 - 1$.)

$f(3) = (3)^2 - 1 = 8$

As $f(3)$ is defined, condition (i) in the definition is met.

(Now examine the one-sided limits to see if $\lim\limits_{x \to 3} f(x)$ exists.)

$$\lim_{x\to 3-} f(x) = \lim_{x\to 3} (x^2 - 1)$$
$$= (3)^2 - 1 = 8$$

and

$$\lim_{x\to 3+} f(x) = \lim_{x\to 3} (2x + 1)$$
$$= 2(3) + 1 = 7$$

As $\lim_{x\to 3-} f(x) \neq \lim_{x\to 3+} f(x)$, $\lim_{x\to 3} f(x)$ is not defined.

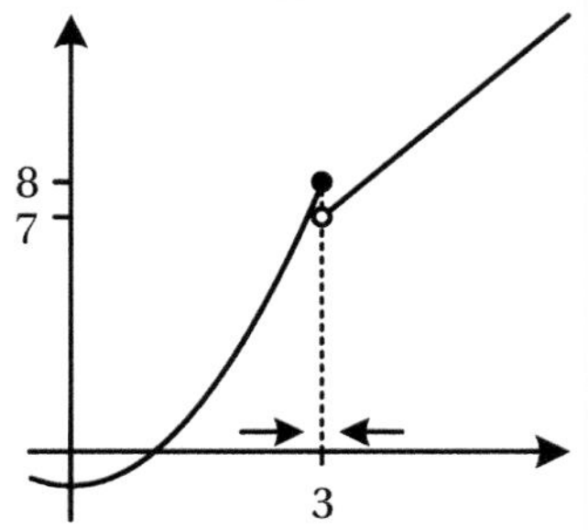

This breaks condition (ii) in the definition. Hence, f is not continuous at $x = 3$.

A number of observations can be made about the functions, and the corresponding curves, that we have already met.

1. All polynomial functions are continuous for all real numbers.
2. All sine and cosine functions we have met are continuous for all real numbers, but tangent functions are not always continuous.

Exercises 25.3

1. $y = f(x)$ is a function defined for all $x \in \mathbb{R}$.

   As x approaches 2 from the left, $f(x)$ approaches 6.

   As x approaches 2 from the right, $f(x)$ approaches 4.

   Explain why $\lim_{x\to 2} f(x)$ does not exist.

2. $y = f(x)$ is a function defined for all $x \in \mathbb{R}$.

   As x approaches 5 from the left, $f(x)$ approaches 8.

   As x approaches 5 from the right, $f(x)$ approaches 12.

   Explain why $\lim_{x\to 2} f(x)$ does not exist.

3. The function f is given by

   $$f: x \to \begin{cases} 2 - x^2 & \text{if } x < 0 \\ 3x + 2 & \text{if } x \geq 0 \end{cases}$$

   Determine if $\lim_{x\to 0} f(x)$ exists.

4. The function f is given by

   $$f: x \to \begin{cases} 5x - 7 & \text{if } x \leq 2 \\ x^2 + x - 3 & \text{if } x > 2 \end{cases}$$

   Determine if $\lim_{x\to 2} f(x)$ exists.

5. The function f is given by

   $$f: x \to \frac{x^2 - 1}{x^2 - 3x + 2}.$$

   (i) Does $\lim_{x\to 1} f(x)$ exist? Explain.

   (ii) Explain why f is not continuous at $x = 1$.

6. The function f is given by

$$f : x \rightarrow \frac{x^2 + x - 6}{x^2 - 4x + 4}.$$

(i) Does $\lim_{x \to 2} f(x)$ exist? Explain.

(ii) Explain why f is not continuous at $x = 2$.

7. The function f is given by

$$f : x \rightarrow \begin{cases} x^2 - 5x & \text{if } x \leq 1 \\ 3x + k & \text{if } x > 1 \end{cases}$$

Find the value of $k \in \mathbb{R}$ if f is continuous at $x = 1$.

8. The function f is given by

$$f : x \rightarrow \begin{cases} x^3 - 5x^2 + 3 & \text{if } x < 2 \\ kx - 5 & \text{if } x \geq 2 \end{cases}$$

Find the value of $k \in \mathbb{R}$ if f is continuous at $x = 2$.

In each of the following questions, we are shown the graph of a function $y = f(x)$. In each case, determine

(i) if $\lim_{x \to a} f(x)$ exists, and if so find its value,

(ii) if f is continuous at $x = a$.

Note that a solid circle indicates the value of the function at that point. A hollow circle indicates that the function is defined along the curve up to that point, but not at the point.

9.

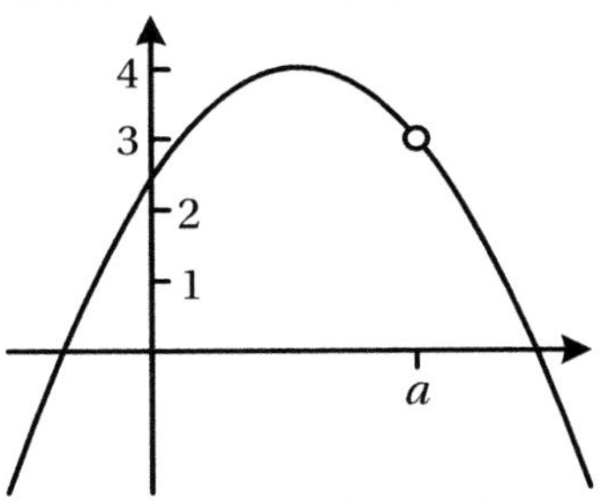

10.

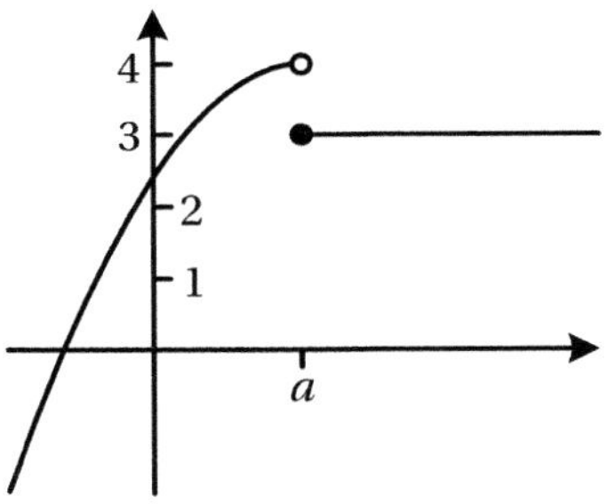

11.

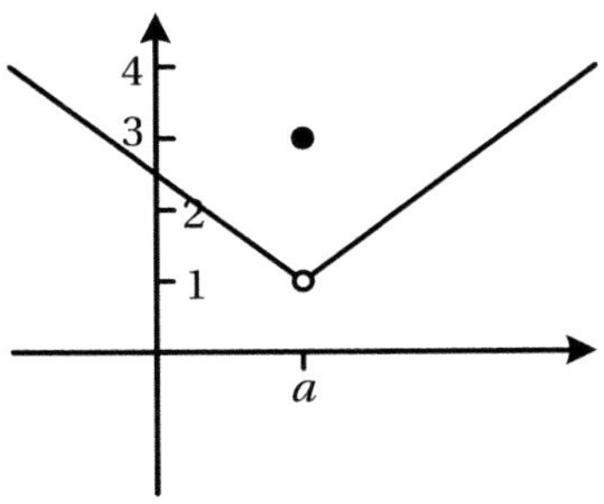

12.

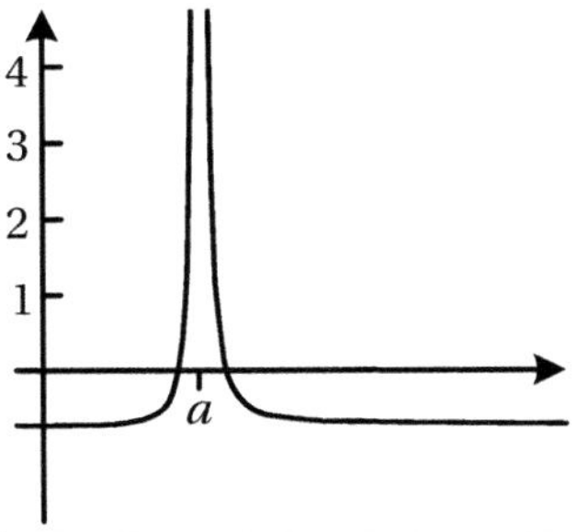

25.4 The Concept of Differentiation

Consider the linear function

$f: \mathbb{R} \to \mathbb{R} : x \to 2x + 1$

and the corresponding curve (which is a straight line)

$y = 2x + 1.$

The slope of this line may be interpreted as **the rate of change of *y* as *x* changes**.

From co-ordinate geometry, we know that the slope of a line is given by

$$\text{slope} = \frac{y_2 - y_1}{x_2 - x_1} = \frac{\text{rise}}{\text{run}} = \frac{\Delta y}{\Delta x},$$

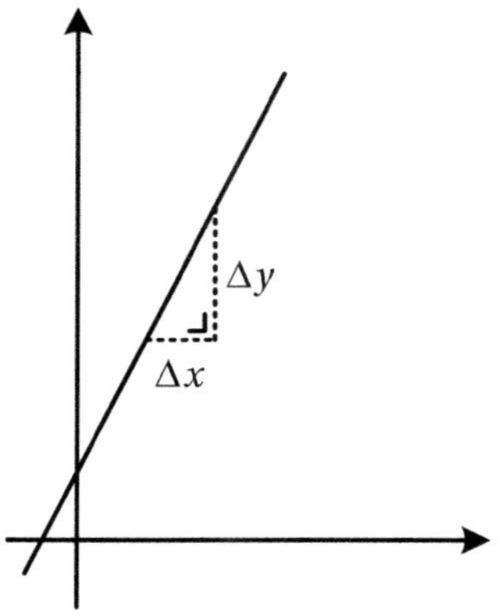

where Δx and Δy are called the *x* and *y* **increments**, and correspond to the 'run' and the 'rise' respectively. Δx is called 'delta *x*'.

For the line $y = 2x + 1$, the slope is 2. We can now interpret this as

'the rate of change of *y* as *x* changes on the line $y = 2x + 1$ is 2'.

For a curve (line) representing a linear function, the slope, i.e. the rate of change, is the same at all points on the curve.

Now consider the function

$f: \mathbb{R} \to \mathbb{R} : x \to x^2$

and the corresponding curve

$y = x^2.$

The idea of the rate of change of *y* as *x* changes is more complicated here, as this rate of change varies as we move along the curve.

Consider the point (1,1) on the curve $y = x^2$. To estimate the rate of change, we can take another point on the curve, say (2,4). Then we can make the following observations.

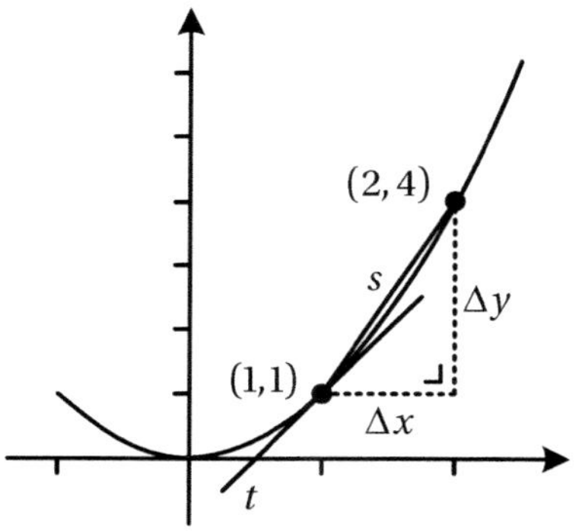

(i) For the line segment, *s*, from (1,1) to (2,4),

$$\Delta x = x_2 - x_1 = 2 - 1 = 1$$

and $$\Delta y = y_2 - y_1 = 4 - 1 = 3$$

Then the slope of *s* is the **average rate of change** of *f* on the interval from $x = 1$ to $x = 2$, i.e.

$$\text{average rate of change} = \frac{\Delta y}{\Delta x} = \frac{3}{1} = 3.$$

(ii) By taking a different second point other than (2,4), e.g. (3,9), we get a different average rate of change, but over a different interval.

(iii) The **instantaneous rate of change** at the point (1,1) is defined to be the slope of the tangent, t, to the curve at this point. You can think of the instantaneous rate of change as being like the speed shown on the speedometer of a car, i.e. the speed at that instant. As you can see from the diagram, the slope of t is not the same as the slope of s.

It was the problem of finding the instantaneous rate of change of a function, i.e. the slope of the tangent, that occupied the attention of some of the greatest mathematical minds in the late 17th century.

Two of them, Newton in England and Leibniz in Germany, independently came up with a solution to the problem. In our modern notation, which is largely due to Leibniz, the solution goes as follows.

Suppose f is a function and the corresponding curve is $y = f(x)$. We want to obtain the instantaneous rate of change, i.e. the slope of the tangent, at the point $(x, y) = (x, f(x))$ on the curve.

We start by considering the point $(x + h, f(x + h))$ further along the curve. Then

$$\Delta x = (x + h) - x = h$$

and

$$\Delta y = f(x + h) - f(x).$$

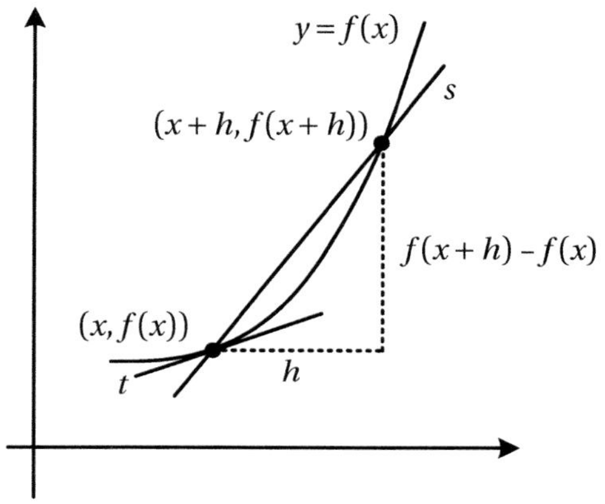

Then the average rate of change, i.e. the slope of the line s, is given by

$$m_s = \frac{\Delta y}{\Delta x} = \frac{f(x+h) - f(x)}{(x+h) - x} = \frac{f(x+h) - f(x)}{h} \quad \dots \mathbf{1}$$

Now comes the crucial element of the argument.

If we let Δx (i.e. h) get smaller, i.e. we let $\Delta x \to 0$, or $h \to 0$, then the line s approaches the tangent t. We can write

$$\text{line } t = \lim_{\Delta x \to 0} (\text{line } s) = \lim_{h \to 0} (\text{line } s).$$

If one line (s) approaches another line (t), then the slope of the first approaches the slope of the second. Thus, we can write m_t, the slope of the tangent t, in terms of limits as

$$m_t = \lim_{\Delta x \to 0} m_s = \lim_{h \to 0} m_s$$

Using the expression in **1** for m_s, we get

$$m_t = \lim_{\Delta x \to 0} \frac{\Delta y}{\Delta x} = \lim_{h \to 0} \frac{f(x+h) - f(x)}{h}.$$

This is the expression that we will use for the slope of the tangent, i.e. the instantaneous rate of change of $y = f(x)$ as x changes.

There are a number of concepts and some terminology and notation that needs to be understood in connection with the idea of finding the slope of the tangent to a curve, i.e. finding the instantaneous rate of change of a function.

1. Leibniz introduced the notation

$$\frac{dy}{dx}$$

to stand for the slope of the tangent. For Leibniz, dx and dy, called x and y **differentials**, stood for theoretical changes in the x and y values respectively so that the fraction composed of the second over the first gives the slope of the tangent. Note that dx and dy are not the same as Δx and Δy. The diagram opposite shows the idea.

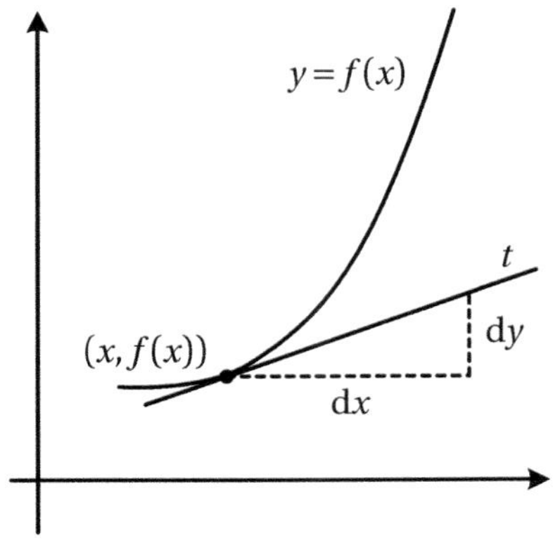

Thus, we can write

$$\frac{dy}{dx} = \lim_{\Delta x \to 0} \frac{\Delta y}{\Delta x} = \lim_{h \to 0} \frac{f(x+h) - f(x)}{h}.$$

2. Since its discovery, many different terms have been used for this method to find an expression for the slope of the tangent, or instantaneous rate of change. Variously called the method of the ratio of differences, the method of the ratio of differentials, amongst others, we now tend to refer to the process as **differentiation**, or as **differential calculus**. Taking a function, or curve, and finding the instantaneous rate of change or slope of the tangent is called **differentiating** the function or curve.

3. About 100 years after Leibniz, a French/Italian mathematician called Lagrange introduced another notation for the slope of the tangent, or instantaneous rate of change. He wrote $f'(x)$, called 'f prime of x' or 'f dash of x', to represent the slope of the tangent. This emphasises the fact that the expression for the slope of the tangent will, in general, be a function of x. This function comes from, or is derived from, the original function. Thus, the expression for the slope of the tangent is called the **derivative**, or sometimes the slope function.

Definition of the Derivative

The slope of the tangent to the curve $y = f(x)$, or the instantaneous rate of change of y as x changes, is called the derivative of y with respect to x, and is given by

$$\begin{aligned}\frac{dy}{dx} &= f'(x)\\ &= \lim_{h \to 0} \frac{f(x+h) - f(x)}{h}\\ &= \lim_{\Delta x \to 0} \frac{\Delta y}{\Delta x}.\end{aligned}$$

The notation $\frac{dy}{dx}$ can be thought of as the fraction, or ratio, of the differentials dy and dx, but in practice we refer to it as '$d\,y\,d\,x$', for historical reasons. Note also that 'dx' does not mean d multiplied by x, but rather d of x, like $\sin x$ means sine of x.

25.5 Differentiation From First Principles

When it comes to calculating the derivative, $\frac{dy}{dx}$, we prefer to use the definition

$$\frac{dy}{dx} = \lim_{h \to 0} \frac{f(x+h) - f(x)}{h}$$

rather than $\frac{dy}{dx} = \lim_{\Delta x \to 0} \frac{\Delta y}{\Delta x}$

because the first expression avoids the use of the increments, Δy and Δx, also called infinitesimals, which caused serious problems for many early mathematicians.

Calculating the derivative by using the limit definition is called **differentiating from first principles**. Although many functions can be differentiated from first principles, on our course, we are only required to be able to differentiate linear and quadratic functions from first principles.

1. Differentiation from First Principles of Linear Functions

A linear function is one of the form

$f: x \to ax + b$

where a and b are real constants. Example 1 shows how we can differentiate such functions from first principles.

Example 1

The function f is defined by

$f: x \to 5 - 3x.$

(i) Differentiate f with respect to x from first principles.

(ii) Explain why the instantaneous rate of change of $f(x)$ for any value of x is the same as the average rate of change of $f(x)$ over any interval.

Solution

(i) Let $y = f(x) = 5 - 3x$. Then

$$\begin{aligned}\frac{dy}{dx} &= f'(x)\\ &= \lim_{h \to 0} \frac{f(x+h) - f(x)}{h}\\ &= \lim_{h \to 0} \frac{[5 - 3(x+h)] - [5 - 3x]}{h}\\ &= \lim_{h \to 0} \frac{(5 - 3x - 3h) - (5 - 3x)}{h}\\ &= \lim_{h \to 0} \frac{-3h}{h}\\ &= \lim_{h \to 0} (-3)\\ &= -3\end{aligned}$$

(ii) The derivative, $\frac{dy}{dx} = f'(x)$, gives the instantaneous rate of change of $y = f(x)$. In this case $\frac{dy}{dx} = -3$, a constant. Hence, the instantaneous rate of change at all points on the curve is –3, i.e. for each one unit increase in x, y decreases by 3 units.
The average rate of change is the slope of the line joining two points on the curve. But because in this case the curve is the line $y = 5 - 3x$, any average rate of change will just be its slope, i.e. –3.
Hence, the instantaneous rate of change and the average rate of change are the same for a linear function.

2. Differentiation from First Principles of Quadratic Functions

A quadratic function is one of the form

$f : x \rightarrow ax^2 + bx + c$

where a, b and c are real constants. Example 2 shows how we can differentiate such functions from first principles.

Example 2

The function f is given by

$f : x \rightarrow 2x^2 - 3x + 5.$

(i) Differentiate f with respect to x from first principles.

(ii) Give an interpretation of the derivative in terms of the curve.

(iii) Find the instantaneous rate of change of f at $x = 2$, i.e. find $f'(2)$.

(iv) Find the average rate of change of f over the interval from $x = 2$ to $x = 3$.

Solution

(i) Let $y = f(x) = 2x^2 - 3x + 5$. Then

$$
\begin{aligned}
\frac{dy}{dx} &= f'(x) \\
&= \lim_{h \to 0} \frac{f(x+h) - f(x)}{h} \\
&= \lim_{h \to 0} \frac{[2(x+h)^2 - 3(x+h) + 5] - [2x^2 - 3x + 5]}{h} \\
&= \lim_{h \to 0} \frac{[2x^2 + 4xh + 2h^2 - 3x - 3h + 5] - [2x^2 - 3x + 5]}{h} \\
&= \lim_{h \to 0} \frac{4xh + 2h^2 - 3h}{h} \\
&= \lim_{h \to 0} \frac{h(4x + 2h - 3)}{h} \\
&= \lim_{h \to 0} (4x + 2h - 3) \\
&= 4x - 3
\end{aligned}
$$

(ii) The derivative, $\frac{dy}{dx} = f'(x) = 4x - 3$, is an expression (a function) derived from the given function $y = f(x) = 2x^2 - 3x + 5$. It gives the slope of the tangent to the curve at any point on the curve, and, hence, is sometimes called the 'slope function'. It may also be interpreted as an expression for the instantaneous rate of change at each point on the curve.

(iii) *(To calculate the instantaneous rate of change at $x = 2$, we substitute 2 for x in the expression for $f'(x)$, i.e. we calculate $f'(2)$.)*

Instantaneous rate of change when $x = 2$

$$
\begin{aligned}
&= f'(2) \\
&= 4(2) - 3 = 5
\end{aligned}
$$

(iv) $f(2) = 2(2)^2 - 3(2) + 5 = 7$ and

$f(3) = 2(3)^2 - 3(3) + 5 = 14.$

Thus, the average rate of change of f over the interval from $x = 2$ to $x = 3$ is

$$\frac{\Delta y}{\Delta x} = \frac{14 - 7}{3 - 2} = 7$$

It is important to realise that differentiation, i.e. obtaining the derivative, is not always possible. It can be shown that for a function $f(x)$ to be differentiable at $x = a$, it is necessary for the function to be continuous at $x = a$. This means that $f(a)$ must be defined, as must $\lim_{x \to a} f(x)$, and $\lim_{x \to a} f(x)$ must be equal to $f(a)$.

But this is not enough. For $f(x)$ to be differentiable at $x = a$, it is necessary for the left derivative

$$f_-'(x) = \lim_{h \to 0-} \frac{f(x+h) - f(x)}{h}$$

and the right derivative

$$f_+'(x) = \lim_{h \to 0+} \frac{f(x+h) - f(x)}{h}$$

to both be defined and equal.

One example of a familiar function that is not differentiable at a point is

$$f: x \to |x|$$

which is not differentiable at $x = 0$.

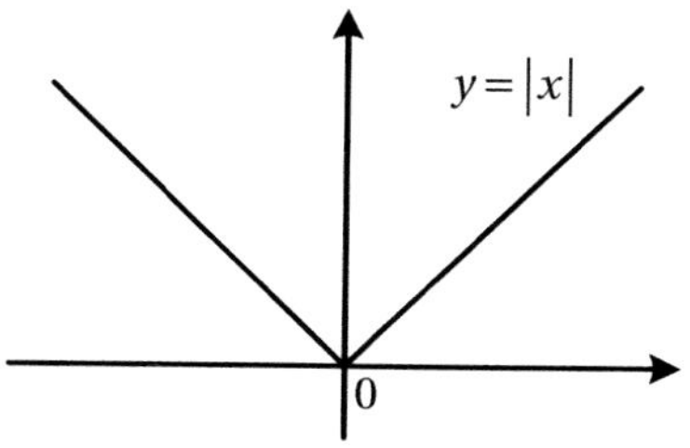

This function may also be written

$$f: x \to \begin{cases} x, & \text{if } x \geq 0 \\ -x, & \text{if } x < 0 \end{cases}$$

and the curve $y = |x|$ is shown opposite.

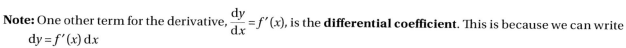

From the diagram,

$$f_-'(0) = -1,$$

i.e. the slope of the curve to the left of 0 is -1, while

$$f_+'(0) = 1$$

i.e. the slope of the curve to the right of 0 is 1. As $f_-'(0) \neq f_+'(0)$, $f(x) = |x|$ is not differentiable at $x = 0$.

Note: One other term for the derivative, $\frac{dy}{dx} = f'(x)$, is the **differential coefficient**. This is because we can write

$$dy = f'(x)\, dx$$

and $f'(x)$, the derivative, is the coefficient of the differential dx.

Exercises 25.5

1. The function f is defined for all $x \in \mathbb{R}$ by

$$f: x \to 2x + 5.$$

(i) Find, from first principles, the derivative of $y = f(x)$.
(ii) Interpret the derivative in terms of the instantaneous rate of change of f.
(iii) How does this compare with the average rate of change of f as x changes?

2. The function f is defined for all $x \in \mathbb{R}$ by

$$f: x \to 3 - 4x.$$

(i) Find, from first principles, the derivative of $y = f(x)$.
(ii) Interpret the derivative in terms of the instantaneous rate of change of f.
(iii) How does this compare with the average rate of change of f as x changes?

3. The function f is defined for all $x \in \mathbb{R}$ by

$$f: x \to x^2 - 2x + 4.$$

(i) Find, from first principles, the derivative of $y = f(x)$.
(ii) The derivative is sometimes described as the 'slope function'. Explain what this means in the light of this derivative.
(iii) Find the instantaneous rate of change of f at $x = 3$.
(iv) Find the average rate of change of f over the interval from $x = 3$ to $x = 4$.

4. The function f is defined for all $x \in \mathbb{R}$ by

$$f : x \rightarrow x^2 + 4x - 7.$$

(i) Find, from first principles, the derivative of $y = f(x)$.
(ii) The derivative is sometimes described as the 'slope function'. Explain what this means in the light of this derivative.
(iii) Find the instantaneous rate of change of f at $x = 1$.
(iv) Find the average rate of change of f over the interval from $x = 1$ to $x = 2$.

Differentiate each of the following functions with respect to x from first principles.

5. $f : x \rightarrow 7x - 8$
6. $f : x \rightarrow 9 - 2x$
7. $f : x \rightarrow \frac{1}{2}x + \frac{4}{3}$
8. $f : x \rightarrow \frac{4}{5} - \frac{3}{2}x$
9. $f : x \rightarrow x^2 - 6x + 8$
10. $f : x \rightarrow 3x^2 + 5x - 2$
11. $f : x \rightarrow -x^2 + 3x - 8$
12. $f : x \rightarrow -2x^2 + 3x - 7$
13. $f : x \rightarrow \frac{1}{2}x^2 - 2x + \frac{7}{2}$
14. $f : x \rightarrow \frac{2}{3}x^2 + \frac{1}{2}x + 4$

Revision Exercises 25

1. (i) Use the *Formulae and Tables* to write

$$\sin(x + h) - \sin x$$

as the product of a cosine and a sine.

(ii) Use the limit result, $\lim\limits_{\theta \to 0} \frac{\sin \theta}{\theta} = 1$, to express the limit

$$\lim_{h \to 0} \frac{\sin(x + h) - \sin x}{h}$$

in terms of x.

(iii) Use the result from part (ii) to explain why the derivative of the function

$$f : x \rightarrow \sin x$$

is given by $f'(x) = \cos x$.

2. (i) Use the *Formulae and Tables* to write

$$\cos(x + h) - \cos x$$

as the product of two sines.

(ii) Use the limit result, $\lim\limits_{\theta \to 0} \frac{\sin \theta}{\theta} = 1$, to express the limit

$$\lim_{h \to 0} \frac{\cos(x + h) - \cos x}{h}$$

in terms of x.

(iii) Use the result from part (ii) to explain why the derivative of the function

$$f : x \rightarrow \cos x$$

is given by $f'(x) = -\sin x$.

3. Consider the function f defined as follows:

$$f: x \rightarrow \begin{cases} \dfrac{1}{x-1}, & \text{for } x < 1 \\ x^2 - 1, & \text{for } x \geq 1 \end{cases}$$

(i) Is there any value of $x \in \mathbb{R}$ for which f is not defined? Explain.
(ii) Explain why f is not continuous at $x = 1$.
(iii) Is f differentiable at $x = 1$? Explain.
(iv) Find, from first principles, the derivative of f for $x > 1$.

4. Consider the function f defined as follows:

$$f: x \rightarrow \begin{cases} \dfrac{x+3}{x+2}, & \text{for } x > -2 \\ 1 - 2x^2, & \text{for } x \leq -2 \end{cases}$$

(i) Is there any value of $x \in \mathbb{R}$ for which f is not defined? Explain.
(ii) Explain why f is not continuous at $x = -2$.
(iii) Is f differentiable at $x = -2$? Explain.
(iv) Find, from first principles, the derivative of f for $x < -2$.

5. Consider the function f defined for all $x \in \mathbb{R}$ by

$$f: x \rightarrow |x - 1|,$$

where $|\,|$ means the modulus.
(i) Give an alternative definition of f as a piece-wise defined function.
(ii) Use this definition to explain why f is continuous at $x = 1$.
(iii) Find, from first principles, the derivative of f for $x < 1$.
(iv) Find, from first principles, the derivative of f for $x > 1$.
(v) Explain why f is not differentiable at $x = 1$.

6. The function f is defined for all $x \in \mathbb{R}$ by

$$f: x \rightarrow ax^2 + bx + c$$

(i) Find, from first principles, the derivative of f with respect to x.
(ii) Find, in terms of a, b and k, an expression for the instantaneous rate of change of f at $x = k$.
(iii) Find an expression for the average rate of change of f over the interval from $x = k - h$ to $x = k + h$.
(iv) Show that this average rate of change is equal to the instantaneous rate of change from part (ii). *(Please note: This is not true for most functions.)*

7. For a curve $y = f(x)$, $\dfrac{dy}{dx} = 2x^3 + 6x - \dfrac{1}{x}$. Find the slope of the tangent to this curve at the point where $x = 1$.

8. For a curve $y = f(x)$, $\dfrac{dy}{dx} = \dfrac{2x-1}{(x-1)^2}$. Find the slope of the tangent to this curve at the point where $x = 2$.

9. If $f: x \rightarrow \sqrt{x}$, for $x > 0$, evaluate $\lim\limits_{h \to 0} \dfrac{f(9+h) - f(9)}{h}$.

10. Evaluate $\lim\limits_{x \to 6} \dfrac{\sqrt{x+3} - 3}{x^2 - 7x + 6}$.

Differentiation by Rule

In the last chapter, we saw how the derivative of a function gives a measure of the instantaneous rate of change of the function and the slope of the tangent to the corresponding curve. The process of obtaining the derivative is called differentiation, and in the last chapter we discovered how to differentiate linear and quadratic functions from first principles, i.e. by using the limit definition.

The process of differentiation is so important in maths and its applications that it is in our interest to speed up the calculation of the derivative, so that we can move on swiftly to using it. To this end, we introduce a number of so-called standard derivatives, and a few rules of differentiation. All of these are given on page 25 of the *Formulae and Tables*. We then combine these to quickly obtain the derivatives of many functions, including some very involved ones.

This is similar to the concept of young school children learning tables in maths so that they can complete calculations more efficiently.

26.1 Differentiation by Rule of Algebraic and Trig Functions

Standard Derivatives

The following standard derivatives are given on page 25 of the *Formulae and Tables*.

$f(x)$	$f'(x)$
x^n	nx^{n-1}
$\cos x$	$-\sin x$
$\sin x$	$\cos x$
$\tan x$	$\sec^2 x$

Each of these standard derivatives can be verified by using first principles. There are a number of issues to be discussed about these standard derivatives.

1. The notation for differentiation can be written in a number of equivalent ways. For example, from the *Formulae and Tables*, we are told

   if $f(x) = x^n$, then $f'(x) = nx^{n-1}$

   But we can also write

   if $y = x^n$ then $\dfrac{dy}{dx} = nx^{n-1}$

   and even, replacing y with x^n,

   $$\frac{d(x^n)}{dx} = nx^{n-1}.$$

2. The first standard derivative tells us that if we differentiate a power of x, we bring the index down in front, keep the base and reduce the index by one, i.e.

   $$\frac{d(x^n)}{dx} = nx^{n-1}$$

Some examples of this standard derivative are given below.

(i) $\frac{d(x^8)}{dx} = 8x^7$

which is equivalent to saying that the instantaneous rate of change of $f(x) = x^8$ is given by $8x^7$, or that the slope of the tangent at any point on the curve $y = x^8$ is given by $8x^7$.

(ii) $\frac{d(x^2)}{dx} = 2x^1 = 2x$

i.e. when we differentiate x^2 we get $2x$.

(iii) $\frac{d(x)}{dx} = \frac{d(x^1)}{dx} = 1x^0 = 1$

i.e. when we differentiate x we get 1.

(iv) $\frac{d(1)}{dx} = \frac{d(x^0)}{dx} = 0x^{-1} = 0$

i.e. when we differentiate 1 we get 0.

(v) $\frac{d\left(\frac{1}{x^2}\right)}{dx} = \frac{d(x^{-2})}{dx} = -2x^{-3} = \frac{-2}{x^3}$

(vi) $\frac{d(\sqrt{x})}{dx} = \frac{d(x^{\frac{1}{2}})}{dx} = \frac{1}{2}x^{\frac{1}{2}-1} = \frac{1}{2}x^{-\frac{1}{2}} = \frac{1}{2} \cdot \frac{1}{x^{\frac{1}{2}}} = \frac{1}{2\sqrt{x}}$

which shows that to differentiate a surd, we start by writing it as a power.

3. The fourth standard derivative is

$$\frac{d(\tan x)}{dx} = \sec^2 x.$$

Page 13 of the *Formulae and Tables* tells us that

$$\sec x = \frac{1}{\cos x}$$

and so $\sec^2 x = \left(\frac{1}{\cos x}\right)^2 = \frac{1}{\cos^2 x}.$

Thus, we can also write

$$\frac{d(\tan x)}{dx} = \sec^2 x = \frac{1}{\cos^2 x}.$$

Example 1

Differentiate with respect to x: **(i)** x^4, **(ii)** $\frac{1}{x^3}$, **(iii)** $\frac{1}{\sqrt{x}}$.

Solution

(i) $\frac{d(x^4)}{dx} = 4x^3$

(ii) $\frac{d\left(\frac{1}{x^3}\right)}{dx} = \frac{d(x^{-3})}{dx}$

$= -3x^{-4}$

$= \frac{-3}{x^4}$

(iii) $\frac{d\left(\frac{1}{\sqrt{x}}\right)}{dx} = \frac{d(x^{-\frac{1}{2}})}{dx}$

$= -\frac{1}{2}x^{-\frac{3}{2}}$

$= -\frac{1}{2x^{\frac{3}{2}}}.$

Rules of Differentiation

The rules of differentiation are used with the standard derivatives to greatly increase the number of functions that can be differentiated. The rules themselves can also be proved by making use of first principles, but we are not required to do so.

Rule 1

If c is a constant, and u is a function of x, then

$$\frac{\mathrm{d}(c.u)}{\mathrm{d}x} = c\frac{\mathrm{d}u}{\mathrm{d}x}.$$

To differentiate a constant times a function of x, we can take the constant outside and multiply it by the derivative of the function of x. For example,

$$\frac{\mathrm{d}(5\sin x)}{\mathrm{d}x} = 5\frac{\mathrm{d}(\sin x)}{\mathrm{d}x} = 5\cos x.$$

Example 2

Differentiate with respect to x:

(i) $7x^4$

(ii) $-9x$

(iii) 12

Solution

(i) $\frac{\mathrm{d}(7x^4)}{\mathrm{d}x} = 7\frac{\mathrm{d}(x^4)}{\mathrm{d}x}$

$= 7(4x^3)$

$= 28x^3$

(In practice, we would not write down the middle lines. Instead, we would bring down the index and multiply it by whatever coefficient the power has.)

(ii) $\frac{\mathrm{d}(-9x)}{\mathrm{d}x} = -9\frac{\mathrm{d}(x)}{\mathrm{d}x}$

$= -9(1)$

$= -9$

(In practice, to differentiate a multiple of x, the outcome is just the multiple.)

(iii) $\frac{\mathrm{d}(12)}{\mathrm{d}x} = 12\frac{\mathrm{d}(1)}{\mathrm{d}x}$

$= 12(0)$

$= 0$

(In practice, when we differentiate a constant on its own, the outcome is 0.)

Rule 2

If u and v are functions of x, then

$$\frac{\mathrm{d}(u \pm v)}{\mathrm{d}x} = \frac{\mathrm{d}u}{\mathrm{d}x} \pm \frac{\mathrm{d}v}{\mathrm{d}x}.$$

To differentiate the sum or difference of two functions of x, differentiate them separately and keep the plus or minus sign between the two parts.

Rule 2 is often used in conjunction with Rule 1. For example

$$\frac{\mathrm{d}}{\mathrm{d}x}(3x^4 + 2\sin x) = \frac{\mathrm{d}}{\mathrm{d}x}(3x^4) + \frac{\mathrm{d}}{\mathrm{d}x}(2\sin x) = 12x^3 + 2\cos x.$$

Example 3

Find $\frac{\mathrm{d}y}{\mathrm{d}x}$ if **(i)** $y = 2x^2 - \frac{1}{x}$, **(ii)** $y = 3\cos x + 2\tan x$.

Solution

(i) *(We should write $\frac{1}{x}$ as x^{-1} before differentiating.)*

$$y = 2x^2 - \frac{1}{x} = 2x^2 - x^{-1}$$

$$\frac{\mathrm{d}y}{\mathrm{d}x} = 4x - (-1)x^{-2}$$

$$= 4x + x^{-2}$$

$$= 4x + \frac{1}{x^2}$$

(ii) $y = 3\cos x + 2\tan x$

$$\frac{\mathrm{d}y}{\mathrm{d}x} = 3(-\sin x) + 2\sec^2 x$$

$$\frac{\mathrm{d}y}{\mathrm{d}x} = -3\sin x + 2\sec^2 x.$$

Once a derivative has been found, we can then evaluate it at any value of x for which it is defined, i.e. we can use it to determine the instantaneous rate of change of the function, or the slope of the tangent to the corresponding curve. It is important to remember to only substitute values for x after the derivative has been obtained.

Example 4

A function is defined for all $x \in \mathbb{R}$ by

$$f: x \rightarrow x^3 + 2x^2 - 5x + 1.$$

(i) Find the derivative $f'(x)$.

(ii) Find the instantaneous rate of change of f when $x = 3$.

(iii) Find the slope of the tangent to the curve $y = f(x)$ at the point where $x = -1$.

Solution

(i) $f(x) = x^3 + 2x^2 - 5x + 1$

Then,

$f'(x) = 3x^2 + 4x - 5$

(ii) The instantaneous rate of change of f at $x = 3$ is $f'(3)$.

$$f'(3) = 3(3)^2 + 4(3) - 5$$
$$= 34$$

(iii) The slope of the tangent to the curve $y = f(x)$ at $x = -1$ is $f'(-1)$, i.e. the value of $\frac{dy}{dx}$ at $x = -1$. Thus slope of tangent

$$= 3(-1)^2 + 4(-1) - 5$$
$$= -6.$$

The remaining standard derivatives and rules of differentiation will be discussed in the following sections.

Exercises 26.1

Differentiate each of the following with respect to x.

1. x^6 **2.** x^{10} **3.** x^{24} **4.** x^{18}

5. $\frac{1}{x}$ **6.** $\frac{1}{x^2}$ **7.** $\frac{1}{x^3}$ **8.** $\frac{1}{x^4}$

9. $5x^3$ **10.** $6x^7$ **11.** $12 \sin x$ **12.** $8 \cos x$

13. $-2 \tan x$ **14.** $-3 \cos x$ **15.** -10 **16.** 0

Find the derivative of each of the following functions.

17. $f: x \to 4x + 7$

18. $f: x \to 5x - 2$

19. $f: x \to x^2 - 4x + 6$

20. $f: x \to 3x^2 - 7x - 11$

21. $f: x \to x^3 + 4x^2 - 8x + 3$

22. $f: x \to 4x^3 - 5x^2 + 7x - 6$

23. $f: x \to 4x^2 - 2 + \frac{3}{x}$

24. $f: x \to 6x + \frac{3}{x^2} + 4\sqrt{x}$

25. $f: x \to 3 \sin x + 5 \cos x$

26. $f: x \to -2 \cos x + 7 \sin x$

27. $f: x \to 5 \sin x + 2 \tan x$

28. $f: x \to 6 \cos x - \frac{2}{x^2}$

29. A function is given by

$$f: x \to 3x^2 - 4x + 6$$

(i) Find the derivative $f'(x)$.

(ii) Find the instantaneous rate of change of f when $x = 2$.

(iii) Find the slope of the tangent to the curve $y = f(x)$ at $x = 1$.

30. A function is given by

$$f: x \to 4x^2 + 12x - 6$$

(i) Find the derivative $f'(x)$.

(ii) Find the instantaneous rate of change of f when $x = -1$.

(iii) Find the slope of the tangent to the curve $y = f(x)$ at $x = 2$.

31. If $y = 2x - \frac{1}{x}$, find the value of $\frac{dy}{dx}$ at $x = 2$.

32. If $y = 3 \sin x + 2 \cos x$, find the value of $\frac{dy}{dx}$ at $x = \frac{\pi}{2}$.

26.2 The Product Rule

The next rule of differentiation is used to find the derivative of a function which is in the form of a product of two factors, each containing x, e.g. $y = x^2 \sin x$ or $y = (2x^3 + 3)\cos x$.

In general, if $y = uv$, where $u = u(x)$ and $v = v(x)$, i.e. u and v are functions of x, then $\frac{dy}{dx}$ is given by the following rule, called the Product Rule. This rule is given on page 25 of the *Formulae and Tables*.

Rule 3 (The Product Rule)

If $y = uv$,

where $u = u(x)$ and $v = v(x)$, then

$$\frac{dy}{dx} = u\frac{dv}{dx} + v\frac{du}{dx}.$$

Example 1

Find the derivative of $y = x^2 \sin x$.

Solution

(y is the product of x^2 and $\sin x$, both of which contain x. We let $u = x^2$ and $v = \sin x$ and use the Product Rule.)

$$y = \underbrace{x^2}_{u}\underbrace{\sin x}_{v}$$

Let $u = x^2$ $\quad v = \sin x$

Then $\frac{du}{dx} = 2x$ $\quad \frac{dv}{dx} = \cos x$

Thus,

$$\frac{dy}{dx} = (x^2)(\cos x) + (\sin x)(2x) \qquad \leftarrow u\frac{dv}{dx} + v\frac{du}{dx}$$

$$= x^2 \cos x + 2x \sin x.$$

For straightforward functions, many students use the Product Rule directly in the form

$$\frac{\mathrm{d}(\text{1st} \times \text{2nd})}{\mathrm{d}x} = (\text{1st})\frac{\mathrm{d}(\text{2nd})}{\mathrm{d}x} + (\text{2nd})\frac{\mathrm{d}(\text{1st})}{\mathrm{d}x},$$

but for more complicated functions it is a good idea to write down u, v, $\frac{\mathrm{d}u}{\mathrm{d}x}$ and $\frac{\mathrm{d}v}{\mathrm{d}x}$.

Exercises 26.2

Use the Product Rule to find $\frac{\mathrm{d}y}{\mathrm{d}x}$ for each of the following functions.

1. $y = (x^2 + 2)(3x^2 - 1)$

2. $y = (4x - 2)(x^2 + x + 5)$

3. $y = (5x - 3)(x^2 + 2x - 4)$

4. $y = (x^2 - 1)(x^2 + x - 1)$

5. $y = x(2x + \sqrt{x})$

6. $y = \sqrt{x}\,(2x - 1)$

7. $y = x^2 \sin x$

8. $y = (3x - 1)\cos x$

9. $y = (1 + \sin x)(2 - \cos x)$

10. $y = (x^2 + 1)\tan x$

11. $y = x(\sin x + \cos x)$

12. $y = (2x^2 - 3)\sin x$

26.3 The Quotient Rule

The Quotient Rule is the rule we use to differentiate a fraction (quotient) where both the top and the bottom contain x, e.g. $y = \frac{2x - 1}{x^2 + 3}$ and $y = \frac{1 - \sin x}{1 + \sin x}$. The Quotient Rule, listed below, is given on page 25 of the *Formulae and Tables*.

Rule 4 (The Quotient Rule)

If $\quad y = \frac{u}{v}$,

where $u = u(x)$ and $v = v(x)$, then

$$\frac{\mathrm{d}y}{\mathrm{d}x} = \frac{v\frac{\mathrm{d}u}{\mathrm{d}x} - u\frac{\mathrm{d}v}{\mathrm{d}x}}{v^2}.$$

Having found $\frac{\mathrm{d}y}{\mathrm{d}x}$, we may be asked to use algebra or trigonometry to write it in some specified form.

Example 1

Find $\frac{\mathrm{d}y}{\mathrm{d}x}$ if $y = \frac{3x - 1}{2x + 5}$, and express your answer in the form $\frac{a}{(bx + c)^2}$, where $a, b, c \in \mathbb{Z}$.

Solution

$$y = \frac{3x-1}{2x+5}$$

(For the Quotient Rule, u is always the top line and v is always the bottom line.)

Let $\quad u = 3x - 1 \qquad v = 2x + 5$

Then $\quad \frac{du}{dx} = 3 \qquad \frac{dv}{dx} = 2$

Then

$$\frac{dy}{dx} = \frac{(2x+5)(3) - (3x-1)(2)}{(2x+5)^2}$$
$$= \frac{6x + 15 - 6x + 2}{(2x+5)^2}$$
$$= \frac{17}{(2x+5)^2}.$$

For straightforward fractions, many students use the Quotient Rule in the form:

$$\frac{d\left(\frac{\text{top}}{\text{bottom}}\right)}{dx} = \frac{(\text{bottom})\frac{d(\text{top})}{dx} - (\text{top})\frac{d(\text{bottom})}{dx}}{(\text{bottom})^2},$$

but for more complicated fractions, it is a good idea to write down u, v, $\frac{du}{dx}$, $\frac{dv}{dx}$ before using the Quotient Rule.

Exercises 26.3

Use the Quotient Rule to find $\frac{dy}{dx}$ for each of the following functions.

1. $y = \frac{2x}{x+1}$

2. $y = \frac{x+3}{2x-1}$

3. $y = \frac{4x-3}{2x+1}$

4. $y = \frac{5x+3}{3x-4}$

5. $y = \frac{x^2-1}{x^2+2}$

6. $y = \frac{x^2+5}{2x^2-1}$

7. $y = \frac{x^2+x+1}{2x-3}$

8. $y = \frac{2x+1}{x^2-2x+3}$

9. $y = \frac{\sin x}{2+\cos x}$

10. $y = \frac{1+\sin x}{1-\cos x}$

11. $y = \frac{x}{1+\sin x}$

12. $y = \frac{2+\sin x}{3+\cos x}$

13. If $y = \frac{4x-1}{x+2}$, express $\frac{dy}{dx}$ in the form $\frac{a}{(x+b)^2}$, where $a, b \in \mathbb{Z}$.

14. If $y = \frac{3x-2}{x+4}$, express $\frac{dy}{dx}$ in the form $\frac{a}{(x+b)^2}$, where $a, b \in \mathbb{Z}$.

15. If $y = \frac{2x+k}{x+3}$ and $\frac{dy}{dx} = \frac{5}{(x+3)^2}$, find the value of $k \in \mathbb{R}$.

16. If $y = \frac{3x+k}{x-1}$ and $\frac{dy}{dx} = \frac{-5}{(x-1)^2}$, find the value of $k \in \mathbb{R}$.

17. If $y = \frac{\cos x}{1+\sin x}$, show that $\frac{dy}{dx} = \frac{-1}{1+\sin x}$.

18. If $y = \frac{\sin x}{1-\cos x}$, show that $\frac{dy}{dx} = \frac{1}{\cos x - 1}$.

26.4 The Chain Rule

The Chain Rule is the rule we use to differentiate many composite functions, i.e. functions of the form $y = u(v(x)) = u \circ v(x)$. But first we need to review a few ideas.

In the notation for differentiation, there is nothing special or unique about the letter x. All we require is that we have the same letter or variable on the top line as on the bottom line. Then the standard derivatives can be used. For example:

(i) $\dfrac{dt^3}{dt} = 3t^2$,

(ii) $\dfrac{d \sin u}{du} = \cos u$.

A problem arises when the variable or letter on the top line is not the same as the variable or letter on the bottom line, e.g. we cannot calculate directly

$$\frac{d(u^4)}{dx}.$$

The only variable that we can differentiate u^4 directly with respect to is u. Hence, to obtain $\dfrac{d(u^4)}{dx}$, we proceed as follows:

$$\begin{aligned}\frac{d(u^4)}{dx} &= \frac{d(u^4)}{du} \cdot \frac{du}{dx}\\ &= 4u^3 \frac{du}{dx}\end{aligned}$$

This is an example of the Chain Rule in action. In practice, the Chain Rule is used to differentiate a function of one variable with respect to a different variable.

In theory, if $y = u \circ v(x) = u(v(x))$, then

$$\begin{aligned}\frac{dy}{dx} &= \frac{d[u \circ v(x)]}{dx}\\ &= \frac{d[u(v(x))]}{dv(x)} \cdot \frac{dv(x)}{dx}\\ &= \frac{du}{dv} \cdot \frac{dv}{dx}.\end{aligned}$$

In prime notation, if $f(x) = u \circ v(x)$, then

$$f'(x) = (u \circ v)'(x) = u'(v(x)).v'(x).$$

Rule 5 (The Chain Rule)

If $y = f(x) = u(v(x)) = u \circ v(x)$, then

$$\begin{aligned}\frac{dy}{dx} &= f'(x) = (u \circ v)'(x)\\ &= \frac{du}{dv} \cdot \frac{dv}{dx}\\ &= u'(v(x)) \,.\, v'(x)\end{aligned}$$

The Chain Rule is not required to differentiate all functions that may be considered to be composite. For example, $y = 3x^2$, may be considered to be the composite of the functions $v(x) = x^2$ and $u = 3x$, i.e. $y = u(v(x)) = u(x^2) = 3x^2$. But the Chain Rule is not required to differentiate y. Below we look at the types of composite functions that require the Chain Rule for differentiation.

1. Chain Rule for Powers

The Chain Rule must be used to differentiate a power of the form

$y = u^n$

if n is a constant and u is anything other than exactly one x. For example, we would need the Chain Rule to differentiate $y = (2x - 1)^4$, $y = (\sin x + 3)^6$ or $y = (3x^2 + 5)^{-2}$.

Then, by the Chain Rule,

$$\frac{dy}{dx} = \frac{d(u^n)}{dx} = \frac{d(u^n)}{du} \cdot \frac{du}{dx} = nu^{n-1} \cdot \frac{du}{dx}$$

Chain Rule 1: Powers

$$\frac{d(u^n)}{dx} = nu^{n-1} \cdot \frac{du}{dx}$$

i.e. (differentiate the power, keeping the base) by (differentiate the base)

Two examples are:

(i) If $y = (5x^2 - 2x + 1)^4$, then $\frac{dy}{dx} = \underbrace{4(5x^2 - 2x + 1)^3}_{\text{differentiate the power}} \cdot \underbrace{(10x - 2)}_{\text{differentiate the base}}$

(ii) If $y = (3 \sin x - 2)^5$, then $\frac{dy}{dx} = \underbrace{5(3 \sin x - 2)^4}_{\text{differentiate the power}} \cdot \underbrace{(3 \cos x)}_{\text{differentiate the base}}$

Having found the derivative, we can be asked to use algebra or trig to write it in a specified form.

Example 1

If $y = \sqrt{2x^2 + 1}$, find $\frac{dy}{dx}$ in terms of x and show that it can be written as $\frac{2x}{y}$.

Solution

(When differentiating roots, again we should start by writing them as powers.)

$$y = \sqrt{2x^2 + 1} = (2x^2 + 1)^{\frac{1}{2}}$$

By the Chain Rule,

$$\frac{dy}{dx} = \frac{1}{2}(2x^2 + 1)^{-\frac{1}{2}} \cdot (4x)$$

Then

$$\frac{dy}{dx} = 2x \cdot \frac{1}{\sqrt{2x^2 + 1}}$$

$$\frac{dy}{dx} = \frac{2x}{\sqrt{2x^2 + 1}}$$

As $y = \sqrt{2x^2 + 1}$,

$$\frac{dy}{dx} = \frac{2x}{y}.$$

Note that $\sin^3 x$ is really a power, i.e. $\sin^3 x = (\sin x)^3$, and is differentiated as a power.

Example 2

If $y = \sin^4 x$, find $\frac{dy}{dx}$.

Solution

$$y = \sin^4 x = (\sin x)^4$$

Then

$$\frac{dy}{dx} = 4(\sin x)^3(\cos x)$$

$$= 4 \sin^3 x \cos x.$$

2. Chain Rule for Trigonometric Functions

The Chain Rule must be used to differentiate a trig function of the form

$y = \cos u$ or $y = \sin u$ or $y = \tan u$

if the angle u is anything other than exactly one x. For example, we would need the Chain Rule to differentiate $y = \cos(2x^2 - 5)$, $y = \sin 5x$ or $y = \tan(2 - x^2)$.

Suppose $y = \sin u$. Then, by the Chain Rule,

$$\frac{dy}{dx} = \frac{d \sin u}{dx} = \frac{d \sin u}{du} \cdot \frac{du}{dx} = \cos u . \frac{du}{dx}$$

We can use a similar approach to differentiate $\cos u$ or $\tan u$, with respect to x.

Chain Rule 2: Trig Functions

$$\frac{d(\sin u)}{dx} = \cos u . \frac{du}{dx}$$

$$\frac{d(\cos u)}{dx} = -\sin u . \frac{du}{dx}$$

$$\frac{d(\tan u)}{dx} = \sec^2 u . \frac{du}{dx}$$

i.e. (differentiate the trig function, keeping the angle) by (differentiate the angle).

Example 3

Find $\frac{dy}{dx}$ if: **(i)** $y = \sin 4x$ **(ii)** $y = \cos(3x^2 - 2)$ **(iii)** $y = \tan(1 - x^2)$

Solution

(i) $y = \sin 4x$

$$\frac{dy}{dx} = \underbrace{\cos 4x}_{\text{differentiate the sin}} . \underbrace{(4)}_{\text{differentiate the angle}}$$

$$= 4 \cos 4x$$

(ii) $y = \cos(3x^2 - 2)$

$$\frac{dy}{dx} = \underbrace{-\sin(3x^2 - 2)}_{\text{differentiate the cos}} \cdot \underbrace{(6x)}_{\text{differentiate the angle}}$$

$$= -6x\sin(3x^2 - 2)$$

(iii) $y = \tan(1 - x^2)$

$$\frac{dy}{dx} = \underbrace{\sec^2(1 - x^2)}_{\text{differentiate the tan}} \cdot \underbrace{(-2x)}_{\text{differentiate the angle}}$$

$$= -2x\sec^2(1 - x^2)$$

Exercises 26.4

Find $\frac{dy}{dx}$ for each of the following functions.

1. $y = (2x^2 - 1)^4$
2. $y = (x^2 - x + 5)^3$
3. $y = (8x^2 - 5)^4$
4. $y = (2\sin x + \cos x)^5$
5. $y = \sqrt{5x + 2}$
6. $y = \sqrt{x^2 + 3}$
7. $y = \sqrt{3 + 2\sin x}$
8. $y = \sqrt{4 - \cos x}$
9. $y = \frac{1}{3x + 2}$
10. $y = \frac{1}{4x - 5}$
11. $y = \frac{1}{(x^2 - 1)^2}$
12. $y = \frac{1}{(4x + 3)^3}$
13. $y = \sin^2 x$
14. $y = \cos^4 x$
15. $y = \sin^6 x$
16. $y = \tan^2 x$
17. $y = \tan^3 x$
18. $y = \sin^7 x$
19. $y = \sin 7x$
20. $y = \sin 9x$
21. $y = \cos 3x$
22. $y = \cos 5x$
23. $y = \tan 4x$
24. $y = \tan 8x$
25. $y = \sin(5x - 3)$
26. $y = \cos(2x^2 + 3)$
27. $y = \tan(x^2 - 6)$
28. $y = \sin(3 - x^2)$
29. $y = \sin(4x^2 + 2x - 1)$
30. $y = \cos(x^2 - 3x + 2)$
31. $y = \sin\left(\frac{1}{x}\right)$
32. $y = \cos\left(1 + \frac{1}{x}\right)$

33. $f: x \to x^2$ and $g: x \to \sin x$. Use the Chain Rule to find
    (i) $(f \circ g)'(x)$ **(ii)** $(g \circ f)'(x)$.
34. $f: x \to \cos x$ and $g: x \to 1 + x^2$. Use the Chain Rule to find
    (i) $(f \circ g)'(x)$ **(ii)** $(g \circ f)'(x)$.
35. $f: x \to \sqrt{x}$ and $g: x \to 2\sin x$. Use the Chain Rule to find
    (i) $(f \circ g)'(x)$ **(ii)** $(g \circ f)'(x)$.
36. $f: x \to x^2 + 1$ and $g: x \to 4\cos x$. Use the Chain Rule to find
    (i) $(f \circ g)'(x)$ **(ii)** $(g \circ f)'(x)$.

26.5 Combination of Rules

Some composite functions require more than one application of the Chain Rule in order to find the derivative. For example, consider the function

$$y = \sin^3(2x + 1).$$

To find $\frac{dy}{dx}$, we start by identifying the function as a power, i.e.

$$y = [\sin(2x + 1)]^3$$

Then, using the Chain Rule,

$$\frac{dy}{dx} = \underbrace{3[\sin(2x+1)]^2}_{\textit{differentiate the power}} \cdot \underbrace{\frac{d\sin(2x+1)}{dx}}_{\textit{differentiate the base}}$$

But the base is itself a composite function, in the form sin u. We will have to use the Chain Rule again.

$$\frac{dy}{dx} = 3\sin^2(2x + 1) \cdot \underbrace{\cos(2x + 1)}_{\textit{differentiate the sin}} . \underbrace{(2)}_{\textit{differentiate the angle}}$$

Tidying up,

$$\frac{dy}{dx} = 6\sin^2(2x + 1)\cos(2x + 1).$$

Example 1

Find $\frac{dy}{dx}$ if $y = x^2 \sin 2x$.

Solution

(It is essential to recognise this as the product of x^2 and sin 2x. Because the angle is 2x, we will need the Chain Rule to differentiate sin 2x.)

$$y = x^2 \sin 2x$$

Let $u = x^2$ $\qquad$ $v = \sin 2x$

$\frac{du}{dx} = 2x$ $\qquad$ $\frac{dv}{dx} = \cos 2x.(2) = 2\cos 2x$

Then, by the Product Rule,

$$\frac{dy}{dx} = u\frac{dv}{dx} + v\frac{du}{dx}$$
$$= (x^2)(2\cos 2x) + (\sin 2x)(2x)$$
$$= 2x^2\cos 2x + 2x\sin 2x.$$

Example 2

If $y=\sqrt{\dfrac{x+1}{x-1}}$, show that $\dfrac{dy}{dx}=\dfrac{-1}{(x+1)^{\frac{1}{2}}(x-1)^{\frac{3}{2}}}$.

Solution

$$y=\sqrt{\frac{x+1}{x-1}}=\left(\frac{x+1}{x-1}\right)^{\frac{1}{2}}$$

(To differentiate this we start by using the Chain Rule to differentiate the power. Then we use the Quotient Rule to differentiate the base. We will have to use algebra to tidy up the answer.)

$$\frac{dy}{dx}=\frac{1}{2}\left(\frac{x+1}{x-1}\right)^{-\frac{1}{2}}\cdot\frac{(x-1)(1)-(x+1)(1)}{(x-1)^2}$$

$$=\frac{1}{2}\frac{(x+1)^{-\frac{1}{2}}}{(x-1)^{-\frac{1}{2}}}\cdot\frac{-2}{(x-1)^2} \qquad \ldots\left(\frac{a}{b}\right)^n=\frac{a^n}{b^n}$$

$$=\frac{-1}{(x+1)^{\frac{1}{2}}(x-1)^{-\frac{1}{2}}(x-1)^2} \qquad \ldots a^{-\frac{1}{2}}=\frac{1}{a^{\frac{1}{2}}}$$

$$=\frac{-1}{(x+1)^{\frac{1}{2}}(x-1)^{\frac{3}{2}}} \qquad \ldots a^{\frac{-1}{2}}.a^2=a^{-\frac{1}{2}+2}=a^{\frac{3}{2}}$$

Exercises 26.5

1. Differentiate $(3+\cos 2x)^2$ with respect to x.
2. Differentiate $(2+3\sin 3x)^4$ with respect to x.
3. Find $\dfrac{dy}{dx}$ if $y=\sin^2 3x$.
4. Find $\dfrac{dy}{dx}$ if $y=\cos^3 4x$.
5. Find $\dfrac{dy}{dx}$ if $y=\sin^3(3x-1)$.
6. Find $\dfrac{dy}{dx}$ if $y=\sqrt{1+\sin 2x}$.
7. Find $\dfrac{dy}{dx}$ if $y=\sqrt{4\cos 3x-1}$.
8. Find $\dfrac{dy}{dx}$ if $y=x(1+3x^2)^3$.
9. Find $\dfrac{dy}{dx}$ if $y=x\sqrt{5x+1}$.
10. Find $\dfrac{dy}{dx}$ if $y=(x+1)\sqrt{x^2+3}$.

11. Find $\frac{dy}{dx}$ if $y = \cos 2x \sin 3x$.

12. Find $\frac{dy}{dx}$ if $y = \cos x(1 + \sin x)^3$.

13. Find $\frac{dy}{dx}$ if $y = \frac{\sin 3x}{1 + \cos 3x}$, and find the value of $\frac{dy}{dx}$ at $x = 0$.

14. Find $\frac{dy}{dx}$ if $y = \frac{x}{\sqrt{1 - 4x^2}}$.

15. If $y = \frac{1 + \cos 2x}{1 - \cos 2x}$, find the value of $\frac{dy}{dx}$ when $x = \frac{\pi}{4}$.

16. If $y = \frac{\cos 2x}{1 - \sin 2x}$, find the value of $\frac{dy}{dx}$ when $x = 0$.

17. If $y = \frac{\sqrt{2x+1}}{x+3}$, show that $\frac{dy}{dx} = \frac{2 - x}{\sqrt{2x+1}(x+3)^2}$.

18. If $y = \sqrt{\frac{x}{x+1}}$, find the value of $\frac{dy}{dx}$ when $x = 1$.

19. Find $\frac{dy}{dx}$ if $y = \sin 3x + \cos 2x$.

20. If $y = 2x - \sin 2x$, find $\frac{dy}{dx}$ and write your answer in the form $k \sin^2 x$, where $k \in \mathbb{R}$.

26.6 Implicit Differentiation

Consider the function $y = \sqrt{x}$. To find $\frac{dy}{dx}$, we can proceed as normal:

$$y = \sqrt{x}$$
$$y = x^{\frac{1}{2}}.$$
$$\frac{dy}{dx} = \frac{1}{2}x^{-\frac{1}{2}} = \frac{1}{2\sqrt{x}}.$$

Alternatively, we can write

$$y = \sqrt{x}$$
$$y^2 = x.$$

Now we can differentiate each term on both sides with respect to x. To differentiate y^2 with respect to x, we have to use the Chain Rule. This technique is known as **implicit differentiation**, as y, wherever it occurs, is an implicit, or implied, function of x.

$$\frac{d(y^2)}{dx} = \frac{d(x)}{dx}$$
$$\frac{d(y^2)}{dy} \cdot \frac{dy}{dx} = 1$$
$$2y\frac{dy}{dx} = 1$$

$$\frac{dy}{dx} = \frac{1}{2y}$$

$$\frac{dy}{dx} = \frac{1}{2\sqrt{x}}, \qquad \text{as before.}$$

When implicit differentiation is used to find $\frac{dy}{dx}$, the answer may contain y as well as perhaps x. Unlike in the example above, it may not be possible to remove the y.

Implicit differentiation can be used to find $\frac{dy}{dx}$ for many curves in the plane, even when they do not represent y as a single function of x.

For example, the equation

$$x^2 + y^2 - 2x + 6y - 3 = 0$$

represents a circle, and implicit differentiation can be used to find $\frac{dy}{dx}$, i.e. the slope of the tangent at any point on this circle. The following example shows how to use implicit differentiation for a curve such as this.

Example 1

Find $\frac{dy}{dx}$ for the circle with equation $x^2 + y^2 - 2x + 6y - 3 = 0$.
Hence, find the slope of the tangent to this circle at the point (4, –1).

Solution

(Differentiate each term on both sides with respect to x.)

$$x^2 + y^2 - 2x + 6y - 3 = 0$$

$$2x + 2y\frac{dy}{dx} - 2 + 6\frac{dy}{dx} = 0$$

(Now rearrange the terms to leave all the $\frac{dy}{dx}$ *terms on one side and all other terms on the other. Then isolate* $\frac{dy}{dx}$*.)*

$$2y\frac{dy}{dx} + 6\frac{dy}{dx} = -2x + 2$$

$$\frac{dy}{dx}(2y + 6) = -2x + 2$$

$$\frac{dy}{dx} = \frac{-2x + 2}{2y + 6} = \frac{-x + 1}{y + 3}$$

At the point (4, –1), the slope of the tangent is given by

$$m = \frac{-(4) + 1}{(-1) + 3} = \frac{-3}{2}.$$

Exercises 26.6

1. If $y^3 = 2x^2 + 5$, show that $\frac{dy}{dx} = \frac{4x}{3y^2}$.
2. If $y^2 = x^3 + 2x$, show that $\frac{dy}{dx} = \frac{3x^2 + 2}{2y}$.

3. The equation of a circle is $x^2 + y^2 - 4x - 8y = 0$. Find $\frac{dy}{dx}$ and use it to find the slope of the tangent to this circle at the point (6,2).

4. The equation of a circle is $x^2 + y^2 + 8x - 2y + 4 = 0$. Find $\frac{dy}{dx}$ and use it to find the slope of the tangent to this circle at the point (–1,3).

5. If $y = \sqrt{\frac{2x}{x^2+1}}$, by squaring both sides, show that $\frac{dy}{dx} = \frac{1-x^2}{y(x^2+1)^2}$.

6. If $y = \sqrt{\frac{x^2+2}{x^2+1}}$, by squaring both sides, show that $\frac{dy}{dx} = \frac{-x}{y(x^2+1)^2}$.

26.7 Differentiation of Inverse Trigonometric Functions

Suppose the derivative of the function

$$y = f(x)$$

is $\frac{dy}{dx} = f'(x)$.

Now suppose the inverse function is $y = f^{-1}(x)$. We can find the derivative of the inverse function by rewriting and using implicit differentiation.

$$y = f^{-1}(x)$$
$$f(y) = x$$
$$f'(y)\frac{dy}{dx} = 1$$
$$\frac{dy}{dx} = \frac{1}{f'(y)}.$$

This theory can now be applied to the problem of finding the derivatives of the inverse trig functions, $y = \cos^{-1} x$, $y = \sin^{-1} x$ and $y = \tan^{-1} x$. The derivatives of these functions are given in the following form on page 25 of the *Formulae and Tables.*

f(x)	f′(x)
$\cos^{-1}\frac{x}{a}$	$-\frac{1}{\sqrt{a^2-x^2}}$
$\sin^{-1}\frac{x}{a}$	$\frac{1}{\sqrt{a^2-x^2}}$
$\tan^{-1}\frac{x}{a}$	$\frac{a}{a^2+x^2}$

In practice, it is best to only use these when $a = 1$.

(i) $\frac{d(\cos^{-1} x)}{dx} = -\frac{1}{\sqrt{1-x^2}}$, **(ii)** $\frac{d(\sin^{-1} x)}{dx} = \frac{1}{\sqrt{1-x^2}}$,

(iii) $\frac{d(\tan^{-1} x)}{dx} = \frac{1}{1+x^2}$.

However, if the function *exactly* matches $\cos^{-1}\frac{x}{a}$, $\sin^{-1}\frac{x}{a}$ or $\tan^{-1}\frac{x}{a}$, where a is a constant, then it is safe to use the formulae in the tables.

Example 1

If $y = \sin^{-1} x$, show that $\frac{dy}{dx} = \frac{1}{\sqrt{1 - x^2}}$.

Solution

$$y = \sin^{-1} x$$

Then $\quad \sin y = x$

Using implicit differentiation,

$$\cos y \frac{dy}{dx} = 1$$

$$\frac{dy}{dx} = \frac{1}{\cos y}$$

$$= \frac{1}{\sqrt{1 - \sin^2 y}} \qquad \ldots \cos^2 y + \sin^2 y = 1 \textit{ and}$$

$$= \frac{1}{\sqrt{1 - x^2}} \qquad -\frac{\pi}{2} \le y \le \frac{\pi}{2} \textit{ means } \cos y > 0$$

OR

$$y = \sin^{-1} x$$

Then

$$\sin y = x$$

Using implicit differentiation,

$$\cos y \frac{dy}{dx} = 1$$

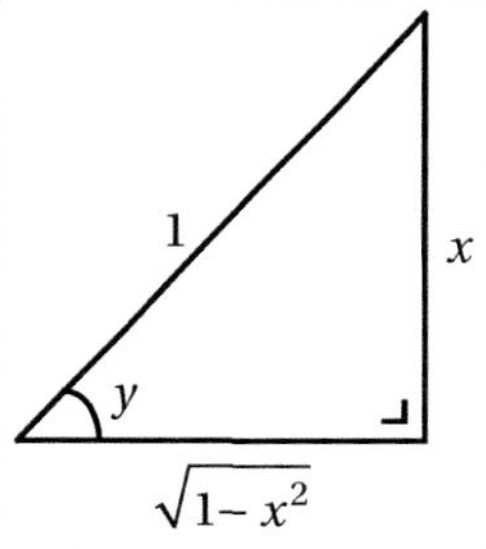

From the triangle opposite,

$$\cos y = \frac{\sqrt{1 - x^2}}{1} = \sqrt{1 - x^2}$$

Thus, $\frac{dy}{dx} = \frac{1}{\sqrt{1 - x^2}}$.

Example 2

Find $\frac{dy}{dx}$ if $y = \sin^{-1} \frac{x}{4}$.

Solution

(We can use the formula from the tables, with a = 4.)

$$y = \sin^{-1} \frac{x}{4}$$

$$\frac{dy}{dx} = \frac{1}{\sqrt{4^2 - x^2}}.$$

Like other basic functions, $\sin^{-1} x$ and $\tan^{-1} x$ can occur in products and quotients.

Example 3

Find $\frac{dy}{dx}$ if $y = (3x^2 - 1)\tan^{-1} x$.

Solution

(The given function is a product.)

$$\frac{dy}{dx} = (3x^2 - 1)\left(\frac{1}{1 + x^2}\right) + (\tan^{-1} x)(6x)$$

$$= \frac{3x^2 - 1}{1 + x^2} + 6x\tan^{-1} x$$

3. Chain Rule for Inverse Trigonometric Functions

The Chain Rule must be used to differentiate inverse trig functions of the form

$y = \cos^{-1} u, \quad y = \sin^{-1} u \quad \text{or} \quad y = \tan^{-1} u$

if u is anything other than exactly one x. For example, we would need the Chain Rule to differentiate

$\sin^{-1}2x, \quad \tan^{-1}(3x + 1) \;$ or $\; \tan^{-1}\left(\frac{1}{x}\right)$.

Suppose $y = \sin^{-1} u$. Then, by the Chain Rule,

$$\frac{dy}{dx} = \frac{d \sin^{-1} u}{dx} = \frac{d \sin^{-1} u}{du} \cdot \frac{du}{dx} = \frac{1}{\sqrt{1 - u^2}} \cdot \frac{du}{dx}$$

$\cos^{-1} u$ and $\tan^{-1} u$ can be approached in the same way.

Chain Rule 3: Inverse Trig Functions

$$\frac{d(\cos^{-1} u)}{dx} = -\frac{1}{\sqrt{1 - u^2}} \cdot \frac{du}{dx}$$

$$\frac{d(\sin^{-1} u)}{dx} = \frac{1}{\sqrt{1 - u^2}} \cdot \frac{du}{dx}$$

$$\frac{d(\tan^{-1} u)}{dx} = \frac{1}{1 + u^2} \cdot \frac{du}{dx}$$

i.e. (differentiate the inverse trig function, keeping the value) by (differentiate the value).

Example 4

Find $\frac{dy}{dx}$ if $y = \tan^{-1}(4x + 1)$.

Solution

$$y = \tan^{-1}(4x + 1)$$

$$\frac{dy}{dx} = \underbrace{\frac{1}{1 + (4x + 1)^2}}_{\text{differentiate the } \tan^{-1}} \cdot \underbrace{(4)}_{\text{differentiate the value}}$$

$$= \frac{4}{1 + (4x + 1)^2}.$$

Exercises 26.7

1. By using implicit differentiation, show that if $y = \cos^{-1} x$, then $\frac{dy}{dx} = -\frac{1}{\sqrt{1-x^2}}$.

2. By using implicit differentiation, show that if $y = \tan^{-1} x$, then $\frac{dy}{dx} = \frac{1}{1+x^2}$.

Find $\frac{dy}{dx}$ for each of the following functions.

3. $y = x^2 + 3\cos^{-1} x$

4. $y = 3x^3 + 2x + \tan^{-1} x$

5. $y = x^2 \sin^{-1} x$

6. $y = (2x+1)\sin^{-1} x$

7. $y = (1 + x^3)\tan^{-1} x$

8. $y = 2\sin^{-1} x + 3\tan^{-1} x$

9. $y = \cos^{-1}(2x)$

10. $y = \sin^{-1}(5x)$

11. $y = \tan^{-1}(4x)$

12. $y = \tan^{-1}(7x)$

13. $y = \cos^{-1}(x+2)$

14. $y = \tan^{-1}(x-1)$

15. $y = \sin^{-1}(2x-3)$

16. $y = \cos^{-1}(4x-2)$

17. $y = \tan^{-1}(x^2)$

18. $y = \sin^{-1}(x^2-1)$

19. $y = (\sin^{-1} x)^2$

20. $y = \tan^{-1}(\cos x)$

21. If $y = \sin^{-1}(\cos x)$, show that $\frac{dy}{dx} = k$, where k is a constant.

22. Differentiate $\tan^{-1}\left(\frac{1}{x}\right)$.

26.8 Differentiation of Exponential Functions

The (natural) exponential function, $y = e^x$, first introduced in Chapter 8, is one of the most important functions in the theory of differentiation. It is the only basic function that is its own derivative. The famous Swiss mathematician, Leonard Euler, defined e^x as the infinite polynomial:

$$e^x = 1 + x + \frac{x^2}{2!} + \frac{x^3}{3!} + \frac{x^4}{4!} + \ldots$$

By differentiating term by term, we obtain

$$\frac{d(e^x)}{dx} = 0 + 1 + \frac{2x}{2!} + \frac{3x^2}{3!} + \frac{4x^3}{4!} + \ldots$$

$$\frac{d(e^x)}{dx} = 1 + x + \frac{x^2}{2!} + \frac{x^3}{3!} + \ldots$$

$$\frac{d(e^x)}{dx} = e^x.$$

We can also use the definition of e^x to approximate the important constant e.

$$e = e^1 = 1 + 1 + \frac{1}{2!} + \frac{1}{3!} + \frac{1}{4!} + \ldots$$

This series very quickly converges (gets closer) to approximately 2·71828.

The standard derivatives of e^x and e^{ax} are given on page 25 of the *Formulae and Tables.*

$f(x)$	$f'(x)$
e^x	e^x
e^{ax}	ae^{ax}

The exponential function can occur in products and quotients.

Example 1

Find $\dfrac{dy}{dx}$ if $y = (2x + 1)e^x$.

Solution

(The given function is a product.)

$$y = (2x + 1)e^x$$
$$\frac{dy}{dx} = (2x + 1)(e^x) + (e^x)(2)$$
$$= e^x(2x + 1 + 2)$$
$$= e^x(2x + 3)$$

4. Chain Rule for Natural Exponential Functions

The Chain Rule must be used to differentiate exponential functions of the form

$$y = e^u$$

if u is anything other than exactly one x. For example, we would need the Chain Rule to differentiate e^{2x+1}, $e^{\sin x}$ or $e^{x^2 + \cos x}$.

Suppose $y = e^u$. Then, by the Chain Rule,

$$\frac{dy}{dx} = \frac{d(e^u)}{dx} = \frac{d(e^u)}{du} . \frac{du}{dx} = e^u . \frac{du}{dx}$$

In practice, it is easy to use the Chain Rule on exponential functions: write down what you are given and multiply by differentiating the index.

Chain Rule 4: Natural Exponential Functions

$$\frac{d(e^u)}{dx} = e^u . \frac{du}{dx}$$

i.e. (what we are given) by (differentiate the index).

Example 2

If $y = e^{x^2 + \sin x}$, find $\dfrac{dy}{dx}$.

Solution

$$\frac{dy}{dx} = e^{x^2 + \sin x} . (2x + \cos x).$$

Exercises 26.8

Find $\frac{dy}{dx}$ for each of the following functions.

1. $y = x^3 + 2e^x$
2. $y = 2\sin x - e^x$
3. $y = \tan^{-1} x + 3e^x$
4. $y = xe^x$
5. $y = (x^2 + 3)e^x$
6. $y = x(3e^x - 1)$
7. $y = \frac{e^x}{x}$
8. $y = \frac{2x+3}{e^x}$
9. $y = \frac{e^x + 1}{e^x - 1}$
10. $y = e^{-x}$
11. $y = e^{4x+2}$
12. $y = e^{\cos x}$
13. $y = e^{2x^2-3x+1}$
14. $y = e^{2\sin x+3}$
15. $y = e^{\sqrt{x+1}}$
16. $y = (x^2 + 1)e^{2x}$
17. $y = e^{3x}\cos x$
18. $y = e^{-x}\sin 2x$
19. $y = e^{-2x}\sin 3x$
20. $y = \frac{e^{2x} + 1}{e^x}$
21. $y = \frac{e^{3x} + 1}{e^{3x} - 1}$

22. Find $\frac{dy}{dx}$ if $y = \sin^{-1}(e^x)$.

23. Find $\frac{dy}{dx}$ if $y = \frac{x^2e^{3-x}}{e^{1+x}}$, by first simplifying y.

24. Find $\frac{dy}{dx}$ if $y = \frac{e^x - e^{-x}}{e^x + e^{-x}}$.

26.9 Differentiation of Logarithmic Functions

The natural logarithmic function, $y = \log_e x = \ln x$, is another key function in the theory of differentiation. Its derivative is given on page 25 of the *Formulae and Tables*.

$f(x)$	$f'(x)$
$\ln x$	$\frac{1}{x}$

Implicit differentiation can be used to verify this derivative, as the following example shows.

Example 1

If $y = \log_e x$, show that $\frac{dy}{dx} = \frac{1}{x}$, for $x > 0$.

Solution

$$y = \log_e x$$
$$e^y = x$$

Using implicit differentiation,

$$e^y \frac{dy}{dx} = 1$$
$$x\frac{dy}{dx} = 1$$
$$\frac{dy}{dx} = \frac{1}{x}.$$

The natural log function can occur in products and quotients.

Example 2

Find $\frac{dy}{dx}$ if $y = x^2 \log_e x$.

Solution

(The given function is a product.)

$$y = x^2 \log_e x$$

$$\frac{dy}{dx} = (x^2)\left(\frac{1}{x}\right) + (\log_e x)(2x)$$

$$= x + 2x \log_e x$$

$$= x(1 + 2\log_e x)$$

5. Chain Rule for Natural Logarithmic Functions

The Chain Rule must be used to differentiate natural log functions of the form

$$y = \log_e u$$

if u is anything other than exactly one x. For example, we would need the Chain Rule to differentiate $\log_e(1 + x^2)$, $\log_e(\sin x + 2)$ or $\ln(x + \sqrt{x})$.

Suppose $y = \log_e u$. Then, by the Chain Rule,

$$\frac{dy}{dx} = \frac{d(\log_e u)}{dx} = \frac{d(\log_e u)}{du} \cdot \frac{du}{dx} = \frac{1}{u} \cdot \frac{du}{dx}$$

In practice, it is easy to use the Chain Rule on natural log functions: put one over the value inside the log and multiply by differentiating the value.

Chain Rule 5: Logarithmic Functions

$$\frac{d(\ln u)}{dx} = \frac{1}{u} \cdot \frac{du}{dx}$$

i.e. (differentiate the log) by (differentiate the value).

Example 3

Find $\frac{dy}{dx}$ if $y = \log_e(\sin x + 3)$.

Solution

$$y = \log_e(\sin x + 3)$$

$$\frac{dy}{dx} = \underbrace{\frac{1}{\sin x + 3}}_{\text{differentiate the log}} \cdot \underbrace{(\cos x)}_{\text{differentiate the value}}$$

$$= \frac{\cos x}{\sin x + 3}$$

The laws of logs can often be used to simplify a log, removing the need to use a Product, Quotient or Chain Rule when differentiating. For example,

(i) $\log_e x^3 = 3\log_e x$ ... don't need the Chain Rule

(ii) $\log_e (x \sin x) = \log_e x + \log_e \sin x$ ... don't need the Product Rule

(iii) $\log_e \left(\frac{x}{\cos x}\right) = \log_e x - \log_e \cos x$ ... don't need the Quotient Rule

Example 4

If $y = \ln\sqrt{x^2+1}$, find $\frac{dy}{dx}$.

Solution

$$y = \ln (x^2+1)^{\frac{1}{2}} = \frac{1}{2}\ln (x^2+1)$$

Then

$$\frac{dy}{dx} = \frac{1}{2}\cdot\frac{1}{x^2+1}.2x$$

$$\frac{dy}{dx} = \frac{x}{x^2+1}$$

Being able to differentiate natural log functions allows us to differentiate general exponential functions, i.e. exponential functions where the base is not necessarily *e*.

For example, consider the function

$y = a^x$, where $a > 0$ is a constant.

Taking logs to the base *e* on both sides, and using implicit differentiation, we get,

$$\log_e y = \log_e a^x$$

$$\ln y = x \ln a$$

$$\frac{1}{y}\frac{dy}{dx} = \ln a$$

$$\frac{dy}{dx} = y\ln a$$

$$\frac{dy}{dx} = a^x \ln a$$

This standard derivative is given on page 25 of the *Formulae and Tables*.

f (x)	f′(x)
a^x	$a^x \ln a$

Example 5

If $y = 2^x$, find $\frac{dy}{dx}$.

Solution

$$\frac{dy}{dx} = 2^x \ln 2.$$

6. Chain Rule for General Exponential Functions

The Chain Rule must be used to differentiate general exponential functions of the form a^u, where u is anything other than exactly one x. For example, we would need the Chain Rule to differentiate 2^{3x+1} or $10^{3+\sin x}$.

Suppose $y = a^u$. Then, by the Chain Rule,

$$\begin{aligned}\frac{\mathrm{d}(a^u)}{\mathrm{d}x} &= \frac{\mathrm{d}(a^u)}{\mathrm{d}u} \cdot \frac{\mathrm{d}u}{\mathrm{d}x} \\ &= a^u \ln a \,.\, \frac{\mathrm{d}u}{\mathrm{d}x}\end{aligned}$$

Chain Rule 6: General Exponential Functions

$$\frac{\mathrm{d}(a^u)}{\mathrm{d}x} = a^u \ln a . \frac{\mathrm{d}u}{\mathrm{d}x}$$

i.e. (differentiate the exponential) by (differentiate the index).

Example 6

Find $\frac{\mathrm{d}y}{\mathrm{d}x}$ if $y = 5^{2+3\sin x}$.

Solution

$y = 5^{2+3\sin x}$

Then

$$\frac{\mathrm{d}y}{\mathrm{d}x} = [5^{2+3\sin x} . \ln 5](3\cos x)$$

Exercises 26.9

Find $\frac{\mathrm{d}y}{\mathrm{d}x}$ for each of the following functions.

1. $y = x^2 + \ln x$

2. $y = 3\ln x - 4x^3$

3. $y = 3\sin x - 2\ln x$

4. $y = x^3 \ln x$

5. $y = (2x - 1)\ln x$

6. $y = (\sin x + 2)\ln x$

7. $y = \ln(1 + x^2)$

8. $y = \ln(3x^2 - 2)$

9. $y = x^2 \ln(2x + 1)$

10. $y = \ln(x^2 \sin x)$

11. $y = \ln(x^3\sqrt{x+1})$

12. $y = \ln\left(\frac{3x^2}{\sqrt{x^2+1}}\right)$

13. $y = \ln(x\sin^2 x)$

14. $y = \ln\left(\frac{\cos x}{\sqrt{x}}\right)$

15. $y = \frac{\ln x}{x^2}$

16. $y = 3^x$

17. $y = 8^x$

18. $y = 10^x$

19. $y = 2^{x^2+3x}$

20. $y = 4^{\sin x + \cos x}$

21. $y = 6^{2x^2} + \sqrt{x}$

22. If $y = x^x$, show that $\ln y = x\ln x$. Hence, use the Product Rule to find $\frac{\mathrm{d}y}{\mathrm{d}x}$ in terms of x.

Revision Exercises 26

1. If $y = \sqrt{x+1} + \dfrac{1}{\sqrt{x+1}}$, show that $\dfrac{dy}{dx} = \dfrac{x}{2(x+1)\sqrt{x+1}}$.

2. If $y = \dfrac{1}{x + \sqrt{x^2+1}}$, show that $\sqrt{x^2+1}\,\dfrac{dy}{dx} = -y$.

3. If $y = \dfrac{1-\cos x}{1+\cos x}$, show that $\dfrac{dy}{dx} = t + t^3$, where $t = \tan\dfrac{x}{2}$.

4. If $y = \sqrt{\dfrac{x^2-1}{x^2+1}}$, find the value of $\dfrac{dy}{dx}$ when $x = \sqrt{3}$ and write it in the form $\sqrt{\dfrac{a}{b}}$, where $a, b \in \mathbb{N}$.

5. If $y = \tan\left(\dfrac{1-x}{1+x}\right)$, find the value of $\dfrac{dy}{dx}$ when $x = 1$.

6. If $y = \dfrac{x}{\sqrt{x^2+1}}$, show that $\dfrac{dy}{dx} = \dfrac{y^3}{x^3}$.

7. If $y = \cos\left(2x + \dfrac{\pi}{4}\right)$, show that $\dfrac{dy}{dx}$ can be written in the form $k\cos\left(2x - \dfrac{\pi}{4}\right)$.

8. Find the value of the constant k if $y = kx^2$ is a solution of the equation

$$x\frac{dy}{dx} + \frac{1}{2}\left(\frac{dy}{dx}\right)^2 + y = 0,$$

where $x \in \mathbb{R}$ and $k \neq 0$.

9. If $y = \sqrt{\dfrac{1+2x}{1-2x}}$, find the values of $k \in \mathbb{N}$ and $p, q \in \mathbb{Q}$ if

$$\frac{dy}{dx} = \frac{k}{(1+2x)^p(1-2x)^q}.$$

10. If $y = \left\{x + \sqrt{1+x^2}\right\}^n$, prove that $\dfrac{dy}{dx} = \dfrac{ny}{\sqrt{1+x^2}}$.

11. Find $\dfrac{dy}{dx}$ if $y = (\tan^{-1}\sqrt{x})^2$.

12. If $y = \sin^{-1}\left(\dfrac{x}{1+x}\right)$, show that $\dfrac{dy}{dx} = \dfrac{1}{(1+x)\sqrt{1+2x}}$.

13. If $y = \log_e\sqrt{\dfrac{x^2-1}{x^2+1}}$, show that $\dfrac{dy}{dx} = \dfrac{2x}{x^4-1}$.

14. If $y = \log_e\left(x + \sqrt{x^2+1}\right)$, show that $\dfrac{dy}{dx}$ can be expressed in the form $\dfrac{p}{(1+x^2)^q}$, $p, q \in \mathbb{R}$.

15. Given $y = \ln\left(\dfrac{3+x}{\sqrt{9-x^2}}\right)$, find $\dfrac{dy}{dx}$ and express it in the form $\dfrac{a}{b-x^n}$.

16. Let $f(x) = \tan^{-1}\dfrac{x}{2}$ and $g(x) = \tan^{-1}\dfrac{2}{x}$, for $x > 0$.

(i) Find $f'(x)$ and $g'(x)$.
(ii) Hence, show that $f(x) + g(x)$ is a constant.
(iii) Find the value of $f(x) + g(x)$.

17. Given that $y = \ln \dfrac{1+x^2}{1-x^2}$ for $0 < x < 1$, find $\dfrac{dy}{dx}$ and write your answer in the form $\dfrac{kx}{1-x^k}$ where $k \in \mathbb{N}$.

18. If $\sin y = \frac{1}{2}(1-x^2)$ for $-\sqrt{3} < x < \sqrt{3}$,

calculate the value of a and the value of b when

$$\left(\frac{dy}{dx}\right)^2 = \frac{a}{3-x^2} - \frac{b}{1+x^2}, \qquad a, b \in \mathbb{N}.$$

27 Curve Sketching

Differential Calculus is a very powerful tool for analysing graphs and sketching curves. We start by considering one of the original objectives of differentiation, i.e. finding the slope of the tangent to a curve.

Next up, we see differentiation being used to identify some of the key features of curves. A knowledge of these features will allow us to construct curves in a more precise way than by just constructing a table of values.

First, we discuss where a curve is increasing and where it is decreasing. Then we see how to find the stationary points, including turning points and points of inflection. For some curves, finding the asymptotes can be an important asset when sketching.

Finally, we put all these features together to sketch a variety of curves. We also consider variations, such as constructing derivative curves and matching curves to their derivative curves.

27.1 Slope and Equation of Tangent

To find the slope of the tangent to a curve at a point (x_1, y_1) on the curve:

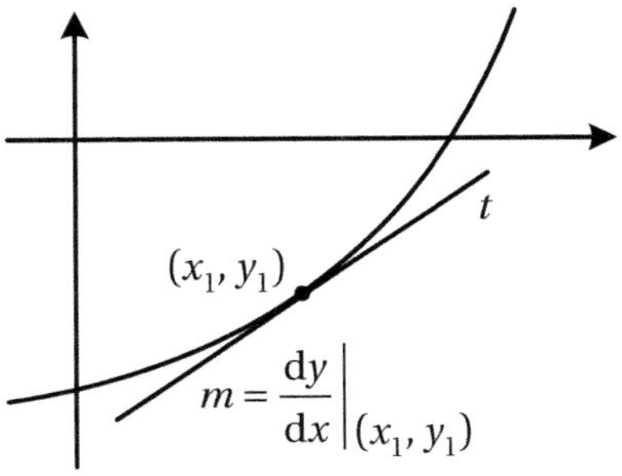

1. Find the derivative, $\frac{dy}{dx}$, using whatever methods are required.
2. Evaluate $\frac{dy}{dx}$ at the point (x_1, y_1) to get the slope, i.e.
$$m = \left.\frac{dy}{dx}\right|_{(x_1, y_1)}.$$

If the equation of the tangent, t, is also required:

3. Use the equation of a line formula
$$y - y_1 = m(x - x_1)$$
to get the equation of the tangent.

Example 1

Find the equation of the tangent to the curve
$$y = \frac{x^2 + 3}{x - 1}$$
at the point (2,7).

Solution

$\left(\textit{Use the Quotient Rule to find } \frac{dy}{dx}.\right)$

$$y = \frac{x^2 + 3}{x - 1}$$

$$\frac{dy}{dx} = \frac{(x-1)(2x) - (x^2+3)(1)}{(x-1)^2}$$
$$= \frac{2x^2 - 2x - x^2 - 3}{(x-1)^2}$$
$$= \frac{x^2 - 2x - 3}{(x-1)^2}$$

At (2,7):

$$m = \frac{(2)^2 - 2(2) - 3}{(2-1)^2} = \frac{-3}{1} = -3$$

The equation of the tangent is

$y - y_1 = m(x - x_1)$

$y - 7 = -3(x - 2)$

$y - 7 = -3x + 6$

$3x + y = 13.$

Example 2

Let $f(x) = x^3 - 3x^2 + 12x - 5$.

Find the co-ordinates of the two points on the curve $y = f(x)$ at which the tangent to the curve has a slope of 12.

Solution

(We need to get $\frac{dy}{dx}$, which is the general expression for the slope; put $\frac{dy}{dx}$ equal to 12 and solve this for x; then work out the y co-ordinates of the points.)

$y = x^3 - 3x^2 + 12x - 5$

$\frac{dy}{dx} = 3x^2 - 6x + 12$

Put $\frac{dy}{dx} = 12$:

$3x^2 - 6x + 12 = 12$

$3x^2 - 6x = 0$

$x^2 - 2x = 0$

$x(x - 2) = 0$

$x = 0$ or $x - 2 = 0$

$x = 0$ or $x = 2$

$x = 0$: $y = (0)^3 - 3(0)^2 + 12(0) - 5 = -5$

One point is (0, –5).

$x = 2$: $y = (2)^3 - 3(2)^2 + 12(2) - 5 = 15$

The other point is (2,15).

Exercises 27.1

1. Find the equation of the tangent to the curve $y = 3x^3 - 4x^2 + 2x - 10$ at the point $(1,-9)$.
2. Find the equation of the tangent to the curve $y = 9x - x^3$ at the point $(-1,-8)$.
3. Find the equation of the tangent to the curve $y = \sqrt{x^2 + 7}$ at the point (3,4).
4. Find the equation of the tangent to the curve $y = x \sin 2x$ at the point $\left(\frac{\pi}{4}, \frac{\pi}{4}\right)$.
5. Find the equation of the tangent to the curve $y = x + \tan x$ at the point $(0,0)$.
6. Find the equation of the tangent to the curve $y = \frac{2x+3}{x-2}$ at the point (3,9).
7. Find the co-ordinates of the point on the curve $y = x^2 - x + 7$ at which the tangent has a slope of 11.
8. Find the co-ordinates of the point on the curve $y = 3x^2 - 2x + 1$ at which the tangent has a slope of -8.
9. Find the co-ordinates of the point on the curve $y = x^2 - 2x + 5$ at which the tangent is parallel to the line $y = 3x$.
10. Find the co-ordinates of the point on the curve $y = 2x^2 + 3x - 5$ at which the tangent is parallel to the line $y = -x$.
11. Find the co-ordinates of the two points on the curve $y = x^3 - 3x^2 - 21x + 5$ at which the tangents have a slope of 3.
12. Find the co-ordinates of the two points on the curve $y = x^3 - 6x^2 + 15x - 4$ at which the tangents have a slope of 6.

27.2 Increasing and Decreasing

The sign of the derivative at a point on a curve can tell us whether a curve is increasing or decreasing at that point.

A curve is ***increasing*** (i.e. going up as we go from left to right) at a point if the tangent to the curve is increasing. Another way of saying this is that the tangent has a positive slope. Thus, $\frac{dy}{dx}$ is positive at that point. We can also say that the curve has a positive rate of change at the point.

Likewise, the curve is ***decreasing*** (i.e. going down as we go from left to right) if the slope of the tangent to the curve is negative. Thus, $\frac{dy}{dx}$ is negative at that point. We can also say that the curve has a negative rate of change at the point.

Increasing and Decreasing

(i) A curve is increasing where $\frac{dy}{dx} > 0$.

(ii) A curve is decreasing where $\frac{dy}{dx} < 0$.

Example 1

Explain why the curve

$$y = \frac{3x+1}{x-2}$$

is decreasing for all $x \in \mathbb{R}$, $x \neq 2$.

Solution

$\left(\textit{Any mention of increasing or decreasing means we should examine the sign of } \frac{dy}{dx}.\right)$

$$y = \frac{3x+1}{x-2}$$

$$\frac{dy}{dx} = \frac{(x-2)(3)-(3x+1)(1)}{(x-2)^2} \qquad \textit{... Quotient Rule}$$

$$\frac{dy}{dx} = \frac{-7}{(x-2)^2}$$

As $-7 < 0$ and $(x-2)^2 > 0$, for all $x \in \mathbb{R}$, $x \neq 2$,

$$\frac{dy}{dx} < 0,$$

for all $x \in \mathbb{R}$, $x \neq 2$. Thus, the curve is decreasing for all $x \in \mathbb{R}$, $x \neq 2$.

Differentiation can now be used to verify some results we obtained when investigating graphs in algebra and trigonometry. For example, by differentiation, we can verify that a quadratic curve is increasing on one side of its turning point, and decreasing on the other side. Another case is highlighted in Example 2.

Example 2

$f: x \to e^{ax}$, where $a \neq 0$ is a constant.

Verify that the curve $y = f(x)$ is increasing for all $x \in \mathbb{R}$ if $a > 0$, and is decreasing for all $x \in \mathbb{R}$ if $a < 0$.

Solution

The curve is $y = e^{ax}$. Then

$$\frac{dy}{dx} = (e^{ax})(a) = ae^{ax}.$$

As $e^{ax} > 0$, for all $x \in \mathbb{R}$, the sign of $\frac{dy}{dx}$ will depend only on the sign of a.

(i) If $a > 0$, then $\frac{dy}{dx} > 0$ and so the curve is increasing for all $x \in \mathbb{R}$.

(ii) If a < 0, then $\frac{dy}{dx} < 0$ and so the curve is decreasing for all $x \in \mathbb{R}$.

Exercises 27.2

1. Explain why the curve $y = x^2 + 2x - 1$ is increasing at the point (1,2).
2. Explain why the curve $y = \frac{x+2}{x-4}$ is decreasing at the point (5,7).
3. Determine the values of $x \in \mathbb{R}$ for which the curve $y = 2x^2 - 6x + 3$ is
   (i) increasing **(ii)** decreasing.
   Hence write down the co-ordinates of the turning point of this curve.
4. Determine the values of $x \in \mathbb{R}$ for which the curve $y = 3x^2 - 12x + 8$ is
   (i) increasing **(ii)** decreasing.
   Hence write down the co-ordinates of the turning point of this curve.
5. Show that the curve $y = \frac{2x-1}{x+3}$ is increasing for all $x \in \mathbb{R}$, $x \neq -3$.
6. Prove that the curve $y = \frac{2x-3}{x-4}$ is decreasing for all $x \neq 4$.
7. Prove that the curve $y = \frac{x+3}{2x-1}$ is decreasing for all $x \neq \frac{1}{2}$.
8. Explain why the curve $y = \tan^{-1} x$ is increasing for all $x \in \mathbb{R}$.
9. Show that the curve $y = \ln x$ is increasing for all $x \in \mathbb{R}$, $x > 0$.
10. Explain why the curve $y = 2x - \cos x$ is increasing for all $x \in \mathbb{R}$.
11. Determine the values of $x \in \mathbb{R}$ for which the curve $y = x^3 - 3x^2 - 9x + 4$ is decreasing.
12. Determine the values of $x \in \mathbb{R}$ for which the curve $y = x^3 - 9x^2 + 15x - 2$ is increasing.

27.3 Stationary Points

A **stationary point** of a curve is a point on the curve at which the tangent to the curve exists and is horizontal. The diagram opposite shows a curve $y = f(x)$ which has a stationary point at A.

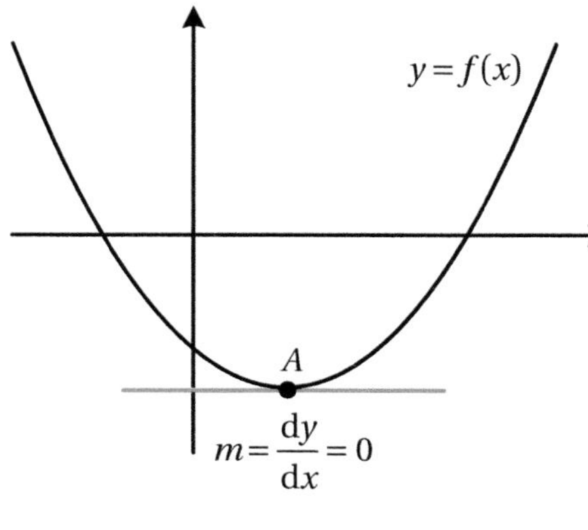

For the tangent to exist at a point on a curve, $\frac{dy}{dx}$ must exist at that point. Thus, for example, $y = |x|$ cannot have a stationary point at (0, 0), as its derivative is not defined at that point.

The slope of a horizontal line is 0. Hence, we can restate the definition of a stationary point of a curve as a point where the derivative exists and is equal to zero.

Stationary Point of a Curve

A stationary point of a curve is a point on the curve at which the curve is differentiable, and

(i) the tangent is horizontal **or**
(ii) the tangent has a slope of zero **or**
(iii) $\frac{dy}{dx} = 0$.

To find the stationary points of the curve $y = f(x)$:

(i) find $\frac{dy}{dx}$,

(ii) put $\frac{dy}{dx} = 0$ and solve for x; any solution is the x co-ordinate of a stationary point,

(iii) find the y co-ordinates of the stationary points.

Example 1

Find the co-ordinates of the two stationary points of the curve

$y = 2x^3 - 3x^2 - 12x + 7$.

Solution

$y = 2x^3 - 3x^2 - 12x + 7$

$\frac{dy}{dx} = 6x^2 - 6x - 12$

Put $\frac{dy}{dx} = 0$:

$6x^2 - 6x - 12 = 0$

$x^2 - x - 2 = 0$

$(x + 1)(x - 2) = 0$

$x + 1 = 0$ or $x - 2 = 0$

$x = -1$ or $x = 2$

$x = -1$: $y = 2(-1)^3 - 3(-1)^2 - 12(-1) + 7$

$y = -2 - 3 + 12 + 7$

$y = 14$

One stationary point is $(-1,14)$.

$x = 2$: $y = 2(2)^3 - 3(2)^2 - 12(2) + 7$

$y = 16 - 12 - 24 + 7$

$y = -13$

The other stationary point is $(2,-13)$.

There are three types of stationary points, shown in the diagram opposite as the points A, B and C.

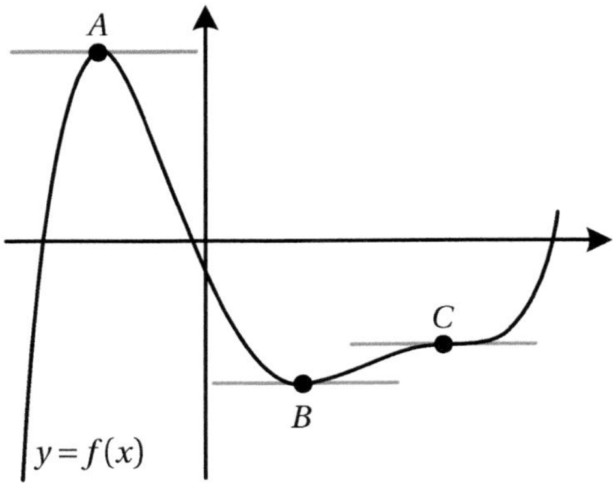

Two of these (A and B) are called **turning points**, as the curve turns around at these points. The third, C, is not a turning point, but is a point at which the tangent goes from one side of the curve to the other, i.e. the tangent cuts across the curve. Each of these three points has its own name.

A: Local Maximum Point

This is the highest point on the curve in the locality of A. It may not be the highest point overall. At a local maximum point (local max, for short), the curve goes from increasing on the left, to decreasing on the right. In other words, $\frac{dy}{dx}$ goes from positive, through zero, to negative.

B: Local Minimum Point

This is the lowest point on the curve in the locality of B. It may not be the lowest point overall. At a local minimum point (local min, for short), the curve goes from decreasing on the left, to increasing on the right. In other words, $\frac{dy}{dx}$ goes from negative, through zero, to positive.

C: Saddle Point (Horizontal Point of Inflection)

At a saddle point, the curve is increasing on both sides, or decreasing on both sides. In other words, $\frac{dy}{dx}$ goes from positive, through zero, to positive, or negative, through zero, to negative.

These observations form the basis of the first method, called the **First Derivative Test**, for determining the nature of a stationary point.

First Derivative Test for Stationary Points

(i) If $\frac{dy}{dx}$ goes from $+ \rightarrow 0 \rightarrow -$, then the point is a **local max.**

(ii) If $\frac{dy}{dx}$ goes from $- \rightarrow 0 \rightarrow +$, then the point is a **local min.**

(iii) If $\frac{dy}{dx}$ goes from $+ \rightarrow 0 \rightarrow +$, or from $- \rightarrow 0 \rightarrow -$, then the point is a **saddle point.**

In practice, we take sample values of x on each side of each stationary point. By evaluating $\frac{dy}{dx}$ at each of these values of x, we can determine the nature of each stationary point. This can be laid out in the form of a table, as shown in Example 2.

Example 2

Find the stationary point of the curve

$$y = x^3 - 6x^2 + 12x - 5$$

and determine the nature of this stationary point.

Solution

$$y = x^3 - 6x^2 + 12x - 5$$

$$\frac{dy}{dx} = 3x^2 - 12x + 12$$

$$= 3(x^2 - 4x + 4)$$

$$= 3(x-2)^2$$

Put $\frac{dy}{dx} = 0$: $3(x-2)^2 = 0$

$$(x-2)^2 = 0$$

$$x - 2 = 0$$

$$x = 2$$

$x = 2$: $y = 3$. Thus, the stationary point is (2,3).

(Take $x = 1$ and $x = 3$ as sample values on each side of $x = 2$.)

x	1	2	3
$\frac{dy}{dx}$	+	0	+
shape	/	—	/

At $x = 1$, $\frac{dy}{dx} = 3$ (+)

At $x = 3$, $\frac{dy}{dx} = 3$ (+).

From the table, (2,3) is a saddle point (horizontal point of inflection).

Exercises 27.3

1. Find the co-ordinates of the stationary points of the curve $y = 3x^2 - x^3$.
2. Find the co-ordinates of the stationary points of the curve $y = 2x^3 - 3x^2 - 6$.
3. Find the co-ordinates of the stationary points of the curve $y = 2x^3 + 3x^2 - 12x$.
4. Find the co-ordinates of the stationary point of the curve $y = x^2 + \frac{16}{x}$.
5. Find the co-ordinates of the stationary point of the curve $y = x^3$. Show that this point is not a turning point.

6. Find the co-ordinates of the stationary points of the curve $y = x^3 - 6x^2 + 9x - 2$, and use the First Derivative Test to determine the nature of these turning points.

7. Find the co-ordinates of the stationary points of the curve $y = (x^2 - 1)^3$, and use the First Derivative Test to determine the nature of these turning points.

8. Find the co-ordinates of the stationary points of the curve $y = (x - 1)^2 (x - 3)^3$, and use the First Derivative Test to determine the nature of these turning points.

27.4 The Second Derivative and its Interpretation

Consider the function

$$y = x^3 - 3x.$$

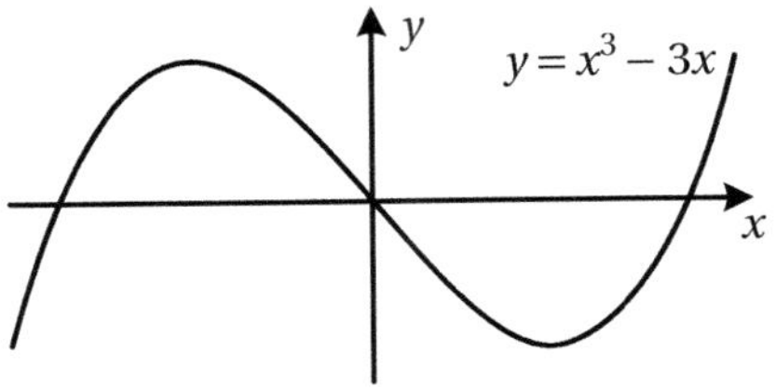

The derivative of this function,

$$\frac{dy}{dx} = 3x^2 - 3$$

gives the slope of the tangent at any point on the curve $y = x^3 - 3x$. It may also be regarded as an expression for the rate of change of y as x changes.

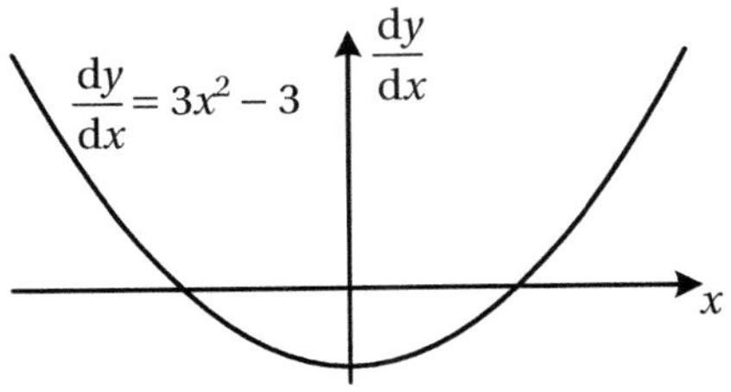

But $\frac{dy}{dx} = 3x^2 - 3$ is a curve in its own right, and as such has tangents which have slopes. Once again, the slopes of the tangents can be found by differentiating.

This can be written

$$\frac{d}{dx}\left(\frac{dy}{dx}\right) = \frac{d}{dx}(3x^2 - 3)$$

$$\frac{d^2y}{dx^2} = 6x.$$

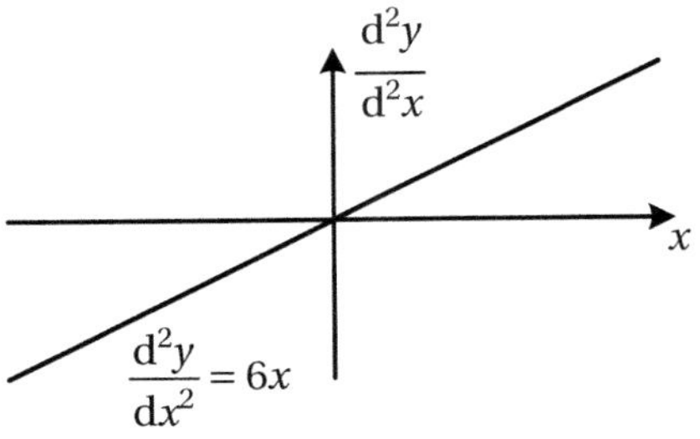

This 'derivative of the derivative' is written as $\frac{d^2y}{dx^2}$, or as $f''(x)$, and is referred to as the **second derivative**.

It may also be referred to as the 'slope of the slope function' or as the 'rate of change of the rate of change'.

One example of the second derivative in real life is that of acceleration. The acceleration of an object, e.g. a car, is the rate of change of the velocity. But velocity is the rate of change of distance. Hence, acceleration can be considered to be the 'rate of change of the rate of change of the distance', i.e. a second derivative. We will investigate this in more detail in the next chapter.

When there is any doubt as to which derivative is involved, $\frac{dy}{dx} = f'(x)$ can also be referred to as the **first derivative**.

In practice, the methods and rules used to find the second derivative from the first derivative are the same as those used to find any derivative, e.g. standard derivatives, product, quotient and chain rules.

Example 1

If $y = x \sin x$, find $\dfrac{d^2y}{dx^2}$.

Solution

$\left(\textit{We get } \dfrac{dy}{dx} \textit{ first and differentiate again to find } \dfrac{d^2y}{dx^2}.\right)$

$y = x \sin x$

$\dfrac{dy}{dx} = (x)(\cos x) + (\sin x)(1)$ ... *Product Rule*

$= x \cos x + \sin x$

Then

$\dfrac{d^2y}{dx^2} = (x)(-\sin x) + (\cos x)(1) + \cos x$

... *Product Rule for x cos x*

$= -x \sin x + 2 \cos x.$

The Sign of the Second Derivative

The sign of the (first) derivative, $\dfrac{dy}{dx}$, tells us whether the curve, $y = f(x)$, is increasing (positive) or decreasing (negative). What does the sign of the second derivative tell us about the curve, $y = f(x)$?

The sign of the second derivative tells us about the **curvature** of the curve, i.e. which way the curve is facing.

The curvature is generally described in terms of which way the curve is **concave**. There are two possibilities for a curve which is everywhere differentiable on an interval: concave upwards and concave downwards.

1. **Concave Upwards**

The curve $y = f(x)$ is concave upwards between the points A and B if every line segment joining two points on the curve between A and B, e.g. [CD], lies completely above the curve.

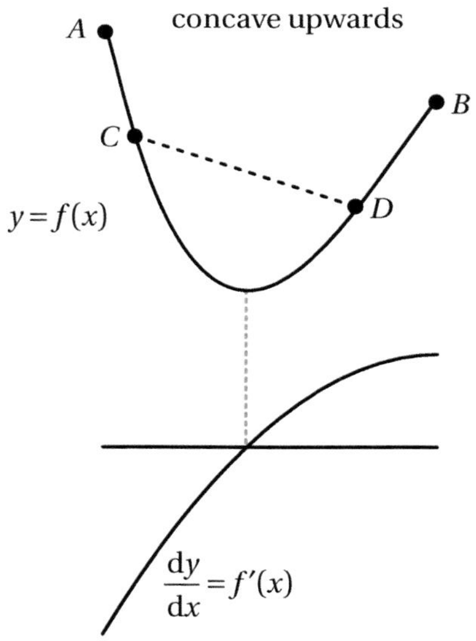

If the derivative, $\dfrac{dy}{dx}$, is increasing at all points between A and B, then the curve $y = f(x)$ is concave upwards in this region. Thus, if

$$\frac{d}{dx}\left(\frac{dy}{dx}\right) > 0$$

or $$\frac{d^2y}{dx^2} > 0$$

then the curve is concave upwards.

2. **Concave Downwards**

The curve $y = f(x)$ is concave downwards between the points A and B if every line segment joining two points on the curve between A and B, e.g. [CD], lies completely below the curve.

If the derivative, $\frac{dy}{dx}$, is decreasing at all points between A and B, then the curve $y = f(x)$ is concave downwards in this region. Thus, if

$$\frac{d}{dx}\left(\frac{dy}{dx}\right) < 0$$

or $$\frac{d^2y}{dx^2} < 0$$

then the curve is concave downwards.

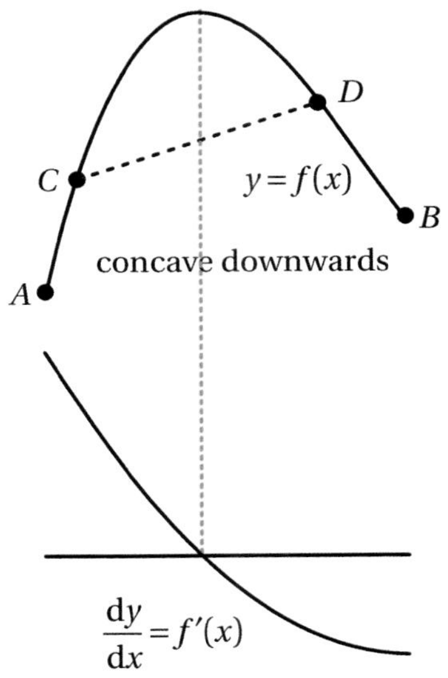

Curvature

(i) A curve is concave upwards where $\frac{d^2y}{dx^2} > 0$.

(ii) A curve is concave downwards where $\frac{d^2y}{dx^2} < 0$.

Example 2

Show that the curve $y = e^x$ is concave upwards, for all $x \in \mathbb{R}$.

Solution

(Any mention of concave means that we have to look at the sign of the second derivative.)

$$y = e^x$$

$$\frac{dy}{dx} = e^x$$

$$\frac{d^2y}{dx^2} = e^x$$

As $e^x > 0$, for all $x \in \mathbb{R}$, $\frac{d^2y}{dx^2} > 0$ for all $x \in \mathbb{R}$. Hence, the curve is concave upwards for all $x \in \mathbb{R}$.

Exercises 27.4

Find $\frac{d^2y}{dx^2}$ for each of the following functions.

1. $y = \sin x$

2. $y = 3x^3 + 5x^2 - 1$

3. $y = (2x - 1)^7$

4. $y = \cos(2x + 3)$

5. $y = (3x^2 + 1)^3$

6. $y = \sin^3 x$

7. If $y = 5x^3 + 2x^2$, show that

$$x^2\frac{d^2y}{dx^2} - 4x\frac{dy}{dx} + 6y = 0.$$

8. If $y = 7x - \frac{2}{x}$, show that

$$x^2\frac{d^2y}{dx^2} + x\frac{dy}{dx} - y = 0.$$

9. Show that the quadratic curve $y = ax^2 + bx + c$
(i) is concave upwards, for all $x \in \mathbb{R}$, if $a > 0$
(ii) is concave downwards, for all $x \in \mathbb{R}$, if $a < 0$.

10. $y = ax^3 + bx^2 + cx + d$, where $a > 0$, is a cubic curve.
Express, in terms of a and b, the values of x for which the curve is concave upwards.

11. Verify that the curve $y = \ln x$ is concave downwards, for all $x > 0$.

12. Determine the values of $x \in \mathbb{R}$ for which the curve $y = xe^x$ is concave upwards.

13. Explain why the curve $y = \sin x$ is concave downwards for all $0 < x < \pi$.

14. Show that the curve $y = \frac{x+2}{x+1}$ is concave upwards for all $x \in \mathbb{R}$, $x > -1$.

27.5 The Second Derivative Test

The second derivative provides an alternative method for distinguishing between turning points, i.e. for distinguishing between a local max and a local min.

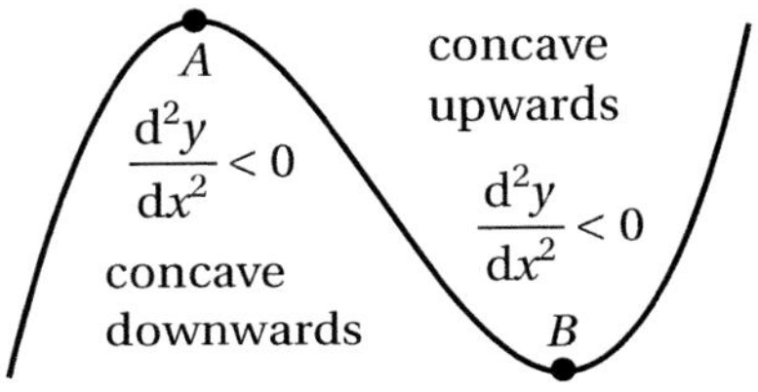

The curve shown opposite has a local max at A and a local min at B. The difference between the two points is that at the local max, the curve is concave downwards, while at the local min, the curve is concave upwards.

This gives us the so-called Second Derivative Test for Turning Points.

Second Derivative Test for Turning Points

Suppose (x_1, y_1) is a stationary point.

(i) if $\frac{d^2y}{dx^2} < 0$ at the point (x_1, y_1), then (x_1, y_1) is a **local max**

(ii) if $\frac{d^2y}{dx^2} > 0$ at the point (x_1, y_1), then (x_1, y_1) is a **local min.**

It is important to note that the Second Derivative Test cannot identify saddle points. If $\frac{d^2y}{dx^2} = 0$ at a stationary point, then the point may be a local max, a local min or a saddle point. On our course, the only way we have of being sure what type of stationary point is involved, is to use the First Derivative Test.

Example 1

Find the co-ordinates of the local maximum and local minimum points of the curve $y = x^3 - 3x^2 - 24x + 10$.

Solution

(Get the stationary points first.)

$$y = x^3 - 3x^2 - 24x + 10$$

$$\frac{dy}{dx} = 3x^2 - 6x - 24$$

Put $\frac{dy}{dx} = 0$:

$$3x^2 - 6x - 24 = 0$$
$$x^2 - 2x - 8 = 0$$
$$(x + 2)(x - 4) = 0$$
$$x + 2 = 0 \quad \text{or} \quad x - 4 = 0$$
$$x = -2 \quad \text{or} \quad x = 4$$

$x = -2$: $y = (-2)^3 - 3(-2)^2 - 24(-2) + 10$

$y = -8 - 12 + 48 + 10 = 38$

One point is (–2,38).

$x = 4$: $y = (4)^3 - 3(4)^2 - 24(4) + 10$

$y = 64 - 48 - 96 + 10 = -70$

The other point is (4,–70).

(Now we find the second derivative and use it to determine the nature of the stationary points.)

Then

$$\frac{dy}{dx} = 3x^2 - 6x - 24$$
$$\frac{d^2y}{dx^2} = 6x - 6$$

$x = -2$: $\frac{d^2y}{dx^2} = 6(-2) - 6 = -18 < 0$

Thus, (–2,38) is the local maximum point.

$x = 4$: $\frac{d^2y}{dx^2} = 6(4) - 6 = 18 > 0$

Thus, (4,–70) is the local minimum point.

Example 2

$f(x) = x^2 \ln x$, for $x \in \mathbb{R}$, $x > 0$.

Show that $f(x)$ has a local minimum at $x = \frac{1}{\sqrt{e}}$, and find this local minimum value.

Solution

Let $y = f(x) = x^2 \ln x$.

Then

$$\frac{dy}{dx} = (x^2)\left(\frac{1}{x}\right) + (\ln x)(2x)$$
$$= x + 2x \ln x$$
$$= x(1 + 2 \ln x)$$

Put $\frac{dy}{dx} = 0$:

$$x(1 + 2 \ln x) = 0$$

$1 + 2 \log_e x = 0$ ... *as $x > 0$*

$$\log_e x = -\frac{1}{2}$$

$$x = e^{-\frac{1}{2}}$$

$$x = \frac{1}{e^{\frac{1}{2}}} = \frac{1}{\sqrt{e}}$$

Then

$$\frac{d^2y}{dx^2} = (x)\left(\frac{2}{x}\right) + (1 + 2\ln x)(1)$$

$$= 2 + 1 + 2\ln x$$

$$= 3 + 2\ln x$$

$x = \frac{1}{\sqrt{e}}$:

$$\frac{d^2y}{dx^2} = 3 + 2\log_e e^{-\frac{1}{2}} = 3 - \log_e e = 3 - 1 = 2 > 0$$

Thus, $y = f(x)$ has a local minimum at $x = \frac{1}{\sqrt{e}}$.

(The local minimum value is the value of y at the local minimum point.)

$$x = \frac{1}{\sqrt{e}}:\ y = \left(\frac{1}{\sqrt{e}}\right)^2 \log_e e^{-\frac{1}{2}}$$

$$= \left(\frac{1}{e}\right)\left(-\frac{1}{2}\right)$$

$$= \frac{-1}{2e}.$$

Exercises 27.5

1. Find the stationary points of the curve $y = 3x^4 + 4x^3 - 12x^2$ and determine the nature of each stationary point.
2. Find the stationary points of the curve $y = 3x^4 - 4x^3 - 12x^2 + 2$. Determine the nature of these stationary points.
3. Find the co-ordinates of the local maximum and local minimum points of the curve $y = x + \frac{4}{x+2}$.
4. Find the stationary points of the curve $y = \frac{4x-3}{x^2+1}$ and determine the nature of each stationary point.
5. Find the co-ordinates of the turning point of the curve $y = x + \frac{4}{x^2}$, and determine whether this point is a local maximum or local minimum.
6. The curve $y = ax^2 + bx + 6$ has a local minimum at the point (2,–2). Find the values of the constants a and b.
7. The curve $y = x^3 + ax^2 - 9x + b$ has a local maximum at the point (–1,11). Find the values of the constants a and b. Find the co-ordinates of the local minimum point.
8. Show that $f(x) = \sqrt{4x - x^2}$ has a maximum value when $x = 2$.
9. Find the stationary point of the curve $y = xe^{-x}$ and determine the nature of the point.
10. Find the co-ordinates of the local maximum and local minimum points of the curve $y = xe^{-x^2}$.

11. Find all the stationary points of the curve $y = x^2e^{-x}$, and determine the nature of these points.

12. Find the stationary point of the curve $y = \log_e(x^2 + 1)$ and determine the nature of the point.

13. Find the stationary point of the curve $y = x \log x$, for $x > 0$, and determine the nature of this point.

14. $f(x) = \frac{\ln x}{x}$, for $x > 0$.

Find the co-ordinates of the turning point of the curve $y = f(x)$, and determine the nature of this turning point.

15. $f(x) = (x - a)^2(b - x)$, where $a < b$.
Find the co-ordinates of the local maximum and local minimum points of the curve $y = f(x)$.

16. The curve $y = (x^2 + 1)e^{ax}$ has a turning point at $x = 1$. Find the value of $a \in \mathbb{R}$.

27.6 Points of Inflection

There is another type of important point that a curve may possess. This is called a point of inflection.

A **point of inflection** is a point on a curve at which the curve goes from being concave upwards to concave downwards, or vice versa.

The curve shown opposite has a point of inflection at the point C, because the curve is concave downwards to the left of C, and concave upwards to the right of C.

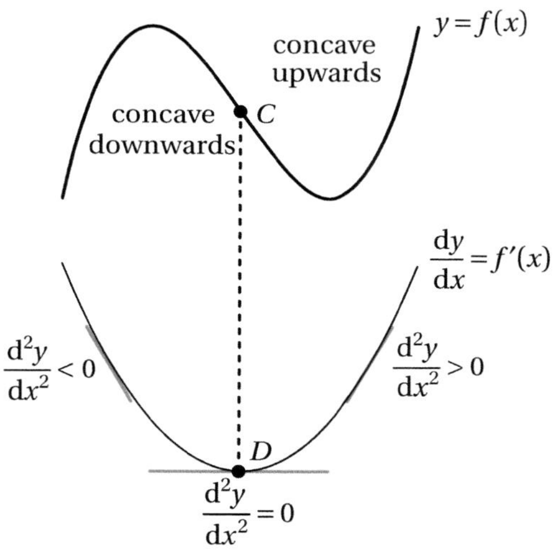

From the slope curve, $\frac{dy}{dx} = f'(x)$ drawn directly underneath, we can see that the slope curve must have a turning point at D, which has the same x co-ordinate as C.

For this to be the case, we need the slope of the slope, $\frac{d^2y}{dx^2}$, to go from $- \to 0 \to +$ or from $+ \to 0 \to -$.

Put another way, for the curve $y = f(x)$ to have a point of inflection at C, the second derivative, $\frac{d^2y}{dx^2}$, must be zero at C and change sign about C.

Point of Inflection

The curve $y = f(x)$ has a point of inflection at $C(x_1, y_1)$ if

(i) $\frac{d^2y}{dx^2} = 0$ at C, and

(ii) $\frac{d^2y}{dx^2}$ changes sign at C.

To investigate if $\frac{d^2y}{dx^2}$ changes sign at a point, take sample x values, one on each side of the point, and by examining the signs of the second derivative with these values of x, see if there is a change of sign.

Example 1

Find any points of inflection on the curve $y = \ln(x^2 + 1)$, which is defined for all $x \in \mathbb{R}$.

Solution

$$y = \ln(x^2 + 1)$$

$$\frac{dy}{dx} = \frac{1}{x^2+1}.(2x) = \frac{2x}{x^2+1}$$

and $$\frac{d^2y}{dx^2} = \frac{(x^2+1)(2) - (2x)(2x)}{(x^2+1)^2}$$

$$\frac{d^2y}{dx^2} = \frac{2x^2 + 2 - 4x^2}{(x^2+1)^2}$$

$$\frac{d^2y}{dx^2} = \frac{-2x^2 + 2}{(x^2+1)^2}$$

Put $\frac{d^2y}{dx^2} = 0$:

$$\frac{-2x^2+2}{(x^2+1)^2} = 0$$

$$-2x^2 + 2 = 0$$

$$2 = 2x^2$$

$$x^2 = 1$$

$$x = \pm 1$$

(Thus, there are two possible points of inflection, one at $x = -1$ and the other at $x = 1$. But we need to check if the second derivative changes sign about each of values of x. Let's evaluate the second derivative at $x = -2, 0, 2$.)

$x = -2$: $\frac{d^2y}{dx^2} = \frac{-2(-2)^2 + 2}{((-2)^2+1)^2} = \frac{-6}{25}$, which is negative

$x = 0$: $\frac{d^2y}{dx^2} = \frac{-2(0)^2 + 2}{((0)^2+1)^2} = \frac{2}{1}$, which is positive

$x = 2$: $\frac{d^2y}{dx^2} = \frac{-2(2)^2 + 2}{((2)^2+1)^2} = \frac{-6}{25}$, which is negative

Thus, the second derivative changes sign about both $x = -1$ and $x = 1$. Hence, there are two points of inflection.

$x = -1$: $y = \ln\left((-1)^2 + 1\right) = \ln 2$

$(-1, \ln 2)$ is one point of inflection.

$x = 1$: $y = \ln\left(1^2 + 1\right) = \ln 2$

$(1, \ln 2)$ is the other point of inflection.

Suppose the second derivative, $\frac{d^2y}{dx^2}$, is zero at the point $C(x_1, y_1)$ on the curve $y = f(x)$, but that the second derivative does not change sign about $x = x_1$.

Then the curve does **not** have a point of inflection at C. Rather, the curve is concave upwards at C (if the second derivative is positive on both sides of C) or it is concave downwards at C (if the second derivative is negative on both sides of C). Example 2 gives an example of this situation.

Example 2

$f: x \rightarrow x^4$ is defined for all $x \in \mathbb{R}$.

(i) Show that $f''(0) = 0$, i.e. that the second derivative is 0 when $x = 0$.

(ii) Show that the curve $y = f(x)$ does not have a point of inflection at $(0, f(0))$.

(iii) Describe the behaviour of the curve at the point $(0, f(0))$.

Solution

(i) $y = f(x) = x^4$

$f'(x) = 4x^3$

$f''(x) = 12x^2$

Then

$f''(0) = 12(0)^2 = 0$

(ii) As $f''(-1) = 12(-1)^2 = 12$ and $f''(1) = 12(1)^2 = 12$, the second derivative does not change sign about $x = 0$. Hence, $(0, f(0)) = (0,0)$ is not a point of inflection.

(iii) As $f'(0) = 0$, (0,0) is a stationary point of the curve $y = x^4$. $f'(-1) = -4$ and $f'(1) = 4$. Hence, by the First Derivative Test, (0,0) is a local min. Also, as the second derivative is positive on both sides of (0,0), the curve is concave upwards at this point. The curve is shown opposite.

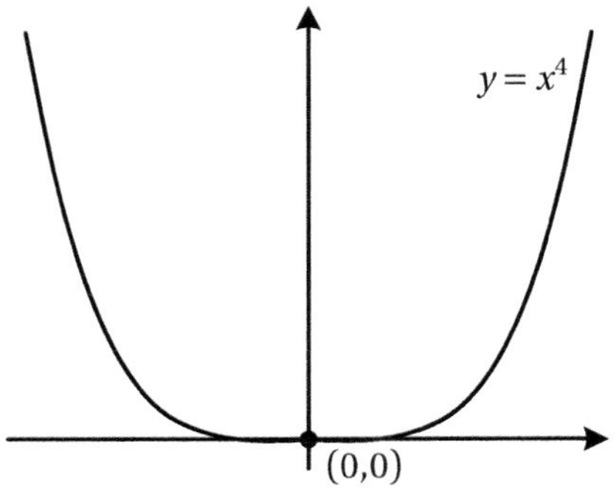

The alternative name for a saddle point, as a horizontal point of inflection, highlights the fact that as well as being a stationary point (horizontal tangent), it is also a point of inflection. It is the only type of point that is both a stationary point and a point of inflection.

Summary

Suppose the curve $y = f(x)$ is differentiable at $C(x_1,y_1)$ and around C. We are now in a position to summarise what we can say about the features and shape of the curve, based on the values of the first and second derivatives at C.

1. $\frac{dy}{dx} > 0$ at C.

The curve is increasing at C.

2. $\frac{dy}{dx} < 0$ at C.

The curve is decreasing at C.

3. $\frac{dy}{dx} = 0$ at C.

The curve has a stationary point at C. This could be a turning point (local max or local min) or it could be a saddle point.

4. $\frac{dy}{dx}$ goes $+ \rightarrow 0 \rightarrow -$ through C.

The curve has a local max at C.

5. $\frac{dy}{dx}$ goes $- \rightarrow 0 \rightarrow +$ through C.

The curve has a local min at C.

6. $\frac{dy}{dx}$ goes $+ \rightarrow 0 \rightarrow +$ or $- \rightarrow 0 \rightarrow -$ through C.

The curve has a saddle point at C.

7. $\frac{dy}{dx} = 0$ and $\frac{d^2y}{dx^2} < 0$ at C.
The curve has a local max at C.

8. $\frac{dy}{dx} = 0$ and $\frac{d^2y}{dx^2} > 0$ at C.
The curve has a local min at C.

9. $\frac{dy}{dx} = 0$ and $\frac{d^2y}{dx^2} = 0$ at C.
C is a stationary point, but to determine its nature we need to examine the sign of the first derivative on each side of C.

10. $\frac{d^2y}{dx^2} > 0$ at C.
The curve is concave upwards at C.

11. $\frac{d^2y}{dx^2} < 0$ at C.
The curve is concave downwards at C.

12. $\frac{d^2y}{dx^2} = 0$ and changes sign at C (i.e. $\frac{d^2y}{dx^2}$ goes $+ \to 0 \to -$ or $- \to 0 \to +$ at C).
The curve has a point of inflection at C.

13. $\frac{d^2y}{dx^2} = 0$ and goes $+ \to 0 \to +$ at C (no change of sign).
The curve is concave upwards at C.

14. $\frac{d^2y}{dx^2} = 0$ and goes $- \to 0 \to -$ at C (no change of sign).
The curve is concave downwards at C.

Exercises 27.6

1. Find the point of inflection of the curve $y = x^3 - 12x + 8$.
2. Find the point of inflection of the curve $y = 2x^3 - 18x^2 + 9x - 2$.
3. Find the two points of inflection of the curve $y = x^4 - 6x^3 + 12x^2 - 8x$.
4. Find the two points of inflection of the curve $y = x^4 - 8x^3 + 18x^2 - 7x + 4$.
5. Find the three points of inflection of the curve $y = 3x^5 - 10x^3$.
6. Show that the curve $y = e^{-x^2}$ has two points of inflection, and find their co-ordinates.
7. Find the co-ordinates of the point of inflection of the curve $y = xe^{2x}$.
8. Show that the curve $y = \frac{2x-1}{x+2}$ has no points of inflection.
9. Show that the curve $y = \frac{3x-1}{2x+3}$ has no points of inflection.
10. If P and Q are the local maximum and local minimum points of the curve $y = x^3 - 3x^2 - 24x + 60$, show that the point of inflection is the midpoint of $[PQ]$.
11. Show that the curve $y = x^5$ has a point of inflection at (0,0).
12. Show that the curve $y = x^4 + 3$ has no points of inflection.

27.7 Asymptotes

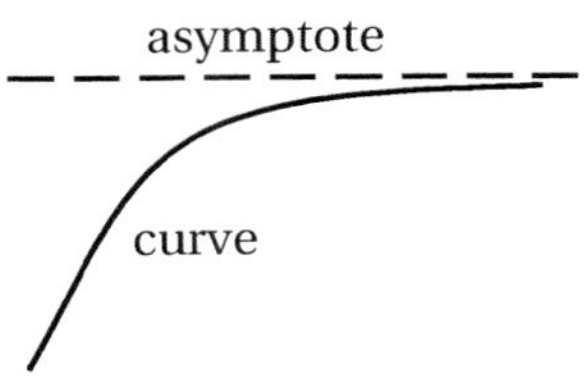

An ***asymptote*** of a curve is a straight line which approximates the curve as the curve tends to infinity.

Only certain types of curve have asymptotes.

For the most part, it is only curves with equations of the form

$$y = \frac{u(x)}{v(x)}$$

i.e. in the form of a fraction. However, there are other curves with asymptotes, e.g. $y = e^x$, $y = \ln x$ and $y = \tan^{-1} x$, which we have met previously.

There are two types of asymptote on our course: vertical and horizontal asymptotes.

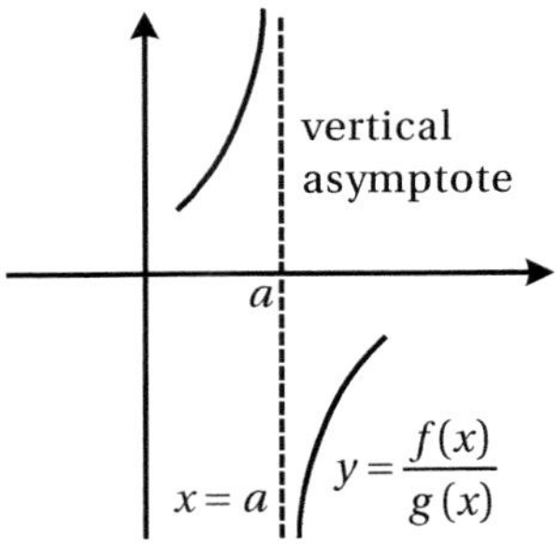

1. Vertical Asymptotes

The vertical asymptotes of $y = \frac{u(x)}{v(x)}$ are found by putting $v(x) = 0$. If $x = a$ is a solution of this equation, then the vertical line $x = a$ is a vertical asymptote of the curve. It acts like a vertical line that the curve tries to get over or under, but which it cannot cross.

Example 1

Find the vertical asymptote of the curve $y = \frac{2x+3}{x-1}$.

Solution

(Put the bottom line equal to zero.)

Vertical asymptote:

$$x - 1 = 0$$

$$x = 1.$$

2. Asymptote Limits

To find the horizontal asymptotes of a curve, we need to be able to work out limits of the form $\lim\limits_{x\to\infty} \frac{u(x)}{v(x)}$. To evaluate these, we need the following special limits.

Special Limits

1. $\lim\limits_{x\to\infty} \frac{1}{x^n} = 0$, as long as $n > 0$, e.g. $\lim\limits_{x\to\infty} \frac{1}{x^2} = 0$.

2. $\lim\limits_{x\to\infty} r^x = 0$, if $-1 < r < 1$, e.g. $\lim\limits_{x\to\infty} \frac{1}{e^x} = \lim\limits_{x\to\infty} \left(\frac{1}{e}\right)^x = 0$, as $-1 < \frac{1}{e} < 1$.

In addition, we have a number of rules for calculating limits as the variable tends to infinity.

Rules of Limits

Suppose $\lim_{x\to\infty} u(x)$ and $\lim_{x\to\infty} v(x)$ are real numbers, and k is a constant. Then

1. $\lim_{x\to\infty} k = k$

2. $\lim_{x\to\infty} ku(x) = k\lim_{x\to\infty} u(x)$

3. $\lim_{x\to\infty} (u(x) \pm v(x)) = \lim_{x\to\infty} u(x) \pm \lim_{x\to\infty} v(x)$

4. $\lim_{x\to\infty} (u(x).v(x)) = \left(\lim_{x\to\infty} u(x)\right)\left(\lim_{x\to\infty} v(x)\right)$

5. $\lim_{x\to\infty} \frac{u(x)}{v(x)} = \frac{\lim_{x\to\infty} u(x)}{\lim_{x\to\infty} v(x)}$, as long as $\lim_{x\to\infty} v(x) \neq 0$.

If a limit is initially indeterminate (generally $\frac{\infty}{\infty}$), then we can use a combination of the Special Limits and Rules to calculate the limit. This generally involves dividing above and below by the dominant term (the highest power of x, or if x is the index, then the power with the largest base).

We also have to be able to calculate a limit of the form $\lim_{x\to-\infty} f(x)$. Rule 6 deals with this.

6. $\lim_{x\to-\infty} f(x) = \lim_{x\to\infty} f(-x)$,

i.e. substitute $-x$ for x in the function and take the limit as $x \to \infty$.

Example 2

$f: x \to \frac{2x+3}{3x+1}$.

(i) Find $\lim_{x\to\infty} f(x)$.

(ii) Show that $\lim_{x\to-\infty} f(x) = \lim_{x\to\infty} f(x)$.

Solution

(i) $\lim_{x\to\infty} f(x) = \lim_{x\to\infty} \frac{2x+3}{3x+1}$

$= \lim_{x\to\infty} \frac{2+3\left(\frac{1}{x}\right)}{3+\left(\frac{1}{x}\right)}$ *... dividing above and below by x*

$= \frac{2+3(0)}{3+(0)} = \frac{2}{3}$

(ii) $\lim_{x\to-\infty} f(x) = \lim_{x\to\infty} f(-x)$

$= \lim_{x\to\infty} \frac{2(-x)+3}{3(-x)+1}$ *... replacing each x with –x*

$= \lim_{x\to\infty} \frac{-2+3\left(\frac{1}{x}\right)}{-3+\left(\frac{1}{x}\right)}$

$= \frac{-2+3(0)}{-3+(0)}$

$= \frac{2}{3} = \lim_{x\to\infty} f(x)$

Limits as the variable tends to infinity (although in a slightly different context) will be examined again in a later chapter.

3. Horizontal Asymptotes

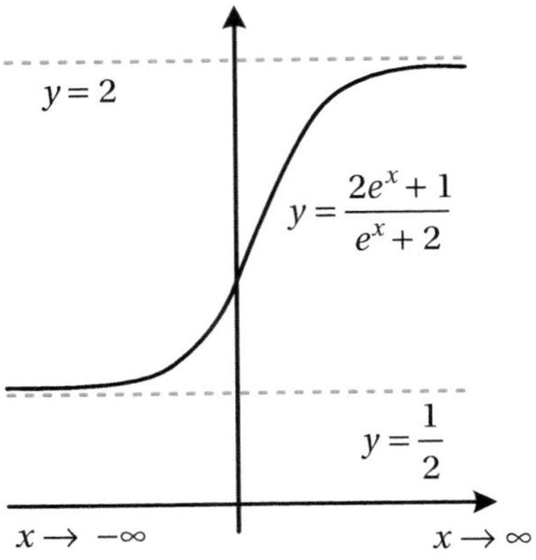

A horizontal asymptote is a horizontal line that approximates a curve as the curve tends to infinity.
A curve representing a function can have at most two horizontal asymptotes: one on the right (as x tends to ∞) and one on the left (as x tends to $-\infty$).

The diagram opposite shows the curve $y = \frac{2e^x + 1}{e^x + 2}$ which has the line $y = 2$ as a horizontal asymptote on the right (as $x \to \infty$) and the line $y = \frac{1}{2}$ as a horizontal asymptote on the left (as $x \to -\infty$).

The horizontal asymptotes of the curve $y = f(x)$, when they exist, are:

(i) On the right: $y = \lim_{x \to \infty} f(x)$

(ii) On the left: $y = \lim_{x \to -\infty} f(x)$, or $y = \lim_{x \to \infty} f(-x)$.

You should note the following.

1. Knowing the asymptotes of a curve is very useful when it comes to sketching a curve, as the asymptotes provide a frame for the curve.
2. Polynomial curves and trig curves do not have asymptotes. We generally only consider asymptotes for certain curves of the form $y = \frac{u(x)}{v(x)}$.
3. A rational curve is one of the form $y = \frac{u(x)}{v(x)}$, where u and v are polynomials in x.
   For the horizontal asymptotes of a rational curve, you should note the following cases.
   (i) If the degree of $u(x)$ is greater than the degree of $v(x)$, then the curve will have no horizontal asymptotes.
   (ii) If the degree of $u(x)$ is equal to the degree of $v(x)$, then the curve will have the same horizontal asymptote on the left as on the right.
   (iii) If the degree of $u(x)$ is less than the degree of $v(x)$, then the x-axis will be the horizontal asymptote for the curve, both on the left and on the right.

Example 3

Find the horizontal asymptote(s), if any, of the curve $y = \frac{3x^2 + x - 1}{x^2 + 2}$.

Solution

(As the top line and the bottom line both have a degree of 2, there will be a horizontal asymptote, but it will be the same on both sides.)

$$y = \frac{3x^2 + x - 1}{x^2 + 2}$$

Right Horizontal Asymptote:

$$y = \lim_{x \to \infty} \frac{3x^2 + x - 1}{x^2 + 2}$$

$$y = \lim_{x \to \infty} \frac{3 + \frac{1}{x} - \frac{1}{x^2}}{1 + 2.\frac{1}{x^2}}$$

$$y = \frac{3 + 0 - 0}{1 + 2(0)}$$

$y = 3$ is the horizontal asymptote on the right.

Left Horizontal Asymptote:

$y = 3$ is the horizontal asymptote on the left (check yourself!).

Exercises 27.7

Find the vertical asymptotes of each of the following curves.

1. $y = \dfrac{2}{x - 3}$
2. $y = \dfrac{x + 1}{x + 2}$
3. $y = \dfrac{4 - x}{x^2 - 1}$
4. $y = \dfrac{5x + 3}{e^x - 1}$

Evaluate each of the following limits.

5. $\lim\limits_{x \to \infty} \dfrac{4x + 1}{x - 2}$
6. $\lim\limits_{x \to \infty} \dfrac{x - 3}{2x + 5}$
7. $\lim\limits_{x \to \infty} \dfrac{3 - x^2}{3x^2 + 2}$
8. $\lim\limits_{x \to \infty} \dfrac{6x}{2x^2 - 1}$

9. Evaluate each of the following limits by dividing above and below by e^x:

   (i) $\lim\limits_{x \to \infty} \dfrac{e^x}{3e^x + 1}$ (ii) $\lim\limits_{x \to \infty} \dfrac{2e^x - 3}{e^x + 2}$ (iii) $\lim\limits_{x \to \infty} \dfrac{5e^x + 4}{2e^x - 1}$.

10. (i) Find $\lim\limits_{x \to \infty} \dfrac{3x + 2}{4x + 5}$.

    (ii) Show that $\lim\limits_{x \to -\infty} \dfrac{3x + 2}{4x + 5} = \lim\limits_{x \to \infty} \dfrac{3x + 2}{4x + 5}$.

11. Show that $\lim\limits_{x \to \infty} \dfrac{x^2 + 3x}{2x^2 + 1} = \lim\limits_{x \to -\infty} \dfrac{x^2 + 3x}{2x^2 + 1}$.

12. (i) Find $\lim\limits_{x \to \infty} \dfrac{3e^x - 1}{2e^x + 3}$.

    (ii) Show that $\lim\limits_{x \to -\infty} \dfrac{3e^x - 1}{2e^x + 3} \neq \lim\limits_{x \to \infty} \dfrac{3e^x - 1}{2e^x + 3}$.

Find the horizontal asymptotes of each of the following curves.

13. $y = \dfrac{x + 1}{x + 2}$
14. $y = \dfrac{2x - 1}{3x + 2}$
15. $y = \dfrac{3x^2 + 1}{2x^2 - 5}$
16. $y = \dfrac{3 + e^x}{2e^x + 7}$

Find all the asymptotes of each of the following curves.

17. $y = \dfrac{x + 2}{x - 5}$
18. $y = \dfrac{2x - 1}{x + 3}$
19. $y = \dfrac{5e^x + 1}{2e^x - 4}$
20. $y = \dfrac{3}{2x^2 + 3}$

27.8 Curve Sketching

In previous chapters, we have seen how to sketch polynomial curves given in fully factorised form, certain exponential and logarithmic curves and certain trigonometric curves.

To sketch a general curve $y = f(x)$, we need to gather information about the curve. We can use the techniques outlined in this chapter. Very often the information gathering steps are outlined in a question. But if not, the following are the features we should investigate.

1. **Intercepts**
   We can often find the x intercept (where the curve intersects the x axis) by putting $y = 0$, and the y intercept (where the curve intersects the y axis) by putting $x = 0$. Plotting these points then helps to locate the curve.

2. **Asymptotes**
   When any asymptotes exist, we should find them. In this case, drawing the asymptotes gives us a frame for the curve.

3. **First Derivative**
   Finding $\frac{dy}{dx}$ allows us to determine where the curve is increasing and decreasing and any stationary points. We can also use the First Derivative Test to determine the nature of each stationary point.

4. **Second Derivative**
   Finding $\frac{d^2y}{dx^2}$ allows us to identify the nature of turning points, determine where the curve is concave upwards and concave downwards, and find any points of inflection. We may not be required to find all, or indeed any, of these features.

Some types of curve require us to pay particular attention to one or more of the above features.

Type 1: Polynomial Curves

Finding the y intercept is generally useful, when dealing with polynomial curves. These curves have no asymptotes, but may have stationary points and/or points of inflection. It is important to remember that we have encountered some polynomial curves before, and useful facts from our previous discussions can prove very helpful.

Example 1

The equation of a curve is $y = 3x^4 - 8x^3 + 6x^2 - 5$.

(i) Show that this curve has two stationary points, one of which is not a turning point. Find the co-ordinates of these points.

(ii) This curve has two points of inflection. Find the co-ordinates of these points and describe the shape of the curve around each.

(iii) Sketch a rough graph of this curve.

Solution

(i) $y = 3x^4 - 8x^3 + 6x^2 - 5$

$$\frac{dy}{dx} = 12x^3 - 24x^2 + 12x$$

$$= 12x(x^2 - 2x + 1)$$

$$= 12x(x - 1)^2$$

Put $\frac{dy}{dx} = 0$:

$12x(x-1)^2 = 0$

$x = 0 \quad \text{or} \quad x - 1 = 0$

$x = 0 \quad \text{or} \quad x = 1$

Thus, the curve has two stationary points.

Then: $x = 0 : y = -5$ One point is (0,–5).

$x = 1 : y = -4$ The other point is (1,–4).

(Because we are asked to show that one of the stationary points is not a turning point, we should use the First Derivative Test instead of the Second Derivative Test. Take sample values on each side, and between, x = 0 and x = 1. This can be laid out in the form of a table.)

x	-1	0	0.5	1	2
$\frac{dy}{dx}$	–	0	+	0	+
shape	\	_	/	—	/

(*Note*: *At* $x = -1$, $\frac{dy}{dx} = 12(-1)(-2)^2 < 0$.

At $x = 0{\cdot}5$, $\frac{dy}{dx} = 12(0{\cdot}5)(-0{\cdot}5)^2 > 0$

At $x = 2$, $\frac{dy}{dx} = 12(2)(1)^2 > 0$.)

From the table, (0,–5) is a local min and (1,–4) is a saddle point. Only (0,–5) is a turning point.

(ii) $\frac{dy}{dx} = 12x^3 - 24x^2 + 12x$

$\frac{d^2y}{dx^2} = 36x^2 - 48x + 12$

Put $\frac{d^2y}{dx^2} = 0$:

$36x^2 - 48x + 12 = 0$

$3x^2 - 4x + 1 = 0$

$(3x-1)(x-1) = 0$

$x = \frac{1}{3} \quad \text{or} \quad x = 1$

$x = \frac{1}{3}: \quad y = -\frac{124}{27} \approx -4{\cdot}59$

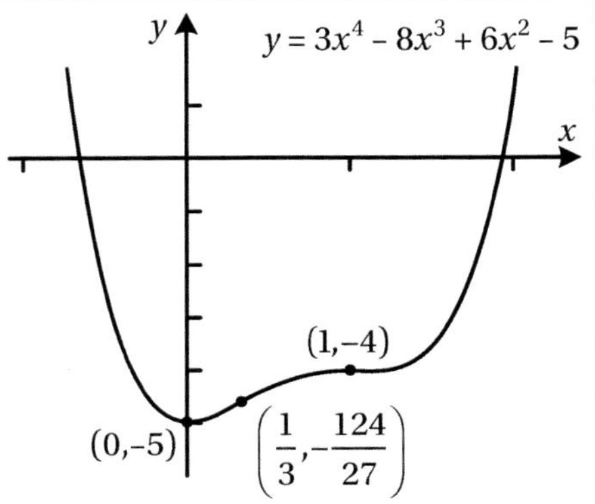

Thus, the points of inflection are $\left(\frac{1}{3}, -\frac{124}{27}\right)$ and (1,–4). The curve is concave upwards to the left of $\frac{1}{3}$ and to the right of 1. It is concave downwards in between.

(iii) The graph is shown above. *(The shape agrees with that expected of a polynomial curve of even degree with a positive leading coefficient.)*

Type 2: Other Curves

For other curves, we go through any information gathering steps that may be outlined. In the absence of these, we follow the guidelines at the beginning of this section. For curves of the form $y = \frac{u(x)}{v(x)}$, it is important to consider asymptotes.

Example 2

$f: x \to \frac{1}{e^x - 1}$ is a function defined for all $x \in \mathbb{R}, x \neq 0$.

(i) Find the vertical asymptote and the two horizontal asymptotes of the curve $y = f(x)$.

(ii) Show that the curve $y = f(x)$ is decreasing for all $x \in \mathbb{R}, x \neq 0$.

(iii) Draw a rough sketch of the curve $y = f(x)$.

Solution

(i) $y = \frac{1}{e^x - 1}$.

Vertical asymptote:

$$e^x - 1 = 0$$
$$e^x = 1$$
$$x = \log_e 1$$
$$x = 0$$

Horizontal asymptote (right):

$$y = \lim_{x \to \infty} \frac{1}{e^x - 1} = \lim_{x \to \infty} \frac{\frac{1}{e^x}}{1 - \frac{1}{e^x}} = \frac{0}{1 - 0}$$
$$y = 0$$

Horizontal asymptote (left):

$$y = \lim_{x \to -\infty} \frac{1}{e^x - 1}$$
$$y = \lim_{x \to \infty} \frac{1}{e^{-x} - 1} = \lim_{x \to \infty} \frac{1}{\frac{1}{e^x} - 1} = \frac{1}{0 - 1}$$
$$y = -1$$

(ii) $y = \frac{1}{e^x - 1} = (e^x - 1)^{-1}$

$$\frac{dy}{dx} = -(e^x - 1)^{-2}.(e^x) = \frac{-e^x}{(e^x - 1)^2}$$

As $-e^x < 0$ and $(e^x - 1)^2 > 0$, for all $x \in \mathbb{R}$, $x \neq 0$, $\frac{dy}{dx} < 0$ and the curve is decreasing for all $x \in \mathbb{R}, x \neq 0$.

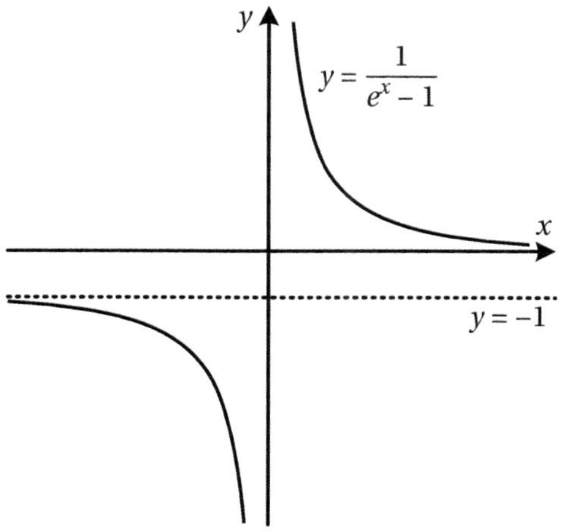

(iii) *(To sketch the graph, we start by drawing the asymptotes.*

From the left, the curve approaches the line $y = -1$.
It then decreases as it approaches the vertical asymptote, $x = 0$, or the y-axis.

As the curve is decreasing everywhere, it comes from plus infinity on the y-axis down to the horizontal asymptote on the right, i.e. the x-axis.)

Exercises 27.8

1. Let $f(x) = x^3 - 9x^2 + 15x + 3, x \in \mathbb{R}$.
(i) Find the co-ordinates of the local maximum and local minimum points of the curve $y = f(x)$.
(ii) Find the co-ordinates of the point of inflection.
(iii) Draw a rough sketch of the curve $y = f(x)$.

2. Let $f(x) = x^3 - 3x^2 - 24x + 36, x \in \mathbb{R}$.
(i) Find the co-ordinates of the local maximum and local minimum points of the curve $y = f(x)$.
(ii) Find the co-ordinates of the point of inflection.
(iii) Draw a rough sketch of the curve $y = f(x)$.

3. The equation of a curve is $y = (x - 1)^2(x - 5)^2$.
(i) Show that the curve has a local maximum at the point (3,16).
(ii) Find the co-ordinates of the two local minimum points.
(iii) Draw a rough sketch of $y = f(x)$.

4. The equation of a curve is $y = -x^2(x - 2)^2$.
(i) Show that the curve has a local minimum at the point (1,–1).
(ii) Find the co-ordinates of the two local maximum points.
(iii) Draw a rough sketch of the curve, for $-1 \le x \le 3$.

5. The equation of a curve is $y = x^4 - 8x^3 + 10x^2 - 5$.
(i) Show that the curve has a local maximum at the point (1,–2).
(ii) Find the co-ordinates of the two local minimum points.
(iii) Draw a rough sketch of the curve.

6. Let $f(x) = x^3 + 3x^2 + ax + b, x \in \mathbb{R}$ and a and b are constants.
(i) If the curve $y = f(x)$ has a local minimum point at (3,–71), find the value of a and the value of b.
(ii) Find the co-ordinates of the local maximum point.
(iii) Draw a rough sketch of the curve $y = f(x)$.

7. Let $f(x) = \frac{x - 1}{x + 2}, x \in \mathbb{R}$ and $x \neq -2$.
(i) Find the equations of the asymptotes of the curve $y = f(x)$.
(ii) Show that the curve $y = f(x)$ has no turning points or points of inflection.
(iii) Draw a rough graph of the curve $y = f(x)$.

8. Let $f(x) = \frac{x - 3}{x - 1}$, for $x \in \mathbb{R}, x \neq -1$.
(i) Find the asymptotes of the curve $y = f(x)$.
(ii) Show that the curve $y = f(x)$ has no turning points and no points of inflection.
(iii) Determine where the curve crosses the x-axis and the y-axis.
(iv) Draw a rough sketch of $y = f(x)$.
(v) Determine the co-ordinates of the two points on the curve at which the tangents have a slope of 2.

9. Let $f(x) = \frac{x+4}{x+1}$, for $x \in \mathbb{R}$, $x \neq -1$.
   (i) Find the asymptotes of the curve $y = f(x)$.
   (ii) Show that the curve $y = f(x)$ has no turning points and no points of inflection.
   (iii) Determine where the curve crosses the x-axis and the y-axis.
   (iv) Draw a rough sketch of $y = f(x)$.
   (v) Determine the co-ordinates of the two points on the curve at which the tangents have a slope of $-\frac{3}{4}$.

10. $f: x \to \frac{e^x}{e^x + 1}$ is a function defined for all $x \in \mathbb{R}$.
   (i) Find the horizontal asymptotes of the curve $y = f(x)$.
   (ii) Show that the curve $y = f(x)$ has no turning points.
   (iii) Find the co-ordinates of the point of inflection of the curve $y = f(x)$ and determine where the curve is concave upwards, and where it is concave downwards.
   (iv) Sketch a rough graph of the curve $y = f(x)$.

27.9 Sketching and Matching Derivative Curves

If we are given the graph of a curve, $y = f(x)$, we can sketch the graph of its derivative, $\frac{dy}{dx} = f'(x)$, by using our knowledge of the sign of the derivative.

Example 1

The diagram opposite shows a section of the curve

$y = f(x)$.

Draw a graph of the slope of this curve, i.e. construct a graph of

$$\frac{dy}{dx} = f'(x).$$

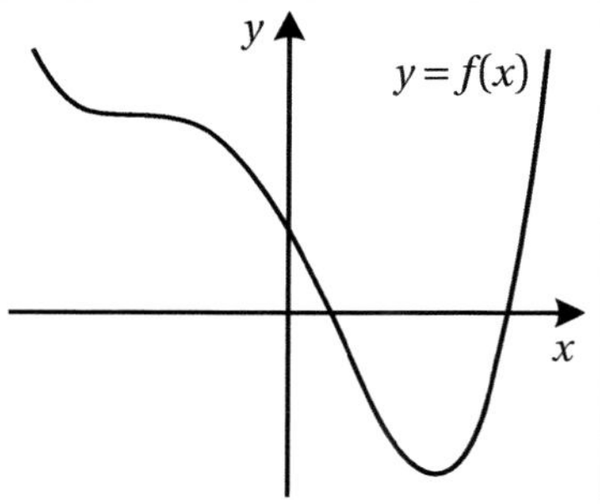

Solution

(It is a good idea to line up the graph of the derivative under the given graph.

Identify the key points on the given curve: A, a saddle point, B, a local min and C a point of inflection. The slope curve will be zero at A and at B. At A and at C, the slope curve will have turning points. To the left of B, the slope is negative, except at A. To the right of B, the slope is positive.)

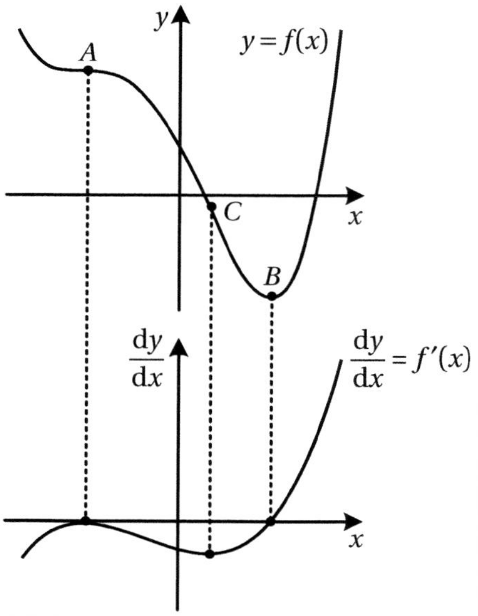

The same methods may be used to construct the graph of the second derivative from the graph of the first derivative.

We may also be asked to match the graph of a function with the graphs of its first and second derivatives.

Example 2

Below are shown three graphs, *A*, *B* and *C*. One of these represents the function $y = f(x)$, and the others represent the first derivative, $\frac{dy}{dx} = f'(x)$, and the second derivative, $\frac{d^2y}{dx^2} = f''(x)$.

A

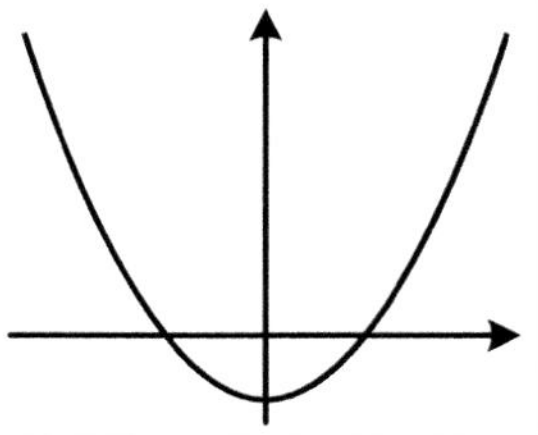

B

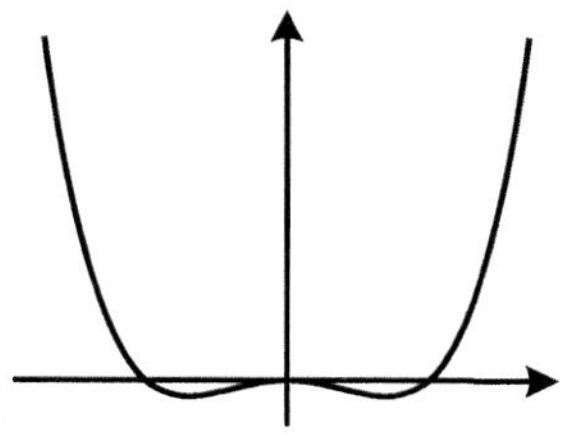

C

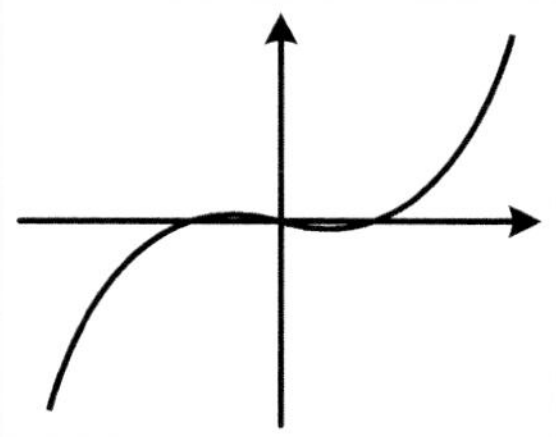

(i) Match the graphs, *A*, *B* and *C*, with the function $y = f(x)$, its first derivative and its second derivative.

(ii) Give reasons for your choices.

Solution

(i) *B*: $y = f(x)$

C: $\frac{dy}{dx} = f'(x)$

A: $\frac{d^2y}{dx^2} = f''(x)$.

(ii) The graph in *C* has two stationary points. Thus, its derivative will intersect the x-axis twice. As the graph in *B* intersects the x-axis three times, it cannot be the derivative of *C*. The graph in *A* intersects the x-axis twice. Hence, it must be the derivative of *C*. This means that the graph in *C* must be the derivative of the graph in *B*.

Exercises 27.9

1. **(i)** From algebra, sketch the polynomial curve $y = f(x) = (x + 1)(x - 1)^3$.

(ii) Sketch the slope function for this curve, i.e. sketch $\frac{dy}{dx} = f'(x)$.

2. **(i)** From algebra, sketch the polynomial curve $y = f(x) = -(x - 1)^2(x - 3)^3$.

(ii) Sketch the slope function for this curve, i.e. sketch $\frac{dy}{dx} = f'(x)$.

3. **(i)** Draw the graph of $y = \sin x$, for $-\pi \le x \le \pi$.

(ii) Sketch the graph of $\frac{dy}{dx}$, for $-\pi \le x \le \pi$. What can you say about this curve, and how does it relate to the earlier work on derivatives?

4. The diagram opposite shows a trigonometric graph, $y = f(x)$.
Copy this graph and indicate underneath a sketch of the slope function of this curve, i.e. sketch

$$\frac{dy}{dx} = f'(x).$$

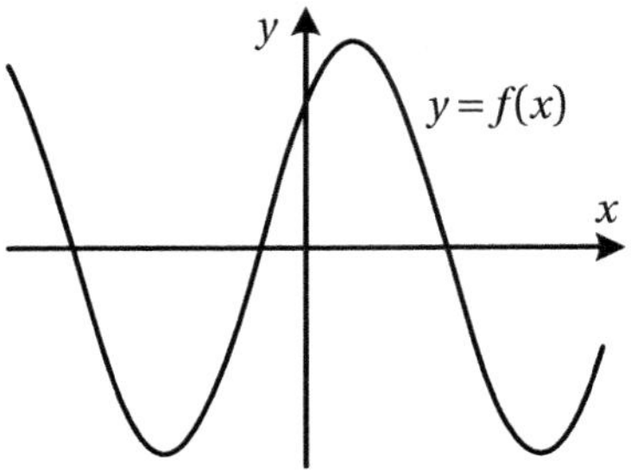

5. The diagram opposite shows a graph of part of the curve

$$y = f(x) = \frac{xe^{-x}}{x+1}.$$

Copy this graph and indicate underneath a sketch of the slope function of this curve, i.e. sketch

$$\frac{dy}{dx} = f'(x).$$

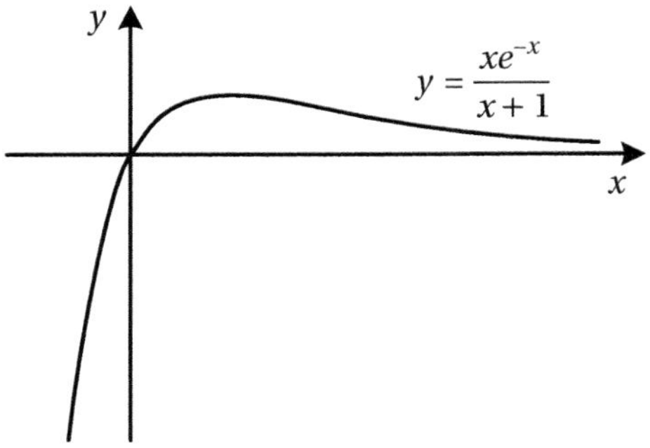

6. The diagram opposite shows a graph of part of the curve

$$y = f(x) = x^2e^{-x}.$$

Copy this graph and indicate underneath a sketch of the slope function of this curve, i.e. sketch

$$\frac{dy}{dx} = f'(x).$$

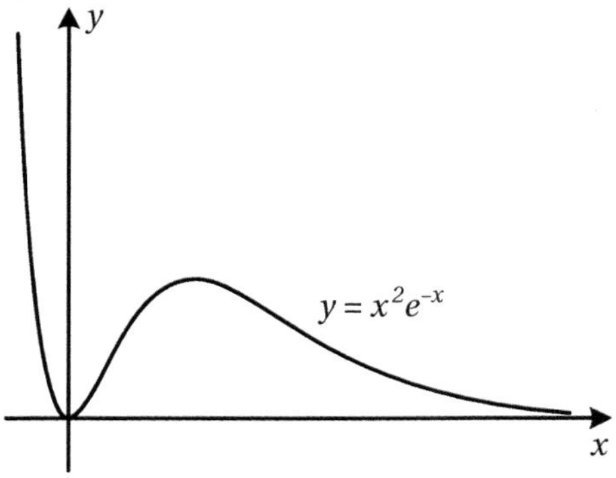

7. Below are shown three graphs, A, B and C. One of these represents the function $y = f(x)$, and the others represent the first derivative, $\frac{dy}{dx} = f'(x)$, and the second derivative, $\frac{d^2y}{dx^2} = f''(x)$.

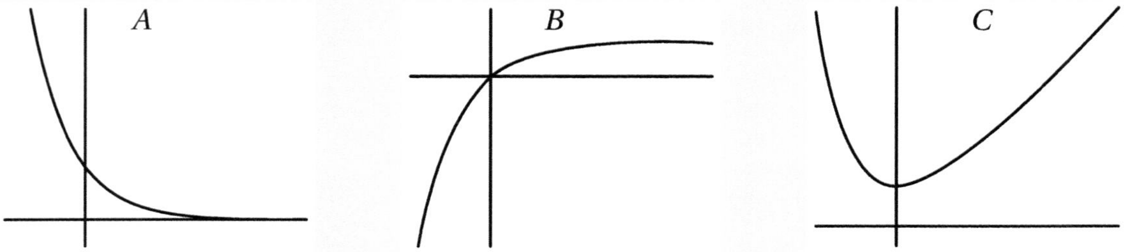

(i) Match the graphs, A, B and C, with the function $y = f(x)$, its first derivative and its second derivative.

(ii) Give reasons for your choices.

8. Below are shown three graphs, A, B and C. One of these represents the function $y = f(x)$, and the others represent the first derivative, $\frac{dy}{dx} = f'(x)$, and the second derivative, $\frac{d^2y}{dx^2} = f''(x)$.

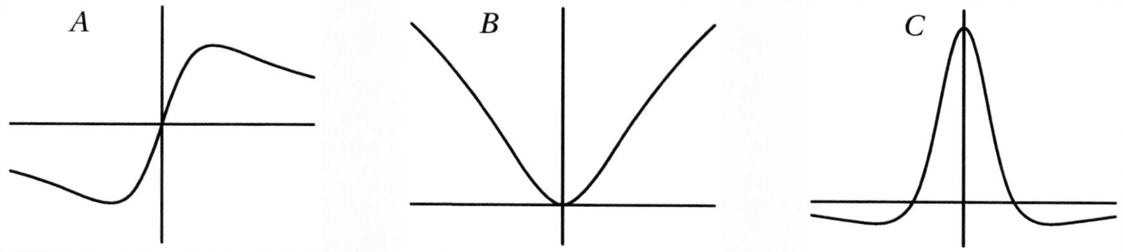

(i) Match the graphs, A, B and C, with the function $y = f(x)$, its first derivative and its second derivative.
(ii) Give reasons for your choices.

Revision Exercises 27

1. Given that $y = \frac{x^2 - 1}{2x^2 + 1}$, find $\frac{dy}{dx}$ and state the values of x for which $\frac{dy}{dx}$ is positive. Find the greatest and least values of y for $0 \leq x \leq 1$.

2. Show that the curve $y = \frac{\sin x + \cos x}{\sin x - \cos x}$ is decreasing for all values of x for which $\tan x \neq 1$.

3. Find the stationary point of the curve $y = \tan^{-1} x - \log(1 + x^2)$ and determine its nature.

4. Find the co-ordinates of the local maximum and local minimum points of the curve $y = (x^2 - 2)e^{-2x}$.

5. Show that every cubic curve

$$y = ax^3 + bx^2 + cx + d, \qquad \text{where } a \neq 0,$$

has one point of inflection.

6. $f(x) = \log_e 3x - 3x$, where $x > 0$.

(i) Show that $\left(\frac{1}{3}, -1\right)$ is a local maximum point of $f(x)$.

(ii) Deduce that the graph of $f(x)$ does not intersect the x-axis.

7. $f(x) = \frac{\ln x}{x}$ where $x > 0$.

Show that the maximum of $f(x)$ occurs at the point $\left(e, \frac{1}{e}\right)$.

8. Below are shown three graphs, A, B and C. One of these represents the function $y = f(x)$, and the others represent the first derivative, $\frac{dy}{dx} = f'(x)$, and the second derivative, $\frac{d^2y}{dx^2} = f''(x)$.

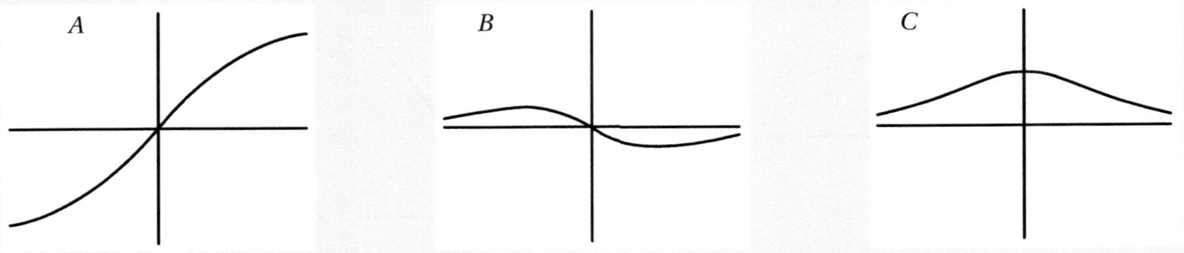

(i) Match the graphs, A, B and C, with the function $y = f(x)$, its first derivative and its second derivative.

(ii) Give reasons for your choices.

9. Use the point (0,0) on the curve $y = x^4 + 4x$ to verify the following statement: "If the second derivative is zero at a point on a curve, but does not change sign at that point, then that point does not have to be a local maximum point or local minimum point of the curve."

Applications of Differentiation 28

Differentiation has applications in many fields of study, not at all confined to maths. The idea of finding the greatest or least value of a quantity, e.g. the greatest profit or the least force, occurs in maths, physics, finance, engineering, among many other disciplines. In this chapter, we examine some practical examples of maximum and minimum problems in a number of settings.

Another application of differentiation is to the problem of analysing rates of change. From the very beginning of differentiation, the derivative was introduced as the measurer of the instantaneous rate of change. There are many practical examples, e.g. the velocity and the acceleration of a moving object.

We also consider what are called 'related rates' problems. These involve being given one rate of change, and being asked to find the rate of change of a connected quantity. For example, water may be pouring into a conical container at a certain rate, and we may be asked to determine the rate of increase of the height of the water at a particular instant.

28.1 Maximum and Minimum Problems

Differential calculus is ideally suited to maximising and minimising real life quantities. To do so, however, we first have to build a mathematical model of the problem. This usually involves introducing variables (letters) to represent measurements and formulating expressions for the quantities to be maximised or minimised.

Because these questions can vary so much, it is important to take a structured approach. This allows us to break a large, difficult problem into a number of shorter, more manageable steps.

To tackle a **max-min modelling question**:

Step 1: Identify the variables and constants to be used in the question, very often with the aid of a diagram. The variables may be identified for us in the question, or we may have to introduce our own.

Step 2: Read the question and identify the quantity that is to be a max or a min (greatest, least, most, largest, etc). Give this quantity an obvious name, e.g. V for volume, A for area, and write this quantity in terms of one or more of the variables.

If the quantity to be a max or a min is expressed in terms of one variable, then go to Step 4. On the other hand, if it is expressed in terms of two or more variables, then we need to go to Step 3.

Step 3: Read the question again, and find the constant expression linking the variables. Use this expression to write one variable in terms of the other, and then write the quantity to be a max or a min in terms of one variable. (We must not get to Step 4 until we have the quantity to be a max or a min in terms of one variable.)

Step 4: Differentiate the quantity to be a max or a min with respect to the one remaining variable and put the derivative equal to zero. Solve this equation.

If there is only one solution, then it must be of the required type. However, if there is more than one solution, then we will need to check each using the First Derivative Test or the Second Derivative Test, to identify the one we require.

Sometimes, there will be more than one solution, but by considering those which make sense, or are physically possible, we may be able to identify the required solution without testing.

Step 5: Read the question (yet again!) to make sure that all the requirements have been found. For example, if in Step 4 we have found r, a radius, and we are asked to find a volume, then the value of r must be used to find the corresponding volume.

Example 1

The area of a rectangle is 12 m^2. Find the dimensions of the rectangle if the perimeter is to be a minimum.

Solution

Let the dimensions be x m and y m. Perimeter, P, to be a minimum:

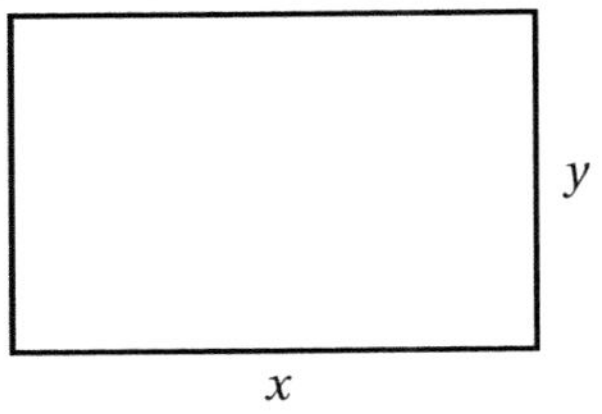

$$P = 2x + 2y. \qquad \text{... \textit{two variables}}$$

Given: Area = 12

$$xy = 12$$

$$y = \frac{12}{x} \qquad \text{... \textit{y in terms of x}}$$

Thus, $P = 2x + 2\left(\frac{12}{x}\right) = 2x + \frac{24}{x} = 2x + 24x^{-1}$ ... *one variable*

Then $\frac{dP}{dx} = 2 - \frac{24}{x^2}$

Put $\frac{dP}{dx} = 0$:

$$2 - \frac{24}{x^2} = 0$$

$$2 = \frac{24}{x^2}$$

$$x^2 = 12$$

$$x = \sqrt{12} \text{ m} \qquad \text{... \textit{as } } x = -\sqrt{12} \text{ \textit{is not possible}}$$

and $y = \frac{12}{\sqrt{12}} = \sqrt{12}$ m, are the required dimensions.

There are some important points to remember.

1. Many of the formulae for areas and volumes can be required in questions involving plane figures and solid objects. Most of these formulae are given in the *Formulae and Tables*.
2. If, in a max/min problem, we are asked to derive an equation, it is almost certain that it will be required as we proceed with the question.
3. If we are told that a certain quantity is 'constant' or 'given', then we put it equal to c, a constant.
4. For questions connected with the x, y plane, if a point lies on a curve, we can use the fact that the co-ordinates of the point satisfy the equation of the curve.

Example 2

A cylinder of radius r and height $2h$ is to be cut from a solid sphere of radius a. The circumference of the top and the base of the cylinder lie on the sphere, as shown opposite.

(i) If V is the volume of the cylinder, show that $V = \pi(a^2h - h^3)$.

(ii) Find, in terms of a, the dimensions of the cylinder of maximum volume that can be cut from the sphere.

(iii) Find, in terms of a, the volume of this cylinder.

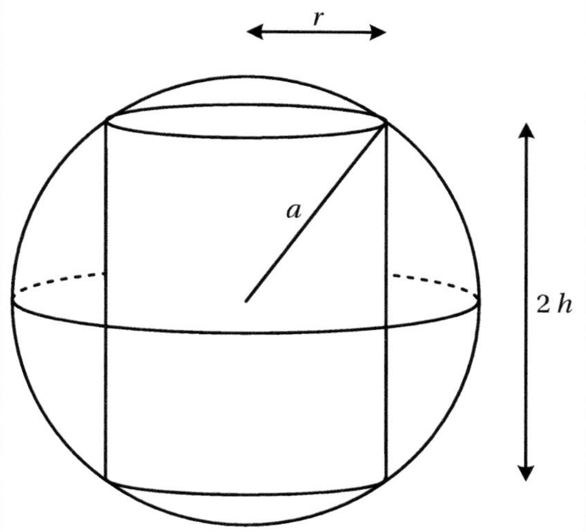

Solution

(i) *(Draw a vertical section of the sphere and cylinder, as shown opposite. Let O be the centre of the sphere, and let P and Q be the points shown. Let S belong to [PQ] such that OS ⊥ PQ. Then, by geometry, |PS| = h.)*

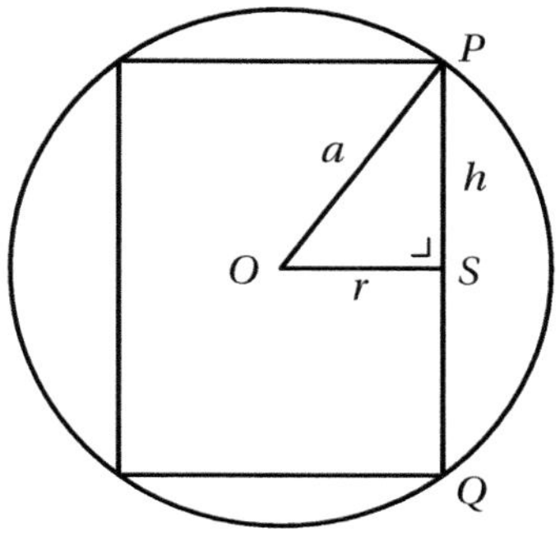

By Pythagoras' Theorem,

$$r^2 + h^2 = a^2$$
$$r^2 = a^2 - h^2$$

Then

$V = \pi r^2 h$ ... *two variables, r and h*

$V = \pi(a^2 - h^2)h$

$V = \pi(a^2h - h^3)$ ... *one variable, h*

(ii) *(Now we differentiate V with respect to the one remaining variable, h.)*

$$\frac{dV}{dh} = \pi(a^2 - 3h^2)$$

Put $\frac{dV}{dh} = 0$:

$$\pi(a^2 - 3h^2) = 0$$
$$a^2 - 3h^2 = 0$$
$$h^2 = \frac{a^2}{3}$$

$h = \frac{a}{\sqrt{3}}$ ... *as $h = -\frac{a}{\sqrt{3}}$ is not physically possible*

Then

$$r^2 = a^2 - \frac{a^2}{3} = \frac{2a^2}{3}$$

and $r = \frac{\sqrt{2}a}{\sqrt{3}}.$

The dimensions of the cylinder of maximum volume are a radius of $r = \frac{\sqrt{2}a}{\sqrt{3}}$ and a height of $2h = \frac{2a}{\sqrt{3}}.$

(iii) The maximum volume of the cylinder is

$$V = \pi\left(a^2\left(\frac{a}{\sqrt{3}}\right) - \left(\frac{a}{\sqrt{3}}\right)^3\right)$$

$$V = \pi\left(\frac{a^3}{\sqrt{3}} - \frac{a^3}{3\sqrt{3}}\right)$$

$$V = \pi\left(\frac{3a^3}{3\sqrt{3}} - \frac{a^3}{3\sqrt{3}}\right)$$

$$V = \frac{2\pi a^3}{3\sqrt{3}}.$$

You should note the following about Example 2.

1. As there was only one physically possible value of h for which $\frac{dV}{dh} = 0$, we were allowed to assume that this gave a max. If required, we could have verified this as follows:

$$\frac{d^2V}{dh^2} = -6\pi h$$

which is negative when $h = \frac{a}{\sqrt{3}}$.

2. The range of possible values of h was $0 \le h \le a$. There is a theorem in maths which says that if a function is differentiable on a closed interval, such as $V = \pi(a^2h - h^3)$ is on the interval $[0, a]$, then its (absolute) maximum and its (absolute) minimum must occur either at a turning point or at an endpoint of the interval.

At $h = 0$ and at $h = a$, $V = 0$. Thus, the minimum possible value of V is zero.

Example 3

$P(x, y)$ is a point on the curve $y = (x - 2)^2$ in the domain $2 < x < 8$.

Q is the point (8,0) and R is on the x-axis such that $PR \perp RQ$.

(i) What value of x maximises the area of the triangle PQR?

(ii) Find the maximum area of the triangle PQR.

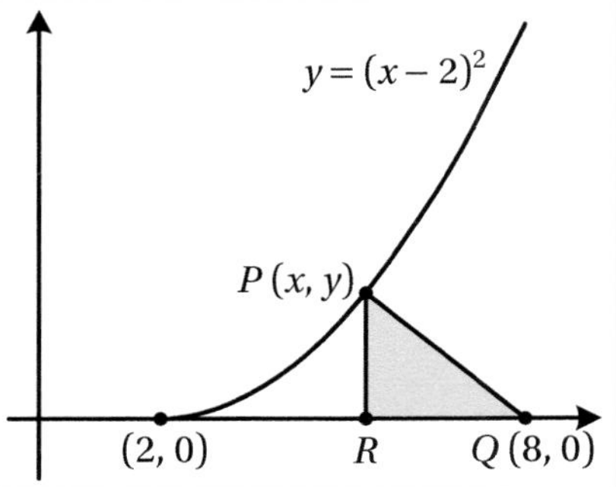

Solution

(i) Let A be the area of the triangle PQR. Then

$$A = \frac{1}{2}|RQ|.|PR|$$

$$A = \frac{1}{2}(8 - x)y \qquad \textit{... as } R = (x, 0)$$

$$A = \frac{1}{2}(8 - x)(x - 2)^2 \qquad \textit{... as P is on the curve } y = (x - 2)^2$$

Then, by the Product Rule,

$$\frac{dA}{dx} = \frac{1}{2}\left[(8 - x).2(x - 2) + (x - 2)^2(-1)\right]$$

$$\frac{dA}{dx} = \frac{1}{2}\left[2(8 - x)(x - 2) - (x - 2)^2\right]$$

$$\frac{dA}{dx} = \frac{1}{2}[2(8x - 16 - x^2 + 2x) - (x^2 - 4x + 4)]$$

$$\frac{dA}{dx} = \frac{1}{2}[-3x^2 + 24x - 36]$$

Put $\frac{dA}{dx} = 0$:

$$\frac{1}{2}[-3x^2 + 24x - 36] = 0$$

$$3x^2 - 24x + 36 = 0$$

$$x^2 - 8x + 12 = 0$$

$$(x - 2)(x - 6) = 0$$

$$x - 2 = 0 \text{ or } x - 6 = 0$$

$$x = 2 \text{ or } x = 6$$

As we are told that $2 < x < 8$, $x = 6$ is the only physically possible solution.

Thus, $x = 6$ gives a max value for A.

(ii) The maximum value of A is then

$$A = \frac{1}{2}(8 - 6)(6 - 2)^2 = 16.$$

For questions involving business and economics, we should note the following basic ideas:

1. Revenue = (Quantity sold) × (Price per unit)
2. Profit = (Revenue) – (Cost).

Example 4

A company sells q items at a unit cost of €p. The number of items that can be sold is linked to the unit cost price by the equation

$$p = 16 - 3q.$$

The total cost in euro, $C(q)$, of producing these q items is given by

$$C(q) = \frac{1}{3}q^3 - 4q^2 + 8q + 3.$$

(i) Find the expression for the profit function, $P(q)$.
(ii) Calculate how many units, q, that must be produced to maximise the profit.
(iii) What is the maximum profit?

Solution

(i) *(First of all, we must get an expression for the revenue.)*

Let the revenue be $R(q)$. Then

$$R(q) = p.q$$

$$R(q) = (16 - 3q)q$$

$$R(q) = 16q - 3q^2$$

Then

$$P(q) = R(q) - C(q)$$

$$P(q) = (16q - 3q^2) - \left(\frac{1}{3}q^3 - 4q^2 + 8q + 3\right)$$

$$P(q) = -\frac{1}{3}q^3 + q^2 + 8q - 3$$

(ii) Thus,

$$\frac{dP}{dq} = -q^2 + 2q + 8$$

Put $\frac{dP}{dq} = 0$:

$$-q^2 + 2q + 8 = 0$$
$$q^2 - 2q - 8 = 0$$
$$(q-4)(q+2) = 0$$
$$q - 4 = 0 \quad \text{or} \quad q + 2 = 0$$
$$q = 4 \quad \text{or} \quad q = -2$$

As $q \geq 0$, $q = 4$ will maximise the profit.

(iii) The maximum profit is then

$$P(4) = -\tfrac{1}{3}(4)^3 + (4)^2 + 8(4) - 3$$
$$= \frac{71}{3} = €23{\cdot}67.$$

Exercises 28.1

1. If $x + y = 6$, find the maximum possible value of $P = xy$.

2. Two positive quantities x and y are connected by the relation $x + y = 10$.
   Find the maximum value of x^2y.

3. A plastic cylinder has one end open and the other end closed. The external surface area of the cylinder is 108π. Find its maximum volume.
   (Ignore the thickness of the plastic.)

4. A tin box has a square base, of side length x m, and height y m.
   The box is open at the top, and is made to hold 4 m^3.
   Write the total external surface area in terms of x and y, and hence in terms of x only.
   Find the least possible area of sheet tin that can be used in its construction.

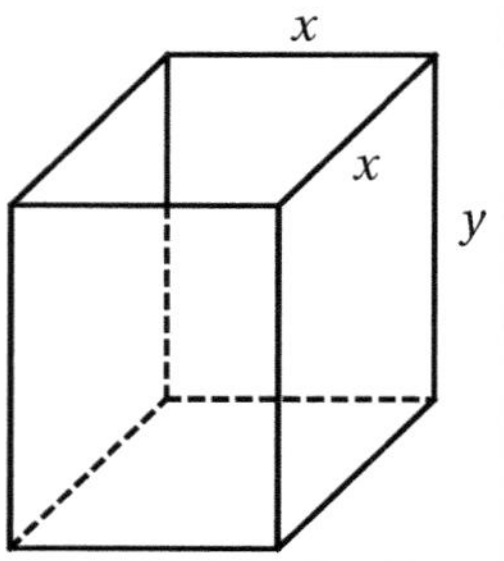

5. A cylindrical block has a base of radius x cm and a volume of 800 cm^3. Show that the total surface area is $2\pi x^2 + \frac{1600}{x}$ cm^2.
   Find the minimum possible surface area of the cylinder.

6. A prism of square section contains 64 m^3 of clay, the sides of the square being x metres. Express the length of the prism in terms of x, and find the total area of the faces. Show that the total area is a minimum when the prism is a cube.

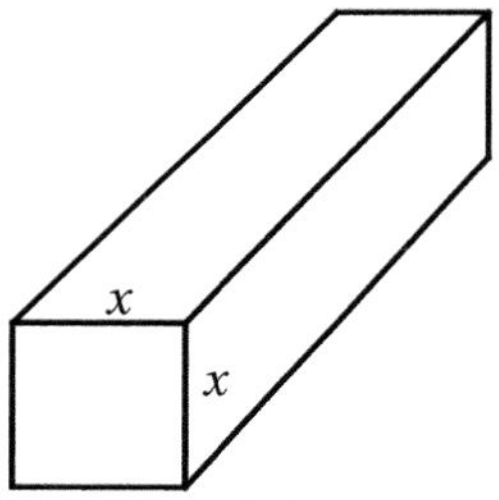

7. The slant height of a right circular cone is 10 cm, see diagram.
   Find the maximum volume of the cone, in terms of π.

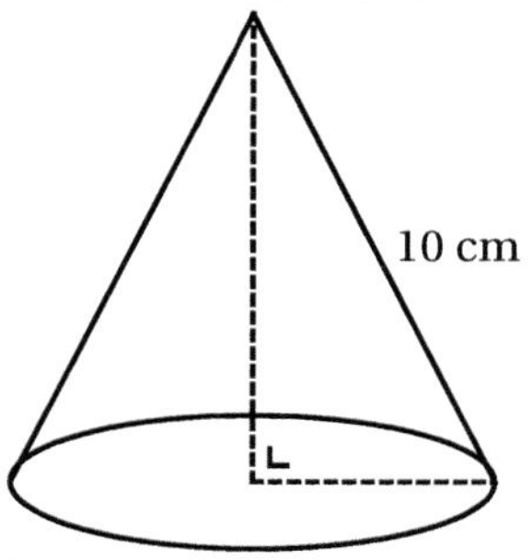

8. Find the radius of the base of a cone of volume 3π cm^3, if the slant height is a minimum.

9. Find the area of the largest rectangle that can be drawn inside a circle of radius r cm.

10. A right circular cone 11 cm in height and of base diameter 8 cm is to enclose a cylinder (see two dimensional drawing).
Express the height (h) of the cylinder in terms of its radius (r).
Find the maximum volume of the cylinder in terms of π.

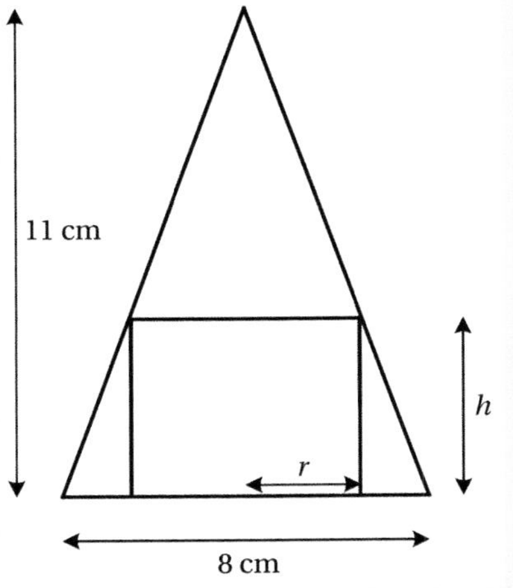

11. A rectangular field, to contain a given area, is to be fenced off along a straight river. If no fencing is needed along the river, show that the least amount of fencing will be required when the length of the field is twice its width.

12. Find the volume of the largest circular cone that can be cut from a solid sphere of radius r cm. Express your answer in terms of π.

13. An isosceles triangle has angles A, B and B.
Write A in terms of B.
Prove that the maximum value of

$$\cos A + \cos B$$

is $\frac{9}{8}$.

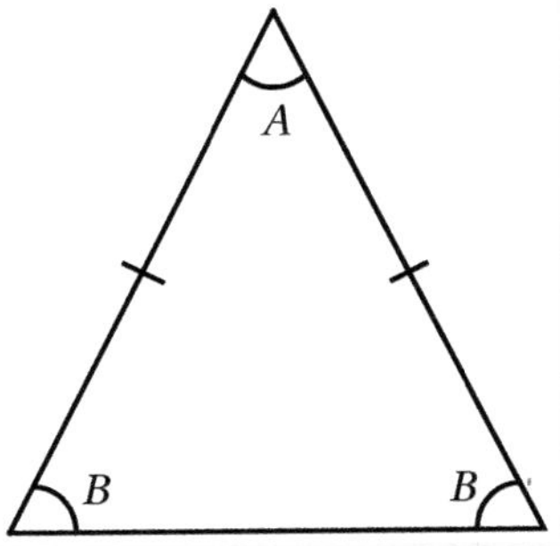

14. A line l contains the point (1,2) and has slope $m < 0$. l crosses the x-axis at P and the y-axis at Q. Find the minimum value of the area of the triangle OPQ, where O is the origin.

15. Two vertices of a rectangle are on the positive x-axis. The other two vertices are on the lines $y = 4x$ and $y = -5x + 6$.
If (x_1, y) is on the line $y = 4x$ and (x_2, y) is on the line $y = -5x + 6$, write x_1 and x_2 in terms of y. Thus, write the area of the rectangle in terms of y. What is the maximum possible area of the rectangle?

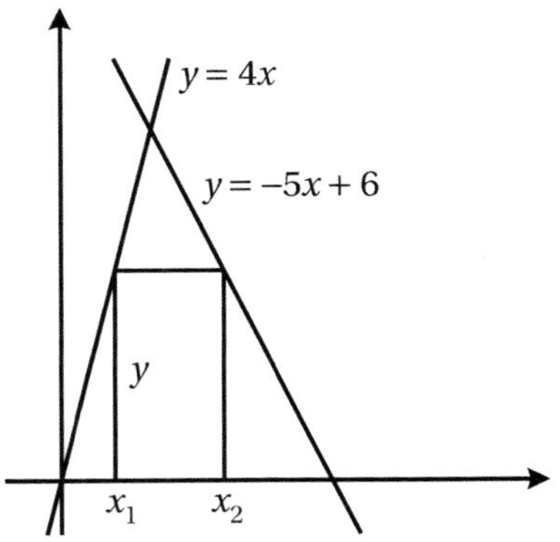

16. A company sells q items at a unit cost of €p. The number of items that can be sold is linked to the unit cost by the equation

$$p = 30 - 5q.$$

The total cost in euro, $C(q)$, of producing these q items is given by

$$C(q) = 2q^3 - 11q^2 + 12q + 4.$$

(i) Find an expression for the profit function, $P(q)$.
(ii) Calculate how many units, q, must be produced in order to maximise the profit.
(iii) What is this maximum profit?

17. The weekly production function for a particular firm is given by

$$f(x) = 100xe^{-0{\cdot}02x}$$

where x is the size of the workforce and $f(x)$ is the number of units produced.
(i) Determine the size of the workforce that will maximise weekly production.
(ii) What is the maximum weekly production?

18. A car retailer has calculated a cost function, $C(q)$, which expresses the annual cost of purchasing and maintaining his stock of cars as a function of q, the number of cars ordered each time the stock is renewed. This is given by:

$$C(q) = \frac{4860}{q} + 15q + 750000,$$

where C is in euro.
(i) Determine the value of q which minimises the cost function.
(ii) What is the minimum value of the cost function?

28.2 Rates of Change

From its introduction, the derivative $\frac{\mathrm{d}y}{\mathrm{d}x}$ was designed as a method of measuring the rate of change of y as x changes. In terms of graphs, this is equivalent to measuring the slope of the tangent to a curve.

Any rate of change can be expressed in derivative form. For example,

(i) 'the rate of change of volume, V, as the radius, r, changes' can be written $\frac{\mathrm{d}V}{\mathrm{d}r}$,

(ii) 'the rate of change of revenue, R, as the quantity sold, q, changes' can be written $\frac{\mathrm{d}R}{\mathrm{d}q}$,

(iii) 'the rate of change of a population, P, as time, t, changes' can be written $\frac{\mathrm{d}P}{\mathrm{d}t}$.

Note that if the second variable is not mentioned, then it is always assumed to be time, t.
For example, 'the rate of change of area, A' would be written $\frac{\mathrm{d}A}{\mathrm{d}t}$.

Example 1

The volume, V cm^3, of a rectangular box is given by

$$V = 3x(x+4)(x+6),$$

where x is in cm. Find the rate of change of the volume as x changes, when $x = 2$ cm.

Solution

(We need to find $\frac{dV}{dx}$. We start by simplifying V.)

$$V = 3x(x+4)(x+6)$$
$$V = 3x(x^2 + 10x + 24)$$
$$V = 3x^3 + 30x^2 + 72x$$

Then $\quad \frac{\mathrm{d}V}{\mathrm{d}x} = 9x^2 + 60x + 72$

$x = 2$: $\quad \frac{\mathrm{d}V}{\mathrm{d}x} = 9(2)^2 + 60(2) + 72$

$$= 228 \text{ cm}^2$$

(Note that the units are $\frac{\text{units of } V}{\text{units of } x} = \frac{cm^3}{cm} = cm^2$.)

Example 2

The area, A m^2, of a region is given by

$$A = 8t^2 + \sin 2t,$$

where t is in seconds. Find the rate of change of the area when $t = \frac{\pi}{2}$ s.

Solution

$\left(\textit{The rate of change of the area is } \frac{dA}{dt}.\right)$

$$A = 8t^2 + \sin 2t$$

$$\frac{\mathrm{d}A}{\mathrm{d}t} = 16t + \cos 2t(2)$$

$$= 16t + 2\cos 2t$$

Then

$$t = \frac{\pi}{2}: \quad \frac{\mathrm{d}A}{\mathrm{d}t} = 16\left(\frac{\pi}{2}\right) + 2\cos \pi$$

$$= 8\pi + 2(-1)$$

$$= (8\pi - 2)\ \mathrm{m^2 s^{-1}}.$$

Two important rates of change are ***velocity*** (speed) and ***acceleration***. Suppose a particle moves along a straight line (the x-axis) and its displacement from the origin (i.e. its location) is called x.

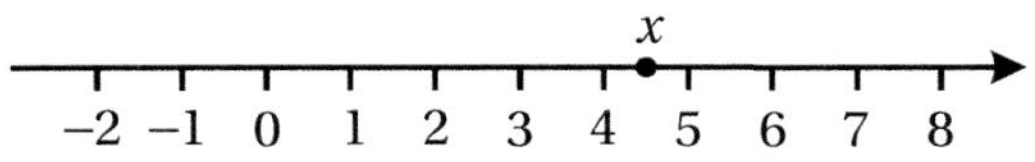

Then:

$$\textbf{velocity} = v = \frac{\mathrm{d}x}{\mathrm{d}t}$$

$$\textbf{acceleration} = a = \frac{\mathrm{d}v}{\mathrm{d}t} = \frac{\mathrm{d}^2x}{\mathrm{d}t^2}$$

If the name of the variable representing displacement is s, then naturally

$$v = \frac{\mathrm{d}s}{\mathrm{d}t} \quad \text{and} \quad a = \frac{\mathrm{d}^2s}{\mathrm{d}t^2}.$$

Questions involving displacement, velocity and acceleration often refer to the following concepts:

(i) greatest/least displacement: put $v = 0$

(ii) greatest/least speed (velocity): put $a = 0$

In each case, we solve to find the time, t, and then calculate anything else that may be required.

In practice, questions involving greatest or least displacement, velocity or acceleration amount to max and min problems. Thus, if we have to distinguish between greatest and least, we can use either the First Derivative Test or the Second Derivative Test.

Example 3

The position, s metres, of a particle relative to a fixed point after t seconds is given by

$$s = 2t^3 - 4t^2 + 2t.$$

(i) Find the two times when the particle is instantaneously at rest.

(ii) Find the acceleration after 2 seconds.

(iii) Find the displacement when the acceleration is 4 $\mathrm{ms^{-2}}$.

(iv) Find the minimum velocity of the particle in its motion.

Solution

(i) *(The particle is instantaneously at rest when the velocity is zero.)*

$v = \frac{ds}{dt} = 6t^2 - 8t + 2$

Put $v = 0$: $6t^2 - 8t + 2 = 0$

$3t^2 - 4t + 1 = 0$

$(3t - 1)(t - 1) = 0$

$3t - 1 = 0$ or $t - 1 = 0$

$t = \frac{1}{3}$ or $t = 1$

(ii) $a = \frac{dv}{dt} = 12t - 8$

At $t = 2$: $a = 12(2) - 8$

$a = 16 \text{ ms}^{-2}$

(iii) When $a = 4$,

$12t - 8 = 4$

$t = 1$

When $t = 1$,

$s = 2(1)^2 - 4(1)^2 + 2(1) = 0.$

(iv) *(The minimum velocity is when its derivative, i.e. the acceleration, is zero.)*

$a = 0$: $12t - 8 = 0$

$t = \frac{8}{12} = \frac{2}{3}$

$t = \frac{2}{3}$: $v = 6\left(\frac{2}{3}\right)^2 - 8\left(\frac{2}{3}\right) + 2 = -\frac{2}{3} \text{ ms}^{-1}.$

(This value of v must be a minimum, but we could have verified it, if required.)

Exercises 28.2

1. The volume, $V \text{ m}^3$, of a container depends on the dimension x m according to

$V = x(2x^2 - x + 4).$

Find the rate of change of the volume as x changes, when $x = 3$.

2. The volume, V, of a solid is given by $V = \frac{5}{3}r^2 + 10r^2$.

Find the rate of change of the volume with respect to r, when $r = 4$.

3. If $x = \theta^2 \sin\theta$, find the rate of change of x with respect to θ, at $\theta = \frac{\pi}{4}$.

4. At any time t seconds, the distance x metres of a particle moving in a straight line is given by $x = \frac{t}{4} - \log_e(1 + t)$. Find:

(i) the initial velocity and acceleration,
(ii) the time when the velocity is zero,
(iii) the acceleration when the velocity is zero.

5. The distance, x metres, travelled by a body in t seconds is given by

$x = 3t^3 - 4t^2 + 6t - 5.$

Find the velocity and the acceleration when (i) $t = 0$, (ii) $t = 2{\cdot}5$.

6. A missile fired from ground level rises x metres vertically in t seconds, where

$$x = 100t - \frac{25}{2}t^2.$$

Find
(i) the initial velocity of the missile,
(ii) the time at which the height of the missile is a maximum,
(iii) the maximum height reached,
(iv) the velocity with which the missile strikes the ground.

7. The displacement, x cm, of the end of a spring at time t seconds is given by

$$x = 3e^{-2t} \sin 20\pi t.$$

Find the velocity of the end of the spring after 2 seconds.

8. The displacement, x cm, of the end of a spring at time t seconds is given by

$$x = 4e^{-t} \sin 4\pi t.$$

Find the velocity of the end of the spring after 4 seconds.

28.3 Related Rates of Change

Sometimes, we are given one rate of change and asked to find a related, or connected, rate of change. We can use the Chain Rule to find this rate of change.

For example, suppose we are told that the radius of a circle is increasing at 5 cms^{-1} and we want to find the rate of increase of the area of the circle.

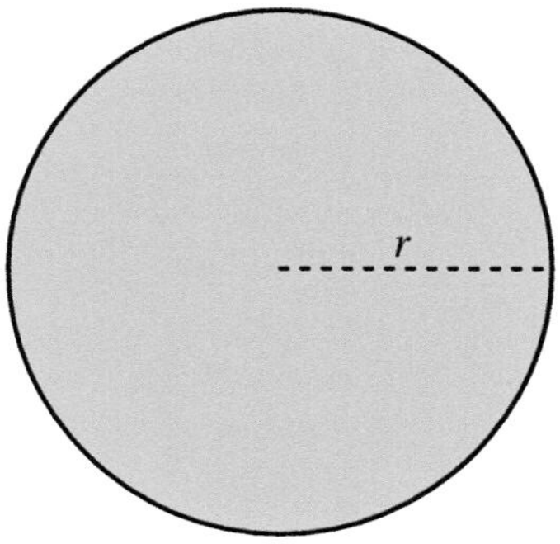

Let r be the radius of the circle and A be its area. Then we are told that the rate of change of the radius, r, (with respect to time) is 5. Hence,

$$\frac{dr}{dt} = 5 \text{ cms}^{-1}.$$

We want to find the rate of change of the area, A, (with respect to time), i.e. we want $\frac{dA}{dt}$. We can use the Chain Rule as follows:

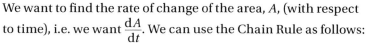

$\frac{dA}{dt}$	=	$\frac{dr}{dt}$	.	?
↑		↑		↑
what we want		*what we are given*		*now figure out what goes here*

To get $\frac{dA}{dt}$, we should multiply $\frac{dr}{dt}$ by $\frac{dA}{dr}$, because then the dr above and below can be cancelled, leaving us with the required $\frac{dA}{dt}$. Thus,

$$\frac{dA}{dt} = \frac{dr}{dt} \cdot \frac{dA}{dr}.$$

So, the first step is to calculate $\frac{dA}{dr}$. From the formula for the area of a circle,

$$A = \pi r^2$$

$$\frac{dA}{dr} = 2\pi r.$$

Now, as $\frac{dr}{dt} = 5$, by the Chain Rule,

$$\frac{dA}{dt} = \frac{dr}{dt}.\frac{dA}{dr}$$
$$= (5)(2\pi r)$$
$$= 10\pi r \text{ cm}^2\text{s}^{-1}$$

We can now evaluate this for any value of r. For example, the rate of increase of the area when the radius is 2 cm is $10\pi(2) = 20\pi \text{ cm}^2\text{s}^{-1}$.

Example 1

A liquid is poured into an inverted cone (apex down) at a rate of $3 \text{ cm}^3\text{s}^{-1}$.

The cone has a radius of 20 cm and a height of 48 cm.

Find the rate at which the height of the liquid in the cone is increasing when the height of the liquid above the apex is 36 cm.

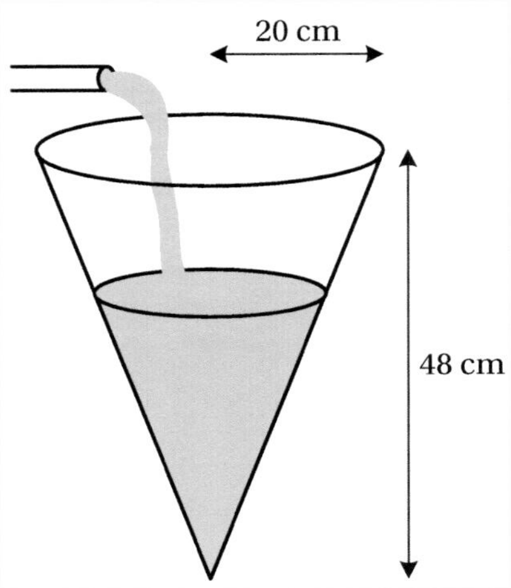

Solution

(Let r cm be the radius of the liquid and let h cm be its height. Let V cm³ be the volume of the liquid.)

Want: $\frac{dh}{dt}$

Given: $\frac{dV}{dt} = 3 \text{ cm}^3\text{s}^{-1}$.

By the Chain Rule:

$$\frac{dh}{dt} = \frac{dV}{dt}.\frac{dh}{dV}$$

(We need to find $\frac{dh}{dV}$. We do this in two stages. First, we write V in terms of h only. This requires that we write r in terms of h.)

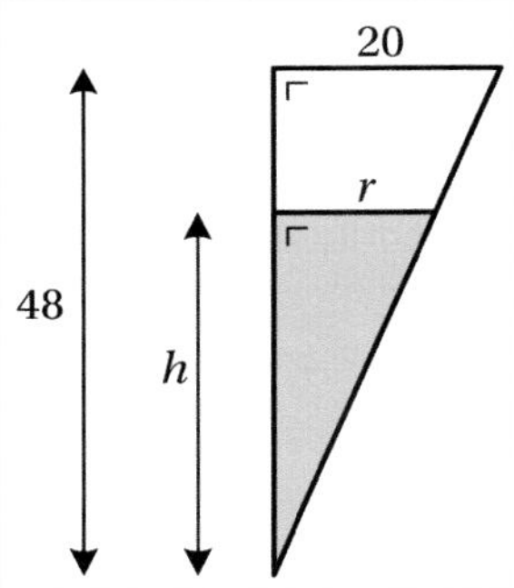

By similar triangles,

$$\frac{r}{20} = \frac{h}{48}$$
$$r = \frac{20h}{48} = \frac{5h}{12}$$

Then

$$V = \frac{1}{3}\pi r^2 h$$
$$V = \frac{1}{3}\pi\left(\frac{5h}{12}\right)^2 h$$
$$V = \frac{1}{3}\pi\left(\frac{25h^2}{144}\right)h$$
$$V = \frac{25\pi}{432}h^3$$

$\left(\textit{Secondly, by finding } \frac{dV}{dh}\textit{, we can invert to find } \frac{dh}{dV} = \frac{1}{\frac{dV}{dh}} \right).$

Then $\frac{dV}{dh} = \frac{25\pi}{432}(3h^2) = \frac{25\pi}{144}h^2$

and $\frac{dh}{dV} = \frac{1}{\frac{dV}{dh}} = \frac{1}{\frac{25\pi h^2}{144}} = \frac{144}{25\pi h^2}$

By the Chain Rule,

$$\frac{dh}{dt} = \frac{dV}{dt} \cdot \frac{dh}{dV}$$

$$= (3)\left(\frac{144}{25\pi h^2}\right) = \frac{432}{25\pi h^2}$$

When $h = 36$,

$$\frac{dh}{dt} = \frac{432}{25\pi(36)^2}$$

$$= \frac{1}{75\pi} \text{ cms}^{-1} \approx 0{\cdot}00424 \text{ cms}^{-1}.$$

Example 2

A rope is attached to the bow of a boat, A, and passes through B, a ring at the edge of the dock. B is 4 m vertically above A.

The boat is pulled in towards the dock by the rope at the rate of $0{\cdot}1$ ms^{-1}, i.e. $|AB|$ is decreasing at the rate of $0{\cdot}1$ ms^{-1}.

Determine how fast the boat is approaching the dock when $|AB|$ is 5 m.

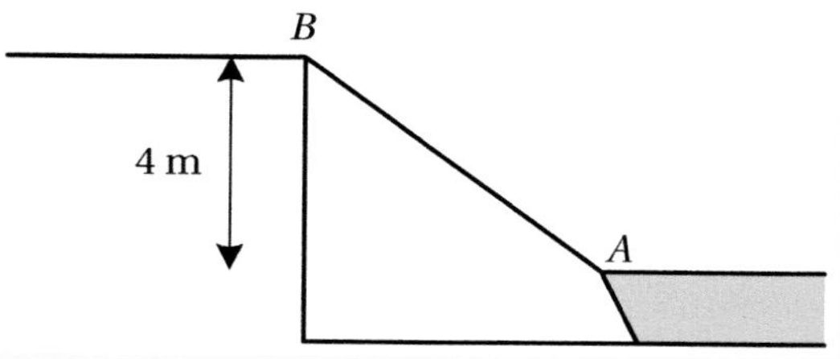

Solution

(Let $|AB| = x$ m and let y m be the distance from A to the vertical dock wall.)

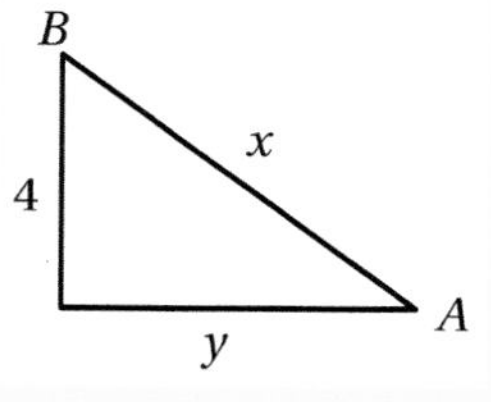

Want: $\frac{dy}{dt}$

Given: $\frac{dx}{dt} = -0{\cdot}1$ ms^{-1}

By the Chain Rule,

$$\frac{dy}{dt} = \frac{dx}{dt} \cdot \frac{dy}{dx}$$

$\left(\textit{To find } \frac{dy}{dx}\textit{, we will get y in terms of x.} \right)$

By Pythagoras,

$$y^2 + 4^2 = x^2$$

$$y = \sqrt{x^2 - 16} = (x^2 - 16)^{\frac{1}{2}}$$

Then

$$\frac{dy}{dx} = \frac{1}{2}(x^2 - 16)^{-\frac{1}{2}}.(2x) = \frac{x}{\sqrt{x^2 - 16}}$$

Thus,

$$\frac{dy}{dt} = \frac{dx}{dt}.\frac{dy}{dx}$$

$$= -\frac{1}{10}.\frac{x}{\sqrt{x^2 - 16}}$$

$$= -\frac{x}{10\sqrt{x^2 - 16}}$$

When $x = 5$,

$$\frac{dy}{dt} = -\frac{5}{10\sqrt{25 - 16}} = -\frac{1}{6},$$

i.e. the boat is approaching the dock at $\frac{1}{6}$ ms^{-1}.

An alternative approach to Example 2 is to start with the equation

$$y^2 + 4^2 = x^2$$

or $y^2 + 16 = x^2$.

Then we use implicit differentiation (and the Chain Rule) to differentiate both sides with respect to t.

$$\frac{d(y^2)}{dt} + \frac{d(16)}{dt} = \frac{d(x^2)}{dt}$$

$$\frac{d(y^2)}{dy}.\frac{dy}{dt} + (0) = \frac{d(x^2)}{dx}.\frac{dx}{dt}$$

$$2y\frac{dy}{dt} = 2x\frac{dx}{dt}$$

$$\frac{dy}{dt} = \left(\frac{x}{y}\right)\frac{dx}{dt}$$

When $x = 5$, $y = \sqrt{25 - 16} = 3$ and we are given $\frac{dx}{dt} = -0{\cdot}1 = -\frac{1}{10}$. Thus,

$$\frac{dy}{dt} = \left(\frac{5}{3}\right)\left(\frac{-1}{10}\right) = -\frac{1}{6}\ ms^{-1},$$

as before.

Exercises 28.3

1. Let $V = \pi r^2(2r + 4)$.

(i) If $\frac{dr}{dt} = 4$, find $\frac{dV}{dt}$ when $r = 2$.

(ii) If $\frac{dV}{dt} = 6$, find $\frac{dr}{dt}$ when $r = 1$.

2. Let $A = 100\sqrt{x}$.

(i) If $\frac{dx}{dt} = 4$, find $\frac{dA}{dt}$ when $x = 9$.

(ii) If $\frac{dA}{dt} = 20$, find $\frac{dx}{dt}$ when $x = 4$.

3. The path of a football is given by the equation $y = x - \frac{x^2}{40}$, $x \geq 0$.
If $\frac{dx}{dt} = 10\sqrt{2}$ for all t, find $\frac{dy}{dt}$ when $x = 10$.

4. The area, A cm^2, of the image of a rocket on a radar screen is given by

$$A = \frac{12}{r^2},$$

where r km is the distance of the rocket from the screen. The rocket is approaching the screen at 0·5 kms^{-1}, i.e. $\frac{dr}{dt} = -0{\cdot}5$ kms^{-1}. When the rocket is 10 km away from the screen, at what rate is the area of the image changing?

5. A spherical balloon is being inflated so that its volume is increasing at a constant rate of 24 cm^{3}s^{-1}. Find the rate of increase of the radius when the radius is 30 cm.

6. The volume of a sphere is increasing at a steady rate of 3 cm^{3}s^{-1}.
(i) Find the rate of change of the radius length, r, in terms of r.
(ii) Find the rate of change of the surface area of the sphere when the radius is 12 cm.

7. Sand is being poured at a rate of 100 cm^{3}s^{-1} to form a conical pile whose height is always three times the radius of its base. Find the rate at which the radius of the conical pile is changing when its height is 48 cm.

8. Oil is dripping onto a surface at the rate of $\frac{\pi}{10}$ cm^{3}s^{-1} and forms a circular film which may be considered to have a uniform depth of 0·1 cm. Find the rate at which the radius of the circular film is increasing when the radius is 5 cm.

9. A light is at the top of a pole 10 m high. A ball is dropped from the same height from a point 6 m away from the light. If the ball falls $5t^2$ m in t seconds, how fast is the shadow of the ball moving along the horizontal ground through the base of the pole 1 second after being dropped?

10. A horizontal trough is 4 m long and 1 m deep. Its cross-section is an isosceles triangle of base 1·5 m with its vertex downwards. Water runs into the trough at the rate of 0·03 m^{3}s^{-1}. Find the rate at which the water level is rising when the water has been running for 25 seconds.

Revision Exercises 28

1. A square of side length x cm is cut from each of the corners of a rectangular piece of cardboard with dimensions 15 cm by 24 cm. The cardboard is then folded to form an open box of depth x cm.
(i) Show that the volume of the box is $(4x^3 - 78x^2 + 360x)$ cm^3.
(ii) Find the value of x for which the volume of the box is a maximum.

2. A solid cylinder of radius r and height h has a fixed volume K.
(i) Express h in terms of r, π and K.
(ii) Find the ratio $r : h$ when the total surface area of the cylinder is a minimum. Give your answer as a ratio of natural numbers.

3. A lump of modelling clay of volume 72 cm^3 is moulded into the shape of a rectangular box with sides of length x cm, $2x$ cm and y cm. Find the minimum surface area of this rectangular box.

4. In a certain production firm, the total revenue function, $R(x)$, and the total cost function, $C(x)$, for a particular product are given by

$$R(x) = 8x - x^2$$

and $$C(x) = 4 + 3x$$

respectively, where x is the number of units produced and sold in thousands, and $R(x)$ and $C(x)$ are in millions of euro.

(i) Determine the profit function, $P(x)$.

(ii) How many of the goods must be produced and sold in order to maximise the profit? What is the maximum profit?

(iii) Determine the values of x for which the profit is increasing.

(iv) For what values of x is the profit positive?

5. The weekly production function, $f(x)$, for a particular firm is given by

$$f(x) = 500xe^{-0{\cdot}05x}$$

where $f(x)$ is the number of units produced and x is the size of the workforce.

(i) Calculate the size of the workforce that will maximise weekly production.

(ii) What is the maximum weekly production?

6. A new state welfare agency wants to know the number of analysts to hire to process welfare applications. Efficiency experts estimate that the average cost, $f(x)$, of processing an application when the number of analysts is x is given by

$$f(x) = 0{\cdot}001x^2 - 5\ln x + 60$$

where $f(x)$ is in euro.

(i) Determine the number of analysts that should be hired to minimise the average cost per application.

(ii) What is the minimum average cost per application?

7. A charity organisation is planning a fund-raising campaign in a major city having a population of 2 million. The proportion, P, of the population who will make a donation is estimated by the function

$$P = 1 - e^{-0{\cdot}02x}$$

where x is the number of days for which the campaign is conducted. Past experience indicates that the average contribution per donor is €2. The cost of the campaign is estimated to be €10000 per day.

(i) By calculating the total contributions minus the total costs, find an expression for $N(x)$, the net proceeds after x days.

(ii) For how many days should the campaign be conducted to maximise the net proceeds?

(iii) Calculate the maximum net proceeds.

8. The height h and the base radius r of a right circular cone vary in such a way that the volume remains constant. Find the rate of change of h with respect to r at the instant when h and r are equal.

9. The radius of the base of a right circular cylinder is r cm and its height is $2r$ cm.

(i) Find the rate at which the volume is increasing, when the radius is 2 cm and is increasing at the rate of $0{\cdot}25\ \text{cms}^{-1}$.

(ii) Find the rate at which the total surface area is increasing when the radius is 5 cm and the volume is increasing at the rate of $5\pi\ \text{cm}^3\text{s}^{-1}$.

10. An astronaut is at a height x km above the earth, as shown. He moves vertically away from the earth's surface at a velocity $\frac{dx}{dt}$ of $\frac{r}{5}$ kmh^{-1}, where r is the length of the earth's radius.
He observes the angle θ, in radians, as shown.
Show that

$$\theta = \sin^{-1}\left(\frac{r}{r+x}\right).$$

Hence, find $\frac{d\theta}{dt}$ when $x = r$.

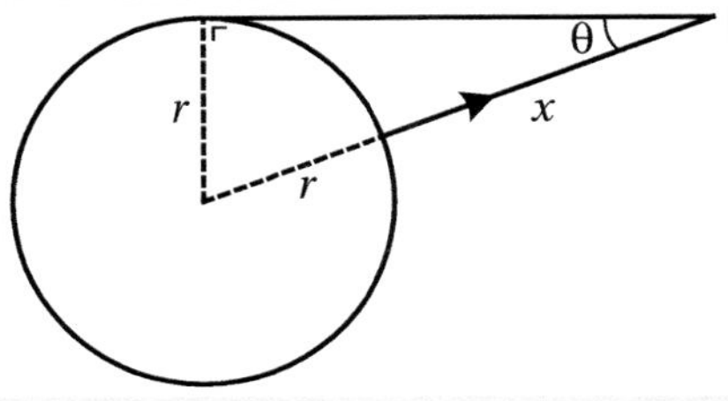

29 Sequences and Series

Sequences, i.e. lists of numbers generally, but not always following some pattern, have been around for thousands of years, as have series, which are the sums of the terms in a sequence. The first known summation of a series was produced by the Greek mathematician, Archimedes, in the 3rd century BC. He used the sum of a series to approximate the area under an arc of a particular type of curve and gave a remarkably accurate approximation of π.

In more modern times, much work has been done on sequences and series, especially since it was discovered that many functions in common use can be approximated by certain series, especially trigonometric series.

Two of the most important types of sequences and series on our course are called arithmetic and geometric. These sequences and series have many practical uses in real-life situations, especially in the realm of financial mathematics. These will be examined in a later chapter. In this chapter, we just meet a couple of simple applications.

29.1 Sequences, Patterns, Rules and Formulae

A **sequence** is an ordered list of objects, or numbers. By 'ordered' we mean that there is a clear idea of the first element in the list, called the **first term**, the second element, called the **second term**, and so on. If we change the order, we make a different sequence. So, unlike a set, the same objects can occur again and again in a sequence.

If the name of the sequence is u (it doesn't have to be u, it could be T or v, etc) then the terms can be called u_1 (the first term), u_2 (the second term) and so on. We call u_n, where $n = 1, 2, 3, \ldots$, the nth term, or the **general term**.

The terms of a sequence do not have to follow any regular pattern. For example, consider the following sequence of the number of students in a maths class each day since the beginning of the year:

24, 23, 24, 24, 22, 23, 22, 21, 23, 24, 24, ...

But in most sequences of interest, the terms do follow a regular pattern. Spotting the pattern allows us to continue the sequence, something we are unable to do with the sequence above.

Consider the following pattern of shapes made from matchsticks.

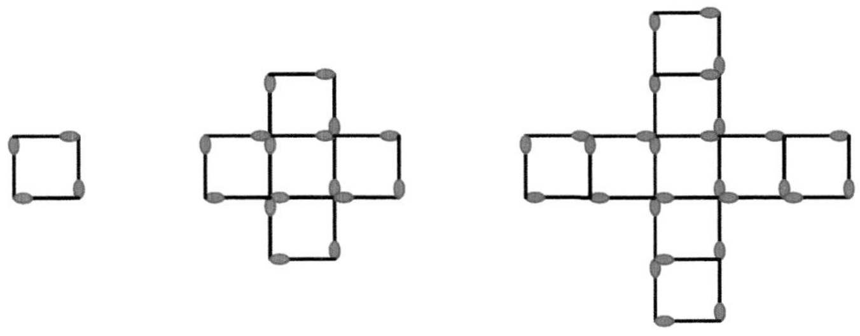

From this pattern, we can form a number of different sequences. Some of these are given below.

Sequence 1: The Shapes

(i) By inspection, we can see that the next term in the pattern will have three squares on the left and right of the centre square, as well as above and below the centre square. We can describe in words how to make the next shape by means of a **rule**.

Rule: Add one extra square to the left, right, top and bottom of the previous shape.

If we were not given a diagram showing what the first few terms look like, we could also include an instruction as to how to start, e.g. starting with one square, add one extra square to the left, right, top and bottom of the last shape.

Try drawing the next two terms in this sequence.

Sequence 2: The Number of Squares

(i) The first shape has one square, the second five, the third nine, and so on. This gives us the sequence of numbers:

1, 5, 9, ...

You should be able to see that we add 4 to the previous term to get the next term. Thus, we can continue this sequence:

1, 5, 9, 13, 17, 21, ...

We can now describe a rule to calculate the next term.

Rule: Add 4 to the previous term to get the next term.

Again, if we are not given the first term, we could make the rule more precise: starting with 1, add 4 to the previous term to get the next term.

(ii) If u_n is a term of the sequence, then the next term of the sequence can be written u_{n+1}. From the rule above, we can see that u_{n+1} can be obtained from u_n by adding 4. This gives what is known as a **recursion formula**.

Recursion Formula: $u_{n+1} = u_n + 4$

On its own, this is not enough to generate the terms of the sequence: we need to know where to start. To give this, we can specify the **initial term**, $u_1 = 1$.

If the rule of the sequence tells us how to get the next term in terms of the previous terms, then a recursion formula can be easy to write down. However, it is not all that easy to work with. For example, how could you use the recursion formula to find u_{1000}?

(iii) If u is the name of this sequence, then we would like to develop a **formula** for u_n. This would allow us to calculate u_{100} or $u_{1000000}$ without having to list all the terms in between.

As we are adding 4 to each term to get the next term, $4n$ should be part of the rule for u_n. But the first term, u_1, can be written $4(1) - 3 = 1$. This suggests that

$$u_n = 4n - 3$$

Formula: $u_n = 4n - 3$

This is called **sequence notation**, and works like function notation, e.g.

$u_2 = 4(2) - 3 = 5$

and $u_3 = 4(3) - 3 = 9$.

As we can see, both of these are correct. When working out a formula for the general term, you should always check a few terms to make sure you are correct.

Then, for example, $u_{1000} = 4(1000) - 3 = 3997$.

Sequence 3: The Number of Matchsticks

(i) The numbers of matchsticks in the first three shapes are 4, 16, 28. Thus, the sequence of the number of matchsticks is

4, 16, 28, ...

To discover the pattern in these numbers, notice that as we go from one shape to the next, we need to add 3 more matchsticks to the left, right, top and bottom: a total of 12 extra matchsticks. This gives us the rule for the number sequence.

Rule: Add 12 to the previous number to get the next number.

To be able to use the rule to generate the terms of the sequence, we also need to know that the first term is 4.

(ii) We can also describe the sequence by a recursion formula and an initial term.

Recursion Formula: $u_{n+1} = u_n + 12$

Initial Term: $u_1 = 4$

(iii) As we add 12 to each term to get the next term, we expect u_n to contain $12n$. But $u_1 = 12(1) - 8 = 4$, $u_2 = 12(2) - 8 = 16$ and so on. Thus, we have a formula for the terms in the sequence.

Formula: $u_n = 12n - 8$

There are other possible sequences we can take from the shapes indicated, e.g. the length of the perimeter. You might like to try this for yourself.

You should note that if the rule of a sequence describes how to make each term directly from the term number, then in general a recursion formula is not a good idea. For example, given the sequence

1, 4, 9, 16, 25, ...

Rule: Square the term number.
Formula: $u_n = n^2$

Although it is possible to find a recursion formula to describe this sequence, one is not convenient here.

Example 1

Describe each of the following sequences by a rule (in words) and, where appropriate, give a recursion formula or formula for the sequence.

(i) 2, 6, 10, 14, 18, ...

(ii) 6, 12, 24, 48, 96, ...

(iii) 2, 3, 5, 7, 11, ...

Solution

(i) *(We add 4 to each term to get the next term.)*

Rule: Add 4 to each term to get the next term.

Recursion Formula: $u_{n+1} = u_n + 4$

Formula: $u_n = 4n - 2$

(Note that $u_1 = 4(1) - 2$, $u_2 = 4(2) - 2$, $u_3 = 4(3) - 2$. *This gives us our formula.)*

(ii) *(Each term after the first is double the previous term.)*

Rule: Multiply the previous term by 2 to get the next term.
Recursion Formula: $u_{n+1} = u_n \times 2$
Formula: $u_n = 6 \times 2^{n-1}$
(Note that $u_1 = 6$, $u_2 = 6 \times 2^{2-1}$, $u_3 = 6 \times 2^{3-1}$. This gives us the formula.)

(iii) *(You will have to recognise that the numbers given are the first few prime numbers. We can write down a rule, but a recursion formula or formula are not appropriate.)*

Rule: Take the next prime number.

Exercises 29.1

1. The diagram below shows a pattern of shapes made from matchsticks.

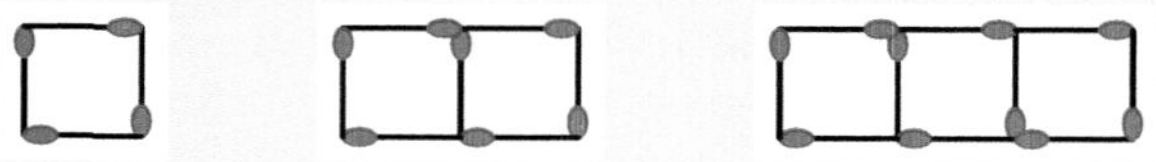

(i) Copy the pattern and draw the next two shapes in the pattern. Describe by a rule how to construct the next shape.
(ii) Write down the sequence for the number of squares present in each shape in the pattern. Describe this number sequence by a rule and a recursion formula. Give a formula for this sequence.
(iii) Write down the sequence for the number of matches used in each shape. Describe this number sequence by a rule and a recursion formula. Give a formula for this sequence, and find the hundredth term in this sequence.
(iv) Write down the sequence for the number of perimeter matches in each shape. Describe this number sequence by a rule and a recursion formula.

2. The diagram below shows a pattern of shapes made from match sticks.

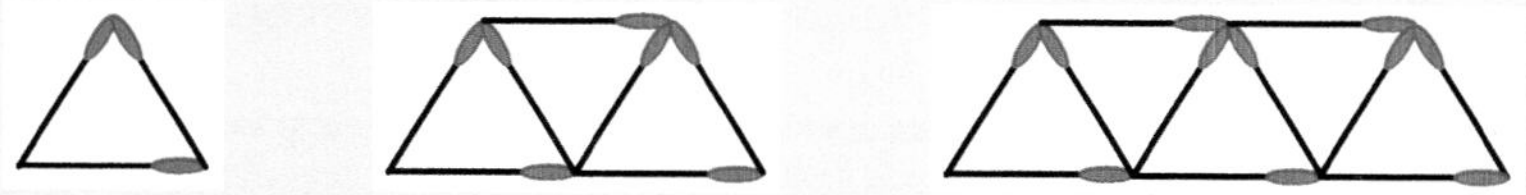

(i) Copy the diagram and draw the next two shapes in the pattern. Describe by a rule how to construct the next shape.
(ii) Write down the sequence for the number of equilateral triangles present in each shape in the pattern. Describe this number sequence by a rule and a recursion formula. Give a formula for this sequence.
(iii) Write down the sequence for the number of matches used in each shape. Describe this number sequence by a rule and a recursion formula. Give a formula for this sequence, u_n, and find u_{86}.

For each of the following number sequences,
(i) write down the next two terms in the sequence,
(ii) describe by a rule how to construct the terms of the sequence, and give a recursion formula if appropriate,
(iii) write down a formula for u_n, the nth term of the sequence.

3. 1, 6, 11, 16, ...
4. 8, 4, 2, 1, ...
5. $1, \frac{1}{2}, \frac{1}{3}, \frac{1}{4}, \ldots$
6. 12, 8, 4, 0, ...
7. 2, 8, 18, 32, ...
8. $\frac{1}{2}, \frac{2}{3}, \frac{3}{4}, \frac{4}{5}, \ldots$

9. For a sequence, $u_n = \frac{2n-1}{n+1}$. Find the first three terms of the sequence and find u_{23}.

10. For a sequence, $u_n = n^2 - 7n + 12$. Find the first three terms of this sequence and find which terms of the sequence have a value of 0.

11. For a sequence, $u_n = 3 \times 2^{n-1}$. Find the first three terms of this sequence and find the term of the sequence which has a value of 12288.

12. For a sequence, $u_n = \frac{n^2+2n}{n+3}$. Find the first three terms of this sequence and find which term has a value of $\frac{33}{4}$.

13. Verify that $u_n = \frac{n(n-1)}{2} + 1$ is a formula for the sequence 1, 2, 4, 7, ...

14. Verify that $u_n = 2n^2 + n + 1$ is a formula for the sequence 4, 11, 22, 37, ...

15. Verify that $u_n = n^2 + \frac{1}{n}$ is a formula for the sequence $2, \frac{9}{2}, \frac{28}{3}, \frac{65}{4}, \ldots$

16. Verify that $u_n = 2^n + 3^n$ is a formula for the sequence 5, 13, 35, 97, ...

29.2 Limits of Sequences

Consider the sequence whose formula is $u_n = \frac{n}{n+1}$. The terms of this sequence are

$$\frac{1}{2}, \frac{2}{3}, \frac{3}{4}, \frac{4}{5}, \ldots$$

As we continue writing the terms of this sequence, it is clear that the terms get closer and closer to 1. For example, $u_{1000} = \frac{1000}{1001} = 0{\cdot}999$ and $u_{1000000} = \frac{1000000}{1000001} = 0{\cdot}999999$. As n gets larger and larger, which we write in maths as '$n \to \infty$', i.e. as n tends to infinity, the terms of the sequence get closer and closer to 1. We write this as follows:

as $n \to \infty$, $u_n \to 1$.

The number that the terms of the sequence get closer and closer to is called the **limit** of the sequence. Thus, we can say that the limit of u_n (as $n \to \infty$) is 1. This can be written

$$\lim_{n \to \infty} u_n = 1$$

or as $$\lim_{n \to \infty} \frac{n}{n+1} = 1.$$

The limits of some sequences can be seen by inspection, often by writing a number of terms.

It is also important to recognise that not all sequences have limits. For example, the sequence 1, 4, 9, 16, ... has no limit as the terms increase without bound.

Example 1

A sequence is given by $u_n = \frac{2^n}{2^{n+1}+1}$.

(i) Write out the first four terms of the sequence.

(ii) Find, by inspection, $\lim_{n \to \infty} u_n$.

Solution

(i) $u_1 = \frac{2}{4+1} = \frac{2}{5}$, $u_2 = \frac{4}{8+1} = \frac{4}{9}$, $u_3 = \frac{8}{16+1} = \frac{8}{17}$, $u_4 = \frac{16}{32+1} = \frac{16}{33}$.

In decimal form, these terms are

$u_1 = 0{\cdot}4$, $u_2 = 0{\cdot}44444$, $u_3 = 0{\cdot}470588$, $u_4 = 0{\cdot}484848$

(ii) By examining the first few terms, $\lim_{n\to\infty} u_n = 0{\cdot}5 = \frac{1}{2}$.

However, the limits of most sequences cannot be found so easily. We need a more structured approach. There are a number of special limits and rules that we can use to calculate the limits of more complicated sequences.

Special Limit 1

$$\lim_{n\to\infty} \frac{k}{n^p} = 0, \quad \text{where } k \in \mathbb{R} \text{ and } p > 0.$$

By taking a few examples, it is easy to see that this special limit makes sense. For example, $\lim_{n\to\infty} \frac{100}{n^2} = 0$ because n^2 becomes exceptionally large while 100 remains constant. Overall, as n increases, the fraction becomes smaller and smaller, and has a limit of 0.

Special Limit 2

$$\lim_{n\to\infty} r^n = 0, \quad \text{if } -1 < r < 1.$$

For example, $\lim_{n\to\infty} \left(\frac{2}{3}\right)^n = 0$ because $\left(\frac{2}{3}\right)^2 = \frac{4}{9}$, $\left(\frac{2}{3}\right)^3 = \frac{8}{27}$ and higher powers of $\frac{2}{3}$ get closer and closer to 0.

In addition, there are a number of limit rules that we can use to help calculate limits.

Limit Rules

Let $\lim_{n\to\infty} u_n = A$, $\lim_{n\to\infty} v_n = B$ where $A, B, c \in \mathbb{R}$.

1. $\lim_{n\to\infty} c = c$ (c a constant)
2. $\lim_{n\to\infty} c.u_n = cA$
3. $\lim_{n\to\infty} (u_n \pm v_n) = A \pm B$
4. $\lim_{n\to\infty} (u_n.v_n) = AB$
5. $\lim_{n\to\infty} \frac{u_n}{v_n} = \frac{A}{B}$, provided $B \neq 0$

In practice, the general approach, when trying to evaluate the limit of a fraction is to **divide above and below by the dominant term**. The dominant term (on the top or bottom or both) is the largest term as $n \to \infty$.

We divide above and below by the dominant term to avoid getting the meaningless $\frac{\infty}{\infty}$ which is called an indeterminate form. On the other hand, we may obtain

$$\frac{\infty}{k}, \quad \text{where } k \in \mathbb{R}$$

which allows us say that the limit is $\pm\infty$, or strictly, the limit does not exist.

Example 2

Evaluate **(i)** $\lim\limits_{n\to\infty} \dfrac{3n-1}{2n+3}$ **(ii)** $\lim\limits_{n\to\infty} \dfrac{n^3+3n-1}{2n^2+3}$ **(iii)** $\lim\limits_{n\to\infty} \dfrac{5(3^n)+4(2^n)}{2(3^n)+1}$.

Solution

(i) *(The dominant term is n. This is what we divide above and below by.)*

$$\lim_{n\to\infty} \frac{3n-1}{2n+3} = \lim_{n\to\infty} \frac{3-\frac{1}{n}}{2+\frac{3}{n}}$$

$$= \frac{\lim\limits_{n\to\infty} 3 - \lim\limits_{n\to\infty} \frac{1}{n}}{\lim\limits_{n\to\infty} 2 + \lim\limits_{n\to\infty} \frac{3}{n}} \quad \text{... by the Limit Rules}$$

$$= \frac{3-0}{2+0} \quad \text{... by Special Limit 1}$$

$$= \frac{3}{2}$$

(ii) *(The dominant term is n^3.)*

$$\lim_{n\to\infty} \frac{n^3+3n^2-1}{2n^2+3} = \lim_{n\to\infty} \frac{1+\frac{3}{n}-\frac{1}{n^3}}{\frac{2}{n}+\frac{3}{n^3}}$$

$$= \frac{1+0-0}{0+0}$$

$$= \frac{1}{0}$$

$$= \pm\infty \quad \text{(or strictly does not exist)}$$

(iii) *(The dominant term is 3^n.)*

$$\lim_{n\to\infty} \frac{5(3^n)+4(2^n)}{2(3^n)+1} = \lim_{n\to\infty} \frac{5+4\frac{2^n}{3^n}}{2+\frac{1}{3^n}}$$

$$= \lim_{n\to\infty} \frac{5+4\left(\frac{2}{3}\right)^n}{2+\left(\frac{1}{3}\right)^n}$$

$$= \frac{5+4(0)}{2+(0)} = \frac{5}{2}.$$

With practice, we can often write down the limits of sequences by inspection. For example,

(i) $\lim\limits_{n\to\infty} \dfrac{3n^2-1}{5n^2+n+4} = \dfrac{3}{5}$ (coefficients of equal highest powers above and below)

(ii) $\lim\limits_{n\to\infty} \dfrac{4^n+2(3^n)}{3(4^n)+2^n} = \dfrac{1}{3}$ (coefficients of equal dominant 4^n terms above and below)

The following limit makes use of the fact that $\lim_{x\to\infty}\sqrt{u_n} = \sqrt{\lim_{n\to\infty} u_n}$, i.e. we can remove the square root outside the limit, as long as we are dealing with a single square root term.

Example 3

Evaluate $\lim_{n\to\infty}\dfrac{n+2}{\sqrt{2n^2+1}}$.

Solution

(We start by writing the sequence as a single square root.)

$$\begin{aligned}\lim_{n\to\infty}\frac{n+2}{\sqrt{2n^2+1}} &= \lim_{n\to\infty}\frac{\sqrt{(n+2)^2}}{\sqrt{2n^2+1}}\\ &= \lim_{n\to\infty}\sqrt{\frac{n^2+4n+4}{2n^2+1}}\\ &= \sqrt{\lim_{n\to\infty}\frac{n^2+4n+4}{2n^2+1}}\\ &= \sqrt{\lim_{n\to\infty}\frac{1+\frac{4}{n}+\frac{4}{n^2}}{2+\frac{1}{n^2}}}\\ &= \sqrt{\frac{1}{2}} = \frac{1}{\sqrt{2}}.\end{aligned}$$

Exercises 29.2

Find the following limits by inspection, and verify your result by using the Special Limits and the Limit Rules.

1. $\lim_{n\to\infty}\dfrac{n+2}{3n+1}$
2. $\lim_{n\to\infty}\dfrac{5n-4}{2n+3}$
3. $\lim_{n\to\infty}\dfrac{7n-1}{2n+6}$
4. $\lim_{n\to\infty}\dfrac{4-3n}{1+5n}$
5. $\lim_{n\to\infty}\dfrac{n^2-2n+5}{2n^2-n+3}$
6. $\lim_{n\to\infty}\dfrac{2n^2+3n-1}{5n^2+3}$
7. $\lim_{n\to\infty}\dfrac{n^2-4n+2}{3n^2+5n+6}$
8. $\lim_{n\to\infty}\dfrac{4n^2-5n+3}{2n^2+8n-3}$
9. $\lim_{n\to\infty}\dfrac{4n+3}{n^2+1}$
10. $\lim_{n\to\infty}\dfrac{2n+1}{5n^2+n+8}$
11. $\lim_{n\to\infty}\dfrac{n^2+3}{2n+1}$
12. $\lim_{n\to\infty}\dfrac{4n^2+3}{3n+5}$
13. $\lim_{n\to\infty}\dfrac{2n^4-5n^2+3}{(2n^2-1)(n^2+3)}$
14. $\lim_{n\to\infty}\left(\dfrac{n}{n+1}-\dfrac{n+1}{n}\right)$
15. $\lim_{n\to\infty}\dfrac{5^n+2^n}{5^n}$
16. $\lim_{n\to\infty}\dfrac{3(2^n)-1}{5(2^n)+3}$
17. $\lim_{n\to\infty}\dfrac{5^n+4^n}{3(5^n)+1}$
18. $\lim_{n\to\infty}\dfrac{4(3^n)+3(2^n)}{2(3^n)+5(2^n)}$
19. $\lim_{n\to\infty}\dfrac{\sqrt{3n-1}}{\sqrt{2n+3}}$
20. $\lim_{n\to\infty}\dfrac{\sqrt{n^2-1}}{\sqrt{3n^2+5}}$
21. $\lim_{n\to\infty}\dfrac{n}{\sqrt{2n^2+3}}$
22. $\lim_{n\to\infty}\dfrac{n+2}{\sqrt{3n^2+4}}$

29.3 Arithmetic Sequences and Series

An **arithmetic sequence** is a sequence such as

3, 7, 11, 15, ...

in which each term after the first is constructed by adding the same fixed constant to the previous term.

In general, the sequence $T_1, T_2, T_3, \ldots, T_{n-1}, T_n, \ldots$ is arithmetic if

$T_n = T_{n-1} + \text{constant}$

which can be re-arranged to give the following definition.

> **Definition of an Arithmetic Sequence**
>
> The sequence $T_1, T_2, T_3, \ldots$ is arithmetic if
>
> $T_n - T_{n-1} = \text{constant}.$

It is handy to note that the formula for an arithmetic sequence will be of the form

$T_n = cn + k,$ where c and k are constants.

To prove that a sequence is arithmetic, we must use the definition. But to show that a sequence is not arithmetic it is usually enough to list the first few terms and show that the idea of adding a fixed constant is not maintained.

Sequence notation can be used to obtain T_{n-1}. For example, if

$T_n = 7n - 4$

then $T_{n-1} = 7(n-1) - 4 = 7n - 11.$

Example 1

Investigate which of the following sequences are arithmetic:

(i) $T_n = 4n - 3,$ **(ii)** $T_n = n^2 + 4.$

Solution

(i) *(From the formula, we suspect that this sequence is arithmetic. To prove that it is, we must use the definition.)*

$T_{n-1} = 4(n-1) - 3 = 4n - 7$

Thus $T_n - T_{n-1} = (4n - 3) - (4n - 7)$

$= 4$ (a constant)

Hence, $T_n = 4n - 3$ is an arithmetic sequence.

(ii) *(From the formula, we suspect this sequence is not arithmetic.)*

$T_1 = 5$, $T_2 = 8$ and $T_3 = 13$.

As $T_2 - T_1 = 8 - 5 = 3$ and $T_3 - T_2 = 13 - 8 = 5$ are not equal, $T_n = n^2 + 4$ is not arithmetic.

An **arithmetic series** is similar to an arithmetic sequence, except the terms are separated by '+' signs instead of commas. For example,

4, 7, 10, 13, ...

is an arithmetic sequence, and the corresponding arithmetic series is

4 + 7 + 10 + 13 + ...

We can test a series to see if it is arithmetic in the same way we tested the sequences above.

There is **standard notation** used with arithmetic sequences and series.

(i) a = **first term** = T_1
(ii) d = **common difference** = $T_2 - T_1$

For example, for the arithmetic sequence 2, 7, 12, 17, ...,
$a = 2$ and $d = 7 - 2 = 5$ (the amount we add to each term to get the next)
and for the arithmetic series $3 + 7 + 11 + 15 + \ldots$
$a = 3$ and $d = 7 - 3 = 4$.

The general or nth term, T_n, can be written in terms of a and d according to the following formula.

General Term of an Arithmetic Sequence or Series

If a is the first term of an arithmetic sequence (or series) and d is its common difference, then

$$T_n = a + (n - 1)d.$$

To see this:

$T_1 = a$
$T_2 = a + d$
$T_3 = a + 2d$

and so on. We just add the common difference, d, to each term to get the next.

a and d are key to questions on arithmetic sequences and series. Very often, we are given information that we can use to write down and solve two equations involving a and d.

Example 2

In an arithmetic sequence, the fourth term is 14, and the tenth term is four times the second term. Find T_n and the value of n if $T_n = 1001$.

Solution

[1] $T_4 = 14$: $\quad a + 3d = 14 \quad$ **...1**

[2] $T_{10} = 4T_2$: $\quad a + 9d = 4(a + d)$

$a + 9d = 4a + 4d$

$-3a + 5d = 0 \quad$ **...2**

Solving simultaneously:

1 × 3: $\quad 3a + 9d = 42$

2: $\quad -3a + 5d = 0$

$14d = 42$

$d = 3$

1: $\quad a + 9 = 14$

$a = 5$

Thus, $\quad T_n = a + (n - 1)d$

$T_n = 5 + (n - 1)3$

$T_n = 3n + 2$

Also, if $\quad T_n = 1001$

$3n + 2 = 1001$

$3n = 999$

$n = 333$

The sum of the first n terms of a sequence or series can be written S_n, i.e. for the sequence

$$T_1, T_2, T_3, \ldots$$

or the series

$$T_1 + T_2 + T_3 + \ldots$$

we have

$$S_n = T_1 + T_2 + T_3 + \ldots + T_n.$$

The definition of S_n holds for all sequences and series, not just arithmetic. S_n can be called a **finite series**, a **partial sum** or just a **series**.

For arithmetic sequences and series, there is a formula for S_n in terms of a, d and n.

Sum of the first *n* Terms of an Arithmetic Sequence or Series

If a is the first term of an arithmetic sequence (or series) and d is its common difference, then

$$S_n = \frac{n}{2}[2a + (n-1)d].$$

To demonstrate this:

$$\begin{aligned} S_n &= [a] + [a+d] + \ldots + [a+(n-2)d] + [a+(n-1)d] \\ S_n &= [a+(n-1)d] + [a+(n-2)d] + \ldots + [a+d] + [a] \\ \hline 2S_n &= [2a+(n-1)d] + [2a+(n-1)d] + \ldots + [2a+(n-1)d] + [2a+(n-1)d] \\ 2S_n &= n[2a+(n-1)d] \\ S_n &= \frac{n}{2}[2a+(n-1)d]. \end{aligned}$$

Example 3

(i) Find a formula for S_n for the arithmetic series

$$1 + 2 + 3 + 4 + \ldots.$$

(ii) Use this formula to evaluate

$$101 + 102 + \ldots + 500.$$

Solution

(i) For this arithmetic series, $a = 1$ and $d = 2 - 1 = 1$. Then

$$\begin{aligned} S_n &= \frac{n}{2}[2(1) + (n-1)(1)] \\ &= \frac{n}{2}(2 + n - 1) \\ &= \frac{n(n+1)}{2} \end{aligned}$$

(ii)

$$\begin{aligned} 101 + 102 + \ldots + 500 &= (1 + 2 + \ldots + 500) - (1 + 2 + \ldots + 100) \\ &= S_{500} - S_{100} \\ &= \frac{(500)(501)}{2} - \frac{(100)(101)}{2} \\ &= 125250 - 5050 \\ &= 120200 \end{aligned}$$

Example 4

The sum of the first ten terms of an arithmetic series is 120 and the sum of the first twenty terms is 840. Find the sum of the first thirty terms.

Solution

(We will use the given information to write down two equations in a and d.)

For the given series, let a be the first term and the common difference be d.

[1] $S_{10} = 120$: $\frac{10}{2}[2a + 9d] = 120$

$2a + 9d = 24$ **... 1**

[2] $S_{20} = 840$: $\frac{20}{2}[2a + 19d] = 840$

$2a + 19d = 84$ **... 2**

Then:

1 × −1: $-2a - 9d = -24$

2: $2a + 19d = 84$

$10d = 60$

$d = 6$

1: $2a + 54 = 24$

$2a = -30$

$a = -15$

Then $S_{30} = \frac{30}{2}[2(-15) + 29(6)]$

$= 15(-30 + 174)$

$= 2160.$

An arithmetic sequence, $T_n = cn + k$, may also be called a **linear sequence**. Like a linear function, a linear sequence satisfies the condition that the 'change' between successive terms is constant. This change may be referred to as the **first difference**.

A sequence of the form $T_n = an^2 + bn + c$ is called a **quadratic sequence**. Like a quadratic function, a quadratic sequence satisfies the condition that the 'change of the changes' is constant. The 'change of the changes' can also be referred to as the **second differences**. If we are given a sequence by a list of terms, we can determine if it is quadratic by calculating the second differences. If a sequence, T_n, is quadratic, i.e. $T_n = an^2 + bn + c$, it can be shown that $a = \frac{1}{2}$ (constant second differences).

Example 5

A sequence is 4, 6, 10, 16, ... and the pattern is continued.

(i) Verify that the sequence is not arithmetic.

(ii) Show that the sequence is quadratic.

(iii) If the general term of this sequence can be written $T_n = an^2 + bn + c$, find the value of a, b and c.

Solution

(i) As $T_2 - T_1 = 6 - 4 = 2$ and $T_3 - T_2 = 10 - 6 = 4$ are not equal, the first differences are not constant. Hence the sequence is not arithmetic.

(ii) Now we calculate the second differences. This can be laid out as follows.

4		6		10		16	Terms
	2		4		6		First differences
		2		2			Second differences

As the second differences are constant, the sequence is quadratic.

(iii) Let $T_n = an^2 + bn + c$. From

$$a = \frac{1}{2}\text{(constant second differences)}$$

$$a = \frac{1}{2}(2) = 1$$

Then

$T_1 = 4$: $1 + b + c = 4$

$b + c = 3$ **... 1**

$T_2 = 6$: $1(4) + b(2) + c = 6$

$2b + c = 2$ **... 2**

Then by the method of simultaneous equations:

1 × –1: $-b - c = -3$

2: $2b + c = 6$

$b = -1$

and

1: $1 + c = -3$

$c = 4$

Thus, $T_n = n^2 - n + 4$.

In the same way, a sequence of the form $T_n = an^3 + bn^2 + cn + d$ is called a **cubic sequence**. We can identify a sequence as being cubic by checking if the 'change of the change of the changes', i.e. the third difference, is constant, like with a cubic function.

Exercises 29.3

Investigate if each of the following sequences is arithmetic.

1. $T_n = 2n$ **2.** $T_n = 1 - 3n$ **3.** $T_n = 5n - 3$ **4.** $T_n = 1 - n^2$

5. For the arithmetic sequence 4, 9, 14, ...
(i) write down T_n,
(ii) find the value of n if $T_n = 599$.

6. Find T_n and T_{20} for the arithmetic sequence 4, 7, 10, ...

7. Find T_n and T_{41} for the arithmetic sequence –3, 5, 13, ...

8. Find which term of the arithmetic sequence –2, 5, 12, ... is 96.

9. Find which term of the arithmetic sequence 23, 15, 7, ... is –217.

10. The seventh term of an arithmetic sequence is 15 and the eleventh term is 35. Find the first term, the common difference and the thirtieth term.

11. The fourth term of an arithmetic sequence is 13 and the tenth term is 31. Find the first term and the common difference. Find the 23rd term of the sequence.

12. If $T_6 = 208$ and $T_{11} = 183$ for an arithmetic sequence, find T_n and T_{40}.

13. The sum of the first three terms of an arithmetic sequence is 15, and the sum of the fourth and seventh terms is 31. Find the twentieth term.

14. If the first three terms of an arithmetic sequence are $k + 3$, $2k + 6$ and 8, find the value of $k \in \mathbb{R}$. *(Hint: Use the fact that $T_2 - T_1 = T_3 - T_2$.)*

15. Find a formula for S_n for the arithmetic series $2 + 8 + 14 + \ldots$, and hence find S_{100}.

16. Find a formula for S_n for the arithmetic series $12 + 9 + 6 + \ldots$, and hence find S_{50}.

17. Find the sum of all the odd natural numbers less than 1000 which are multiples of 3.

18. Find the sum of all the odd natural numbers less than 500 which are multiples of 5.

19. In an arithmetic sequence, $T_2 : T_4 = 11 : 13$ and $S_5 = 30$. Find S_{30}.

20. The first term of an arithmetic sequence is 25 and the third term is 19. Find the value of n if $S_n = 82$.

21. How many terms of the series $3a + 5a + 7a + 9a + \ldots\ldots$ must be taken for the sum to equal $624a$?

22. The tenth term of an arithmetic sequence is 10 and the sum of the first 10 terms is –35. Find the first term and the common difference of the sequence.

23. The sum of the first four terms of an arithmetic sequence is twice the fifth term. Show that the common difference of the sequence is the first term.

24. The sum of the first twenty terms of an arithmetic series is 45, and the sum of the first forty terms is 290. Find the first term and the common difference.

25. In an arithmetic series, the sum of the first eight terms is 164 and the sum of the next six terms is 333. Find the first term and the common difference.

26. In an arithmetic series, the sum of the first $2n$ terms is equal to the sum of the next n terms. If the first term is 12 and the common difference is 3, find the non-zero value of n.

27. The sum of the first n terms of an arithmetic series is $2n$, and the sum of the first $2n$ terms is $3n$. Find, in terms of n, the sum of the first $3n$ terms of the series.

28. The first four terms of a sequence are 8, 13, 20, 29, and the pattern is continued.
    (i) Verify that the sequence is not arithmetic.
    (ii) Show that the sequence is quadratic.
    (iii) If $T_n = an^2 + bn + c$, use the first three terms to find the value of a, b and c.
    (iv) Show that the value of a is half the second difference.

29. The first four terms of a sequence are 7, 6, 7, 10, and the pattern is continued.
    (i) Show that the sequence is quadratic.
    (ii) Write down the next three terms of the sequence.
    (iii) If $T_n = an^2 + bn + c$, find the values of a, b and c.

30. The first four terms of a sequence are –2, 5, 16, 31, and the pattern is continued.
    (i) Show that the sequence is quadratic.
    (ii) Write down the next three terms of the sequence.
    (iii) If $T_n = an^2 + bn + c$, find the values of a, b and c.

29.4 Geometric Sequences and Series

A **geometric sequence** is a sequence such as

3, 12, 48, ...

in which each term after the first is constructed by multiplying the previous term by the same fixed constant.

In general, the sequence T_1, T_2, T_3, ... is geometric if

$T_n = T_{n-1} \times$ constant,

which can be rearranged to give the following definition.

Definition of a Geometric Sequence

The sequence T_1, T_2, T_3, ... is geometric if

$$\frac{T_n}{T_{n-1}} = \text{constant.}$$

The appearance of the rule for a geometric sequence is of the form

$T_n = c.k^n$,   where c and k are constants,

or any rule that can be rearranged into this form.

For example, $T_n = 5.2^n$, $T_n = 3^{2n+1}$ are geometric, but $T_n = 4n^2 + 2$ is not. To prove that a sequence is geometric, we must use the definition. On the other hand, to show that a sequence is not geometric, it is usually enough to write out the first few terms and show that the ratio of consecutive terms is not constant.

A geometric sequence may also be referred to as an **exponential sequence**, because of the presence of n in the index. Like an exponential function, a sequence is exponential if the ratio of successive terms is constant.

Once again, a geometric series is similar to a geometric sequence, except that the terms are separated by '+' signs rather than by commas. For example, one geometric sequence is

2, 6, 18, 54, 162, ...

and the corresponding geometric series is

2 + 6 + 18 + 54 + 162 + ...

Like with arithmetic sequences and series, there is a **standard notation** used with geometric sequences and series.

(i) a **= first term** $= T_1$

(ii) r **= common ratio** $= \dfrac{T_2}{T_1}$

For example, for the geometric sequence 3, 6, 12, 24, ...,

$a = 3$ and $r = \dfrac{6}{3} = 2$ (the amount we multiply each term by to get the next)

and for the geometric series 4 + 12 + 36 + 108 + ...

$a = 4$ and $r = \dfrac{12}{4} = 3$.

Example 1

Show that the sequence given by the formula $T_n = 3(2^{n-2})$ is geometric.
For this sequence, find the first term and the common ratio.

Solution

$T_n = 3(2^{n-2})$ and $T_{n-1} = 3(2^{n-3})$.

Thus

$$\frac{T_n}{T_{n-1}} = \frac{3(2^{n-2})}{3(2^{n-3})}$$
$$= 2^{(n-2)-(n-3)} = 2^1 = 2 \qquad \text{(a constant)}$$

Thus, $T_n = 3(2^{n-2})$ is a geometric sequence.

Also,

$$a = T_1 = 3(2^{1-2}) = 3(2^{-1}) = \frac{3}{2}$$

and $r = \dfrac{T_2}{T_1} = \dfrac{3}{\frac{3}{2}} = 3 \times \dfrac{2}{3} = 2.$

The general or nth term, T_n, can be written in terms of a and r according to the following formula.

General Term of a Geometric Sequence or Series

If a is the first term of a geometric sequence (or series) and r is its common ratio, then

$$T_n = ar^{n-1}.$$

To see this:

$T_1 = a, \qquad T_2 = ar, \qquad T_3 = ar^2$

and so on. We just multiply each term by r, the common ratio, to get the next term.

a and r are key to questions on geometric sequences and series. Very often, we are given information that we can use to write down and solve two equations involving a and r.

Example 2

Find the value of the seventh term of a geometric sequence that has 6 as its third term and 1458 as its eighth term.

Solution

We are given that

[1] $T_3 = 6: \quad ar^2 = 6 \qquad$ **... 1**

[2] $T_8 = 1458: \quad ar^7 = 1458 \qquad$ **... 2**

Dividing **2** by **1**,

$$\frac{ar^7}{ar^2} = \frac{1458}{6}$$

$$r^5 = 243$$

$$r = 3$$

1: $a(9) = 6$

$$a = \frac{6}{9} = \frac{2}{3}$$

Thus $\quad T_7 = ar^6 = \frac{2}{3}(3)^6 = 486.$

For a geometric sequence or series, there is a formula for

$$S_n = T_1 + T_2 + T_3 + \ldots + T_n$$

in terms of a, r and n.

Sum of the first *n* terms of a Geometric Sequence or Series

If a is the first term of a geometric sequence (or series) and r is its common ratio, then

$$S_n = \frac{a(1-r^n)}{1-r}, \qquad r \neq 1.$$

To demonstrate this:

$$\begin{aligned} S_n &= a + ar + ar^2 + ar^3 + \ldots\ldots + ar^{n-2} + ar^{n-1} \\ rS_n &= \quad ar + ar^2 + ar^3 + \ldots\ldots\ldots\ldots\ldots + ar^{n-1} + ar^n \quad (-) \\ \hline S_n - rS_n &= a \qquad\qquad\qquad\qquad\qquad\qquad - ar^n \\ (1-r)S_n &= a(1-r^n) \end{aligned}$$

Thus,

$$S_n = \frac{a(1-r^n)}{1-r}.$$

Example 3

(i) Find a formula for S_n for the geometric series $3 + \frac{3}{2} + \ldots$

(ii) Find the value of n if $S_n = \frac{381}{64}$.

Solution

(i) For the series, $a = 3$ and $r = \frac{1}{2}$. Then

$$S_n = \frac{a(1-r^n)}{1-r}$$

$$= \frac{3\left(1-\left(\frac{1}{2}\right)^n\right)}{1-\frac{1}{2}} = \frac{3\left(1-\frac{1}{2^n}\right)}{\frac{1}{2}} \times \frac{2}{2}$$

$$S_n = 6\left(1-\frac{1}{2^n}\right)$$

(ii) $S_n = \frac{381}{64}$

$$6\left(1 - \frac{1}{2^n}\right) = \frac{381}{64}$$

$$1 - \frac{1}{2^n} = \frac{127}{128}$$

$$1 - \frac{127}{128} = \frac{1}{2^n}$$

$$\frac{1}{128} = \frac{1}{2^n}$$

$$2^n = 128$$

$$n = \log_2 128 = 7.$$

Consider the geometric series

$$\frac{1}{2} + \frac{1}{4} + \frac{1}{8} + \ldots$$

which continues forever for an infinite number of terms. It is sometimes possible to sum all the terms of an **infinite geometric series** like this and get a finite sum or total.

For this series,

$$S_1 = \frac{1}{2}$$

$$S_2 = \frac{1}{2} + \frac{1}{4} = \frac{3}{4}$$

$$S_3 = \frac{1}{2} + \frac{1}{4} + \frac{1}{8} = \frac{7}{8}$$

and so on. For example, $S_7 = \frac{127}{128}$ and $S_{20} = \frac{1048575}{1048576}$. From this, we should be able to see that as $n \to \infty$, $S_n \to 1$. This allows us to say that the sum to infinity of this series, written S_∞, is 1.

If we consider $S_1, S_2, S_3, \ldots, S_n, \ldots$ to be a **sequence of partial sums**, then S_∞ is the limit of this sequence, i.e.

$$S_\infty = \lim_{n \to \infty} S_n.$$

If we have a formula for S_n, we can use the techniques for limits to evaluate S_∞, when this limit exists.

Consider the infinite geometric series

$$a + ar + ar^2 + ar^3 + \ldots.$$

For this series we have

$$S_n = \frac{a(1 - r^n)}{1 - r}, \qquad r \neq 1$$

and so

$$S_\infty = \lim_{n \to \infty} S_n = \lim_{n \to \infty} \frac{a(1 - r^n)}{1 - r} = \frac{a\left(1 - \lim_{n \to \infty} r^n\right)}{1 - r}$$

We will only be able to find S_∞ if $\lim_{n \to \infty} r^n$ exists. From Special Limit 2, $\lim_{n \to \infty} r^n = 0$ if $-1 < r < 1$, and this limit does not exist for other values of r.

Thus, we are only able to find the (finite) sum of an infinite geometric series

$$a + ar + ar^2 + ar^3 + \ldots$$

if $-1 < r < 1$. In this case:

$$S_\infty = \frac{a(1-0)}{1-r}$$

$$S_\infty = \frac{a}{1-r}.$$

An infinite series which has a finite sum is called **convergent**, and so an infinite geometric series is convergent if $-1 < r < 1$ or equivalently $|r| < 1$.

Sum to Infinity of a Geometric Series

If a is the first term of a geometric series and r is its common ratio, then the sum to infinity of the series is given by

$$S_\infty = \frac{a}{1-r}, \qquad \text{if } -1 < r < 1.$$

Example 4

The sum of the first two terms of a geometric sequence is 9 and the sum to infinity of the sequence is 25. If the sequence has a positive common ratio r, find the value of r and the third term of the sequence.

Solution

Let the first term of the sequence be a.

[1] $T_1 + T_2 = 9$

$$a + ar = 9$$

$$a(1 + r) = 9 \qquad \textbf{... 1}$$

[2] $\lim\limits_{n\to\infty} S_n = 25$

$$\frac{a}{1-r} = 25$$

$$a = 25(1 - r) \qquad \textbf{... 2}$$

Then, putting **2** into **1**,

$$25(1 - r)(1 + r) = 9$$

$$1 - r^2 = \frac{9}{25}$$

$$r^2 = 1 - \frac{9}{25} = \frac{16}{25}$$

$$r = \frac{4}{5} \qquad \textit{(because we are told that } r > 0\textit{)}$$

1: $a\left(1 + \frac{4}{5}\right) = 9$

$$\frac{9}{5}a = 9$$

$$a = 5$$

Then $T_3 = ar^2 = 5\left(\frac{4}{5}\right)^2 = 5 \times \frac{16}{25} = \frac{16}{5}.$

Exercises 29.4

1. Show that the sequence $u_n = 2(3^{n+2})$ is geometric.

2. Show that the sequence $u_n = 4^{n+2}$ is geometric.

3. Show that the sequence $T_n = 3n^2$ is not geometric.

4. For the geometric sequence 3, 6, 12, ..., find T_n and T_6.

5. For the geometric sequence $1, 3x, 9x^2, ...$, find T_n and T_7.

6. The first two terms of a geometric sequence are 4 and 12. Find the fifth term of the sequence.

7. The first term of a geometric sequence is $\frac{3}{5}$ and the fourth term is $\frac{75}{8}$.
Find the fifth term of the sequence.

8. The second term of a geometric sequence is $\frac{8}{9}$ and its sixth term is $\frac{9}{2}$.
Find the two possible values of the common ratio.

9. In a geometric sequence, $T_3 = 32$, $T_5 = 8$. Find the two possible values for T_4.

Find S_n and S_{10} for each of the following geometric series.

10. $1 + 3a + 9a^2 + ...$

11. $\frac{1}{2} + \frac{1}{4} + \frac{1}{8} + ...$

12. Find S_n, the sum of n terms, of the geometric series

$$2 + \frac{2}{3} + \frac{2}{3^2} + ... + \frac{2}{3^{n-1}}.$$

If $S_n = \frac{242}{81}$, find the value of n.

13. Find S_n, the sum of the first n terms, of the geometric series

$$\frac{1}{12} + \frac{1}{4} + \frac{3}{4} + ...$$

Find the least value of n for which $S_n > 100$.

14. The first term of a geometric sequence is $\frac{3}{5}$ and the fourth term is $\frac{75}{8}$.
Find the 6th term and the sum to 6 terms.

15. The sum of the first seven terms of a geometric series is 7 and the sum of the next seven terms is 896. Find the common ratio.

16. The sum of the first six terms of a geometric series is nine times the sum of the first three terms. Find the common ratio.

17. The nth term of a geometric series is 3^{n-3}. Find the sum of the first eight terms.

18. Find the value of the following infinite geometric series:

(i) $2 + \frac{2}{3} + \frac{2}{9} + ...$

(ii) $x + \frac{x}{1+x} + \frac{x}{(1+x)^2} + ...$

19. Find the sum of the infinite geometric series

$$1 + \frac{3}{2x+1} + \left(\frac{3}{2x+1}\right)^2 + ... + \left(\frac{3}{2x+1}\right)^{n-1} + ...\text{ where } x > 1.$$

20. Find the value of $1 + \sin\theta + \sin^2\theta + \sin^3\theta + ...$, where $\theta = 45°$.

21. Determine the values of $x \in \mathbb{R}$ for which the infinite geometric series

$$x + 2x(1 - x) + 4x(1 - x)^2 + ...$$

has a finite sum. For these values of x, express the sum to infinity in terms of x.

22. For what values of $x \in \mathbb{R}$ does the sum of the infinite geometric series

$$\frac{1}{x} + \frac{1 + 2x}{x} + \frac{(1 + 2x)^2}{x} + ...$$

exist? For these values of x, find the sum of the series in terms of x.

23. A geometric series with common ratio 0·8 has a sum to infinity of 250. Find the fourth term of the series.

24. If the sum to infinity of the geometric series $1 + \left(\frac{2x}{x+1}\right) + \left(\frac{2x}{x+1}\right)^2 + ...$ is 3, find the value of x.

29.5 Applications of Geometric Series

There are many practical applications of geometric series, both finite and infinite. Some we will meet in a later chapter, e.g. mortgage repayments and series of investments. We will look at a few applications here.

One such application is recurring decimals.

A **recurring decimal**, e.g. $3{\cdot}\dot{5}\dot{2} = 3{\cdot}52525252.......$ can be written in the form $\frac{p}{q}$, where $p, q \in \mathbb{N}$ by writing the recurring decimal as an infinite geometric series. For example

$$3{\cdot}52525252.... = 3 + 0{\cdot}52 + 0{\cdot}0052 + 0{\cdot}000052 + ...$$

$$= 3 + \left[\frac{52}{10^2} + \frac{52}{10^4} + \frac{52}{10^6} + ...\right]$$

The square brackets contain an infinite geometric series, with $a = \frac{52}{10^2} = \frac{52}{100}$ and $r = \frac{1}{10^2} = \frac{1}{100}$. Thus

$$3{\cdot}52525252... = 3 + \frac{\frac{52}{100}}{1 - \frac{1}{100}}$$

$$= 3 + \frac{52}{100 - 1} = 3 + \frac{52}{99} = \frac{349}{99}$$

Example 1

By forming an infinite geometric series, write $2{\cdot}1\dot{3}$ in the form $\frac{p}{q}$, $p, q \in \mathbb{N}$.

Solution

$$2{\cdot}1\dot{3} = 2{\cdot}133333.......$$

$$= 2 + \frac{1}{10} + \left[\frac{3}{100} + \frac{3}{1000} + \frac{3}{10000} + ...\right]$$

$$= \frac{21}{10} + \frac{\frac{3}{100}}{1 - \frac{1}{10}} = \frac{21}{10} + \frac{3}{100 - 10}$$

$$= \frac{21}{10} + \frac{3}{90} = \frac{21}{10} + \frac{1}{30} = \frac{63 + 1}{30} = \frac{64}{30} = \frac{32}{15}$$

Example 2

Each hour 2·5% of the mass of radioactive substance present at the beginning of that hour decays. In a laboratory, an experiment starts with P grams of the substance.

(i) Find an expression for the mass that has decayed by the end of the second hour.

(ii) Using geometric series, find an expression for the mass that has decayed in the first n hours.

(iii) Find the value of n for which three quarters of the original mass has decayed.

Solution

(i) Let S_n be the total amount decayed after n hours.

In the first hour: $2{\cdot}5\%$ of $P = \frac{1}{40}P$ decayed

Thus, $S_1 = \frac{1}{40}P$.

Also, $P - \frac{1}{40}P = \frac{39}{40}P$ not decayed

In the second hour: $\frac{1}{40}$ of $\frac{39}{40}P = \frac{1}{40}\left(\frac{39}{40}P\right) = \left(\frac{1}{40}P\right)\left(\frac{39}{40}\right)$ decayed

Thus, $S_2 = \left(\frac{1}{40}P\right) + \left(\frac{1}{40}P\right)\left(\frac{39}{40}\right)$

(ii) In general,

$$S_n = \left(\frac{1}{40}P\right) + \left(\frac{1}{40}P\right)\left(\frac{39}{40}\right) + \left(\frac{1}{40}P\right)\left(\frac{39}{40}\right)^2 + \dots + \left(\frac{1}{40}P\right)\left(\frac{39}{40}\right)^{n-1}$$

This is a geometric series with $a = \frac{1}{40}P$ and $r = \frac{39}{40}$. Thus,

$$S_n = \frac{\frac{1}{40}P\left(1 - \left(\frac{39}{40}\right)^n\right)}{1 - \frac{39}{40}}$$

$$S_n = \frac{P\left(1 - \left(\frac{39}{40}\right)^n\right)}{40 - 39} = P\left(1 - \left(\frac{39}{40}\right)^n\right)$$

(iii) $P\left(1 - \left(\frac{39}{40}\right)^n\right) = \frac{3}{4}P$

$1 - (0{\cdot}975)^n = 0{\cdot}75$

$0{\cdot}25 = (0{\cdot}975)^n$

$n = \log_{0{\cdot}975} 0{\cdot}25$

$n = 54{\cdot}76$

Exercises 29.5

1. By forming an infinite geometric series, write $4{\cdot}2\dot{3} = 4{\cdot}2333333......$ in the form $\frac{p}{q}$, where $p, q \in \mathbb{N}$.
2. By forming an infinite geometric series, write $1{\cdot}\dot{6} = 1{\cdot}66666...$ in the form $\frac{p}{q}$, where $p, q \in \mathbb{N}$.
3. By forming an infinite geometric series, write $4{\cdot}\dot{7} = 4{\cdot}7777...$ in the form $\frac{p}{q}$, where $p, q \in \mathbb{N}$.
4. By forming an infinite geometric series, write $2{\cdot}\dot{5}\dot{1} = 2{\cdot}515151......$ in the form $\frac{p}{q}$, where $p, q \in \mathbb{N}$.

5. By forming an infinite geometric series, write $1{\cdot}\dot{2}\dot{7} = 1{\cdot}272727......$ in the form $\frac{p}{q}$, where $p, q \in \mathbb{N}$.

6. Each year 5% of the mass of a radioactive substance present at the beginning of the year decays. In a laboratory, an experiment begins with P grams of the substance.
   (i) Find an expression for the mass that has decayed by the end of the second year.
   (ii) Using geometric series, find an expression for the total mass that has decayed in the first n years.
   (iii) Find the least value of $n \in \mathbb{N}$ for which 80% of the original mass has decayed.

7. A ball is dropped from a height of 4 metres. It strikes the ground and rebounds to 60% of the height from which it was dropped. It then falls again and each time it strikes the ground, it rebounds to 60% of its previous height.

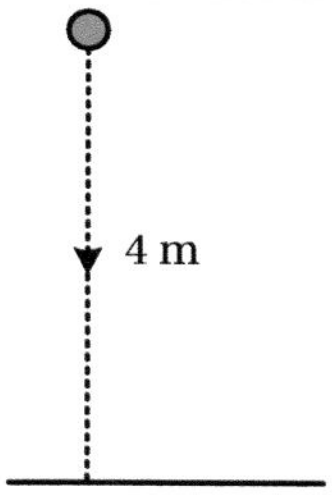

   (i) Find the height to which the ball rises after the first bounce.
   (ii) Use geometric series to find the total distance travelled by the time the ball bounces for the sixth time.
   (iii) Find the total distance travelled by the ball in coming to rest.
   (iv) Does it take for ever for the ball to rest? Explain your answer.

8. A ball is projected vertically upwards from ground level and rises to a height of 10 metres. It falls from this height, strikes the ground and rebounds to 75% of its maximum height. It repeats the process, each time bouncing to 75% of its previous height.
   (i) Find the total distance travelled by the ball by the time it bounces for the tenth time, using geometric series.
   (ii) Using geometric series, find the total distance travelled by the ball in coming to rest.

9. Sean and his dog Pythagoras start out to walk home, a distance of 2 km. Pythagoras runs twice as fast as Sean walks. Pythagoras runs directly to the house, turns around immediately and runs back to Sean. When he reaches Sean, he immediately turns around and runs back to the house, and so on.
   (i) Find how far from the house they are when Pythagoras gets back to Sean for the first time.
   (ii) Using geometric series, find the total distance travelled by Pythagoras before he meets Sean for the fourth time.
   (iii) Using geometric series, find the total distance travelled by Pythagoras before Sean reaches the house.

Revision Exercises 29

1. The diagram below shows a pattern of shapes.

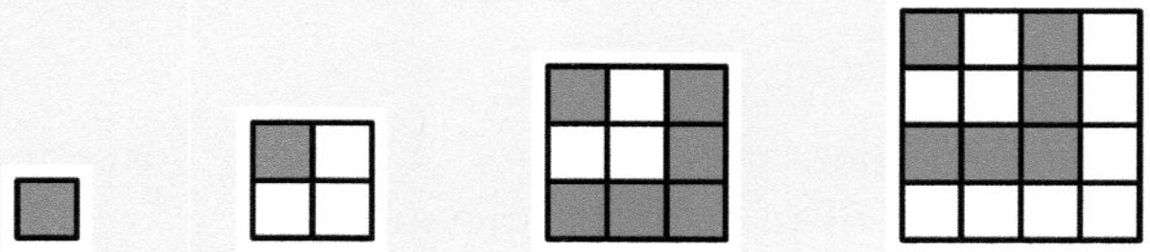

   (i) Copy the diagram and indicate the next two shapes in the pattern. Describe by a rule how to generate the next term.
   (ii) The shapes represent the first few terms of the sequence $u_n = 1 + 3 + 5 + ... + (2n - 1)$, starting with $u_1 = 1$, $u_2 = 1 + 3$. Use the shapes to deduce a formula for $1 + 3 + 5 + ... + (2n - 1)$ in terms of n.
   (iii) Use your formula to find the sum of the first 200 odd natural numbers.

2. Find, by inspection, the limit of the sequence $u_n = \frac{n+1}{2n}$. Use the Special Limits and the Limit Rules to verify your answer.

3. Find, by inspection, the limit of the sequence $u_n = \frac{2n^2 - 3n}{n^2 + 5n + 1}$. Use the Special Limits and the Limit Rules to verify your answer.

4. **(i)** Find a formula for S_n for the arithmetic series $1 + 2 + 3 + 4 + \dots$

(ii) If $u_n = \frac{1}{n}\sqrt{1 + 2 + 3 + \dots + n}$, find, using the Special Limits and Limit Rules, $\lim_{n\to\infty} u_n$.

5. If $S_n = u_1 + u_2 + \dots + u_n$, write down an expression for S_{n-1} in terms of n. Show that
$u_n = S_n - S_{n-1}$.

6. A sequence is given by the recursion formula
$$u_{n+1} = 2u_n$$
and the initial term $u_1 = 6$.
(i) List the next three terms of the sequence.
(ii) What type of sequence is this? Give a reason.
(iii) Write down a formula for u_n in terms of n.
(iv) Find S_{10}, i.e. the sum of the first ten terms of this sequence.

7. A sequence is given by the recursion formula
$$u_{n+1} = \frac{2}{3}u_n$$
and the initial term $u_1 = 2$.
(i) List the next three terms of this sequence.
(ii) What type of sequence is this? Give a reason.
(iii) Write down a formula for u_n in terms of n.
(iv) Express S_n, the sum of the first n terms, in terms of n.
(v) Find the value of n if $S_n = \frac{1330}{243}$.

8. Given that $u_n = 2\left(-\frac{1}{2}\right)^n - 2$ for all $n \in \mathbb{N}$,
(i) write down u_{n+1} and u_{n+2}
(ii) show that $2u_{n+2} - u_{n+1} - u_n = 0$.

9. u_1, u_2, u_3, u_4, u_5 ..... is a sequence where $u_1 = 2$ and $u_{n+1} = (-1)^n u_n + 3$.
Evaluate u_2, u_3, u_4, u_5 and u_{10}.

10. If a is the first term of an arithmetic sequence, d the common difference and l the last term, prove that the sum is
$$\frac{1}{2}(a + l)\left(1 + \frac{l - a}{d}\right).$$
Find the sum of all multiples of 11 between 550 and 990 inclusive.

11. Show that the nth term of the sequence 5, 55, 555, 5555, ... can be written as the sum to n terms of a geometric series and has the value $\frac{5}{9}(10^n - 1)$.

12. a, b and c are three different, non-zero numbers.
a, b, c are the first three terms of an arithmetic sequence.
a, c, b are the first three terms of a geometric sequence.
Find the numerical value of the common ratio of the geometric sequence.

13. The first and third terms of an arithmetic series are a and b respectively.
The sum of the first n terms of this series is denoted by S_n. Find S_4 in terms of a and b.
Given that S_4, S_5 and S_7 are consecutive terms of a geometric series, show that $7a^2 = 13b^2$.

14. **(i)** A sequence is given by $u_n = 5(2)^{n-1}$. Verify that this sequence is geometric.
(ii) Find an expression for S_n for this sequence.
(iii) Another sequence, v_n, is defined by $v_n = \log_2(u_n)$. Verify that v_n is an arithmetic sequence.
(iv) Find a formula for $S_n = v_1 + v_2 + v_3 + \dots + v_n$.

15. The sum to infinity of a geometric series is $\frac{9}{2}$.
The second term of the series is -2.
Find the value of r, the common ratio of the series.

16. In a geometric series, the second term is 8 and the fifth term is 27.
Find the first term and the common ratio.

17. A finite geometric sequence has first terms a and common ratio r.
The sequence has $2m + 1$ terms, where $m \in \mathbb{N}$.
(i) Write down the last term, in terms of a, r and m.
(ii) Write down the middle term, in terms of a, r and m.
(iii) Show that the product of all of the terms of the sequence is equal to the middle term raised to the power of the number of terms.

18. Suppose Ellen deposits €1000 in Bank A. She retains the right to withdraw some or all of this money at any time.
For legal reasons, Bank A is obliged to retain a fraction of this, say one fifth, but can lend the rest.
Suppose it lends €800 of Ellen's money. The money supply is now €(1000 + 800) = €1800.
The €800 lent by Bank A can go directly or indirectly to Bank B. The same legal restriction is on Bank B.
It must retain one fifth, but can loan out the rest, €640.
The money supply is now €(1000 + 800 + 640) = €2440.
(i) Find an expression for the money supply when the money has been lent by five banks, subject to the legal requirement to retain one fifth as a reserve.
(ii) If the process were to continue forever, find the total money supply resulting from Ellen's deposit of €1000.

19. A lab technician placed a bacterial cell into a vial at 8 a.m. The cells divide in such a way that the number of cells double every four minutes. The vial is full one hour later.
Let u_1 be the number of cells present at 8 a.m., u_2 be the number of cells present at 8.04 a.m., u_3 be the number of cells present at 8.08 a.m. etc.
(i) Write down a formula for u_n.
(ii) At what time is the number of cells in the vial 4096?
(iii) At what time is the vial one half full?

20. A ball is dropped from a window which is 10 metres above horizontal ground. It strikes the ground repeatedly and each time rises to 60% of its previous height.
(i) Find the height to which it rises after the third bounce.
(ii) Find the total distance travelled by the ball before it strikes the ground for the fifth time.
(iii) Find the total distance travelled by the ball before it comes to rest.

30 Arithmetic and Money

Arithmetic, in the form of dealing with numbers, is the oldest and most basic form of mathematics. Nevertheless, it is still probably the most important, being used by almost everybody in their daily lives, ranging from buying goods to telling and counting time. People who are involved in science and business, among other occupations, find themselves using arithmetic to a much greater extent. No matter what a person's background or occupation, it is an interesting exercise to keep a record for 24 hours of the number of occasions we interact with arithmetic.

After discussing units of measurement and the different ways that numbers can be presented, e.g. percentages, ratios and proportions, we consider the idea of approximating numbers and the amount of error involved. Then we look at maths in a financial context, in the form of profit, loss, markup, margin, and the use of maths in household bills and currency conversions.

We also meet the idea of personal tax and deductions from earnings. This includes income tax, PRSI, USC and other deductions.

30.1 Units and Approximation

1. Metric System of Measurement

The **metric system of measurement** is a system of measuring based on the metre (m) for length, the kilogram (kg) for mass and the second (s) for time. For the metre and the kilogram, prefixes are used to indicate decimal multiples and submultiples. These are given on page 45 of the *Formulae and Tables*. Some common examples are:

1 kilometre (km) = 1000 metres	($1\text{ km} = 10^3\text{ m}$)
100 centimetres (cm) = 1 metre	($1\text{ m} = 10^2\text{ cm}$)
1000 millimetres (mm) = 1 metre	($1\text{ m} = 10^3\text{ mm}$)
1000 grams (g) = 1 kilogram	($1\text{ kg} = 10^3\text{ g}$)
1000 milligrams (mg) = 1 gram	($1\text{ g} = 10^3\text{ mg}$, $1\text{ kg} = 10^6\text{ mg}$)
1 tonne (t) = 1000 kilograms	($1\text{ t} = 10^3\text{ kg}$)

From the metric units of length, we can derive the metric units of area and volume.

Some of the common metric units of **area** are:

1 square metre = 10000 square centimetres
[$1\text{ m}^2 = (10^2\text{ cm})^2 = 10^4\text{ cm}^2$]
1 hectare = 10000 square metres (1 hectare = 100 ares, but ares are seldom used)
[$1\text{ ha} = 10^4\text{ m}^2$]
1 square kilometre = 1000000 square metres
[$1\text{ km}^2 = (10^3\text{ m})^2 = 10^6\text{ m}^2$]

Some of the common metric units of **volume** are:

1 cubic metre = 1000000 cubic centimetres (sometimes written cc)
[$1\text{ m}^3 = (10^2\text{ cm})^3 = 10^6\text{ cm}^3$]
1 litre = 1000 cubic centimetres
[$1\text{ l} = 10^3\text{ cm}^3$]
1 cubic metre = 1000 litres
[$1\text{ m}^3 = 1000\text{ l}$]
1 millilitre = 1 cubic centimetre
[$1\text{ ml} = 1\text{ cm}^3$]

From the basic metric units, we can form many derived units. Two of those that appear frequently are:

Speed (velocity)
Speed is distance divided by time.
1 metre per second = 1 m/s = 1 ms^{-1}
1 kilometre per hour = 1 km/h = 1 kmh^{-1}

Rate of Change
Rate of change of a quantity is that quantity divided by time. For example, the rate of flow of a liquid into a container is the volume of the liquid entering the container divided by the time taken. The units will be the units of volume divided by the units of time, e.g.
1 litre per second = 1 l/s = 1 ls^{-1}

2. Imperial System of Measurement

The **imperial system of measurement** is the system of units introduced and used by countries that belonged to the old British Empire. Although now largely replaced by the metric system, some imperial units are still in common usage. The conversion factors between metric and imperial units will be given when required. You will be familiar with many of the following imperial units.

Length:	1 foot = 12 inches	(1 inch is about 2·54 cm)
	1 yard = 3 feet	(1 yard is about 0·9144 m)
	1 furlong = 220 yards	(1 furlong is just over 200 m)
	1 mile = 8 furlongs	(1 mile is about 1·609 km)
Area:	1 square mile = 640 acres	(1 acre is about 40% of a hectare)
Volume:	1 gallon = 8 pints	(1 gallon is about 4·546 litres)
Mass:	1 pound = 16 ounces	(1 pound is about 454 grams, or 0·454 kg)
	1 stone = 14 pounds	(1 stone is about 6·35 kilograms)
	1 ton = 160 stone	(1 ton is about 1·016 tonnes)

Speed: 1 mile per hour (1 mph) is about 1·609 kmh^{-1} or 0·45 ms^{-1}.

In both systems, time is measured in seconds, minutes, hours, days, weeks, months and years.

3. Approximation

When we have to perform an exact calculation involving awkward numbers, it can be useful to start by making a rough approximation. This involves **rounding** numbers contained in the calculation, often to the nearest 10, 100, 1000 etc. To round a number in this way, place a line where the rounding is to occur. If the first digit to the right of the line is 4 or less, leave the first digit to the left of the line as it is. If the first digit to the right of the line is 5 or more, add 1 to the first digit to the left of the line. Then replace all digits to the right of the line by zeros.

For example, 2378

(i) to the nearest 10 is $237|8 = 2380$

(ii) to the nearest 100 is $23|78 = 2400$

(iii) to the nearest 1000 is $2|378 = 2000$

A similar method is used to round numbers to a number of **decimal places** or to a number of **significant figures**, although this is usually done at the end of a calculation. To round a number to

n significant figures, place the line behind the nth digit after the first non-zero digit, counted from the left. For example:

(i) 312·4328 correct to two decimal places is 312·43|28 = 312·43

(ii) 27·164 correct to one decimal place is 27·16|4 = 27·2

(iii) 518346 correct to two significant figures is 51|8346 = 520000

(iv) 0·00153892 correct to three significant figures is 0·00153|892 = 0·00154
(there is no need for any additional zeros to the right).

Example 1

A rectangular tank has a base of width 78 cm and length 124 cm. Its height is 152 cm.
Water flows into this tank at the rate of 1 pint every 2 seconds. The tank is initially empty.
(1 pint = 0·568 litres.)

(i) Make a rough estimate of what the volume of the tank should be in litres.

(ii) Calculate exactly the volume of the tank in litres, correct to two decimal places.

(iii) Calculate how long it will take to fill the tank, giving your answer in seconds correct to three significant figures.

(iv) Express the time taken in hours, minutes and seconds, correct to the nearest second.

Solution

(i) *(Round each dimension to the nearest 10.)*

Volume of tank = 80 × 120 × 150
= 1440000 cm^3
= 1440 litres (1 litre = 1000 cm^3)

(ii) Volume of tank = 78 × 124 × 152
= 1470144 cm^3
= 1470·144 litres
= 1470·14 litres, correct to two decimal places.

(iii) Rate of flow = 1 pint every 2 seconds
= (0·5 × 0·568) litres per second
= 0·284 litres per second

From $\text{Rate} = \dfrac{\text{Volume}}{\text{Time}}$

$$\text{Time} = \frac{\text{Volume}}{\text{Rate}} = \frac{1470{\cdot}14}{0{\cdot}284}$$

= 5176·55 = 5180 s, correct to three significant figures.

(iv) Time = 5177 seconds, correct to the nearest second
= 86·283333 minutes
= 86 minutes and 17 seconds (0·283333 × 60 = 17)
= 1 hour 26 minutes 17 seconds.

Exercises 30.1

1. An athlete runs around a racing circuit, which has a length of 440 yards.
   (i) If the athlete runs eight complete circuits, i.e. eight laps, how many kilometres has she travelled?
   (ii) How many laps of the circuit would be required for a 10000 metre race?
   (iii) If she covers three laps in 228 seconds, express her average speed in metres per second, and kilometres per hour. Give your answers correct to two decimal places.
   [1 yard = 0·914 m]

2. The speedometer in an antique car shows only miles per hour (mph). However, all the speed signs are in kilometres per hour (kph). [1 mile ≈ 1·609 km]
   (i) To the nearest mile per hour, find the speed limit in miles per hour that corresponds to a speed limit of 50 km/h.
   (ii) If the speedometer in the car displays 60 mph, at what speed is the car travelling in kilometres per hour? Give your answer to four significant figures.

3. In the imperial system, a vehicle's fuel consumption is measured in miles per gallon (mpg), i.e. the number of miles that the vehicle will travel on one gallon of fuel. In the metric system, fuel consumption is measured in litres per 100 km, i.e. the number of litres of fuel required to travel a distance of 100 km.
   (i) Express a fuel consumption of 30 miles per gallon in litres per 100 km.
   (ii) Express a fuel consumption of 5·3 litres per 100 km in miles per gallon.
   Give your answers correct to two decimal places.
   [1 mile = 1·609 km and 1 gallon = 4·546 litres]

4. A rectangular field measures 322 yards by 197 yards.
   (i) Make a rough estimate of what the area of the field is in square yards.
   (ii) Calculate the exact value of the area of the field in square yards.
   (iii) If 1 acre = 4840 square yards, find the number of acres in the field.
   (iv) A tractor and plough can till a field at the rate of 0·65 hectares per hour.
   Find, to the nearest minute, how long it will take the tractor and plough to till this field, given that 1 yard = 0·9144 metres and 1 hectare = 10000 m^2.

5. A storage container is in the shape of a rectangular box with internal dimensions 3 metres by 4 metres by 12 metres.
   (i) One of these containers is filled with identical packets which measure 20 cm by 25 cm by 10 cm. Find how many packets are present in the container.
   (ii) A warehouse contains 487 of these containers, each filled with the same packets. Estimate the total number of packets in the warehouse and find the exact number of packets.

6. A man cycles from A to B, a distance of 60 km, in 3 hours, and then takes 2 hours to return from B to A.
   (i) Find the total distance cycled and the total time taken.
   (ii) Determine the average speed of the cyclist over the whole journey.

7. A tank has a capacity of 2000 gallons. It is filled from empty at a rate of 1·4 litres per second.
   Find the time it takes to fill the tank. Give your answer in minutes, correct to the nearest minute.
   (1 gallon = 4·546 litres)

8. A fertiliser product is designed to be sprayed at the rate of 6 ounces for every square foot. What weight of fertiliser, in kilograms, will be required for a field of size 2 hectares? (16 ounces = 454 grams, 3 feet = 0·9144 metres, 1 hectare = 10000 m^2)

30.2 Percentages, Ratios and Proportions

'Per cent' means 'for every hundred'. For example 5% stands for $\frac{5}{100}$. Fractions, decimals and percentages can all be converted to each other. From Junior Cert, you should be familiar with the following operations.

1. To convert to a percentage:

(i) a decimal, e.g. 0·1268: multiply by 100 and add the % symbol

$0{\cdot}1268 = 0{\cdot}1268 \times 100\% = 12{\cdot}68\%$

(ii) a fraction, e.g. $\frac{4}{7}$: convert to a decimal and then to a percentage

$\frac{4}{7} = 0{\cdot}5714 = 0{\cdot}5714 \times 100\% = 57{\cdot}14\%$

2. To convert from a percentage:

(i) to a decimal, e.g. 32%: divide by 100 and remove the % symbol

$32\% = \frac{32}{100} = 0{\cdot}32$

(ii) to a fraction, e.g. 45%: divide by 100 and simplify the fraction

$45\% = \frac{45}{100} = \frac{9}{20}$

3. Finding a percentage of a number

To find 24% of €1600, we can multiply €1600 by 24% written either as a decimal or as a fraction,

$$\begin{aligned} 24\% \text{ of } €1600 &= €1600 \times 0{\cdot}24 \\ &= €384 \end{aligned}$$

4. To express one quantity as a percentage of another

One quantity can be expressed as a percentage of another, as long as both are expressed in the same units. We can start by writing the first as a fraction of the second and then convert this to a percentage. For example, to express 572 metres as a percentage of 2·2 km, we convert 2·2 km to 2200 m, and then

$$\text{percentage} = \frac{572}{2200} \times 100\% = 26\%$$

5. Given a percentage

Suppose a company has to pay 24% of the cost of a new research project and it is given a bill of €120 million as its contribution. What is the total cost of the research project?

We can proceed as follows, using what is known as unitary method ('unit' means one).

24% of total cost = €120 million
1% of total cost = €5 million (divide both sides by 24)
100% of total cost = €500 million (multiply both sides by 100)

6. Ratio, proportion and proportional parts

The **ratio** 6 : 8 is equivalent to the fraction $\frac{6}{8}$. This fraction can be simplified and rewritten as a ratio: $6 : 8 = \frac{6}{8} = \frac{3}{4} = 3 : 4$.

This gives us the basic rule for simplifying any ratio: we can multiply or divide all numbers in a ratio by the same number. This also applies to a ratio such as 15 : 10 : 25, which consists of three or more parts.

A **proportion** is an equation stating that two ratios are equal. For example

$6 : 8 = 3 : 4$

is a proportion.

In practice, proportions are used when two quantities are **proportional**, i.e. when one quantity is a constant times the other. For example, suppose we want to find the cost of five apples given that three apples cost 54 cent. The cost is proportional to the number of apples. Let x cent be the cost of five apples. Then

$$x : 5 = 54 : 3$$
$$\frac{x}{5} = \frac{54}{3}$$
$$x = \frac{270}{3}$$
$$x = 90$$

Another use of the term 'proportion' is as a fraction of a whole. For example, if a sum of money is divided between Mary and Susan in the ratio 3 : 2, then the number of portions, or parts, is 3 + 2 = 5, and the proportion that each receives is $\frac{3}{5}$ and $\frac{2}{5}$ respectively.

When a quantity is divided according to a ratio, it is said to be divided proportionately, or in **proportional parts**. We can compare proportions by converting them to fractions, decimals or percentages.

Example 1

Two groups win equal large sums of money in a lotto draw. The first group consists of Alan, Brendan and Ciara. They decide to divide their prize in the ratio 25 : 15 : 20.
The second group of Dermot, Eve and Fiona, decide to divide their prize in the ratio $\frac{7}{8} : \frac{3}{4} : \frac{1}{2}$.

(i) Write each ratio in its simplest form.

(ii) Find out which of Alan and Dermot gets the greater amount.

Solution

(i) Group 1:

$25 : 15 : 20 = 5 : 3 : 4$ ... *dividing each part by 5*

Group 2:

$\frac{7}{8} : \frac{3}{4} : \frac{1}{2} = 7 : 6 : 4$ ... *multiplying each part by 8*

(ii) *(Find out what percentage of the first group's prize Alan gets and what percentage of the second group's prize that Dermot gets.)*

Alan gets 5 parts out of 5 + 4 + 3 = 12 parts. Thus, the percentage of the first group's prize that Alan gets is

$$\frac{5}{12} \times 100\% = 41{\cdot}67\%$$

Dermot gets 7 parts out of 7 + 6 + 4 = 17 parts. Thus, the percentage of the second group's prize that Dermot gets is

$$\frac{7}{17} \times 100\% = 41{\cdot}18\%$$

Thus, Alan gets the greater amount.

7. Percentages in Financial Transactions

Percentages are used frequently in trading and financial transactions, and they are often very visible, e.g. large ads in shop windows saying '20% off' or '50% off'. When it comes to financial transactions, there are a number of terms we should be familiar with. These are highlighted in the following examples.

1. Drive Hard Computers purchased a lap-top from their suppliers for €400 and sold it for €500.

(i) The **purchase price** (**cost price**) is €400 and the **selling price** is €500.

(ii) The **profit** is given by:

$$\text{profit} = \text{selling price} - \text{cost price}$$
$$= €500 - €400$$
$$= €100$$

This is an absolute value: it is not a percentage.

(iii) The **percentage profit** is given by:

$$\%\ \text{profit} = \frac{\text{profit}}{\text{cost price}} \times 100\%$$
$$= \frac{€100}{€400} \times 100\%$$
$$= 25\%$$

This can also be referred to as the **markup** (or more accurately, the **markup percentage**).

(iv) Another way of viewing the transaction states what percentage of the selling price is profit. This is called the **margin**, or more accurately, the **margin percentage**.

$$\text{margin} = \frac{\text{profit}}{\text{selling price}} \times 100\%$$
$$= \frac{€100}{€500} \times 100\%$$
$$= 20\%$$

You should note carefully the difference between the markup and the margin. The first is a percentage of the cost price while the second is a percentage of the selling price.

2. Maria buys a car for €10000 and two years later sells it for €6000.

(i) The cost price is €10000 and the selling price is €6000.

(ii) The **loss** is given by:

$$\text{loss} = \text{cost price} - \text{selling price}$$
$$= €10000 - €6000$$
$$= €4000$$

(iii) The **percentage loss** is given by

$$\%\ \text{loss} = \frac{\text{loss}}{\text{cost price}} \times 100\%$$
$$= \frac{€4000}{€10000} \times 100\%$$
$$= 40\%$$

Example 2

A department store buys a fashion item and places it for sale with a markup of 50%. Later, in a sale, it sells the item at a 10% discount. Find the margin achieved by the store when the item is sold, to the nearest percentage.

Solution

Let X be the cost price. Then the original selling price is then

$X + 50\%$ of $X = 1{\cdot}5X$

In the sale the discount is

10% of $1{\cdot}5X = 0{\cdot}15X$

Thus, the sale price of the item is

$1{\cdot}5X - 0{\cdot}15X = 1{\cdot}35X$

The profit on the item is $0{\cdot}35X$.

The margin achieved is

$$\frac{\text{profit}}{\text{selling price}} \times 100\%$$

$$= \frac{0{\cdot}35X}{1{\cdot}35X} \times 100\%$$

$$= 26\%$$

Exercises 30.2

1. Convert each of the following to a percentage to two decimal places, if necessary.
   (i) $\frac{7}{20}$ (ii) $\frac{3}{8}$ (iii) $\frac{11}{15}$ (iv) $\frac{25}{33}$ (v) $\frac{8}{21}$
2. Convert each of the following to a percentage to two decimal places, if necessary.
   (i) 0·827 (ii) 1·34 (iii) 0·0032 (iv) 2·17 (v) 0·00023
3. Convert each of the following to a fraction in its simplest form and a decimal.
   (i) 24% (ii) 15% (iii) 37·5% (iv) 2·25% (v) 64%
4. Find 45% of 780.
5. Find 28% of 350.
6. Find 14% of €1250.
7. Find 32% of €2300.
8. Express 54 cents as a percentage of €3·60.
9. Express 432 metres as a percentage of 3·6 kilometres.
10. Express 624 grams as a percentage of 2·6 kilograms.
11. Express €117·60 as a percentage of €560.
12. €240 is divided between Stephen and Louise in the ratio 5 : 3.
    How much does each get?
13. €440 is divided between Mark and Conor in the ratio 7 : 4.
    How much does each get?
14. €720 is divided between Paul, Luke and Daniel in the ratio 3 : 2 : 7.
    How much does each get?
15. €1,200 is divided between Maeve, Tom and Greg in the ratio 5 : 8 : 7.
    How much does each get?

16. A sum of money is divided between Alf, Brona and Charlie in the ratio 3 : 7 : 4.
If Alf gets €120
(i) what is the sum of money?
(ii) how much do Brona and Charlie get?

17. A sum of money is divided between Sean, Therese and Mary in the ratio 5 : 2 : 4. If Sean gets €200
(i) what is the sum of money?
(ii) how much do Therese and Mary get?

18. When cooking a certain type of rice, the ratio of rice to water is 5 : 8.
(i) If there are 450 g of rice, how much water should there be?
(ii) How much rice will 560 g of water cook?

19. **(i)** Write $\frac{2}{3} : 3 : 1$ as a ratio of natural numbers.
(ii) Divide €420 in the ratio $\frac{2}{3} : 3 : 1$.

20. **(i)** Write $\frac{3}{4} : \frac{1}{2} : 2$ as a ratio of natural numbers.
(ii) Divide €780 in the ratio $\frac{3}{4} : \frac{1}{2} : 2$.

21. A quantity is divided in the ratio $2 : \frac{3}{4} : \frac{1}{3}$. Express the proportion 2 as a percentage of the quantity.

22. A sum of money is divided between Sean, Maeve and Cliona.
(i) If it is divided in the ratio 4 : 7 : 5, find what percentage of the sum of money each gets.
(ii) If it is instead divided in the ratio 7 : 10 : 8, does Cliona's percentage increase or decrease, and by how much?

23. Two friends Alan and Brendan win a big prize in a club lotto. The winning ticket cost €5. Alan points out that he paid €2·80 towards the cost of the winning ticket, and wants to divide the prize in proportion to the amount each paid for the ticket. Brendan replies that at the same time as buying the ticket, he bought Alan an ice-cream for 80c. He wants this to be added to the cost of the ticket, and the prize divided proportionately. In the end, they agree to divide the prize evenly.
(i) Taking Alan's suggestion, simplify the proportion in which the prize should be divided. What percentage of the prize will Alan get?
(ii) If Brendan's suggestion is adopted, what percentage of the prize will Alan now get?

24. A company buys a machine for €150,000. Five years later, it sells the machine for €35,000. What percentage loss has the company made on the machine?

25. A computer costs €1200 when new. Four years later it is sold for €450. What percentage loss is made on the computer?

26. A car dealer sells a car for €17,400, making a profit of 20%. How much had she paid for the car?

27. In a sale, an item is offered for €42. The shop advertises that this is 25% off the pre-sale price. What was the pre-sale price?

28. A shop buys 20 loaves of bread for €1·20 each. 16 of these loaves are sold for €1·60 each, but the last four have to be thrown out. What percentage profit or loss does the shop make on all the loaves of bread?

29. A fruit shopkeeper buys 40 punnets of strawberries at €3 each. He sells 90% of them at a profit of 20% each. The last 10% he sells at a loss of 15% each.
(i) What was his total cost and total income?
(ii) Calculate the percentage profit or loss that he made on all the strawberries.

30. A shop buys a TV screen for €120 and sells it for €199. Express, to the nearest percent,
(i) the markup.
(ii) the margin.

31. A car trader buys a second hand car from a main dealer for €2,100. He spends €250 making it ready for sale. He then sells it for €3,400 cash. Express, to the nearest percentage,
(i) his markup.
(ii) his margin.

32. A shopkeeper buys a box of 60 packets of biscuits from a wholesaler for €49·99. Calculate, to the nearest cent, the price she sells each packet of biscuits for if
(i) her markup is 33%.
(ii) her margin is 20%.

33. A store offers DVDs at €7 each, or two for €12. Each DVD costs the store €4·50. Calculate the percentage of the DVDs that are sold singly if the average markup is 50%.

34. An electrical store buys a sandwich maker and offers it for sale with a markup of 60%. In a sale, it later reduces the selling price by 15%. Calculate, to the nearest percentage, the margin it achieves on the sale of the sandwich maker.

35. A shoe shop buys a consignment of identical shoes and offers them for sale with a markup of 80%. Having sold some of the shoes, it then sells the remainder at one third off. If the overall markup on the consignment is 56%, determine what percentage of the shoes were sold at the original price.

30.3 Estimation, Percentage Error and Tolerance

1. Estimates, Error and Percentage Error

When performing real world calculations, it is often a good idea to estimate the result first. This is to make sure that the result we get is roughly right. For example, if we have 103 boxes, each containing 48 tins of beans. Then we can take an **estimate** of the total number of tins to be:

$$\text{Estimate} = 100 \times 50 = 5000.$$

If necessary, we can perform the calculation exactly to get the **true value** of the number of tins:

$$\text{True Value} = 103 \times 48 = 4944.$$

When an estimate is made, there is always an **error** involved. This error does not mean a mistake, because the rounding has been done deliberately, but is the difference between the true value and the estimate. The definition of the error is:

$$\begin{aligned} \text{Error} &= \text{True Value} - \text{Estimate} \\ &= 4944 - 5000 \\ &= -56 \end{aligned}$$

Very often, we are not interested in whether the error is plus or minus. So we define the **absolute error**, which is the error made positive. This is written $|\text{True value} - \text{Estimate}|$.

$$\begin{aligned} \text{Absolute Error} &= |\text{True Value} - \text{Estimate}| \\ &= |4944 - 5000| \\ &= |-56| \\ &= 56 \end{aligned}$$

The significance of the error can be found by comparing it with the true value (or the estimate if the true value is not available). This gives us the **relative error**.

$$\text{Relative Error} = \frac{\text{Absolute Error}}{\text{True Value}}$$
$$= \frac{56}{4944}$$
$$= 0{\cdot}011327$$

It is easier to relate to percentages than it is to decimals like this. So we define the **percentage error** as follows.

$$\text{Percentage Error} = \text{Relative Error} \times 100\%$$
$$= 0{\cdot}011327 \times 100\%$$
$$= 1{\cdot}1327\%$$

Example 1

Find, correct to two decimal places, the percentage error in taking

(i) 150 for 153·7.

(ii) 60 + 150 for 58·2 + 153·7.

Solution

(i) absolute error $= |153{\cdot}7 - 150|$
$= |3{\cdot}7|$
$= 3{\cdot}7$

relative error $= \dfrac{3{\cdot}7}{153{\cdot}7} = 0{\cdot}02407$

percentage error $= 0{\cdot}02407 \times 100\% = 2{\cdot}41\%$

(ii) true value $= 58{\cdot}2 + 153{\cdot}7 = 211{\cdot}9$

estimate $= 60 + 150 = 210$

absolute error $= |211{\cdot}9 - 210| = |1{\cdot}9| = 1{\cdot}9$

relative error $= \dfrac{1{\cdot}9}{211{\cdot}9} = 0{\cdot}00897$

percentage error $= 0{\cdot}00897 \times 100\% = 0{\cdot}90\%$

2. Tolerance

Suppose we have an electronic weighing scales that gives weight correct to the nearest gram, i.e. the **precision** of the scales is 1 gram. Now suppose we weigh a sample and the electronic scales displays 65 grams. Then we can say the following.

(i) The actual weight of the sample lies within 0·5 grams of the measurement. Thus, the greatest possible error in the measurement of the weight of the sample is 0·5 grams. This is referred to as the **tolerance** of the measuring instrument, in this case the weighing scales. For a measuring instrument, the **tolerance is one half of the precision of the instrument.**

(ii) The true weight of the sample lies in the interval
[64·5, 65·5]
i.e. [65 – 0·5, 65 + 0·5]
i.e. [measurment – tolerance, measurement + tolerance]
This interval is called the tolerance interval for the weight of the sample. The true weight of the sample can then be written:
65 ± 0·5 grams.

In general, we can write the true value of a quantity as
(obtained measurement) ± (tolerance).

In the context of manufacturing, the tolerance is taken to be the greatest allowable variation in a measurement. For example, suppose a machine produces washers of diameter 13·5 mm and we have a tolerance of 0·1 mm, then any washer with a diameter between 13·4 mm and 13·6 mm will be accepted, but a washer with a diameter outside this interval will be rejected.

Example 2

A machine produces ball-bearings which are supposed to have a mass of 18·5 g.

(i) What is the least possible tolerance is a ball-bearing of mass 18·47 g is not rejected? Give the tolerance interval in this case.

(ii) The machine incorporates a weighing scales which determines whether an individual ball-bearing is to be accepted or rejected. This weighing scales measures weight in grams to three decimal places, e.g. 18·536 g. What is the tolerance of the weighing scales?

Solution

(i) The difference, or error, is

$$18{\cdot}5 - 18{\cdot}47 = 0{\cdot}03 \text{ g}$$

If this ball-bearing is not rejected, then the tolerance must be at least this amount, i.e. 0·03 g.

In this case, the tolerance interval is

$$[18{\cdot}5 - 0{\cdot}03,\ 18{\cdot}5 + 0{\cdot}03]$$
$$= [18{\cdot}47,\ 18{\cdot}53].$$

(ii) The precision of the weighing scales is 0·001 g. Hence, the tolerance is a half of this, i.e.

$$\text{tolerance} = 0{\cdot}0005 \text{ g}.$$

You should note the difference between a measurement given as '18 cm to the nearest cm' and '18 cm, to within one cm'. In the first case, the true value lies in the tolerance interval [17·5, 18·5] cm, and the tolerance is 0·5 cm. In the second case, the true value lies in the tolerance interval [17, 19] cm and the tolerance is 1 cm. In the first case, we would write the true value as 18 ± 0·5 cm, while in the second we would write the true value as 18 ± 1 cm.

3. Accumulation of Error

Suppose $a = (8{\cdot}34 \pm 0{\cdot}01)$ cm and $b = (5{\cdot}14 \pm 0{\cdot}01)$ cm are two estimated lengths. We want to find the tolerance interval and the percentage error for $a + b$ and $a - b$.

[1] Addition: $a + b$

smallest possible value for $a + b = 8{\cdot}33 + 5{\cdot}13 = 13{\cdot}46$ cm

largest possible value for $a + b = 8{\cdot}35 + 5{\cdot}15 = 13{\cdot}50$ cm

Thus, $a + b$ has a tolerance interval [13·46, 13·50] cm, and we can write

$$a + b = (13{\cdot}48 \pm 0{\cdot}02) \text{ cm}.$$

This could also have been obtained by writing

$$\begin{aligned} a + b &= (8{\cdot}34 \pm 0{\cdot}01) + (5{\cdot}14 \pm 0{\cdot}01) \\ &= (8{\cdot}34 + 5{\cdot}14) \pm (0{\cdot}01 + 0{\cdot}01) \\ &= (13{\cdot}48 \pm 0{\cdot}02) \text{ cm} \end{aligned}$$

Also,

$$\text{percentage error} = \frac{0{\cdot}02}{13{\cdot}48} \times 100\% = 0{\cdot}15\%$$

[2] Subtraction: $a - b$

smallest possible value for $a - b = 8{\cdot}33 - 5{\cdot}15 = 3{\cdot}18$ cm

largest possible value for $a - b = 8{\cdot}35 - 5{\cdot}13 = 3{\cdot}22$ cm

Thus, $a - b$ has a tolerance interval [3·18, 3·22] cm, and we can write

$$a - b = (3{\cdot}20 \pm 0{\cdot}02) \text{ cm.}$$

This could also have been obtained by writing

$$\begin{aligned} a - b &= (8{\cdot}34 \pm 0{\cdot}01) - (5{\cdot}14 \pm 0{\cdot}01) \\ &= (8{\cdot}34 - 5{\cdot}14) \pm (0{\cdot}01 + 0{\cdot}01) \\ &= (3{\cdot}20 \pm 0{\cdot}02) \text{ cm.} \end{aligned}$$

Also,

$$\text{percentage error} = \frac{0{\cdot}02}{3{\cdot}20} \times 100\% = 0{\cdot}63\%$$

From our calculations, we should note that for $a > 0$, $b > 0$,

(i) for both $a + b$ and $a - b$, the accumulated absolute error is the sum of the individual absolute errors

(ii) the percentage error will be less for $a + b$ than it is for $a - b$.

In more complicated situations, we may have to use common sense to choose the largest or smallest possible values for certain quantities to maximise or minimise some other quantity. The following example shows how this works.

Example 3

The lengths of the three sides of a triangle, a, b and c were measured as follows:

$a = (5{\cdot}2 \pm 0{\cdot}1)$ cm, $b = (7{\cdot}3 \pm 0{\cdot}1)$ cm and $c = (10{\cdot}6 \pm 0{\cdot}1)$ cm.

A is the angle opposite the side a.

(i) Calculate the percentage error in the measurement of the perimeter $p = a + b + c$.

(ii) Calculate the largest possible value of A, in degrees to two decimal places.

(iii) Calculate the smallest possible value of A, in degrees to two decimal places.

Solution

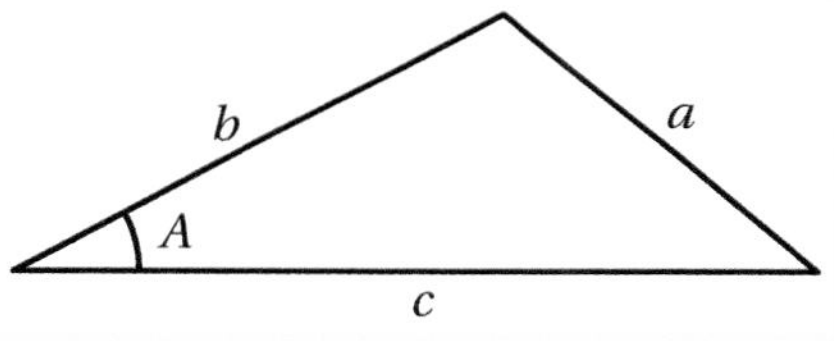

(i) [1] $p = (5{\cdot}2 \pm 0{\cdot}1) + (7{\cdot}3 \pm 0{\cdot}1) + (10{\cdot}6 \pm 0{\cdot}1)$

$= (23{\cdot}1 \pm 0{\cdot}3)$ cm

Absolute error = 0·3 cm

[2] Relative error $= \frac{0{\cdot}3}{23{\cdot}1} = 0{\cdot}012987$

[3] Percentage error $= 0{\cdot}012987 \times 100\% = 1{\cdot}3\%$.

(ii) For the largest possible value of A, we need the largest possible value of a and the smallest possible values of b and c, i.e. $a = 5{\cdot}3$, $b = 7{\cdot}2$ and $c = 10{\cdot}5$.

By the Cosine Rule:

$$a^2 = b^2 + c^2 - 2bc \cos A$$

$$5{\cdot}3^2 = 7{\cdot}2^2 + 10{\cdot}5^2 - 2(7{\cdot}2)(10{\cdot}5) \cos A$$

$$28{\cdot}09 = 162{\cdot}09 - 151{\cdot}2 \cos A$$

$$151{\cdot}2 \cos A = 134$$

$$\cos A = 0{\cdot}8862$$

$$A = 27{\cdot}60°$$

(iii) For the smallest possible value of A, we need the smallest possible value of a and the largest possible values of b and c, i.e. $a = 5{\cdot}1$, $b = 7{\cdot}4$ and $c = 10{\cdot}7$.

By the Cosine Rule,

$$a^2 = b^2 + c^2 - 2bc \cos A$$

$$5{\cdot}1^2 = 7{\cdot}4^2 + 10{\cdot}7^2 - 2(7{\cdot}4)(10{\cdot}7) \cos A$$

$$26{\cdot}01 = 169{\cdot}25 - 158{\cdot}36 \cos A$$

$$158{\cdot}36 \cos A = 143{\cdot}24$$

$$\cos A = 0{\cdot}9045$$

$$A = 25{\cdot}24°.$$

Exercises 30.3

1. The number of nails in a bag is estimated to be 1,200. When counted using a machine, the number of nails is determined to be 1,173. Calculate the relative error and the percentage error in the result.

2. The length of a rod is estimated to be 510 mm. Calculate the percentage error if the true length of the rod is
   (i) 502 mm,
   (ii) 523 mm.

3. The distance between Dublin and Lisbon is estimated to be 1,500 km. The true distance is 1,638·92 km. Calculate the percentage error in the estimate.

4. The number of spectators at an important match is estimated to be 5,500. An accurate count of the attendance gives 5,387 as the number of spectators. Calculate the percentage error in the result.

5. The current accepted height of Mount Everest is 8,850 m. Calculate, correct to one decimal place, the percentage error in giving the height of Mount Everest as 8,800 m.

6. The area of a plot of land is estimated to be 680 square metres. The exact value is 637 square metres. Calculate the percentage error in the result.

7. An old ruler is scaled in inches, with marking showing every eighth of an inch.
   (i) What is the tolerance of the ruler?
   (ii) This ruler measures a stick to have a length of ten and a half inches. What is the tolerance interval for the length of the stick?

8. A ruler is scaled with marks showing every two millimetres.
   (i) What is the tolerance of this ruler?
   (ii) This ruler measures a length to be 10·4 cm. What is the tolerance interval for the length?

9. The weight of a bag of carrots is given as 765 grams. The weighing machine only measures weight to the nearest 5 grams.
   (i) Give a tolerance interval for the true weight of the bag of carrots.
   (ii) If the true weight is 762 grams, calculate the percentage error in the weight of the bag.

10. A pilot reckons that he has fuel enough left for 800 km flight. He knows that the reading is correct to within 40 km.
    (i) Give a tolerance interval for the flight distance remaining.
    (ii) If the true distance remaining is 832 km, calculate the percentage error.

11. Susan is using her graph $y = f(x)$ to estimate $f(2·5)$. By calculation, the correct value of $f(2·5)$ is 11·75. Her teacher is willing to accept any answer that is within 0·25 of the true value.
(i) Give a tolerance interval for the accepted answers.
(ii) If Susan's answer is 11·6, calculate the percentage error.

12. A machine produces batteries which are supposed to have a voltage of 1·5 V.
(i) What is the least possible tolerance if a battery with a voltage of 1·7 V is not rejected?
(ii) The machine incorporates a voltmeter which measures the voltage of individual batteries. The voltmeter measures voltage in volts, correct to two decimal places. What is the tolerance of the voltmeter?

13. A machine cuts rods of steel which are supposed to be of length 1·25 m.
(i) What is the least possible tolerance if a rod of length 1·23 m is not rejected?
(ii) The machine has a device which measures length to the nearest millimetre. What is the tolerance of this device?

14. Calculate, correct to one decimal place, the percentage error in taking 12 + 7 as an approximation for 11·83 + 6·95.

15. Calculate, correct to one decimal place, the percentage error in taking 60 + 35 as an approximation for 58·7 + 34·8.

16. Calculate, correct to one decimal place, the percentage error in taking 45 – 20 as an approximation for 45·3 – 19·6.

17. Calculate, correct to one decimal place, the percentage error in taking 120 – 50 as an approximation for 118·7 – 51·4.

18. In trying to calculate 3·2 × 1·5, Dermot accidently presses 3·2 + 1·5. Calculate, correct to one decimal place, his percentage error.

19. If $a = (3·16 \pm 0·05)$ cm and $b = (7·32 \pm 0·5)$ cm, calculate the percentage error in
(i) $a + b$, **(ii)** $b - a$.

20. If $p = (12·7 \pm 0·15)$ km and $q = (10·5 \pm 0·1)$ km, calculate the percentage error in
(i) $p + q$, **(ii)** $p - q$.

21. $x = 7·2$ and $y = 9·3$, each correct to one decimal place. Write down a tolerance interval and find the percentage error for
(i) $x + y$, **(ii)** $y - x$.

22. $a = 29·14$, $b = 5·92$ and $c = 18·34$, each correct to two decimal places. Calculate the percentage error for
(i) $a + b + c$, **(ii)** $a - b - c$.

23. $\sqrt{2} = 1·41$ and $\sqrt{3} = 1·73$, each correct to two decimal places. Calculate the percentage error in taking these estimates to evaluate
(i) $\sqrt{3} + \sqrt{2}$, **(ii)** $\sqrt{3} - \sqrt{2}$.

24. Stephen uses a ruler to measure the lengths of the sides of a triangle. He obtains the following measurements $a = 12·4$ cm, $b = 8·6$ cm and $c = 7·4$ cm, each correct to the nearest two millimetres, where a, b and c are the lengths of the sides of the triangle and A is the angle opposite the side of length a.
(i) If the true length of a is 12·32 cm, what is the percentage error in the measurement of a?
(ii) What is the tolerance of the ruler?
(iii) What is the percentage error in the measurement of the perimeter $p = a + b + c$?
(iv) Calculate the least possible value of the angle A, in degrees to two decimal places.
(v) Calculate the greatest possible value of the angle A, in degrees to two decimal places.

25. Louise uses a protractor to measure two of the angles, A and B, of a triangle. The protractor measures angles to the nearest degree. Louise obtains the following measurements: $A = 78°$ and $B = 36°$. The side a, which is opposite the angle A, is determined accurately to be 14·37 cm.
(i) Give the tolerance interval for the true value of C, the third angle in the triangle.
(ii) Calculate the greatest possible value of c, the side opposite C.
(iii) Calculate the least possible value of c.

30.4 Estimation of Very Large and Very Small Numbers

1. Order of Magnitude for Very Large and Very Small Numbers

For very large numbers, a crude way of getting an estimate is to consider **order of magnitude**. This term is used in a number of different ways.

An **order of magnitude estimate of a number** is the number rounded to the nearest power of 10. This involves writing the number in scientific notation, in the form $a \times 10^n$, where $1 \leq a < 10$ and $n \in \mathbb{Z}$. If $a < 5$, then the order of magnitude is n, while if $a \geq 5$, then the order of magnitude is $n + 1$.

Consider the following examples.

(i) If $x = 21330000000 = 2{\cdot}133 \times 10^{10}$, then the order of magnitude of x is 10. Thus, in an order of magnitude calculation, we would replace 21330000000 by 10^{10}.

(ii) If $y = 578000000 = 5{\cdot}78 \times 10^8$, then the order of magnitude of y is $8 + 1 = 9$. Thus, in an order of magnitude calculation, we would replace 578000000 by 10^9.

If two numbers **differ by an order of magnitude of one**, then one number is approximately 10 times the other. Likewise, if two numbers differ by an order of magnitude of two, then one is approximately 100 times the other. For example, the mass of the planet Saturn is two orders of magnitude greater than the mass of the earth (it is actually about 96 times greater).

Example 1

An Olympic-sized swimming pool has a length of 50 m, a width of 30 m and an average depth of 3 m. It is proposed to fill this pool from empty with a garden hose which can deliver water at the rate of 1 gallon every 6 seconds. Using order of magnitude estimates, obtain a rough estimate of how long it would take the hose to fill the pool: is it hours, days, weeks, months or years?

Note: 1 gallon = 4·546 litres.

Solution

(What we are really trying to determine here is if it is reasonable or practical to try to fill an Olympic-sized pool with a garden hose.)

Order of magnitude estimates for the dimensions of the pool:

length: $50 = 5 \times 10^1 \approx 10^2$

width: $30 = 3 \times 10^1 \approx 10^1$

depth: $3 = 3 \times 10^0 \approx 10^0$

Thus, if V is our estimate for the volume of the pool, then

$$V = (10^2)(10^1)(10^0) = 10^3 \text{ m}^3$$

As $1 \text{ m}^3 = 10^3$ l, we also have

$$V = (10^3)(10^3) = 10^6 \text{ l}.$$

Order of magnitude estimate for the rate of flow:

$$\text{Rate} = 4{\cdot}546 \text{ litres in 6 seconds}$$
$$\approx 0{\cdot}8 \text{ litres in 1 second}$$
$$\approx 1 = 1 \times 10^0 \approx 10^0 \text{ litres per second.}$$

$$\text{From Rate} = \frac{\text{Volume}}{\text{Time}}$$

$$\text{Time} = \frac{V}{\text{Rate}}$$
$$\approx \frac{10^6}{10^0} = 10^6 \text{ seconds}$$

So how long is this?

(1 minute = 60 s $\approx 10^2$ s, 1 hour = 60 min $\approx 10^2$ min, 1 day = 24 hours $\approx 10^1$ hours)

$$10^6 \text{ s} = \frac{10^6}{10^2 \times 10^2 \times 10^1} = 10^1 = 10 \text{ days.}$$

So, our order of magnitude estimate is in weeks, clearly too long from a practical point of view.

2. Estimation of Large Numbers

Suppose you want to estimate large numbers such as the number of books in a library, the number of spectators at a match, or the number of people taking part in a march. Such estimates are useful for planning purposes, e.g. how long will be required to catalogue all the books, how many security personnel will be needed to supervise the crowd.

The key to the estimation of large numbers such as these is to break the total up into a number of sections, possibly of different types. Then we analyse in detail one such section of each type to find the number in that section. Multiplication and perhaps addition should then give us our estimate.

Example 2

Una wants to estimate the number of books in her local library. She makes a few quick calculations.

- There are 68 bookcases of width 80 cm, each containing 6 shelves. Each shelf contains on average 35 books.
- There are 21 bookcases of width 50 cm, each containing 5 shelves. Each shelf contains on average 16 books.
- There are 10 bookcases of width 40 cm, each containing 4 shelves. Each shelf contains on average 10 books.

What estimate of the number of books will she obtain?

Solution

The bookcases of width 80 cm contain $68 \times 6 = 408$ shelves each containing an average of 35 books. This gives approximately $400 \times 35 = 14000$ books.
The bookcases of width 50 cm contain $21 \times 5 = 105$ shelves each containing an average of 16 books. This gives approximately $100 \times 16 = 1600$ books.
The bookcases of width 40 cm contain $10 \times 4 = 40$ shelves each containing an average of 10 books. This gives approximately $40 \times 10 = 400$ books. Una's estimate for the total number of books in the library is

$$14000 + 1600 + 400 = 16000.$$

Exercises 30.4

1. Obtain an order of magnitude estimate for the number of heart-beats in a human life. (Average number of heartbeats per minute is about 80, average lifespan is about 80 years.)
2. Obtain an order of magnitude estimate for the number of brain cells a human adult has. (Average volume of human brain = 1×10^{-3} m^3, average volume of a brain cell = 1×10^{-15} m^3.)
3. Obtain an order of magnitude estimate for the number of €5 notes which if placed on top of each other, would cover the distance from the earth to the moon. (Distance from the earth to the moon = 400,000 km; ten €5 notes have a thickness of 1 mm.)
4. A country has a national debt of €180 billion, and a population of about 4 million. Obtain an order of magnitude estimate for the average amount owed by each citizen of the country.
5. Obtain an order of magnitude estimate for the number of spectators at all the premiership matches in England in the season 2010–11. (Number of matches is about 400, average attendance is about 25,000.)
6. Obtain an order of magnitude estimate of the number of calories consumed by all the people in Ireland in 1 year. (Population about 5 million, number of calories per person per day is about 800.)
7. How many orders of magnitude greater is
   (i) the radius of the Solar System over the radius of the earth
   (ii) the radius of the Milky Way over the radius of the earth?
   (Radius of earth $\approx 10^7$ m, radius of Solar System $\approx 10^{13}$ m and radius of Milky Way $\approx 10^{17}$ m.)
8. When compared with the height of an ant, which has a height of about 8×10^{-4} m, how many order of magnitudes greater is the height of a human?
9. In order to estimate the number of blades of grass in a rectangular field which is 100 metres by 60 metres, a square of side length 20 cm is picked at random. The number of blades of grass in this square is counted at 215. Estimate the number of blades of grass in the field.
10. Donal wants to estimate the number of grains in a 10 kg bag of rice. He measures out accurately 10 g of rice from the bag. He counts 483 grains, ignoring portions less than half a grain.
    (i) What estimate does he come up with for the number of grains of rice in the bag?
    (ii) What estimate would he have of the total number of grains of rice produced each year worldwide, given that the annual production of rice worldwide is about 680 million tonnes?
11. To estimate the capacity of a sports stadium, Kim divides it into 14 large sections which have roughly the same number of seats. Then she divides one of these sections in four. In one of these smaller sections, she counts twelve rows of 26 seats. What is Kim's estimate of the number of seats in the stadium?

12. Ian, a journalist, wants to estimate the number of people attending a large protest march. He calculates that it takes 1 hour and 20 minutes for the entire march to pass one point on a road twenty two metres wide. He also determines that the march is moving at the rate of 5 km/hour. By analysing quickly photographs he takes of sections of the march, he calculates that each person occupies approximately 1 square metre of space. What number should Ian include for the number of protestors as he files his report on the march?

30.5 Household Finances

1. Currency Transactions

An amount in one currency can be changed into another currency by using the going rate of exchange. Most banks and other institutions that change money charge a fee for the transaction. This can be a fixed fee or a percentage of the amount changed.

Example 1

Seamus has to make a trip to Australia and Japan. He decides to bring €1000 cash with him, equally divided between Australian dollars (AU\$) and Japanese Yen (¥). His bank charges him 2·5% commission for making each exchange.

(i) If on the day he purchases the currency, the exchange rates are €1 = 1·347 AU\$ and €1 = 114·54 ¥, calculate the amounts of foreign currency he receives.

(ii) On his return, he has 150 AU\$ and 20000 ¥ left over. He returns to his bank and converts his remaining money back to euro. Assuming the same exchange rates still hold, how much in total did his cash spending money for the trip cost him?

Solution

(i) $€500 = 500 \times 1{\cdot}347$

$= 673{\cdot}50 \text{ AU\$}$

$€500 = 500 \times 114{\cdot}54$

$= 57270 \text{ ¥}$

(ii) $150 \text{ AU\$} = \dfrac{150}{1{\cdot}347}$

$= €111{\cdot}36$

$20000 \text{ ¥} = \dfrac{20000}{114{\cdot}54}$

$= €174{\cdot}61$

Gross $= €(111{\cdot}36 + 174{\cdot}61)$

$= €285{\cdot}97$

The bank charges 2·5% commission.

Net $= €285{\cdot}97 \times 0{\cdot}975 = €278{\cdot}82$

Original cost $= €1000 +$ commission at 2·5%

$= €(1000 + 1000 \times 0{\cdot}025)$

$= €1025$

Cost of spending money

$= €1025 - €278{\cdot}82$

$= €746{\cdot}18$

2. Rates and Household Charges

Each county council, city council and town council is responsible for maintaining the roads in its area and providing housing, street lighting, water and many other local services. Much of the money needed to pay for these services is raised through **rates**, which are a tax on commercial properties (e.g. shops, factories, offices), and **household charges** such as water charges and waste charges.

To calculates the rates payable on a commercial property, each such property is given what is known as a **rateable valuation** (e.g. a shop may have a rateable valuation of €55 and a factory a rateable valuation of €190). Then each year the county council has to decide how much has to be paid in rates, for each euro of rateable valuation. This is called 'striking the rate'. Then multiplying the rateable valuation by the rate gives the rates due for that year.

For example, in 2010, the rate for commercial properties in Navan Town was €59. Thus, if a commercial property in Navan has a rateable valuation of €135, then its rates bill was

$€(135 \times 59) = €7965.$

Household charges also vary from place to place and from year to year. Some are fixed charges, and some are related to the use made of the services.

3. Value Added Tax (VAT)

Value added tax (VAT for short) is a tax on goods and services that are bought. There are different rates of VAT, each of which is usually expressed as a percentage. In 2011, the standard rate of VAT was 21% and the reduced rate is 13·5%. Some goods and services are exempt from VAT, i.e. are charged at a rate of 0%. The VAT rates can be changed in the budget each year.

For example, books are exempt from VAT, newspapers and magazines are charged at the reduced rate and stationery products are charged VAT at the standard rate. Some prices are quoted 'inclusive of VAT' while others are given 'exclusive of VAT'.

4. Domestic bills and charges

Most households have to pay regular bills for utilities and services such as electricity, gas, waste, water, phone, internet and mobile phones. Some of these are fixed rate charges, others involve calculation of units consumed, as well as fixed charges. Many also involve a VAT charge.

Example 2

An electricity supply company charges domestic users a fixed daily standing charge, as well as for the number of units of electricity used. On top of this, there is a Public Service Obligation (PSO) Levy, which is an amount levied on all customers by the Government to offset the cost of generating electricity from sustainable and renewable sources. On the total of all these charges, VAT is charged. Over a 61-day period, Eithne uses 1217 general units. If the cost of a general unit is €0·141, the daily standing charge is €0·252, the PSO is €5·46 and the rate of VAT is 13·5%, calculate Eithne's electricity bill.

Solution

The bill can be constructed as follows:

61 days @ €0·252/day standing charge	15·37
1217 units @ €0·141	171·60
PSO	5·46
VAT @ 13·5% on 192·44	25·98
Total	218·41

Thus her electricity bill for the period will be €218·41.

5. Costing of Work

It is usual to get a number of quotes from experienced suppliers when a job of work has to be done and paid for. For example, Mary needs to get two bedrooms and a hall, stairs and landing decorated. So she decides to get three quotes for the work done from people recommended by friends. She then chooses the quote that suits her best. A detailed quote is more satisfactory than an 'all in' quote, which can look like it is just a made up figure.

A detailed quote should have separate listings for materials and labour. An allowance for wastage may also be listed, although this may be built into the quantity of materials quoted. The VAT due (at the standard rate for materials and at the reduced rate for labour) should also be given.

Exercises 30.5

1. A man wants to convert 15000 U.S. dollars into euro. The exchange rate is €1 = \$1·47, i.e. 1 euro equals 1·47 U.S. dollars.
   (i) How much does the man get, correct to the nearest euro?
   (ii) If the bank charges €15 commission for the transaction, how much does the man get?

2. A woman wants to change 51200 Mexican pesos into euro. The exchange rate is €1 = 16 pesos. The bank charges €45 for the conversion. How much, in euro, does the woman get?

3. Des has to make an extended business trip to a number of countries. For spending money, he changes €2000 into Indian rupees at an exchange rate of €1 = 64 rupees. Commission is charged at 2% for this transaction.
   (i) Find how much Des gets, correct to the nearest rupee.
   (ii) On leaving India for China, he changes some of his rupees into Chinese yuan. There is a 3% fee for this transaction. If he gets 6510 yuan and the exchange rate is €1 = 9·26 yuan, how many rupees did he change?
   (iii) On his way back through Kuwait, he changes 3400 yuan into Kuwaiti dinar. If €1 = 0·4 dinar, find how many dinar he gets, after a 2% fee.

4. **(i)** A county council estimates that it will need €80,000,000 for the following year. €20,000,000 of this will come from the Government and other sources. If the total rateable valuation for the county is €2,000,000, what rate per euro of rateable valuation does the council need to strike?
   (ii) A shop owner in this county has a rates bill of €7230. What is the rateable valuation of the shop?

5. A shop builds an extension, and so its rateable valuation is increased from €96 to €123. If the rates bill increases by €1525·50, calculate the rate per euro struck by the local authority where the shop is.

6. A dishwasher is selling at €450 plus 21% VAT. What is the total price, inclusive of VAT?

7. A computer is for sale at €1149·50, inclusive of VAT at 21%. What is the price of the computer exclusive of VAT?

8. An item costs €726, inclusive of VAT at 21%. If the rate of VAT is reduced to 20%, find the new cost of the item.

9. An item costs €968 inclusive of VAT at 21%. If the category of the item is changed, and its new rate of VAT is 13·5%, what is the new price of the item?

10. A waste collection company charges €0·20 per kilogram of waste and €3·20 per 'lift', i.e. for each time the bin is emptied. Over a three-month period, Michael has waste of weight 287 kg and his bin was emptied 11 times. If VAT is charged at 13·5%, find Michael's total waste bill for the period.

11. The present reading on the electricity meter in John's house is 63792 units. The previous reading was 62942 units.
    (i) How many units of electricity were used since the previous reading?
    (ii) What is the cost of the electricity used, if electricity costs 14·1 cent per unit?
    (iii) There is also a daily standing charge of €0·252 and a PSO levy of €7·56.
    John's bill covers a period of 62 days. If VAT is charged on all the previous amounts and John's bill comes to €162·34, what is the rate of VAT?

12. A Gas Company charges customers for the volume of gas used, a standing daily charge and a carbon tax. Then VAT is charged on the total. Martin receives his gas bill for a period of 58 days, and the standing daily charge is €0·164. His carbon tax is €12·56. VAT at 13·5% comes to €25·14. If the charge for one unit of gas is €0·03932, find, correct to four significant figures, how many units of gas Martin used in the period.

13. Aoife pays a fixed monthly charge of €15 for her mobile phone. This charge includes 100 free text messages and 50 minutes free call time each month.
    Further call time costs 28 cent per minute and additional text messages cost 11 cent each.
    In one month, Aoife sends 140 text messages and her call time is 2 hours.
    (i) Find the total cost of her fixed charge, text messages and call time.
    (ii) VAT is added to this cost at the rate of 21%.
    Find the amount paid, including VAT.

14. Cormac wants to do some decorating of his apartment. He wants to paper 3 rooms, which he calculates will take 12 rolls, 10 rolls and 7 rolls of wallpaper respectively. The papers he chooses cost €35, €23 and €28 per roll respectively, exclusive of VAT. He decides to buy an extra two rolls for each room to allow for wastage. He also wants to paint the ceilings and the woodwork in these rooms. He buys 20 litres of ceiling paint at €4·50 a litre and 6 litres of gloss paint at €9·50 a litre, both exclusive of VAT.
    He hires a local painter and decorator, who quotes €12 a roll to hang the wallpaper and supply the paste, and €150 a room to paint, all exclusive of VAT. If VAT is charged at 21% on the materials and 13·5% on labour, calculate how much the whole project will cost Cormac.

30.6 Income Tax

In Ireland at present, income is taxed on a tax credit system. While there are many subtle points, such as a difference in income tax for a couple, depending on whether one is working or both are working, the main features of the income tax system are described below.

Under this system, the **gross income** (total income) is taxed. If the gross income for a period is below the **standard rate cut off point**, then all the income is taxed at the **standard rate** (lower rate). In 2011, the standard rate of tax was 20%.

If the gross income is above the standard rate cut off point, then the portion of the income above this point is taxed at the **higher rate**. In 2011, the higher rate of tax was 41%, and the annual standard rate cut off point was €32800 for a single person.

This allows us to calculate the **gross tax**.

For example, suppose Sean earns €32000 in a year. Because this is below the standard rate cut off point, all his income is taxed at the standard rate. For Sean:

Gross Tax: 20% of €32000 = €6400

Suppose Helen earns €48000, which is above the standard rate cut off point. Then the first €32800 of her income is taxed at the standard rate, and the rest

€48000 – €32800 = €15200,

is taxed at the higher rate. So for Helen:

Gross Tax:	20% of €32800 = €6560
	41% of €15200 = €6232
	Total gross tax = €12792

From the gross tax, we subtract the person's **tax credits**, which depends on their individual circumstances. A person's tax credits are based on a personal allowance, and possible additions for medical expenses, mortgage interest relief, etc.

After subtracting the tax credits from the gross tax, we are left with the **net tax**.

For example, if Helen above has tax credits of €3300, then

Gross Tax	= €12792
Tax Credits	= €3300
Net Tax	= €9492

Finally, we subtract the net tax from the gross income to find the **income net of tax**. The income net of tax for Helen above is

Net income = €48000 – €9492 = €38508.

These calculations can all be performed on a yearly, monthly or weekly basis, as long as the appropriate figures are given. All rates and cut off points are subject to change in budgets.

Example 1

Orla earns €64000 in a certain year. The standard rate cut off point is €35400 and her tax credits are €3240. The standard rate of tax is 20% and the higher rate is 41%.

(i) Find the gross tax that Orla has to pay for that year.

(ii) Find her income net of tax for that year.

(iii) What is her monthly income net of tax?

Solution

(i) *(We can lay out the calculation in a number of stages. The first calculation is to find out how much of her income is taxed at the higher rate. We get this by subtracting €35400 from €64000.)*

Gross Income:	€64000		
Standard rate:	€35400 @ 20%	= €7080	
Higher rate:	€28600 @ 41%	= €11726	(+)
	Gross Tax	= €18806	

(ii) Then

Gross Tax	= €18806	
Tax Credits	= €3240	(–)
Net Tax	= €15566	

and

Gross Income	= €64000	
Net Tax	= €15566	(–)
Income Net of Tax	= €48434	

Orla's income net of tax for the year is €48434.

(iii) Her monthly income net of tax is

€48434 ÷ 12 = €4036·17.

Example 2

Peter earns €5200 in a certain month, and has an income net of tax of €3967·50 for the month. The standard rate cut off point for the month is €2950. The standard and higher rates of tax are 20% and 41%, respectively.

(i) Find Peter's gross tax for the month.

(ii) Find Peter's net tax for the month and deduce his tax credits for the month.

Solution

(i) *(We are not given the tax credits. So we have to work forward as far as we can. Then we can work backwards to calculate the tax credits.)*

Gross Income:	€5200	
Standard rate:	€2950 @ 20%	= €590
Higher rate:	€2250 @ 41%	= €922·50
Gross Tax:		= €1512·50

(ii)

Gross Income:	= €5200
Income Net of Tax:	= €3967·50
Net Tax:	= €1232·50

(The difference between the gross tax and the net tax are the tax credits.)

Gross Tax:	= €1512·50
Net Tax:	= €1232·50
Tax Credits:	= €280

Thus, Peter's tax credits for the month are €280.

There are other deductions that are made from almost all tax payers. These are PRSI (pay related social insurance) and USC (universal service contribution or universal social charge). When all deductions have been made, what is left is called **take home pay**.

1. PRSI

In 2011, PRSI was payable at the rate of 4% on all income over €127 a week, or €6604 for a 52 week year. Both the rate and the exempt amount can be changed in any budget. In the 2012 budget, the exempt amount was removed, but could be reintroduced again.

2. USC

This tax was introduced at the beginning of 2011, and applies differently to individuals aged under 70 and those aged over 70. In 2011, for those under 70, USC is applied at the following rates:

On the first €10036 of income:	2%
On the next €5980 of income:	4%
On all income above €16016:	7%

In 2011, an individual earning less than €4004 a year did not have to pay any USC.

Example 3

Emily earns €46500 in a year. For that year, the standard rate cut off point is €30250, the standard and higher rates of tax are 21% and 42% respectively. Her tax credits for the year are €2950. She pays PRSI at 4% on all income over €6604. She also pays USC at the rate of 2% on the first €10036 of income, 4% on the next €5980 and at the rate of 7% on all other income.

(i) Calculate how much Emily pays in income tax, PRSI and USC.

(ii) Determine her monthly take home pay.

Solution

(i) **Income Tax**

Gross Income	€46500		
Standard rate:	€30250@21%	€6352·50	
Higher rate:	€16250@42%	€6825·00	
Gross Tax:		€13177·50	
Tax Credits:		€2950·00	
Net tax:		€10227·50	Tax

PRSI

4% of €(46500 – 6604) = €39896:	€1595·84	PRSI

USC

Low rate:	€10036@2%	€200·72	
Middle rate:	€5980@4%	€239·20	
High rate:	€30484@7%	€2133·88	
USC:		€2573·80	USC

(ii) Total deductions:

Tax	€10227·50
PRSI	€1595·84
USC	€2573·80
Total:	€14397·14

Then,

Gross Income:	€46500
Total Deductions:	€14397·14
Net income:	€32102·86

Thus, Emily's monthly take home pay (net income) is

€(32102·86 ÷ 12) = €2675·24.

Exercises 30.6

1. Paul earns €42000 in a year and has tax credits of €2450 for that year. The standard rate cut off point is €35400 and the standard and higher rates of tax are 20% and 41% respectively.

(i) Calculate Paul's net tax for the year.

(ii) Calculate his monthly pay after tax.

2. Sarah earns €68000 in a year and has tax credits of €3250 for that year. The standard rate cut off point is €35400 and the standard and higher rates of tax are 20% and 41% respectively.
   (i) Calculate Sarah's gross tax for the year.
   (ii) Calculate her monthly pay after tax.

3. Mark earns €5860 in a month and has tax credits of €240 for that month. The standard rate cut off point is €2950 and the standard and higher rates of tax are 20% and 41% respectively.
   (i) Calculate his gross tax for the month.
   (ii) Calculate his pay after tax for the month.

4. Susan earns €6240 in a month and has tax credits of €278 for that month. The standard rate cut off point is €2950 and the standard and higher rates of tax are 20% and 41% respectively.
   (i) Calculate her gross tax for the month.
   (ii) Calculate her pay after tax for the month.

5. Barry has a gross income of €72000 and an income after tax of €53295 for a certain year. The standard rate cut off point is €36500 and the standard and higher rates of tax are 20% and 41% respectively.
   (i) Calculate his gross tax for the year.
   (ii) What are Barry's tax credits for the year?

6. Eithne has a gross income of €84000 and an income after tax of €60212 for a certain year. The standard rate cut off point is €37200 and the standard and higher rates of tax are 20% and 41% respectively.
   (i) Calculate her gross tax for the year.
   (ii) What are Eithne's tax credits for the year?

7. Hugh has an income after tax of €4577 for a particular month. His tax credits are €270 for the month and the standard rate cut off point is €2950. The standard and higher rates of tax are 20% and 41% respectively. Calculate his gross income for the month.

8. Miriam has an income after tax of €5158 for a particular month. Her tax credits are €320 for the month and the standard rate cut off point is €2950. The standard and higher rates of tax are 20% and 41% respectively. Calculate her gross income for the month.

In each of the following questions, assume that PRSI is charged at 4% on all the gross income above the exempt amount. Also assume that USC is charged at the rate of 2% on the first €10036 of annual income, at 4% on the next €5980 and at 7% on all other income. Take a year to be 12 equal months and a year to be 52 weeks.

9. Tomás earns €81000 in a year. His standard rate cut off point is €30100 and tax credits are €3520 for the year. The standard rate of tax is 20% and the higher rate is 41%. The first €127 per week of his income is exempt from PRSI. Calculate Tomás' take home pay for the year and his monthly take home pay.

10. Jane earns €4850 in a month. Her yearly standard rate cut off point is €31560 and her yearly tax credits are €3420. The standard rate of tax is 21% and the higher rate of tax is 42%. The first €127 per week of her income is exempt from PRSI. Calculate Jane's take home pay for the month.

11. Clodagh earns €1150 in a week. Her yearly standard rate cut off point is €29580 and her yearly tax credits are €3280. The standard rate of tax is 20% and the higher rate of tax is 42%. The first €148 per week of her income is exempt from PRSI. Calculate Clodagh's take home pay for the week.

12. Stephen earns €3150 in a month. His yearly standard rate cut off point is €30260 and his yearly tax credits are €3180. The standard rate of tax is 20% and the higher rate of tax is 41%. The first €142 per week of his income is exempt from PRSI. Calculate Stephen's take home pay for the month.

Revision Exercises 30

1. A cake is placed in an oven at 4:10 and is taken out of the oven at 7:25.
   (i) For how many hours and minutes was the cake cooking?
   (ii) The cake was cooked following the instructions for that type of cake which state that the cooking time should be '70 minutes per kilogram, plus 20 minutes'. What was the weight of the cake?

2. The cooking instructions for a turkey state that the cooking time should be '40 minutes per kilogram, plus 20 minutes'.
   (i) For how long should a turkey which weighs 15 pounds be cooked?
   (ii) If this turkey is placed in the oven at 8:45, at what time will it be cooked? [1 pound = 454 grams]

3. A train leaves Athlone at 7:05 and arrives in Galway at 8:21.
   (i) How long does the journey take?
   (ii) If the distance from Athlone to Galway is 93 km, find the average speed, in kilometres per hour, correct to the nearest integer.

4. A woman drives from Wexford to Sligo. She leaves Wexford at 9:35 and arrives in Sligo at 16:23. If the distance from Wexford to Sligo is 307 km, what was her average speed, correct to the nearest km/h?

5. Divide 357 grams in the ratio $\frac{1}{2} : \frac{1}{4} : 1$.

6. A car journey of 559 kilometres took 6 hours and 30 minutes.
   (i) Calculate the average speed, in km/hour, for the journey.
   (ii) If the average petrol consumption for the journey was 8·3 kilometres per litre, calculate the number of litres of petrol used, correct to the nearest litre.
   (iii) The advertising for the car says that the fuel consumption should be 9·2 litres per 100 km. If the car had performed to this standard, how many fewer litres of petrol would have been used on the journey?

7. The answer to 3·58 + 2·47 was given as 6·50. What was the percentage error, correct to one decimal place?

8. Four phone calls cost €3·85, €7·45, €8·40 and €11·55.
   (i) John estimates the total cost of the four calls by ignoring the cent part of the cost of each call. Calculate the percentage error in his estimate.
   (ii) Anne estimates the total cost of the four calls by rounding the cost of each call to the nearest euro. Calculate the percentage error in her estimate.

9. A train leaves Cork at 09:05 and arrives at Dublin at 12:25. The distance from Cork to Dublin is 250 km. Find the average speed of the train in kmh^{-1}.

10. When using a calculator to add 1·7 and 2·2, Natasha strikes the multiplication key instead of the addition key. Calculate the percentage error, correct to one decimal place.

11. A car with wheels of radius 19 inches is designed to last for 150000 km. Taking 1 inch = 2·54 cm,
    (i) obtain an order of magnitude estimate for the number of complete rotations a wheel will undergo in such a lifetime,
    (ii) by rounding to two significant figures, obtain another estimate,
    (iii) by calculating the correct value, determine the percentage error in the answer in part (ii).

12. Sarah wants to estimate the number of seats in a large restaurant. She counts 12 large tables which seat between 6 and 8, about 50 tables which seat 4, and about 20 tables for two.
    (i) What is her estimate of the capacity of the restaurant?
    (ii) If she later finds out that the capacity is 340, calculate her percentage error.

13. Paul has to make the following calculation:

$$\frac{(816 \times 48) - (192 \times 31)}{78 \times 12}$$

(i) Obtain a rough estimate of his answer.
(ii) Calculate the exact answer and determine the percentage error for your estimate in part (i).

14. A rectangle has sides of length $a = (5{\cdot}8 \pm 0{\cdot}1)$ cm and $b = (8{\cdot}4 \pm 0{\cdot}1)$ cm.
(i) Find the tolerance interval for the length of the perimeter of the rectangle.
(ii) Find the percentage error in the length of the perimeter.

15. Eoin is trying to estimate the number of DVDs in a large store. He calculates that there are about 40 sets of shelves, each containing 6 shelves. Each shelf contains about 9 DVDs, to an average depth of 4.
(i) Obtain an estimate for the number of DVDs in the store.
(ii) If the correct number of DVDs is 8378, calculate the percentage error.

16. Obtain an order of magnitude estimate for the number of hydrogen atoms in the sun. The sun is almost exclusively made up of hydrogen. 1 g of hydrogen contains $6{\cdot}02 \times 10^{23}$ hydrogen atoms, and the mass of the sun is 2×10^{30} kg.

17. A tanker delivered oil to a school. Before the delivery, the meter reading showed 11360 litres of oil in the tanker. After the delivery, the meter reading was 7160 litres.
(i) Calculate the cost of the oil delivered if 1 litre of oil cost €1·025.
(ii) When VAT was added to the cost of the oil delivered, the bill to the school amounted to €5209·05. Calculate the rate of VAT added.

18. A supplier agrees to buy 300 computer parts for 3704 Chinese yuan (CNY) each. She plans to sell them for a total of €138000.
(i) Calculate the percentage profit she will make if the exchange rate is €1 = 9·26 CNY.
(ii) By how much will the percentage profit (on the cost price) change if the exchange rate becomes €1 = 9·05 CNY? Give your answer correct to one place of decimals.

19. The standard rate of income tax is 20% and the higher rate is 42%. Colm has weekly tax credits of €50 and a standard-rate cut-off point of €240. Until recently, Colm had a gross weekly income of €900.
(i) Calculate the tax Colm paid each week.
(ii) After getting a pay rise, Colm's weekly after-tax income increased by €20·30. Calculate the increase in Colm's gross weekly income.

20. Yvonne earns €61000 in a year. Her standard rate cut off point is €32700 and tax credits are €3520 for the year. The standard rate of tax is 20% and the higher rate is 41%. The first €127 per week of her income is exempt from PRSI, but she pays PRSI at the rate of 4% on all her income above this. She also pays USC at the rate of 2% on the first €10036 of her income, at 4% on the next €5980, and 7% on all income above this.
(i) Calculate Yvonne's take home pay for the year and her monthly take home pay.
(ii) She is offered the opportunity to earn an extra €6000 a year by working overtime for three nights a week. If she takes the offer, she will have to pay extra childcare costs of €220 a month. Do you think she should take the offer? Give reasons.

Financial Maths

31

Many think of maths as only being useful in science, especially in chemistry and physics. But the applications of maths extend far beyond this, into engineering, architecture, computing, accounting, economics, medicine, even into art.

In this chapter, we focus on the use of maths in the context of financial calculations. Simple financial calculations, such as household finances and tax calculations, have already been covered in a previous chapter.

But a greater amount of maths is required when dealing with loans and investments, including mortgages. When a series of payments at regular intervals is involved, we find that we require results and methods from geometric series to perform our calculations. In the real world, this is the business of actuaries who work for banks and other financial institutions. In this chapter, we will encounter many terms and ideas that are met frequently in news broadcasts, e.g. the effect of a change in interest rates on the monthly repayment of a mortgage.

31.1 Compound Interest and Depreciation

1. Compound Interest Rule

When money is invested with an institution such as a bank, then the institution pays interest for having the use of the money. Interest is usually expressed as a rate per annum (per year). The symbol we will use for the interest rate is i, which is the interest rate expressed as a decimal (or a fraction). For example, for an interest rate of 4%, $i = \frac{4}{100} = 0{\cdot}04$.

Suppose €100 is invested for one year at an interest rate of 4% per annum. Then at the end of one year, the interest gained is 4% of €100, i.e. €100 × 0·04 = €4. The final value of the investment at the end of one year is €100 + €4 = €104.

In general, suppose P, called the **principal**, is invested for a year at a rate of interest of i per annum, then the **final value**, F, at the end of one year is given by

$$F = P + (P \times i)$$
$$F = P(1 + i)$$

This gives us the rule for compound interest calculations. The phrase 'compound interest' refers to the fact that interest gained is immediately treated as principal. The rate of interest assumes that the interest is added at the end of the period, in this case one year.

Compound Interest Rule

To find the future value, F, at the end of one year when the rate of interest is i per annum, multiply the principal, P, at the beginning of the year, by

$(1 + i)$.

This rule may be used for year after year calculations, especially when

(i) the rate of interest varies from year to year,

(ii) some money is added to the investment or removed from the investment at the end of a year before the investment continues.

In some questions, we may have to work backwards to find the principal at the beginning of a year, or we may be asked to calculate the rate of interest for a given year. In such questions, we lay out the calculation on a year to year basis, as seen in Example 1.

Example 1

A sum of money was invested for one year at 6% per annum compound interest.

(i) After one year, the investment was worth €3710. What sum of money was originally invested?

(ii) At the end of the first year, €500 was withdrawn. The rest was invested for a further year, and grew to €3370·50 at the end of this year. What was the rate of interest for this year? Give your answer as a percentage.

Solution

(i) Let €P be the principal at the beginning of the first year.

Year 1: $(i = 0{\cdot}06)$

Beginning: €P

End: €$P \times 1{\cdot}06$

$= €1{\cdot}06P$

Given: $1{\cdot}06P = 3710$

$$P = \frac{3710}{1{\cdot}06}$$

$$P = 3500$$

Thus, the original sum invested was €3500.

(ii) Let i be the rate of interest for the second year.

Year 2:

Beginning: €3710 – €500

= €3210

End: €3210 × $(1 + i)$

Given: $3210(1 + i) = 3370{\cdot}50$

$$1 + i = \frac{3370{\cdot}50}{3210}$$

$$1 + i = 1{\cdot}05$$

$$i = 0{\cdot}05$$

Thus, the rate of interest in the second year is 5%.

2. Compound Interest Formula

Suppose a principal of P is invested at an annual interest rate of i. Then, after 1 year, the future value F is given by

$$F = P(1 + i)$$

If this sum is left to grow, then at the end of year 2,

$$F = [P(1 + i)](i + i) = P(1 + i)^2$$

and after 3 years

$$F = P(1 + i)^3.$$

In general, we have the formula below, which is on page 30 of the *Formulae and Tables*.

Compound Interest Formula

The future value, F, to which a principal, P, grows at a rate of i per annum compound interest after t years is

$$F = P(1 + i)^t.$$

This formula can only be used if

(i) the rate of compound interest stays the same throughout the period, and

(ii) no sums of money are added or removed during the period in question.

The formula can be used to calculate any one of the quantities *F*, *P*, *i* and *t*, given the values of the other three.

Example 2

What sum of money, invested now at 4% per annum compound interest, will amount to €1052·87 after four years? Give your answer correct to the nearest euro.

Solution

(This time F is the sum given and we want to find P. i is 0·04 and t is 4.)

$F = 1052{\cdot}87 \qquad P = ?$

$i = 0{\cdot}04 \qquad t = 4$

Then

$$1052{\cdot}87 = P(1{\cdot}04)^4$$

$$1052{\cdot}87 = P(1{\cdot}04)^4$$

$$1052{\cdot}87 = 1{\cdot}16985856P$$

$$P = \frac{1052{\cdot}87}{1{\cdot}16985856}$$

$$P = 899{\cdot}9976$$

$P = 900,$ correct to the nearest euro.

Thus, the initial sum of money invested is €900.

3. Depreciation (Reducing Balance Method)

Suppose a company buys a new car for one of its sales representatives at a cost of €24000. As the car gets older, its value decreases. This is called **depreciation**. In its company accounts, the company needs to keep track of the change of value of the car for two reasons.

1. The depreciation, or loss in value, is a legitimate business expense, and can be set against profits.
2. The value of the car at the end of each period (usually a year), called its **later value** or **net book value** (NBV), is a company asset and has to be recorded as such.

Data shows that, for the make and model of car bought, the car loses 25% of its value over the period of each year. Suppose the company keeps the car for three years, and we want to determine the depreciation and net book value each year over this period. The following method of calculation is called the **reducing balance method**.

Year 1:	Original value of car	€24000
	Depreciation (25% of original value)	€6000
	NBV	€18000
Year 2:	Value at start Year 2	€18000
	Depreciation (25% of value at start Year 2)	€4500
	NBV	€13500
Year 3:	Value at start Year 3	€13500
	Depreciation (25% of value at start Year 3)	€3375
	NBV	€10125

An alternative, simpler, method of calculating depreciation is called the straight line method, under which the asset loses a fixed amount each year. However, the reducing balance method is a more realistic approach to depreciation and is the only method on our course.

It might also be necessary to work backwards in depreciation questions.

Example 3

A manufacturing company buys a machine, which they know will depreciate at the rate of 15% per year. In the second year, the depreciation of the machine is given as €5737·50 in the company accounts. Find the original cost of the machine.

Solution

Year 2:	Depreciation in Year 2	€5737·50
	15% of value Start Year 2	€5737·50
	1% of value Start Year 2	€382·50
	Value Start Year 2	€38250
Year 1:	Later value at end Year 1	€38250
	85% of original cost	€38250
	1% of original cost	€450
	Original Cost of Machine	€45000

There is a formula for depreciation, just as there is for compound interest. Suppose an asset of value P depreciates at the rate of i per annum. Let F be the later, or future, value after t years. Then

$$F = P(1 - i)^t.$$

Depreciation Formula (Reducing Balance Method)

The future value, F, of an initial value, P, after depreciating at a rate of i per annum for t years is

$$F = P(1 - i)^t.$$

Example 4

A company buys a machine on the understanding that it will be able to dispose of it in eight years time for 10% of its original cost. Find the annual rate of depreciation, as a percentage correct to two decimal places.

Solution

Let P be the original cost. Then $F = (10\% \text{ of } P) = 0{\cdot}1P$. Let i be the annual rate of depreciation. Then

$$0{\cdot}1P = P(1 - i)^8$$

$$(0{\cdot}1)^{\frac{1}{8}} = 1 - i$$

$$i = 1 - 0{\cdot}74989$$

$$i = 0{\cdot}25011$$

Thus, the annual rate of depreciation is 25·01%.

Exercises 31.1

1. €2600 was invested for two years at compound interest.
   (i) In the first year, the rate of interest was 4%. What was the value of the investment at the end of the first year?
   (ii) In the second year, the rate of interest was 5%. What was the value of the investment at the end of the second year?

2. €5800 was invested for two years at compound interest.
   (i) In the first year, the rate of interest was 5%. What was the value of the investment at the end of the first year?
   (ii) In the second year, the rate of interest was 6%. What was the value of the investment at the end of the second year?

3. A sum of money was invested at 7% per annum compound interest. If the value of the investment after one year was €3745, what was the sum of money originally invested?

4. A sum of money was invested at 6% per annum compound interest. If the value of the investment after one year was €5088, what was the sum of money originally invested?

5. €2500 was invested for two years at compound interest.
   (i) In the first year, the rate of interest was 6%. What was the value of the investment at the end of the first year?
   (ii) The value of the investment at the end of the second year was €2782·50. What was the rate of interest for the second year?

6. €3800 was invested for two years at compound interest.
   (i) In the first year, the rate of interest was 5%. What was the value of the investment at the end of the first year?
   (ii) The value of the investment at the end of the second year was €4149·60. What was the rate of interest for the second year?

7. €1200 is invested at 6% per annum compound interest. What is the value of the investment after three years?

8. €2800 is invested at 4% per annum compound interest. What is the value of the investment after five years?

9. €5400 is invested at 5% per annum compound interest. What is the value of the investment after six years? How much interest was gained in this time?

10. €3800 is invested at 7% per annum compound interest. What is the value of the investment after four years? How much interest was gained in this time?

11. What sum of money, invested now at 3% per annum compound interest, will grow to €4919·50 in seven years? Give your answer correct to the nearest euro.

12. What sum of money, invested now at 5% per annum compound interest, will grow to €9648·69 in six years? Give your answer correct to the nearest euro.

13. A machine originally cost a manufacturing company €120000. Its value depreciates at the rate of 20% per annum. Find the depreciation amounts in each of the first four years after being bought.

14. A new car costs €35000. It depreciates at the rate of 25% in each of its first two years. Then a newer model becomes available and the car depreciates at the rate of 30% each year after that. Find the amount of the depreciation in the fourth year.

15. A machine depreciates in value by 15% each year. If the depreciation in the third year after being bought is €6502·50, find the initial cost of the machine.

16. A car depreciates in value by 20% each year. If it depreciates by €3584 in its third year, find the original cost of the car.

17. A company buys a machine knowing that it will be able to sell it for 20% of its original cost in 10 years' time. What is the annual rate of depreciation?

18. The value of a car depreciates at the rate of 18% per annum. Express the value of the car after 5 years as a percentage of the original value.

19. A machine depreciates at a constant rate. After 10 years its value is 27·85% of its original value. Find the annual rate of depreciation, correct to the nearest percentage.

31.2 Present Value and Equivalent Value

1. Present Value

Suppose we are entitled to a sum of €5000 in four years time. What is the value of this sum now, i.e. how much would someone be willing to give me now if I promised them the €5000 in four years' time?

This is called the present value of €5000 due in four years' time. It is the principal that should be invested now, at the going annual interest rate of i to get €5000 in four years time.

From the compound interest formula, if P is the present value, then

$$5000 = P(1+i)^4$$

$$P = \frac{5000}{(1+i)^4}.$$

This gives us the formula for the present value of a future payment.

Present Value Formula

The present value, P, of a payment F due t years in the future when the effective annual rate of interest is i, is given by

$$P = \frac{F}{(1+i)^t}.$$

Example 1

Joe has an insurance policy which is due to mature in 12 years' time, giving him €75000.

(i) If the going rate of interest is 3% per annum compound interest, what is the present value of his insurance policy?

(ii) Explain what is meant by 'present value' in this case.

Solution

(i) $F = 75000$, $i = 0{\cdot}03$ and $t = 12$. Then

$$P = \frac{75000}{(1{\cdot}03)^{12}}$$

$$P = \frac{75000}{1{\cdot}42576}$$

$$P = 52603{\cdot}49$$

Thus, the present value of the insurance policy is €52603·49.

(ii) €52603·49 is the present value of €75000 in 12 years' time because, if Joe invests €52603·49 now at 3% per annum compound interest, its value in 12 years' time will be €75000.

2. Equivalent Value

The idea of present value can be extended to take any point in time as the present. For example, we can use the idea of present value to find the value, in three years' time, of a payment due in ten years' time. We can also use it to find the value, in four years' time, of a payment made two years ago.

With this extended notion of present value, we change the name to **equivalent value**. The equivalent value of a payment depends on the time at which the payment is being evaluated, called the **focal date**. We now look at how to find the equivalent value of a payment made before, after and at the focal date.

(i) Equivalent Value of a Payment made t years before the Focal Date

The equivalent value, P, of a payment, A, made t years before the focal date may be found by using

$$P = A(1+i)^t,$$

as A has been accumulating for t years at an annual rate of compound interest, i. This comes directly from the Compound Interest Formula.

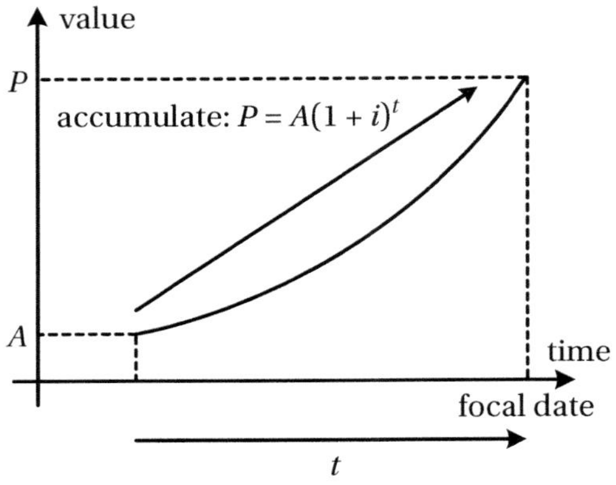

P may also be called the **future value** of the payment A.

We **accumulate** (or **grow**) a payment made in the past to find its equivalent value at a focal date after the payment.

(ii) Equivalent Value of a Payment to be made t years after the Focal Date

The equivalent value, P, of a payment, A, to be made t years after the focal date may be found by using

$$P = \frac{A}{(1+i)^t}$$

which will be recognised as the present value of a payment, A, t years in the future. Some refer to P as a present value although the focal date does not have to be right now.

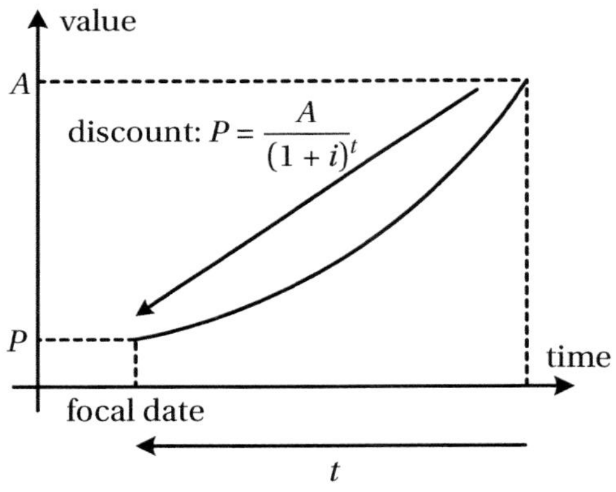

We **discount** a payment to be made in the future to find its equivalent value (present value) at a focal date before the payment.

(iii) Equivalent Value of a Payment made at the Focal Date

The equivalent value, P, of a payment, A, made at the focal date is just the value of the payment, i.e. $P = A$.

In practice, the equivalent value is often referred to as the present value, even when the focal date is not right now, and even when a payment is accumulated forward. This approach is a very powerful tool for dealing with the more complicated situations we will meet later.

Equivalent Value (Present Value)

(i) Grow forward by t years: multiply by $(1 + i)^t$.

$$P = A(1 + i)^t$$

(ii) Discount backward by t years: divide by $(1 + i)^t$.

$$P = \frac{A}{(1 + i)^t}.$$

(iii) At focal date: $P = A$.

3. Net Present Value (NPV)

We can use the concept of present value to analyse proposed financial arrangements involving payments in and payments out at different times. We do this by calculating the **net present value (NPV)**, which is the total present value of all payments received minus the present value of all payments made. If the NPV is positive, the investment is worthwhile, while if the NPV is negative, the investment is not a good idea.

Although it is called the net present value, it could be more accurately called the net equivalent value, because any time can be used as the present, i.e. the focal date.

Example 2

Joe, the managing director of a manufacturing company, calculates that he will need to spend €5000 at the end of each of four years, and €30000 at the end of the fifth year to replace essential machinery. He engages an engineering company to carry out this work.

It is now one year after the first €5000 has been due and it has not been paid. You, as head of the engineering company, are about to undertake the second €5000 replacement, but have become concerned about the lack of payment. You approach Joe, and he offers to pay you €3000 now and €47000 promptly in two years' time to complete the work. If the going rate of interest is 6% per annum, do you think you should accept the offer? Give a reason.

Solution

(We will take the focal date to be today, one year after the first payment is due. We then calculate the effective values of all payments received, by Joe's suggested method, and all payments made, i.e. billed according to the original agreement.)

Equivalent (present) values of payments received:

€3000 now:		€3000
€47000 in 2 years:	$€\frac{47000}{(1{\cdot}06)^2} =$	€41829·83
	Total =	€44829·83

Equivalent (present) values of payments made (billed cost of replacing machinery):

€5000 1 year ago:	€5000(1·06) =	€5300
€5000 now:		€5000

€5000 in 1 year:	$€\frac{5000}{1{\cdot}06} =$	€4716·98
€5000 in 2 years:	$€\frac{5000}{(1{\cdot}06)^2} =$	€4449·98
€30000 in 3 years:	$€\frac{30000}{(1{\cdot}06)^3} =$	€25188·58
	Total =	€44655·54

Thus, the NPV is €(44829·83 – 44655·54) = €174·29. As this is positive, you should accept the offer. (This is unless you don't trust Joe, or believe his company will not be around in two years' time.)

Exercises 31.2

1. If the effective annual rate of interest is 4%, find the present value of a payment of €5000 due in
   (i) one years' time,
   (ii) three years' time,
   (iii) six months' time.
2. If the effective annual rate of interest is 3·5%, find the present value of
   (i) €2000 due in three years' time,
   (ii) €6500 due in two and a half years' time,
   (iii) €4000 due in nine months' time.
3. If the effective annual rate of interest is 5%, find the present value of
   (i) €1500 due in six years' time,
   (ii) €2800 due in ninety months' time,
   (iii) €4800 due in thirteen months' time.
4. If the effective annual rate of interest is 6%, find
   (i) the value in two years' time of €2500 paid five years ago,
   (ii) the value in three years' time of €5600 due in eight years' time,
   (iii) the value two years ago of €7000 due in four years' time.
5. If the effective annual rate of interest is 4·5%, find
   (i) the value in four years' time of €2400 paid two years ago,
   (ii) the value three years ago of €8000 due in four years' time,
   (iii) the value four years ago of €12000 paid eight years ago.
6. If the effective annual rate of interest is 5·75%, find
   (i) the value in twelve years' time of €6500 due in two years' time,
   (ii) the value one year ago of €4800 due in two and a half years' time,
   (iii) the value in two years' time of €6000 due in sixty six months' time.
7. Today is Sinead's 40th birthday. On her 18th birthday, she received money presents totalling €300. She is due to retire when she reaches age 65 years, and on this occasion will receive a lump sum of €150000. Taking the annual interest rate to be 3%,
   (i) find the present value of her 18th birthday present,
   (ii) find the present value of her retirement lump sum.
8. Eithne borrowed €30000 from a bank five years ago, and a further €20000 three years ago. She repaid the bank €15000 two years ago. Taking the annual rate of interest to be 6%,
   (i) find the present value of all the borrowings and payment,
   (ii) find how much Eithne owes the bank today.

9. Helen is due to pay Joe €25000 in two years' time and €30000 in four years' time. She offers to pay him €47000 now instead. Taking the annual rate of discount to be 5%, determine if Joe should accept her offer.

10. An investment company has the option of buying a 20% share of a project for €180000. The project is projected to make a profit of €100000 in one years' time, €250000 in two years' time, €400000 in three years' time and €500000 in four years' time. Taking the annual rate of interest to be 6%,
(i) find the present value of all the projected profits of the project,
(ii) determine if the company should invest in the project.

11. Ciara is looking for an investment of €60000 now in return for a 25% share in the company she is planning to set up. She calculates that she will have to spend €100000 now to get the company going. She also projects a loss of €20000 at the end of the first year, but profits of €30000, €70000 and €120000 at the end of years two, three and four respectively. She also calculates that she can sell the company for €350000 at the end of year four. Taking the annual rate of interest to be 8%, should you invest in her company? Give a reason.

31.3 Interest Rates

1. Effective Rates of Compound Interest

So far, we have only encountered rates of compound interest expressed as an annual rate, e.g. 6% per annum, giving $i = 0{\cdot}06$. In the world of finance, there are many other ways of expressing the rate of compound interest.

To begin with, the **interest period** does not have to be a year. It could be six months, three months, one month, etc. For example, we could have an interest rate of 1% per month, or 3% every six months.

An interest rate of 1% per month means that 1% of the principal at the beginning of a month is added by way of interest at the end of that month.

The time interval at which interest is added to the principal, and converted into principal, is called the **compounding period**. As we will see later, the interest period and the compounding period do not have to be the same. When they are the same, the interest rate is called an **effective rate** of compound interest.

When we have an effective rate of interest, i, whatever the compounding period, we are entitled to use all the compound interest formulae from the last section, e.g.

$$P = A(1 + i)^t$$

and $$P = \frac{A}{(1 + i)^t}$$

where i is the effective rate of compound interest for the compounding period, and t is the number of compounding periods.

For many practical questions, we need to be able to convert between different effective rates of compound interest. The two most important are converting from an effective annual rate to an effective monthly rate, and converting from an effective monthly rate to an effective annual rate. The following example illustrates both conversions.

Example 1

(i) Find the monthly rate of compound interest equivalent to an annual rate of 7%. Give your answer as a percentage, correct to four decimal places.

(ii) Find the annual rate of compound interest equivalent to a monthly rate of 1%. Give your answer as a percentage, correct to four decimal places.

Solution

(i) Let i be the equivalent monthly rate of interest. Let P be the value of a sum, A, at the end of one year. This should be the same whether we use the annual rate or the equivalent monthly rate.

By the annual rate,

$$P = A(1 + 0{\cdot}07)$$

For the monthly rate, there are twelve compounding periods. Thus,

$$P = A(1 + i)^{12}$$

Thus,

$$A(1 + i)^{12} = A(1{\cdot}07)$$

giving

$$(1 + i)^{12} = 1{\cdot}07$$

$$1 + i = 1{\cdot}07^{\frac{1}{12}}$$

$$1 + i = 1{\cdot}005654145$$

$$i = 0{\cdot}005654145$$

giving a rate of 0·5654%, correct to four decimal places.

(Note that this is less than one twelfth of 7%, which is 0·5833%.)

(ii) Let i be the equivalent annual rate. Then by the same reasoning as in part (i),

$$1 + i = (1 + 0{\cdot}01)^{12}$$

$$1 + i = 1{\cdot}01^{12}$$

$$1 + i = 1{\cdot}12682503$$

$$i = 0{\cdot}12682503$$

giving a rate of 12·6825%, correct to four decimal places.

(Note that this is more than $12 \times 1\% = 12\%$.)

From Example 1, we can now state a formula for converting between effective interest rates with different compounding periods.

Converting Between Annual and Monthly Interest Rates

(i) If i is an annual rate of compound interest, then the equivalent monthly rate is

$$(1 + i)^{\frac{1}{12}} - 1.$$

(ii) If i is a monthly rate of compound interest, then the equivalent annual rate is

$$(1 + i)^{12} - 1.$$

Note that to reduce the compounding period, e.g. from a yearly to a monthly rate, and go to a smaller rate, the index is $\frac{1}{12}$, while to increase the compounding period, e.g. from a monthly to a yearly rate, and go to a higher rate, the index is 12. Conversions between other compounding periods can be handled in the same way.

Example 2

A moneylender advertises a weekly compound interest rate of 1%. Taking a year to be 52 weeks, find the equivalent annual rate of compound interest. Give your answer as a percentage, correct to two decimal places.

Solution

Let i be the equivalent annual rate of compound interest. As there are 52 weeks (compounding periods),

$$i = (1 + 0{\cdot}01)^{52} - 1$$
$$i = 1{\cdot}01^{52} - 1$$
$$i = 1{\cdot}677688921 - 1$$
$$i = 0{\cdot}677688921$$

which is an interest rate of 67·77%, correct to two decimal places.

2. Expressions of Interest Rate

(a) Loans, Mortgages and Other Forms of Credit: APR

In the past, lenders tried to confuse potential borrowers by expressing the interest rate charged for credit in ways that borrowers found difficult to comprehend. For example, an interest rate might be quoted as 0·5% per week. This might not sound like a high rate, but is actually equivalent to an annual rate of 29·61%!

Another device used to conceal the true interest rate was to charge set-up fees, management charges, etc. When these were factored in, the interest rate was often significantly higher than that quoted in advertisements.

In recent times, European and Irish legislation has required that lenders display the Annual Percentage Rate (APR) prominently for all proposed loan agreements. There is a very precise definition of APR (given on page 31 of the *Formulae and Tables*). From the point of view of the definition, all charges must be included, along with all repayments.

Annual Percentage Rate (APR)

The APR is the value of i (expressed as a percentage) for which the sum of the present values of all advances is equal to the sum of the present values of all repayments.

(b) Savings and Investments: AER (or EAR or CAR)

For savings and investments, i.e. where savings are made with financial institutions, the term used for the interest rate is Annual Equivalent Rate (AER), or alternatively Equivalent Annual Rate (EAR) or Compound Annual Rate (CAR). We will use the abbreviation AER, although all three are taken as equivalent.

The rules governing the definition of the AER are not as strict as those for the APR, as, for example, it is not as clearly specified what fees and charges have to be taken into account in their calculation.

In our calculations, we will take APR and AER to be the same: the annual rate of compound interest equivalent to that stated. Both are very important, especially for comparison purposes. One difference is that the APR is always a percentage, but the AER can be either a percentage or a decimal. In practice, we use decimals for both.

Example 3

A post office offers investors a Savings Bond promising a 40% increase in value at the end of five years. What is the annual equivalent rate (AER) for this bond? Give your answer as a percentage, correct to two decimal places.

Solution

Let i be the AER for this Savings Bond. Then in five years, €1 becomes €1·40.
Thus

$$1(1+i)^5 = 1{\cdot}40$$
$$1+i = 1{\cdot}4^{\frac{1}{5}}$$
$$i = 1{\cdot}4^{\frac{1}{5}} - 1$$
$$i = 0{\cdot}0696$$

Hence, the AER is 6·96%, correct to two decimal places.

3. Nominal Interest Rates

Suppose a financial institution advertises that for a certain type of loan the interest rate is '12% per annum, compounded monthly'.

What this means is that at the end of each month, one twelfth of the annual interest rate, i.e. $\frac{1}{12}(12\%) = 1\%$, of the principal at the beginning of the month is applied to the capital. Thus after one month

$$P = A\left(1 + \frac{0{\cdot}12}{12}\right) = A(1{\cdot}01)$$

and at the end of one year

$$P = A\left(1 + \frac{0{\cdot}12}{12}\right)^{12}$$
$$P = A(1{\cdot}1268)$$
$$P = A(1 + 0{\cdot}1268)$$

Thus, the annual equivalent rate (AER) is 12·68%. The expression '12% per annum, compounded monthly' is called a nominal interest rate, because '12% per annum' applies in name only.

In general, a rate of interest is a **nominal interest rate** if the interest period and the compounding period are not the same. In '12% per annum, compounded monthly', the interest period is one year (per annum) and the compounding period is one month.

On our course, we do not work with nominal rates of interest. Rather, we convert them to effective interest rates, and continue as before. We can convert to an effective rate based on the compounding period, or on the interest period.

Thus, for example, the following are equivalent:

(i) '12% per annum, compounded monthly'
As discussed above, this is a nominal interest rate.

(ii) '1% per month'
It is understood that this means '1% per month, compounded monthly', and as such is an effective rate of interest.

(iii) '12·68% per annum'
It is understood that this means '12·68% per annum, compounded annually' and as such is an effective rate of interest.

In general, suppose we have a nominal rate of interest of r per annum, compounded m times per annum. Then:

(i) $\frac{r}{m}$ is the effective interest rate for one compounding period,

(ii) if i is the AER (annual equivalent rate), as there are m compounding periods per year,

$$i = \left(1 + \frac{r}{m}\right)^m - 1,$$

using the same method as for converting from a monthly to an annual interest rate.

This formula is given on page 32 of the *Formulae and Tables*.

Converting to an Annual Effective Rate from a Nominal Interest Rate

If r is the nominal annual rate, compounded m times per year, and i is the equivalent annual rate, then

$$i = \left(1 + \frac{r}{m}\right)^m - 1.$$

Example 2

An interest rate is quoted as 8% per annum, compounded quarterly. Find, as a percentage correct to two decimal places, the annual equivalent rate (AER).

Solution

As the compounding period is different from that of the interest period, we are dealing with a nominal rate of interest. From the given information, $r = 0{\cdot}08$ and $m = 4$ (four quarters in a year). Let i be the annual equivalent rate. Then

$$i = \left(1 + \frac{0{\cdot}08}{4}\right)^4 - 1$$

$$i = 0{\cdot}08243216$$

Hence, the AER is 8·24%, correct to two decimal places.

Exercises 31.3

1. Find the equivalent monthly rate for an annual rate of 10% compound interest. Give your answer as a percentage, correct to two decimal places.
2. Find the equivalent monthly rate for an annual rate of 6·8% compound interest. Give your answer as a percentage, correct to two decimal places.
3. Find the equivalent annual rate for a monthly rate of 1·3% compound interest. Give your answer as a percentage, correct to two decimal places.
4. Find the equivalent annual rate for a monthly rate of 0·7% compound interest. Give your answer as a percentage, correct to two decimal places.
5. Find the effective annual rate for each of the following interest rates. Give your answers as percentages correct to two decimal places.
   (i) 0·3% per month
   (ii) 2·5% bi-annually (each six months)
   (iii) 1·7% per quarter.
6. Find the effective annual rate for each of the following interest rates. Give your answers as percentages correct to two decimal places.
   (i) 1·92% per quarter
   (ii) 0·56% per month
   (iii) 0·148% per week (52 weeks in a year).
7. What rate of interest per month is equivalent to an effective annual rate of 7%?
8. What rate of interest per quarter is equivalent to an effective annual rate of 6%?
9. What effective annual rate of interest is equivalent to a nominal annual rate of 9%, compounded monthly?
10. What effective annual rate of interest is equivalent to a nominal annual rate of 12%, compounded quarterly?
11. What effective annual rate of interest is equivalent to a nominal annual rate of 15%, compounded
    (i) every six months,
    (ii) quarterly,
    (iii) monthly,
    (iv) weekly?
12. Ronan has inherited a substantial sum of money which he wants to invest. He researches the interest rates offered by different institutions. A offers a rate of 6% per annum, B offers a rate of 0·45% per month and C offers an annual rate of 5%, compounded monthly. If Ronan wants to maximise his income, which of the three institutions should he invest his money with?
13. Irene won €500000 in a Lotto, and she wants to invest half of it. She has three choices as to which institution to invest this money with. One offers a rate of 0·28% per month, a second offers a rate of 0·9% per quarter and the third offers a rate of 3·5% per annum, compounded weekly.
    (i) What is the greatest value that her investment can have after one year?
    (ii) If she leaves her investment in place for 20 years, what is the difference between the highest and the lowest values of her investment, depending on which institution she invested with?
14. A Government bond offers an interest rate of 60% after ten years. Find the equivalent annual rate of compound interest.

31.4 Loans and Mortgages

1. Series of Payments: Geometric Series

In our calculations, we will find that in evaluating series of payments we often encounter geometric series. Recall that the formula for the sum of the finite geometric series

$$S_n = a + ar + ar^2 + \ldots\ldots + ar^{n-1}$$

is $S_n = \dfrac{a(1-r^n)}{1-r}$.

Also, if $-1 < r < 1$, then the formula for the sum of the infinite geometric series

$$S_\infty = a + ar + ar^2 + \ldots\ldots$$

is $S_\infty = \dfrac{a}{1-r}$.

2. Amortised Loans

In real life, many loans, including mortgages, which are borrowed from financial institutions are paid off by a series of regular repayments. These repayments cover the loan amount and the interest. Such a loan or mortgage is called an **amortised loan**, and the process is known as **amortisation**.

The key principle behind financial transactions such as these is that ***the sum of the equivalent values of all advances (borrowings) at any focal date is equal to the sum of the equivalent values of all repayments at the same focal date, at the going rate of interest.***

In many cases, the focal date will be the date of the first transaction. In that case, all future payments will be discounted to the focal date. However, in many more complicated situations, e.g. topping up loans or repaying loans early, it will be in our interest to consider other focal dates. A good choice of focal date can simplify the calculations involved in a question.

In actuarial work (actuaries are professionals who deal with the complicated maths of financial dealings, risks and probabilities), this principle is called the **Equation of Value**.

Equation of Value

At the rate of interest involved in any given transaction, the value at any time of all the payments made by one party to the transaction and the value, at the same time, of all the payments that party will receive must be equal.

This principle is used extensively in practice. It can also be used to derive a formula for the amount of equal repayments of an amortised loan.

Example 1

Sandra takes a loan now of P. She agrees to repay this loan by a series of t equal yearly payments, A, starting one year from now. The rate of interest throughout is i.

(i) Derive an expression for A in terms of P, t and i.

(ii) Hence, find her level annual repayment if she borrows €10000 over 10 years at 5% per annum.

Solution

(i) *(We will take the focal date to be the moment when Sandra receives the loan.)*
Present value of loan = P

Present value of 1st repayment = $\dfrac{A}{(1+i)}$

Present value of 2nd repayment = $\dfrac{A}{(1+i)^2}$

....

Present value of last repayment = $\dfrac{A}{(1+i)^t}$

By the Equation of Value,

$$P = \frac{A}{(1+i)} + \frac{A}{(1+i)^2} + \dots + \frac{A}{(1+i)^t}$$

(The RHS is a geometric series with $a = \dfrac{A}{(1+i)}$, $r = \dfrac{1}{1+i}$ *and* $n = t$.*)*

$$P = \frac{\frac{A}{(1+i)}\left(1 - \left(\frac{1}{1+i}\right)^t\right)}{1 - \frac{1}{1+i}} \times \frac{1+i}{1+i} \quad \text{... multiply above and below by } 1+i$$

$$P = \frac{A\left(1 - \frac{1}{(1+i)^t}\right)}{(1+i) - 1}$$

$$iP = A\left(\frac{(1+i)^t - 1}{(1+i)^t}\right)$$

$$iP(1+i)^t = A\left((1+i)^t - 1\right)$$

$$A = P\frac{i(1+i)^t}{(1+i)^t - 1}$$

(ii) $P = 10000$, $t = 10$ and $r = 0{\cdot}05$. Then

$$A = 10000\frac{(0{\cdot}05)(1{\cdot}05)^{10}}{(1{\cdot}05)^{10} - 1}$$

$$A = 10000\frac{0{\cdot}08144473}{0{\cdot}62889463}$$

$$A = 1295{\cdot}0457$$

Thus, Sandra's level annual repayment is €1295·05.

The formula for A in terms of P and i is given on page 31 of the *Formulae and Tables*.

Amortisation Formula

Suppose a principal of P is repaid in full by a series of annual repayments of A starting one year later and continuing for t years with an annual percentage rate of i. Then

$$A = P\frac{i(1+i)^t}{(1+i)^t - 1}.$$

As it stands, the amortisation formula can only be used when

(i) there is a single loan, P, given at the beginning of the transactions,
(ii) the loan is completely paid off, along with interest, by a series of t equal, regular repayments starting one period after the loan is given.

This formula can be adapted to repayments over any regular periods of time, not just yearly payments. However, in this case:

(i) i is the interest rate for the compounding period used, e.g. year, month, week,
(ii) t is the number of repayments, not the number of years.

In practice, loans and mortgages tend to be repaid on a monthly basis, as we see in Example 2. Then it is important to calculate the equivalent monthly rate of interest for the interest rate we are given.

Amortisation calculations can be performed by using geometric series, or in most cases by using the amortisation formula above. When using geometric series, a common device is to let

$$v = \frac{1}{1+i}$$

to simplify calculations where sums are being discounted.

Example 2

Suppose David and Jean take a mortgage (i.e. a loan) now of €200000 to buy a house. They agree to repay this loan, plus interest, by a series of equal monthly payments, starting in one month's time and continuing for 20 years. The effective annual rate of interest is 6%.

(i) Find the monthly interest rate that is equivalent to an effective annual rate of 6%. Give your answer in decimal form, correct to eight decimal places.
(ii) Use geometric series to find the monthly repayment David and Jean have to make on their mortgage.
(iii) Use the amortisation formula to check your answer to part (ii).

Solution

(i) Let i be the rate per month that is equivalent to 6% per annum. Then

$$(1+i)^{12} = 1{\cdot}06$$
$$1+i = 1{\cdot}06^{\frac{1}{12}}$$
$$1+i = 1{\cdot}004867551$$
$$i = 0{\cdot}00486755$$

(ii) Let A be their equal monthly repayments, and let

$$v = \frac{1}{1+i} = \frac{1}{1{\cdot}00486755} = 0{\cdot}9951560277.$$

Taking the focal date to be the date of getting the loan, the present value of their loan is 200000. They will have to make 20 × 12 = 240 repayments, starting in 1 month's time. The present values of their repayments can be laid out in the form of a table.

Payment No.	Value	Time (months)	Present Value
1	A	1	$\frac{A}{1+i} = Av$
2	A	2	$\frac{A}{(1+i)^2} = Av^2$
3	A	3	$\frac{A}{(1+i)^3} = Av^3$
....	....	....	....
240	A	240	$\frac{A}{(1+i)^{240}} = Av^{240}$

By the Equation of Value,

$$Av + Av^2 + Av^3 + ... + Av^{240} = 200000$$

(The LHS is a geometric series with $a = Av, r = v$ and $n = 240$.)

$$\frac{Av(1 - v^{240})}{1 - v} = 200000$$

$$A\frac{0{\cdot}9951560277(1 - 0{\cdot}9951560277^{240})}{1 - 0{\cdot}9951560277} = 200000$$

$$141{\cdot}384309A = 200000$$

$$A = 1414{\cdot}58$$

Thus, their monthly mortgage repayment is €1414·58, correct to the nearest cent.

(iii) $P = 200000$ and $i = 0{\cdot}00486755$. $t = 20 \times 12 = 240$ payments. Thus, the monthly repayment, A, is given by

$$A = P\frac{i(1 + i)^t}{(1 + i)^t - 1}$$

$$A = 200000\frac{(0{\cdot}00486755)(1{\cdot}00486755)^{240}}{(1{\cdot}00486755)^{240} - 1}$$

$$A = 200000 \times 0{\cdot}00707292071$$

$$A = 1414{\cdot}58$$

Thus, their monthly mortgage repayment is €1414·58, as in part (ii)

3. Amortisation Schedule

Under an amortised loan, each repayment contains a portion for interest and a portion to repay part of the principal. However, the portion for each varies with each repayment, although the overall repayments remain constant. In the early repayments, the interest portion is large, while in the later repayments the principal repayment portion is larger. The diagram below shows this.

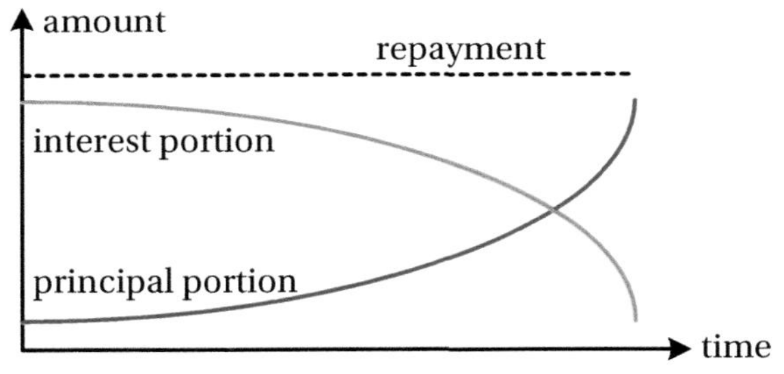

For an amortised loan, we can construct a schedule showing how much of each payment is interest and how much is principal. This is called an **amortisation schedule**. This schedule can be constructed manually, by working on a year by year basis, as Example 3 shows. Alternatively, the schedule can be constructed using software packages such as Microsoft Excel.

The reasons for constructing an amortisation schedule include the fact that, for businesses, the amount of interest paid on a business loan in a given year can be offset against the tax due for that year.

4. Early Repayment of an Amortised Loan

Suppose Mary has taken a 20 year mortgage to buy her apartment. After 14 years, she inherits a sizeable sum of money and wants to pay off the remaining mortgage. How much will this cost her?

Again, there are many ways of calculating this amount. Perhaps the easiest way is to find the equivalent value, taken at the time she wants to pay off the mortgage, of all her remaining payments. However, if we have an amortisation schedule, we can read off directly how much she needs to pay after 14 years to clear the mortgage.

Example 3

Serena borrows €50000 from a bank to fund new machines for her business. She agrees to repay the loan, plus interest, by a series of level annual repayments starting one year later and continuing for six years. The agreed annual interest rate for the loan is 7·5%.

(i) Find the amount of each annual repayment.

(ii) Construct a schedule showing the interest and principal portions of each of Serena's annual repayments.

(iii) At the end of 4 years, Serena finds herself in a position to clear the loan. How much will she have to pay the bank at this stage to clear the loan?

Solution

(i) $P = 50000$, $t = 6$ and $i = 0{\cdot}075$. Then

$$A = P\frac{i(1+i)^t}{(1+i)^t - 1}$$

$$A = 50000\,\frac{0{\cdot}075(1{\cdot}075)^6}{(1{\cdot}075)^6 - 1}$$

$$A = 10652{\cdot}24$$

Thus, her equal annual repayments will be €10652·24.

(ii) The Schedule of Payments (amortisation schedule) is shown below.

Payment No.	Fixed Payment	Interest	Principal	Balance
0				€50000·00
1	€10652·24	€3750·00	€6902·24	€43097·76
2	€10652·24	€3232·33	€7419·91	€35677·84
3	€10652·24	€2675·84	€7976·41	€27701·44
4	€10652·24	€2077·61	€8574·64	€19126·80
5	€10652·24	€1434·51	€9217·73	€9909·06
6	€10652·24	€743·18	€9909·06	€0·00

Notes:

1. Enter the amount borrowed as the balance on the first line.
2. Enter the fixed payment, calculated above, in each space from the first payment to the last payment.
3. Now fill the table in row by row. In each row, calculate the interest by multiplying the balance from the previous row by i, i.e. calculate the (simple) interest for one year.

   For example, for payment 1,

   $$\text{interest} = 50000 \times 0{\cdot}075 = 3750$$
4. To find the principal portion in each row, just subtract the interest from the fixed payment, e.g. for payment 1,

   $$\text{principal} = 10652{\cdot}24 - 3750{\cdot}00 = 6902{\cdot}24$$

5. To calculate the balance, subtract the principal amount from the previous balance, e.g. for payment 1,

   balance = 50000·00 – 6902·24 = 43097·76.

6. This table is self-checking. If the values are correct, the last balance should be zero, or just a few cent, on account of rounding.

(iii) From the table, each payment occurs at the end of that particular year. Thus, the balance still owing at the end of year 4 is €19126·80. This is what she will have to pay to clear the loan at the end of year 4.

Exercises 31.4

1. Dermot and Carole take a mortgage of €180000 to help buy their new house. The APR for the mortgage is 4·5%, and they agree to repay the mortgage by a series of equal monthly repayments.
(i) Find the monthly rate of interest that is equivalent to an APR of 4·5%.
(ii) If the period of the mortgage is 20 years, find the amount of the equal monthly repayments.
(iii) If the period of the mortgage is 25 years, find the amount of the equal monthly repayments.

2. Heather needs to borrow €65000 for essential repairs to her property. Her bank loans her this money at an APR of 6% and she agrees to repay the loan over 15 years.
(i) If she makes equal annual repayments, starting in one year's time, find the amount of each equal annual repayment.
(ii) If she makes equal monthly repayments, starting in one month's time, find the amount of each equal monthly repayment.

3. Ian and Fiona borrow €300000 to buy a house. They pay back the loan and interest by a series of equal monthly repayments, starting one month from now. Find the value of each monthly repayment
(i) if the loan is for 20 years, i.e. there are $20 \times 12 = 240$ repayments, and the effective annual interest rate is 4%,
(ii) if the loan is for 30 years, i.e. there are $30 \times 12 = 360$ repayments, and the effective annual interest rate is 4%,
(iii) if the loan is for 20 years and the effective annual interest rate is 4·5%.

4. Tom and Una take a mortgage of €150000 to buy a new house. It is a 20 year mortgage with $20 \times 12 = 240$ equal monthly repayments starting one month after the loan is drawn down. Initially, the effective annual interest rate was 5%.
(i) Find the monthly interest rate that is equivalent to an effective annual interest rate of 5%.
(ii) Find the amount of each monthly repayment.
(iii) Before they draw down the loan, the interest rate increases to 5·5%. What is the increase in their monthly repayment on the mortgage?

5. Consider a mortgage of €100000 over 20 years, to be repaid by 240 equal monthly repayments starting one month after the mortgage is drawn down. Use the formula on page 31 of *Formulae and Tables* to find the monthly repayment if the effective annual interest rate is
(i) 4% **(ii)** 4·25% **(iii)** 4·5%

Is the increase in monthly repayment the same in going from 4% to 4·25% as it is in going from 4·25% to 4·5%?

6. Olivia borrows €100000 and agrees to repay the loan by a series of 8 equal annual repayments starting in one year's time. The APR for the loan is 9%.
(i) Calculate the amount of each equal annual repayment.
(ii) Construct a schedule showing interest and principal portions of the repayments outlined in part (i).

7. Tomasz borrows €60000 to expand his business. However, according to the business plan produced by his accountant, he will need a one year moratorium before he begins his repayments on the loan. They find a bank that will agree to these terms, but the bank is quoting an APR of 8% and insists that the loan be repaid within 7 years.
   (i) If Tomasz and his accountant agree to repay the loan by 6 equal annual repayments starting in two years' time, find the amount of each equal annual repayment.
   (ii) Construct a schedule showing interest and principal portions of the repayments outlined in part (i).
   (iii) If it is agreed that the loan be repaid by monthly repayments, starting in one year and one month's time, calculate the amount of each equal monthly repayment.

8. Wayne and Julie borrow €200000 to refurbish their hotel. They agree to repay the loan with a series of equal monthly repayments starting in one month's time and with the last payment in ten years' time. The APR for the loan is 6·8%.
   (i) Calculate the amount of the equal monthly repayments.
   (ii) After making 92 monthly repayments, they wish to pay off the remainder of the loan immediately. Calculate how much this will cost them.

9. Five years ago, David borrowed €100000 for his business. He agreed to repay the loan by 10 equal annual repayments starting one year later. The APR for the loan is 6·5%.
   (i) Find the amount of the equal annual repayments.

   Having just made his fifth annual repayment on the loan, David now needs another €50000 in finance. His bank will provide this, but insists on combining what remains of the old loan with the new finance into a single loan which he will have to repay by 8 equal repayments starting in one year's time. The bank also states that the APR for the new loan will be 7%.
   (ii) Find the amount outstanding on his original loan.
   (iii) Find the amount of the equal annual repayments on his new loan.
   (iv) David's accountants require a schedule of interest and principle for the period of his new loan. Construct such a schedule.
   (v) Having just made the third last repayment on his new loan, David finds he is in a position to pay off the rest of the loan immediately. Use your schedule to determine how much he must pay to clear the loan.

10. Dylan borrows P and agrees to pay back the loan with interest by t equal annual repayments of A, starting one year after he gets the loan. The effective annual interest rate is i. Let $v = \frac{1}{1+i}$.
   (i) Use the Equation of Value to show that $P = A(v + v^2 + \dots + v^t)$ and hence that $iP = A(1 - v^t)$.
   (ii) Each annual repayment contains some interest and some repayment of the original loan. Explain why the interest element in the first repayment is iP.
   (iii) The rest of the first repayment pays off some of the loan. Show that this part of the first repayment is Av^t, and that the amount of the loan still outstanding after the first repayment is
   $$P_1 = A(v + v^2 + \dots + v^{t-1}) = P\frac{1 - v^{t-1}}{1 - v^t}.$$
   (iv) Repeat the process to show that the amount of the loan outstanding after the second repayment is
   $$P_2 = P\frac{1 - v^{t-2}}{1 - v^t}.$$
   (v) Write down an expression for the amount of the loan still outstanding after n repayments.
   (vi) Dylan has borrowed €200000 at 5% per annum over 20 years. After making 12 equal annual repayments, starting one year after he gets his loan, he wants to pay off the entire balance of the loan. How much will this cost him?

31.5 Investments, Annuities and Bonds

1. Series of Investments

Many people save regularly for the future, especially to provide themselves with a pension on retirement. The value of a series of regular investments can be found by using the formula for a geometric series.

Example 1

Eric starts a savings policy with his bank. He starts by saving €100 now. Each year, the value of the saving he makes grows by 4% to take account of inflation. He makes 20 annual savings, and his policy matures at the end of the 20th year. Throughout this period, his fund is guaranteed to gain interest at an AER of 3%.

(i) Obtain an expression for F_1, the value of his first payment when the policy matures.

(ii) Obtain an expression for F_2, the value of the second payment when the policy matures.

(iii) Obtain an expression for F_{20}, the value of the last payment when the policy matures.

(iv) Determine the value of Eric's savings policy when it matures, i.e. when he gets the value of the policy.

Solution

(i) The first saving of €100 grows for 20 years at 3% per annum. Thus

$$F_1 = 100(1{\cdot}03)^{20}$$

(ii) His second saving is €100(1·04). This grows for 19 years at 3% per annum. Thus

$$F_2 = 100(1{\cdot}04)(1{\cdot}03)^{19}$$

(iii) The last saving is €$100(1{\cdot}04)^{19}$. This grows for one year at 3% per annum. Thus

$$F_{20} = 100(1{\cdot}04)^{19}(1{\cdot}03)$$

(iv) By the same token,

$$F_3 = 100(1{\cdot}04)^2(1{\cdot}03)^{18}$$

and so on. The value of Eric's savings policy at the end, i.e. on maturity, is

$$\begin{aligned} S_{20} &= F_1 + F_2 + F_3 + \dots + F_{20} \\ &= 100(1{\cdot}03)^{20} + 100(1{\cdot}04)(1{\cdot}03)^{19} + \dots 100(1{\cdot}04)^{19}(1{\cdot}03) \end{aligned}$$

This is a geometric series with $a = 100(1{\cdot}03)^{20} = 180{\cdot}6111$,

$$r = \frac{T_2}{T_1} = \frac{100(1{\cdot}04)(1{\cdot}03)^{19}}{100(1{\cdot}03)^{20}} = \frac{1{\cdot}04}{1{\cdot}03} = 1{\cdot}0097087$$

and $n = 20$. Thus

$$\begin{aligned} S_{20} &= \frac{180{\cdot}6111(1 - 1{\cdot}0097087^{20})}{1 - 1{\cdot}0097087} \\ &= \frac{180{\cdot}6111(-0{\cdot}2131708)}{-0{\cdot}0097087} \\ &= 3965{\cdot}62 \end{aligned}$$

Thus, the value of the policy, when it matures, is €3965·62.

In some cases, we want to find what regular savings are required to achieve a fund of a certain size. Once again, we can use geometric series to answer such questions.

However, it is interesting to note that we can also adapt the amortisation formula to provide an alternative solution. Example 2 shows both these methods.

Example 2

When Larry retires in 24 years time, he wants to have saved a fund of €600000. He decides to make equal annual savings, starting now and finishing one year before he retires. The AER throughout is 4%.

(i) Calculate the value of his equal annual savings.

(ii) If instead he decides to wait four years to make his first payment, find the value of each of his twenty equal savings.

Solution

(i) *(Let A be the value of each of Larry's equal savings. The first saving grows for 24 years and the last grows for one year. We will write down the Equation of Value on his retirement date.)*

Equation of Value:

$$A(1{\cdot}04)^{24} + A(1{\cdot}04)^{23} + \ldots + A(1{\cdot}04) = 600000$$

or

$$A(1{\cdot}04) + A(1{\cdot}04)^2 + \ldots + A(1{\cdot}04)^{24} = 600000$$

$$\frac{A(1{\cdot}04)\left[1 - (1{\cdot}04)^{24}\right]}{1 - 1{\cdot}04} = 600000$$

$$40{\cdot}64590829A = 600000$$

$$A = €14761{\cdot}63$$

or

(Taking the focal date to be one year ago, we can treat Larry's savings as a loan repayment situation, with the first repayment after one year, and use the amortisation formula. However, we also have to find the present value of his retirement fund. This involves discounting 600000 for 25 years.)

For the amortisation formula, $P = \frac{600000}{(1{\cdot}04)^{25}} = 225070{\cdot}0814$ and $t = 24$. Then

$$A = 225070{\cdot}0814\frac{(0{\cdot}04)(1{\cdot}04)^{24}}{(1{\cdot}04)^{24} - 1}$$

$A = €14761{\cdot}63$, as before.

(ii) *(Let A be the new annual savings, starting in four year's time. Hence, we should treat the focal date as three years' time, and discount the 600000 for 21 years.)*

For the amortisation formula, $P = \frac{600000}{(1{\cdot}04)^{21}} = 263300{\cdot}1613$ and $t = 20$. Then

$$A = 263300{\cdot}1613\frac{(0{\cdot}04)(1{\cdot}04)^{20}}{(1{\cdot}04)^{20} - 1}$$

$A = €19374{\cdot}09$.

2. Annuities

An **annuity** is a term which refers to a regular series of payments made from a fund. It is sometimes also applied to the fund from which the payments are made. One example of an annuity is a series of pension payments. Although the word 'annuity' comes from 'annual', meaning yearly, in fact, the period between payments can be anything, e.g. quarterly, monthly.

An annuity can be for a fixed length of time, for the period of a person's life, or for ever (such an annuity is referred to as a perpetuity).

Mathematically, an annuity can be treated the same way as an amortised loan, with the recipient (called the annuitant) taking the place of the financial institution and the financial institution taking the place of the borrower.

To use the amortisation formula to calculate the value of the equal payments, it is important to note that the formula only applies when the first payment is one time period after the start. Alternatively, we can use geometric series and the Equation of Value. This is probably the better option when any complications, such as increasing annual payments, are involved.

Example 3

Sheila's accountant, Marie, has informed her that, on the date of her retirement, she will have a fund of €467500 with which to buy a pension annuity. Sheila asks Marie to make calculations about different possible annuities. Marie finds that the AER at that time is 4·8%, and bases all her calculations on this rate. In answer to Sheila's queries, calculate the following options which can be purchased with her fund.

(i) The value of monthly payments, starting on the date of her retirement and lasting for 25 years (300 payments).

(ii) The value of monthly payments, starting one month after her retirement and continuing indefinitely.

Solution

(i) *(We can start by finding the monthly rate, i, equivalent to an AER of 4·8%. Then let* $v = \frac{1}{1+i}$. *Again, this is a common device with such calculations.)*

$$1 + i = (1{\cdot}048)^{\frac{1}{12}} = 1{\cdot}003914608$$

$$i = 0{\cdot}003914608$$

and $v = \frac{1}{1+i} = 0{\cdot}9961006564$

(We will take the focal date to be the date of Sheila's retirement. Let the monthly payments be A. Then we use the formula for the sum of a geometric series.)

Payment No.	Amount	Present Value
1	A	A
2	A	Av
......	.....	.....
300	A	Av^{299}

Then $A + Av + \dots + Av^{299} = 467500$

$$\frac{A(1 - v^{300})}{1 - v} = 467500$$

$$A = 467500 \frac{1 - 0{\cdot}9961006564}{1 - (0{\cdot}9961006564)^{300}}$$

$$A = €2640{\cdot}87$$

is the value of her monthly payments (annuity).

(Alternatively, we can treat the focal date as one month before her retirement, find the present value of her fund and use the amortisation formula, for which $i = 0{\cdot}003914608$,
$P = \dfrac{467500}{1{\cdot}003914608} = 465677{\cdot}0569$ *and* $t = 300$.*)*

$$A = 465677{\cdot}0569 \frac{0{\cdot}003914608(1{\cdot}003914608)^{300}}{(1{\cdot}003914608)^{300} - 1}$$

$A = €2640{\cdot}87$, as before.

(ii) *(Let the monthly payments be A. We take the focal date to be the date of her retirement. Again let* $v = \dfrac{1}{1+i} = 0{\cdot}9961006564$. *'Continuing indefinitely' means continuing to infinity. Thus, we use the formula for the sum to infinity of a geometric series.)*

By the Equation of Value,

$$Av + Av^2 + Av^3 + \ldots = 467500$$

$$A(v + v^2 + v^3 + \ldots) = 467500$$

By the formula for the sum of an infinite geometric series, with $a = v$ and $r = v$,

$$A\frac{v}{1-v} = 467500$$

$$A = 467500\,\frac{1 - 0{\cdot}9961006564}{0{\cdot}9961006564}$$

$$A = €1830{\cdot}08$$

3. Bonds

A **bond** is a certificate issued by a government or a public company promising to repay the borrowed money on a fixed date, along with interest payments at fixed intervals. A bond is a negotiable security, in that it can be bought and sold. The issuer of the bond owes money to whoever holds the bond on dates when money is due.

The conditions attaching to bonds can differ greatly. The Equation of Value can be used to evaluate a bond at any stage.

Example 4

A company wishes to raise finance to expand their operations. To do so, they issue a number of 10-year €10000 bonds that will pay €200 at the end of every six months, up to and including the maturity date. If the current market interest rate is 4·5% per annum, what is a fair market value of one of these bonds?

Solution

(We will work the question with a time unit of six months. Thus, we have to find the interest rate for six months that is equivalent to an annual rate of 4·5%.)

Let i be the equivalent interest rate for six months. Then

$$(1 + i)^2 = 1{\cdot}045$$

$$i = \sqrt{1{\cdot}045} - 1 = 0{\cdot}02225241501$$

and

$$v = \frac{1}{1+i} = 0{\cdot}9782319761$$

A fair market value for one of these bonds is the present value of all future payments to be received. The present value of the €10000 to be paid in 10 years is

$$\frac{10000}{(1{\cdot}045)^{10}} = 6439{\cdot}27682$$

Let $P_1, P_2, \ldots, P_{20}$ be the present values of each of the six monthly payments. Then

$$\begin{aligned} P_1 + P_2 + \ldots + P_{20} &= 200v + 200v^2 + \ldots + 200v^{20} \\ &= \frac{200v(1 - v^{20})}{1 - v} \\ &= \frac{200(0{\cdot}9782319761)(1 - 0{\cdot}9782319761^{20})}{1 - 0{\cdot}9782319761} \\ &= 3200{\cdot}302689 \end{aligned}$$

Thus, a fair market value is

$6439{\cdot}27682 + 3200{\cdot}302689$

$= €9639{\cdot}58$

Exercises 31.5

1. Aoife is saving for a holiday after the Leaving Cert. She starts by saving €20 in September, and each month after that she increases what she saves by 20% on the previous month. By the time she finishes saving in May, how much has she saved in total?

2. Una takes out a savings policy with a financial institution. She agrees to save €500 now and at the beginning of each year for a total of 25 years. The institution promises her a fixed AER of 6% for the period. Find the total value of her investments at the end of the 25th year.

3. **(i)** Paul invests €100 at the beginning of each year for twelve consecutive years. If the effective annual interest rate is 4% throughout, what is the total value of his investment at the end of the twelfth year?

   (ii) Paul decides that he will increase the amount he saves each year by 5% on the previous year. Assuming he starts by investing €100 at the same effective annual interest rate, what is the total value of his investments at the end of the twelfth year?

4. Eamon wants to save for his retirement, which is due in 40 years. He has calculated that he will need a retirement fund of €1200000. He plans to save a certain amount each year, starting now and continuing for 40 years. He retires one year after his last saving. He invests all his savings at an effective annual rate of 6%.

   (i) If he saves the same amount, €A, each year, find the value of A that will give him his desired retirement fund.

   (ii) If he saves €$\frac{A}{12}$ each month, starting now and continuing for $40 \times 12 = 480$ months, find the value of A that will give him his desired retirement fund.

   (iii) If he saves €A today and makes an annual saving which increases by 5% each year, to take inflation into account, find the value of A which will give him his desired retirement fund.

5. A manufacturing company knows that it has to replace two key machines in the near future. The first machine needs to replaced in four years time at a cost of €600000, and the second machine needs to be replaced in six years time at a cost of €850000. The company proposes to save and invest €A per month, starting now, for the next $6 \times 12 = 72$ months, so that it will just fund the purchase of the two machines. If the effective annual interest rate is 4%, use the Equation of Value to find the value of A.

6. Lucy wants to plan for her retirement. She wants a fund that, from the date of her retirement, will give her €30000 at the beginning of each year for 25 years. The effective annual interest rate throughout is 5%.
   (i) Find the required value of her retirement fund on the date she retires.
   (ii) Her retirement is 26 years away. She plans to invest a fixed amount €A each month, starting now and continuing for $26 \times 12 = 312$ months. Express in terms of A the value of her investments on the date of her retirement.
   (iii) Calculate the value of A which will give her her retirement fund.

7. Siobhan wants to plan for her retirement. She starts by estimating what income she will need after retirement. She calculates that she will need €25000 on the day of her retirement, and at the start of each year after that an amount which is 5% greater than the previous year, for a total of 25 years. The effective annual interest rate throughout is 4%.
   (i) Find the required value of her retirement fund on the date she retires.
   (ii) Her retirement is 30 years away. She plans to invest a fixed amount €A each month, starting now and continuing for $30 \times 12 = 360$ months. Express in terms of A the value now of all her investments. Deduce, in terms of A, the expression for the value of her investments on the date of her retirement.
   (iii) Calculate the value of A which will give her her retirement fund.

8. Colm is planning for his retirement. He calculates that he will need an annuity of €2500 per month from the date of his retirement. He plans that it should start on the day he retires and last for 25 years, i.e. 300 payments. Colm needs to determine the value of the fund, on his retirement date, that will buy this annuity. He has to estimate what the annual interest rate will be on his retirement.
   (i) Calculate the value of the fund if the AER on his retirement is 4%.
   (ii) Calculate the value of the fund if the AER on his retirement is 5%.

9. Frank wants to save for his retirement, and so needs to calculate the size of the fund he will need to purchase an annuity, starting on the date of his retirement and lasting for 20 years. Take the AER on the date of his retirement to be 4·5%.
   (i) Find the value of the fund required to buy an annual payment of €20000 per year.
   (ii) Find the value of the fund required to buy an annual payment which starts at €20000 and increases by 3% per year.

10. Dervla's accountant has told her that on the date of her retirement she will have a retirement fund of €620000 with which to buy an annuity. The AER at the time of her retirement is 5%.
   (i) If she buys an annuity of €A per month, starting one month after she retires and continuing for 25 years (300 payments), calculate the value of A.
   (ii) If she buys an annuity of €A per month, starting on the day she retires and continuing for 25 years (300 payments), calculate the value of A.

11. Phyllis spends €450000 on the date of her retirement buying an annual payment of €A starting immediately and continuing indefinitely. If the AER is 5·5%, calculate the value of A.

12. Igor has a retirement fund of €740000 on the date of his retirement. He buys an annual payment of €A, starting one year after he retires and continuing indefinitely. If the AER is 4·2%, calculate the value of A.

13. The country Opalland issues bonds which promise €10000 in four years time, along with quarterly payments of €500, starting in three months' time and finishing with a payment on the day of maturity. Taking the effective annual interest rate to be 5·7%, determine a fair market value for one of these bonds.

14. A company needs to raise capital to expand and decides to issue bonds. These are 6-year €5000 bonds which will give annual payments of €200 starting immediately and continuing for 6 years. Taking the effective annual interest rate to be 4·3%, determine a fair market value for one of these bonds.

15. Maths Ltd needs to raise funds to acquire another company. To do so, it issues 10-year €20000 bonds which promise yearly payments of €500, starting one year after purchase and continuing for 10 years. Taking the effective annual interest rate to be 6%, determine a fair market value for one of these bonds.

16. A company needs to raise funds to expand. To do so, it issues 8-year €50000 bonds which promise payments of €1000 every six months, starting six months after issue and continuing to the end of the eighth year. Taking the effective annual interest rate to be 5%, determine a fair market value for one of these bonds.

31.6 Continuously Compounding

Consider a nominal interest rate of 5% per annum, i.e. $r = 0{\cdot}05$. Let i be the equivalent annual rate of interest. Let's investigate the effect on the value of i by increasing m, the number of times each year that the interest is compounded (calculated and added to the principal).

Taking a year to be 12 months, 52 weeks or 365 days, we can obtain the following examples of values of i, each given correct to ten decimal places. We know that the number of weeks and days is not entirely accurate, but it makes no difference to the theory that follows.

m	Frequency	Formula	$i =$
1	each year	0·05	0·05
12	each month	$\left(1 + \frac{0{\cdot}05}{12}\right)^{12} - 1$	0·0511618979
52	each week	$\left(1 + \frac{0{\cdot}05}{52}\right)^{52} - 1$	0·0512458419
365	each day	$\left(1 + \frac{0{\cdot}05}{365}\right)^{365} - 1$	0·0512674965

From this table, we should be able to see that as m increases, i gets larger, but tends to a limit that will be shown to be 0·0512710964, correct to ten decimal places. This is the rate of interest if a nominal annual rate of 5% is **compounded continuously**.

The nominal annual rate of interest when interest is being compounded continuously is called the **force of interest**, which is denoted by r in the *Formulae and Tables*. Thus,

$$i = \lim_{m \to \infty} \left(1 + \frac{r}{m}\right)^m - 1$$

or $$1 + i = \lim_{m \to \infty} \left(1 + \frac{r}{m}\right).$$

We can find a more convenient link between the force of interest, r, and the corresponding equivalent annual rate of interest, i, as follows.

First of all, we consider the expression $\left(1 + \frac{1}{m}\right)^m$ as m gets very large. Some sample values are shown below.

m	100	1000	10000	100000	1000000
$\left(1 + \frac{1}{m}\right)^m$	2·70481	2·71692	2·71814	2·71826	2·71828

You should recognise that these values of $\left(1+\frac{1}{m}\right)^m$ are getting closer and closer, as m increases, to the famous number e that we have met on a number of previous occasions.

Thus, we can say that

$$\lim_{m\to\infty}\left(1+\frac{1}{m}\right)^m = e$$

although a formal proof of this is beyond the scope of our course.

Now, to find $\lim_{m\to\infty}\left(1+\frac{r}{m}\right)^m$, let

$$x = \frac{m}{r}.$$

Then $\frac{1}{x} = \frac{r}{m}$ and $m = xr$. Also, as $m \to \infty$, $x \to \infty$.

Thus,

$$\begin{aligned}\lim_{m\to\infty}\left(1+\frac{r}{m}\right)^m &= \lim_{x\to\infty}\left(1+\frac{1}{x}\right)^{xr}\\ &= \lim_{x\to\infty}\left[\left(1+\frac{1}{x}\right)^x\right]^r\\ &= \left[\lim_{x\to\infty}\left(1+\frac{1}{x}\right)^x\right]^r\\ &= e^r\end{aligned}$$

Hence, $1 + i = e^r$

and $i = e^r - 1$.

Rearranging

$$1 + i = e^r$$

$$\log_e(1+i) = r.$$

Compounding Continuously and the Force of Interest

When interest is being compounded continuously, the nominal annual rate of interest, r, is called the force of interest. If i is the equivalent annual interest rate, then

$$i = e^r - 1$$

or $r = \log_e(1+i)$.

Thus, for example, a nominal interest rate of 5%, compounded continuously, gives $r = 0{\cdot}05$ and an equivalent annual rate of

$$i = e^{0{\cdot}05} - 1$$

or $i = 0{\cdot}0512710964$, as mentioned before.

Also, the compound interest formula $F = P(1+i)^t$ can now be written

$$F = P(e^r)^t$$

or $F = Pe^{rt}$,

where r is the nominal annual rate when interest is compounded continuously.

In theory, the force of interest is a very important quantity in the calculation of compound interest, as it is the true rate of growth, or instantaneous rate of growth, per unit of principal. Annual and other rates of interest are then obtained from the force of interest, and are quoted for convenience.

Example 1

The interest rate for a large financial loan is quoted as 3·5% per annum, compounded continuously. Find the equivalent annual rate of compound interest, as a percentage, correct to five decimal places.

Solution

We are given that

$$r = 0{\cdot}035$$

If i is the equivalent annual rate, then

$$i = e^{0{\cdot}035} - 1 = 0{\cdot}0356197$$

which is 3·56197%, correct to five decimal places.

Exercises 31.6

1. An interest rate is quoted as 8% per annum, compounded continuously.
   (i) Find the equivalent annual rate of interest.
   (ii) Find the equivalent monthly rate of interest.
2. An interest rate is quoted as 5·5%, compounded continuously.
   (i) Find the equivalent annual rate of interest.
   (ii) Find the equivalent monthly rate of interest.
3. The annual rate of interest charged by a bank is 6%. Find the corresponding force of interest, i.e. the annual nominal rate of interest, compounded continuously.
4. The annual rate of interest charged by a bank is 10%. Find the corresponding force of interest, i.e. the annual nominal rate of interest, compounded continuously.
5. A rate of interest is quoted as 8% per annum, compounded monthly. Find as a percentage, correct to four decimal places, the corresponding nominal annual rate of interest, if interest is compounded continuously.
6. A rate of interest is quoted as 10% per annum, compounded monthly. Find as a percentage, correct to four decimal places, the corresponding nominal annual rate of interest, if interest is compounded continuously.

Revision Exercises 31

1. €5000 is invested for two years at compound interest.
   (i) The interest in the first year was €275. Calculate the rate of interest for the year.
   (ii) At the end of the second year the investment was worth €5644·25. Calculate the rate of interest for the second year.
2. A pupil saves money each day in the month of November. The pupil saves 10c on the first of November, and every day after that he saves 5c more than the previous day. How much does he save in total in the 30 days of November?

3. A person saves €x at the beginning of each year for 4 consecutive years at an effective annual rate of 10%. The total value of the investments at the end of the fourth year was €51051. Find the value of x.

4. A company invested €100000 in new machinery at the beginning of each year for three consecutive years. The machinery depreciated at the rate of 10% per annum.
   (i) Find the value of the first investment of €100000 at the end of the third year.
   (ii) Find the total value of all the investments at the end of the third year.

5. Eugene invested €2500 for three years at compound interest. The effective rate of annual interest was 4% for the first year and 3% for the second year.
   (i) Calculate the value of the investment after two years.
   (ii) If the investment amounted to €2744·95 after three years, calculate the rate of interest in the third year.

6. Shane takes out a car loan of €15000, at an effective annual interest rate of 9·5%. The loan is to be repaid by equal monthly payments starting one month after he draws down the loan, and is to continue for 3 years, i.e. 36 repayments.
   (i) Find the monthly interest rate, correct to six decimal places, that is equivalent to an annual interest rate of 9·5%
   (ii) By using the Equation of Value when he draws down the loan, find the amount of his monthly repayments.
   (iii) By using the Equation of Value on the date of his last repayment, find the amount of his monthly repayments. What do you notice?

7. Leaky Homes Ltd is a development company. Five years ago it borrowed €23 million from a bank and three years ago it borrowed a further €18 million. Four years ago it repayed €7·2 million and six months ago it repayed a further €9·3 million. It wants to borrow €8·4 million more now, and promises to pay back all its debts with two equal repayments, one in eighteen months' time and the other in three years' time. If the effective annual interest rate for the transactions is 4%, find the values of the two equal repayments, correct to six significant figures.

8. Nora invests €600 at the beginning of each year for three consecutive years at an effective annual rate of interest of 4·5%.
   (i) Find the value of all her investments at the end of the third year.
   (ii) Instead, she decides to invest €50 a month, starting now and continuing for a total of 36 months. The effective annual rate of interest is the same. How much less will her investments be worth at the end of the third year?

9. Lucy is due to retire in exactly 10 years. She wants to boost her pension fund as much as possible between now and then. She cannot afford to save any more than €800 a month between now and the date of her retirement. The effective annual rate for pension fund contributions is 7%.
   (i) If she invests €800 a month, starting now, for the next 120 months, what will be the value of these investments on the date she retires?
   (ii) From other sources, she has an additional €300000 in her pension fund on the date she retires. With her total pension fund she wishes to buy an annuity, starting on the date she retires and continuing each year for a total of 25 years.
   If these payments are equal, and the effective annual interest rate is 4% after her retirement, find the amount she will receive each year for 25 years.

10. Today is John's birthday. He plans to save an amount on his birthday each year, starting today and going for twenty years. He plans to save €200 today but to increase the amount he saves by 5% each year. The effective annual rate of interest throughout is 4%.
   (i) Calculate the value of all John's savings twenty years from now.
   (ii) If tax at 21% is deducted from his interest each year, find the value of all his savings after twenty years.
   Give your answers correct to the nearest euro.

11. A sum of money is invested at an effective annual rate of 6%. Calculate how many years it will take to double in value.

12. A sum of money is invested at an effective annual rate of i. Show that the number of years it takes to double in value can be written $\log_{(1+i)} 2$.

13. A government bond is quoted as offering a rate of interest of 6%, compounded monthly. Find the effective annual rate of interest, as a percentage correct to two decimal places.

14. Tony saves €25 from his wages each week, putting it in a savings account that gives an effective annual rate of interest of 3·75%.

(i) What weekly rate of interest is equivalent to an effective annual rate of interest of 3·75%? Give your answer to six decimal places, taking 1 year = 52 weeks.

(ii) What is the total value of Tony's savings at the end of 10 years, i.e. one week after he has made his 520th saving?

15. A company invest €25000 in machinery at the beginning of each year for twelve consecutive years. The machinery depreciates at the rate of 15% per annum compound depreciation. Find the total value of all the machinery at the end of twelve years, correct to the nearest euro.

16. A company invests €P in new machinery. The machinery depreciates at the rate of i per annum. If the machinery depreciates to one quarter of its original value after 8 years, find i, correct to three decimal places.

32 Proof by Induction

In maths, there are different ways of proving statements. We have already met deductive proof (the most common method, using a series of logical steps to progress from the hypothesis to the conclusion) and proof by contradiction.

Another indirect method of proof is called proof by induction. The stages involved in the method are outlined in the text below. The first known use of the method was by the 16th century mathematician Francesco Maurolico in his book *Arithmeticorum Libri Duo.*

Proof by induction should not be confused with 'inductive reasoning' which is a technique often used in science. Inductive reasoning involves guessing a formula and then verifying it by checking experimental evidence. This would not do as a mathematical proof.

On the other hand, proof by induction, as we will see below, is a proper and rigorous method of mathematical proof.

32.1 Proof by Induction: The Method

Consider the sum of the first n odd natural numbers.

$n = 1$: $1 = 1$
$n = 2$: $1 + 3 = 4$
$n = 3$: $1 + 3 + 5 = 9$
$n = 4$: $1 + 3 + 5 + 7 = 16$
$n = 5$: $1 + 3 + 5 + 7 + 9 = 25$

Noting that $1^2 = 1, 2^2 = 4, 3^2 = 9, 4^2 = 16, 5^2 = 25$, and so on, it *appears* that we can formulate the rule that the sum of the first n odd natural numbers is equal to n^2. As the nth odd natural number is $2n - 1$, it *appears* as if we have the formula:

$$1 + 3 + 5 + \dots + (2n - 1) = n^2$$

However, on the basis of the few examples shown above, it is not safe to propose that the above formula is always correct. For all we know, the formula may fail for some larger value of n which we have not checked. To be confident that the formula is always correct, we need to prove it.

One method that can be used to prove statements such as this formula is called **proof by induction**. This is a method that can be used to prove a proposition, written $P(n)$, put forward as being true for all natural numbers n, from some starting number s upwards.

For the example above, the first number for which we want the formula to hold is 1. Thus, we want to prove:

$$P(n)\text{: } 1 + 3 + 5 + \dots + (2n - 1) = n^2, \qquad \text{for all } n \in \mathbb{N} \text{ (i.e. } s = 1)$$

The method of proof by induction consists of two steps and a conclusion as shown below.

Step 1: Show that $P(s)$ is true, i.e. show that the statement is true for the first number.

$P(1)$: $1 = 1^2$
$1 = 1$ True.
[When $n = 1$, there is only one term on the LHS, i.e. the first term.]

Step 2: Assuming that $P(k)$ is true, show that as a consequence then $P(k+1)$ is true.

Assume $P(k)$ is true:

$$1 + 3 + 5 + \dots + (2k - 1) = k^2$$

[Just substitute k for each n.]

To prove $P(k + 1)$:

$$1 + 3 + 5 + \dots + (2(k+1) - 1) = (k+1)^2$$

$$1 + 3 + 5 + \dots + (2k+1) = (k+1)^2$$

[Just substitute $k + 1$ for each n.]

Proof:

$$\begin{aligned} \text{LHS} &= 1 + 3 + 5 + \dots + (2k-1) + (2k+1) \\ &= [1 + 3 + 5 + \dots + (2k-1)] + (2k+1) \\ &= [k^2] + (2k+1) \qquad \textit{... by the assumption, } P(k) \\ &= k^2 + 2k + 1 \\ &= (k+1)^2 \\ &= \text{RHS} \end{aligned}$$

Thus, $P(k + 1)$ is true, assuming that $P(k)$ is true.

Conclusion: Write the conclusion that the proposition is now proved.

Thus, $P(n)$ is true for all $n \in \mathbb{N}$.   Q.E.D.

The following points should be noted about the method of proof by induction.

1. The theory behind the method goes as follows. First of all, Step 1 verifies that the proposition is definitely true for the starting number, in this case $s = 1$. Then Step 2 establishes a general bridge between the proposition being true for one natural number and it being true for the next natural number. With Step 2, we can now say that because the proposition is true for $n = 1$, it must also be true for $n = 2$.

Applying Step 2 again and again, we can then say that the proposition must then be true for $n = 3$, 4, 5, ... and so on forever. This completes the proof and is illustrated below.

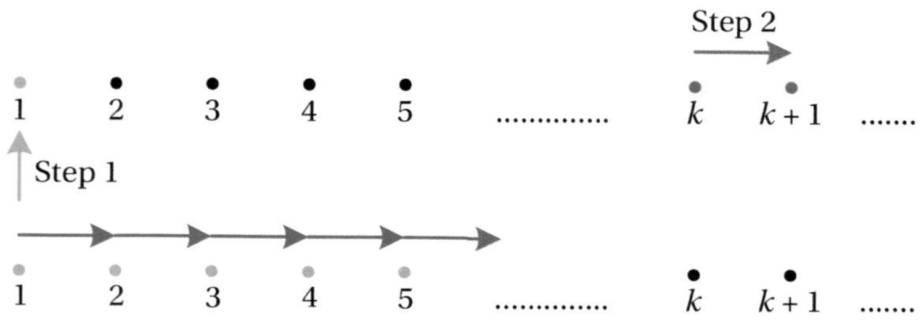

2. Both steps are required to complete the proof. In particular, Step 1 cannot be omitted. Step 2 on its own proves that the proposition will be true for the next natural number if it is true for the previous. However, without Step 1, the proposition might be false for all natural numbers.

3. Don't assume that the starting number, s, is 1. It very often is, but can be different.

4. By the nature of Step 2 of this method, we assume that $P(k)$ is true. This means that we take it as a fact. We do not question how we know it.

5. In proof by induction, the 'induction' is that we (or somebody) guesses the formula in the first place. Then the steps outlined above are used to prove mathematically that the guess is correct.

Exercises 32.1

1. $u_1 = 5$ and $u_{n+1} = \frac{n}{n+1}u_n$ for all $n \in \mathbb{N}$.
   - **(i)** Write down the values of u_2, u_3 and u_4.
   - **(ii)** Hence, by inspection, write an expression for u_n in terms of n.
   - **(iii)** Use proof by induction to justify your answer for part (ii).
2. $u_1 = 1$ and $u_{n+1} = \frac{2}{3}u_n$ for all $n \in \mathbb{N}$.
   - **(i)** Show that $u_n = \left(\frac{2}{3}\right)^n$ is not a correct guess for a formula for u_n.
   - **(ii)** Write down the values of u_2, u_3 and u_4.
   - **(iii)** Hence, by inspection, write an expression for u_n in terms of n.
   - **(iv)** Use proof by induction to justify your answer for part (iii).

32.2 Formula for the Sum of a Series

To prove by induction a formula for the sum of a series, i.e. a statement of the form:

$u_1 + u_2 + \ldots.. + u_n = f(n)$ or $u_2 + u_3 + \ldots.. + u_n = f(n)$, etc,

Step 1: Identify s by comparing first and last on LHS. Prove $P(s)$ true.

Step 2: Assume $P(k)$ is true, i.e.

$\ldots + u_3 + \ldots.. + u_k = f(k)$

Write down $P(k+1)$: $\ldots + u_3 + \ldots.. + u_{k+1} = f(k+1)$

Now write down the LHS, showing the second last term, u_k.

LHS $= \ldots + u_3 + \ldots. + u_k + u_{k+1}$

Group the terms from the first to the second last, and replace them by $f(k)$.

LHS $= (\ldots + u_3 + \ldots. + u_k) + u_{k+1}$

$= f(k) + u_{k+1}$

All that remains is to use the ordinary laws of algebra to show that $f(k) + u_{k+1}$ is equivalent to $f(k+1)$.

Conclusion: Write down the conclusion.

Example 1

Prove by induction that

$(1)(2) + (2)(3) + \ldots.. + n(n+1) = \frac{1}{3}n(n+1)(n+2)$.

Solution

$P(n)$: $(1)(2) + (2)(3) + \ldots. + n(n+1) = \frac{1}{3}n(n+1)(n+2)$

[1] *(The starting number, s, can be found by calculating the value of n which makes the first and last terms on the LHS the same. In this case, though not all, the value of n is 1. Thus, s = 1.)*

$P(1)$: $(1)(2) = \frac{1}{3}(1)(2)(3)$

$2 = 2$

Thus, $P(1)$ is true.

[2] Assume $P(k)$ is true, i.e.

$$(1)(2) + (2)(3) + \ldots. + k(k+1) = \frac{1}{3}k(k+1)(k+2)$$

To prove $P(k+1)$:

$$(1)(2) + (2)(3) + \ldots. + (k+1)(k+2) = \frac{1}{3}(k+1)(k+2)(k+3)$$

(Now take the LHS, showing the second last term – the last term from the assumption. Group the terms from first to second last and replace by what is given in the assumption.)

$$\text{LHS} = \underbrace{(1)(2) + (2)(3) + \ldots. + k(k+1)} + (k+1)(k+2)$$

$$= \underbrace{\frac{1}{3}k(k+1)(k+2)} + (k+1)(k+2) \qquad \text{... by } P(k)$$

$$= \frac{1}{3}k(k+1)(k+2) + \frac{3}{3}(k+1)(k+2)$$

$$= \frac{1}{3}(k+1)(k+2)[k+3] \qquad \text{... taking out the common factor}$$

$$= \frac{1}{3}(k+1)(k+2)(k+3)$$

$$= \text{RHS}$$

Thus, $P(k+1)$ is true, assuming $P(k)$ is true.

Conclusion: Thus, $P(n)$ is true, for all $n \in \mathbb{N}$.

Example 2

Prove by induction that

$$1 + 3 + 9 + \ldots. + 3^n = \frac{1}{2}\left(3^{n+1} - 1\right).$$

Solution

$P(n)$: $1 + 3 + 9 + \ldots + 3^n = \frac{1}{2}\left(3^{n+1} - 1\right)$

[1] *(By comparing the first term, $1 = 3^0$, on the LHS with the last term, 3^n, we can see that the value of n that makes these the same is $n = 0$. Thus, $s = 0$.)*

$P(0)$: $1 = \frac{1}{2}\left(3^1 - 1\right)$

$1 = 1$ True.

[2] Assume $P(k)$ is true, i.e.

$$1 + 3 + 9 + \ldots. + 3^k = \frac{1}{2}\left(3^{k+1} - 1\right)$$

To prove $P(k+1)$:

$$1 + 3 + 9 + \ldots. + 3^{k+1} = \frac{1}{2}\left(3^{k+2} - 1\right)$$

$$\text{LHS} = \underbrace{1 + 3 + 9 + \ldots + 3^k} + 3^{k+1}$$

$$= \underbrace{\frac{1}{2}\left(3^{k+1} - 1\right)} + \frac{2}{2}3^{k+1} \qquad \text{... by } P(k)$$

$$= \frac{1}{2}\left(3^{k+1} - 1 + 2.3^{k+1}\right)$$

$= \frac{1}{2}(3.3^{k+1} - 1)$

$= \frac{1}{2}(3^{k+2} - 1)$

$=$ RHS

Thus, $P(k+1)$ is true, assuming that $P(k)$ is true.

Conclusion: Thus, $P(n)$ is true, for all $n \in \mathbb{N} \cup \{0\}$.

Note: The expression $5 \times 4 \times 3 \times 2 \times 1$ is written 5!, and is called **5 factorial**. $5! = 120$. In general,

$$n! = n(n-1)(n-2)...(2)(1)$$

and 0! is defined to be equal to 1. There is a factorial function button on all modern scientific calculators.

Exercises 32.2

1. Prove by induction that

$$1 + 2 + 3 + ... + n = \frac{n(n+1)}{2}.$$

Use this formula to evaluate

(i) $21 + 22 + 23 + ... + 59 + 60$

(ii) $2 + 4 + 6 + ... + 998 + 1000$.

2. Prove by induction that

$$3 + 7 + 11 + ... + (4n - 1) = 2n^2 + n.$$

Use this formula to evaluate

(i) $3 + 7 + 11 + ... + 99$

(ii) $43 + 47 + 51 + ... + 123$.

3. Prove by induction that

$$1 + \frac{1}{2} + \frac{1}{4} + ... + \frac{1}{2^n} = 2 - \frac{1}{2^n}.$$

4. Prove by induction that

$$\frac{1}{3} + \frac{2}{9} + \frac{4}{27} + ... + \frac{2^{n-1}}{3^n} = 1 - \left(\frac{2}{3}\right)^n.$$

5. Prove by induction that

$$\frac{1}{(1)(2)} + \frac{1}{(2)(3)} + ... + \frac{1}{n(n+1)} = \frac{n}{n+1}.$$

6. Prove by induction that

$$\frac{1}{(1)(3)} + \frac{1}{(3)(5)} + ... + \frac{1}{(2n-1)(2n+1)} = \frac{n}{2n+1}.$$

7. Prove by induction that

$$(1)(3) + (2)(4) + ... + (n-1)(n+1) = \frac{n(n-1)(2n+5)}{6}.$$

8. Prove by induction that

$$(2)(5) + (3)(6) + ... + (n+1)(n+4) = \frac{1}{3}n(n+4)(n+5).$$

9. Prove by induction that

$$1^2 + 2^2 + ... + n^2 = \frac{n(n+1)(2n+1)}{6}.$$

10. Prove by induction that

$$1(1!) + 2(2!) + 3(3!) + ... + n(n!) = (n+1)! - 1.$$

32.3 Divisibility Proofs

30 is divisible by 6, because, when 30 is divided by 6, the remainder is zero. Another way of saying this is that 30 is divisible by 6 because we can write

$30 = 6 \times A, \qquad \text{for some } A \in \mathbb{Z}.$

We know that $A = 5$, but this is not important. Saying that 6 is a factor of 30 is equivalent to saying that 30 is divisible by 6.

In the same way, if $f(k)$ is divisible by 8, then we can write

$f(k) = 8.A, \qquad \text{for some } A \in \mathbb{Z}.$

Likewise, if $f(k)$ is divisible by 11, then $f(k) = 11.A$, for some $A \in \mathbb{Z}$.

We will use this definition of divisibility in the proof by induction questions to follow. A typical such question would be:

"Prove by induction that $3^{2n} - 1$ is divisible by 8, for all $n \in \mathbb{N}$."

We should note the following.

1. If n is in the index, try to write each index as n exactly. Here
   $3^{2n} = (3^2)^n = 9^n$
   Thus, "$P(n)$: $9^n - 1$ is divisible by 8" is a better way of writing the proposition.

2. Write the assumption with an " = " sign, and rearrange to get a single term on the LHS. Here
   $P(k)$: $9^k - 1$ is divisible by 8
   i.e. $9^k - 1 = 8A, \qquad \text{for some } A \in \mathbb{Z}$
   i.e. $9^k = 8A + 1$

3. In the $P(k+1)$ expression, break down the terms so that the 9^k is visible.
   Then substitute $8A + 1$ for this term, and show that 8 can be taken out as a factor.

Example 1

Prove by induction that

$3^{2n} - 1$

is divisible by 8, for all $n \in \mathbb{N}$.

Solution

$P(n)$: $3^{2n} - 1$ is divisible by 8 $\qquad s = 1 \qquad$ *... as $\mathbb{N} = \{1, 2, 3, ...\}$*

or

$P(n)$: $9^n - 1$ is divisible by 8

[1] $P(1)$: $9^1 - 1 = 9 - 1 = 8$ which is divisible by 8. True.

[2] Assume $P(k)$ is true, i.e.

$9^k - 1$ is divisible by 8

i.e. $9^k - 1 = 8A$, for some $A \in \mathbb{Z}$

i.e. $9^k = 8A + 1$

To prove $P(k + 1)$:

$9^{k+1} - 1$ is divisible by 8

Then

$$\begin{aligned} 9^{k+1} - 1 &= 9(9^k) - 1 \\ &= 9(8A + 1) - 1, \quad \textit{... by } P(k) \\ &= 72A + 8 \\ &= 8(9A + 1) \\ &= 8B, \quad \text{for some } B \in \mathbb{Z} \end{aligned}$$

Thus, $9^{k+1} - 1$ is divisible by 8.

Hence, $P(k + 1)$ is true, assuming $P(k)$ is true.

Conclusion: Thus, $P(n)$ is true, for all $n \in \mathbb{N}$.

Example 2

Prove by induction that 3 is a factor of $7^n + 2^{2n} + 1$, for all $n \in \mathbb{N}$.

Solution

("3 is a factor of ..." is another way of saying "... is divisible by 3".)

$P(n)$: $7^n + 2^{2n} + 1$ is divisible by 3, $s = 1$

or

$P(n)$: $7^n + 4^n + 1$ is divisible by 3 ... *as* $2^{2n} = (2^2)^n = 4^n$

[1] $P(1)$: $7^1 + 4^1 + 1 = 7 + 4 + 1 = 12$ is divisible by 3.
True.

[2] Assume $P(k)$ is true, i.e.

$7^k + 4^k + 1$ is divisible by 3

i.e. $7^k + 4^k + 1 = 3A$, for some $A \in \mathbb{Z}$

i.e. $7^k = 3A - 4^k - 1$

To prove $P(k + 1)$:

$7^{k+1} + 4^{k+1} + 1$ is divisible by 3

Then

$$\begin{aligned} 7^{k+1} + 4^{k+1} + 1 &= 7(7^k) + 4(4^k) + 1 \\ &= 7(3A - 4^k - 1) + 4(4^k) + 1 \quad \textit{... by } P(k) \\ &= 21A - 3(4^k) - 6 \\ &= 3(7A - 4^k - 2) \\ &= 3B, \quad \text{for some } B \in \mathbb{Z} \end{aligned}$$

Thus, $7^{k+1} + 4^{k+1} + 1$ is divisible by 3.

Hence, $P(k + 1)$ is true, assuming $P(k)$ is true.

Conclusion: Thus, $P(n)$ is true, for all $n \in \mathbb{N}$.

Example 3

Prove by induction that

$$2n^3 - 3n^2 + n$$

is divisible by 6, for all $n \in \mathbb{N}$, $n \geq 2$.

Solution

$P(n)$: $2n^3 - 3n^2 + n$ is divisible by 6, $\quad s = 2$

[1] $P(2)$: $2(2)^3 - 3(2)^2 + (2) = 16 - 12 + 2 = 6$
which is divisible by 6. True

[2] Assume $P(k)$ is true, i.e.

$$2k^3 - 3k^2 + k \text{ is divisible by } 6$$

i.e. $2k^3 - 3k^2 + k = 6A$, $\quad$ for some $A \in \mathbb{Z}$

i.e. $2k^3 = 6A + 3k^2 - k$

To prove $P(k + 1)$:

$$2(k+1)^3 - 3(k+1)^2 + (k+1) \text{ is divisible by } 6$$

Then

$$\begin{aligned}
&2(k+1)^3 - 3(k+1)^2 + (k+1) \\
&= 2(k^3 + 3k^2 + 3k + 1) - 3(k^2 + 2k + 1) + k + 1 \\
&= 2k^3 + 3k^2 + k \\
&= (6A + 3k^2 - k) + 3k^2 + k \qquad \text{... by } P(k) \\
&= 6A + 6k^2 \\
&= 6(A + k^2) \\
&= 6B, \qquad \text{for some } B \in \mathbb{Z}
\end{aligned}$$

Thus, $P(k + 1)$ is true, assuming $P(k)$ is true.

Conclusion: Hence, $P(n)$ is true for all $n \in \mathbb{N}$, $n \geq 2$.

Exercises 32.3

1. Prove by induction that $2^{2n} - 1$ is divisible by 3, for all $n \in \mathbb{N}$.
2. Prove by induction that $2^{2n} + 14$ is divisible by 6, for all $n \in \mathbb{N}$.
3. Prove by induction that 7 is a factor of $8^{2n} - 1$, for all $n \in \mathbb{N}$.
4. Prove by induction that $10^n - 3^n$ is divisible by 7, for all $n \in \mathbb{N}$.
5. Show by mathematical induction that $7^n + 2^{2n+1}$ is divisible by 3, for all $n \in \mathbb{N}$.
6. Prove by induction that $2^{n+2} + 3^{2n+1}$ is divisible by 7, for all $n \in \mathbb{N} \cup \{0\}$.
7. Prove by induction that
   $5^{2n+2} - 4^{n+1}$ is divisible by 21,
   for all $n \in \mathbb{N} \cup \{0\}$.
8. Prove by induction that
   $n^3 - n$ is divisible by 3,
   for all $n \geq 2$, $n \in \mathbb{N}$.

9. Prove by induction that
$n(n+1)(2n+1)$ is divisible by 6,
for all $n \in \mathbb{N}$.

10. Prove by induction that $2n^3 + 9n^2 + 7n$ is divisible by 6, for all $n \in \mathbb{N}$.

11. Prove that $8^n - 7n + 6$ is divisible by 7, for all $n \in \mathbb{N}$.

12. Prove by induction that $5^n - 4n + 15$ is divisible by 16, for all $n \in \mathbb{N}$.

13. Prove by induction that $4^{n+3} - 3n - 10$ is divisible by 3, for all $n \in \mathbb{N} \cup \{0\}$.

32.4 Inequality Proofs

Certain types of inequality can be proved by induction.

The principle we will use to approach these inequalities is as follows.

(i) Suppose we have the inequality :
$x > y$
and we want to change it to
$x > z$.

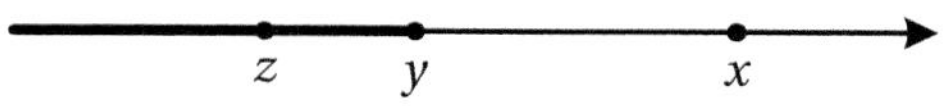

From the diagram opposite, it is clear that this change will definitely be valid as long as $y \geq z$.

(ii) Suppose we have the inequality:
$x < y$
and we want to change it to
$x < z$.

From the diagram opposite, it is clear that this change will definitely be valid as long as $y \leq z$.

To prove an inequality, $P(n)$, by induction:

Step 1: Identify s correctly, and prove $P(s)$ is true.

Step 2: Assume $P(k)$ is true, writing this down.
Write down $P(k+1)$.
Write down $P(k)$ and change both sides so that the LHS is as it should be in $P(k+1)$. Then change the other side into what it should be in $P(k+1)$. Finally, explain why this change is valid.

Conclusion: Draw the usual conclusion.

Note that in explaining why the change of inequality is valid, it is important to remember that k only assumes the same value as n, e.g. if we are proving an inequality for $n \geq 4$, then $s = 4$ and $k \geq 4$.

Example 1

Prove by induction that
$(n+1)! \geq 3^n$, for $n \in \mathbb{N}, n \geq 5$.

Solution

$P(n)$: $(n+1)! \geq 3^n$ $\qquad s = 5$

[1] $P(5)$: $6! \geq 3^5$

$720 \geq 243$ $\qquad$ True.

[2] Assume $P(k)$ is true, i.e.

$(k+1)! \geq 3^k$

To prove $P(k+1)$: $(k+2)! \geq 3^{k+1}$

From $P(k)$: $(k+1)! \geq 3^k$

$(k+2)(k+1)! \geq (k+2)3^k$

$(k+2)! \geq (k+2)3^k$

$(k+2)! \geq 3^{k+1}$

... valid if

$(k+2)3^k \geq 3^{k+1}$

$(k+2)3^k \geq 3 \,.\, 3^k$

$k+2 \geq 3$

$k \geq 1$,

true because $k \geq 5$

Thus, $P(k+1)$ is true, assuming $P(k)$ is true.

Conclusion: Hence, $P(n)$ is true, for all $n \in \mathbb{N}$, $n \geq 5$.

Example 2

Prove by induction that

$n^2 > 3n + 1$, $\qquad$ for $n \in \mathbb{N}$, $n \geq 4$.

Solution

$P(n)$: $n^2 > 3n + 1$ $\qquad s = 4$

[1] $P(4)$: $4^2 > 3(4) + 1$

$16 > 13$ $\qquad$ True.

[2] Assume $P(k)$ is true, i.e.

$k^2 > 3k + 1$

To prove $P(k+1)$:

$(k+1)^2 > 3(k+1) + 1$

or $\qquad k^2 + 2k + 1 > 3k + 4$

By $P(k)$: $\qquad k^2 > 3k + 1$

$k^2 + 2k + 1 > 3k + 1 + 2k + 1$

$(k+1)^2 > 5k + 2$

$(k+1)^2 > 3k + 4$

... valid if

$5k + 2 \geq 3k + 4$

$2k \geq 2$

$k \geq 1$

true as $k \geq 4$

Thus, $P(k+1)$ is true, assuming $P(k)$ is true.

Conclusion: Hence, $P(n)$ is true for all $n \in \mathbb{N}$, $n \geq 4$.

Example 3

Prove by induction that

$$3^n > n^2,$$

for all $n \in \mathbb{N}$, $n \geq 2$.

Solution

$P(n)$: $\quad 3^n > n^2, \qquad s = 2$

[1] $P(2)$: $\quad 3^2 > 2^2$

$9 > 4 \qquad$ True.

[2] Assume $P(k)$ is true, i.e.

$$3^k > k^2$$

To prove $P(k+1)$:

$$3^{k+1} > (k+1)^2 \text{ or}$$
$$3^{k+1} > k^2 + 2k + 1$$

From $P(k)$,

$$3^k > k^2$$
$$3 \times 3^k > 3 \times k^2$$
$$3^{k+1} > 3k^2$$
$$3^{k+1} > k^2 + 2k + 1$$

... valid if

$$3k^2 \geq k^2 + 2k + 1$$
$$2k^2 - 2k \geq 1$$
$$2k(k-1) \geq 1$$

as $k \geq 2$,

$$2k(k-1) \geq 2(2)(1) = 2$$

thus

$$2k(k-1) \geq 1 \text{ is true}$$

Thus, $P(k+1)$ is true, assuming $P(k)$ is true.

Conclusion: Hence, $P(n)$ is true, for all $n \in \mathbb{N}$, $n \geq 2$.

Exercises 32.4

1. Prove by induction that

$$n^2 > 4n + 3$$

for $n \geq 5$, $n \in \mathbb{N}$.

2. Prove by induction that

$$2n^2 \geq 3n + 2$$

for $n \geq 2$, $n \in \mathbb{N}$.

3. Prove by induction that

$$2^n > 2n + 1,$$

for $n \geq 3$, $n \in \mathbb{N}$.

4. Prove by induction that

$$2^n > 3n,$$

for $n \geq 4$, $n \in \mathbb{N}$.

5. Prove by induction that

$$n! \geq 2^{n-1},$$

for $n \geq 3$, $n \in \mathbb{N}$.

6. Prove by induction that if $x > -1$,

$$(1 + x)^n \geq 1 + nx,$$

for all $n \in \mathbb{N}$.

7. Prove, using the method of induction, that if $r > 0$,

$$\frac{1}{(1 + r)^n} \leq \frac{1}{1 + nr}, \text{ for all } n \geq 1.$$

Revision Exercises 32

1. Prove by induction that

$$1 + 4 + 7 + \ldots + (3n - 2) = \frac{n(3n - 1)}{2}.$$

2. Prove by induction that 9 is a factor of $5^{2n+1} + 2^{4n+2}$, for all $n \in \mathbb{N}$.

3. Prove by induction that, for any positive integer n,

$$x + x^2 + x^3 + \ldots + x^n = \frac{x(x^n - 1)}{x - 1}, \text{ where } x \neq 1.$$

4. Prove by induction that $n! > 2^n$, $n \in \mathbb{N}$, $n \geq 4$.

5. Use induction to prove that 8 is a factor of $7^{2n+1} + 1$ for any positive integer n.

6. Prove that for $n \in \mathbb{N}$, $n \geq 3$, $n^3 + 3n^2 - 10n$ is divisible by 3.

7. Prove by induction that

$9(4^{2n}) - 5^{n-1}$ is divisible by 11,

for all $n \in \mathbb{N}$.

8. Prove by induction that

$$n! > n^2 + n,$$

for $n \geq 4$, $n \in \mathbb{N}$.

9. Prove by induction that

$$-(-2) - (-2)^2 - (-2)^3 - (-2)^4 - \ldots\ldots - (-2)^n = \frac{(-2)^{n+1} + 2}{3}.$$

33

Complex Numbers 1

Until the sixteenth century AD, the use of numbers in maths was limited to what we now call real numbers. Around that time, much work was done on the solution of polynomial equations. For a certain type of cubic equation, an Italian mathematician, Gerolamo Cardano, derived a formula. When this formula was used for a cubic with known integer roots, expressions involving the square roots of negative numbers were obtained. This forced the study of such numbers and what we now know as complex numbers were born.

Shortly after Cardano, another Italian, Rafael Bombelli, came up with the basic rules for dealing with complex numbers. Subsequently, many of the greatest mathematicians of the next three centuries worked on and developed the theory of complex numbers. These included Leibniz (more famous for his invention of calculus), Euler (who introduced the modern notation), Gauss, Cauchy, Argand and the Irish mathematician Sir William Rowan Hamilton, who extended complex numbers to three dimensions with his invention of quaternions. Currently, complex numbers are used extensively in maths, science, engineering and computer games.

33.1 Complex Numbers, the Argand Diagram and Modulus

1. Definitions

When the formula $x = \dfrac{-b \pm \sqrt{b^2 - 4ac}}{2a}$ is used to solve the quadratic equation

$$ax^2 + bx + c = 0,$$

it quite often happens that we get the square root of a negative number. In this case, we can always say that the quadratic equation has no real roots, because there is no real number whose square is a negative number. As we know, if $p \in \mathbb{R}$, then $p^2 \geq 0$.

Alternatively, we can extend the definition of what we call numbers to include the square roots of negative numbers. Then it will be possible to say that all quadratic equations have roots. This is the more forward-looking approach, as it gives a new collection of numbers which have many applications in maths and in real life. Some of these will be seen later in this chapter.

To extend our system of numbers, it is only necessary to introduce one new concept, that of the square root of –1. This is denoted by i, and is referred to as the **imaginary unit**, with reference to the original idea that such a number doesn't exist and, hence, is imaginary.

In some ways, this is a misleading name because a number such as $-\frac{1}{2}$ doesn't exist either, and yet we have grown accustomed to using such numbers.

As $i = \sqrt{-1}$

$$i^2 = (\sqrt{-1})^2$$

$$i^2 = -1.$$

This is the preferred definition of the imaginary unit. We can now write the square root of any negative number in terms of i, e.g.

$$\sqrt{-16} = \sqrt{(16)(-1)} = \sqrt{16}\sqrt{-1} = 4i.$$

Any number of the form ki, where $k \in \mathbb{R}$, is called an **imaginary number**.

A **complex number** is a number that involves this new imaginary unit. Specifically, a complex number, z, is a number of the form

$$z = a + bi$$

where $a, b \in \mathbb{R}$. For example, $3 + 2i$, $-4 - i$ and $\frac{1}{2} - \frac{5}{4}i$ are all complex numbers.

There is a certain amount of terminology associated with complex numbers, as there is in all areas of maths.

If

$$z = a + bi$$

then

(i) a is called the **real part** of the complex number, and is written $a = \text{Re}(z)$,

(ii) b is called the **imaginary part** of the complex number, and is written $b = \text{Im}(z)$,

(iii) bi is called the **imaginary term**.

It is interesting to note that every real number is also a complex number. For example,

$$3 = 3 + 0i$$

and so the complex number 3 has a real part of 3 and an imaginary part of 0.

Example 1

State the real part and the imaginary part of each of the following complex numbers:

(i) $z = 4 - 3i$, **(ii)** $z = -7 - i$, **(iii)** $z = 5i$, **(iv)** $z = 9$.

Solution

(i) $z = 4 - 3i$

$\text{Re}(z) = 4$, $\text{Im}(z) = -3$ *(not $-3i$)*

(ii) $z = -7 - i$

$\text{Re}(z) = -7$, $\text{Im}(z) = -1$

(iii) *(Write z as a full complex number first.)*

$z = 5i = 0 + 5i$

$\text{Re}(z) = 0$, $\text{Im}(z) = 5$

(iv) *(Every real number is also a complex number. Write 9 as a full complex number first.)*

$z = 9 = 9 + 0i$

$\text{Re}(z) = 9$, $\text{Im}(z) = 0$.

Powers of i can also be written as complex numbers, as the following example shows. For large powers of i, it is important to note that $i^4 = (i^2)(i^2) = (-1)(-1) = 1$.

Example 2

Simplify each of the following:

(i) i^3 **(ii)** i^{13}.

Solution

(i) $i^3 = (i^2)(i) = (-1)(i) = -i$

(ii) $i^{13} = (i^4)(i^4)(i^4)(i)$

$= (1)(1)(1)(i)$

$= i$

The set of all complex numbers is written as $\mathbb{C}$, and is defined as follows

$$\mathbb{C} = \{a + bi \mid a, b \in \mathbb{R}, i^2 = -1\}.$$

$\mathbb{C}$ includes all real numbers, $\mathbb{R}$, and all imaginary numbers. But most complex numbers are neither real numbers nor imaginary numbers.

Complex Numbers, $\mathbb{C}$

$$\mathbb{C} = \{a + bi \mid a, b \in \mathbb{R}, i^2 = -1\}$$

If $z = a + bi$, then

(i) $a = \text{Re}(z)$

(ii) $b = \text{Im}(z)$.

The Venn Diagram below shows the relationships between the different number systems on our course. The set of natural numbers, $\mathbb{N}$, is a subset of the set of integers, $\mathbb{Z}$, which in turn is a subset of the set of rational numbers, $\mathbb{Q}$. This set is a subset of the set of real numbers, $\mathbb{R}$, which is then a subset of the set of complex numbers, $\mathbb{C}$.

Another subset of $\mathbb{C}$, which is disjoint from $\mathbb{R}$, is the set of imaginary numbers, written as Im, which contains purely imaginary numbers like $-7i$. However, most complex numbers, e.g. $2 - 3i$, belong to neither $\mathbb{R}$ nor to Im.

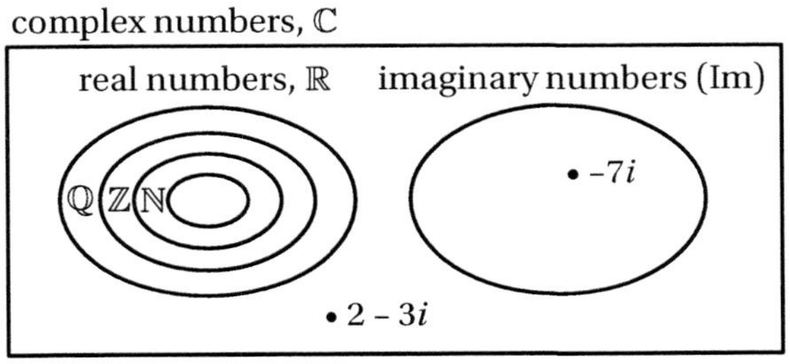

2. Argand Diagram

Complex numbers may be represented graphically on a diagram called an **Argand diagram**, named after the Swiss mathematician Jean-Robert Argand who proposed the theory in 1806.

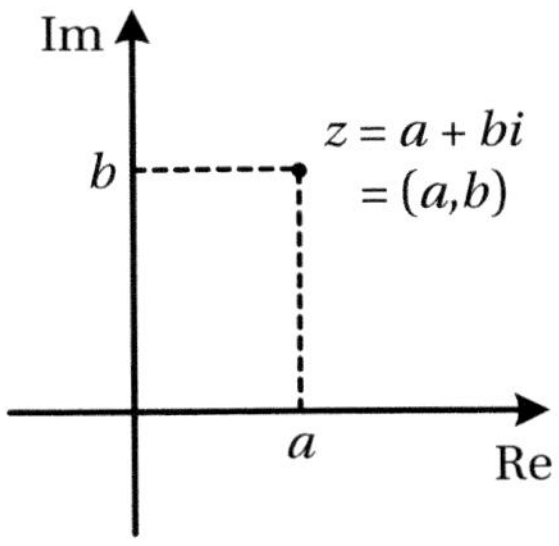

An Argand diagram looks like an ordinary x, y, or Cartesian, plane. However, the x-axis is called the real axis (Re) and the y-axis is called the imaginary axis (Im). The complex number $z = a + bi$ is represented by the point (a,b) on an Argand diagram.

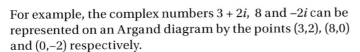

For example, the complex numbers $3 + 2i$, 8 and $-2i$ can be represented on an Argand diagram by the points $(3,2)$, $(8,0)$ and $(0,-2)$ respectively.

3. Modulus of a Complex Number

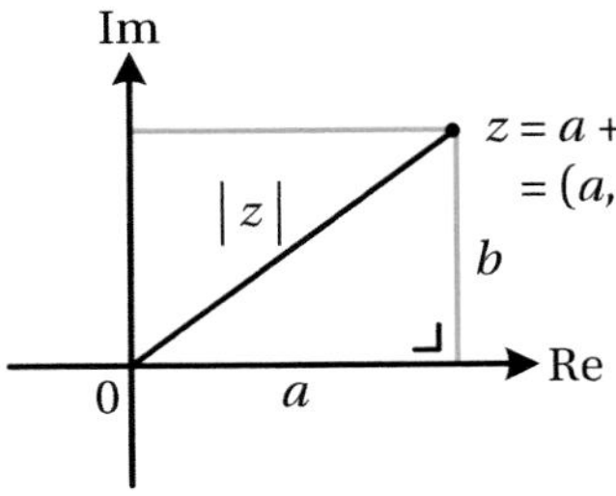

If $z = a + bi$, it is represented by the point (a,b) on an Argand diagram. The **modulus** of z, written $|z|$, is the distance from the origin $0 = 0 + 0i = (0,0)$ to the point representing z on the Argand diagram.

By Pythagoras' Theorem on the triangle shown,

$$|z|^2 = a^2 + b^2$$

$$|z| = \sqrt{a^2 + b^2}$$

The greater the modulus of a complex number, the further it is from the origin.

Example 3

The Argand diagram opposite shows the four complex numbers z_1, z_2, z_3 and z_4.

(i) If one of these is $3 + 3i$, identify which one.

(ii) Write the other complex numbers in the form $a + bi$.

(iii) Determine which of the four complex numbers is furthest from the origin.

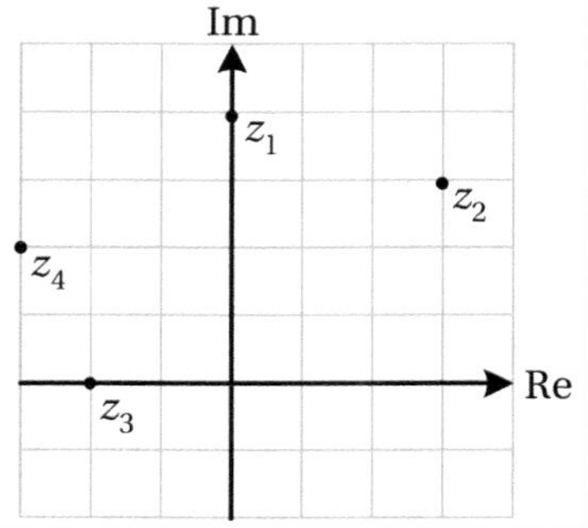

Solution

(i) $3 + 3i = (3,3)$

Thus, $z_2 = 3 + 3i$.

(ii) $z_1 = (0,4) = 0 + 4i = 4i$

$z_3 = (-2,0) = -2 + 0i = -2$

$z_4 = (-3,2) = -3 + 2i$

(iii) $|z_1| = \sqrt{0^2 + 4^2} = \sqrt{16} = 4$ $|z_2| = \sqrt{3^2 + 3^2} = \sqrt{18}$

$|z_3| = \sqrt{(-2)^2 + 0^2} = \sqrt{4} = 2$ $|z_4| = \sqrt{(-3)^2 + 2^2} = \sqrt{13}$

As z_2 is the complex number with the greatest modulus, it is the one furthest from the origin.

Argand Diagram and Modulus

(i) The complex number $z = a + bi$ is represented by the point (a,b) on an Argand diagram.

(ii) The modulus of $z = a + bi$, written $|z|$, is given by

$$|z| = \sqrt{a^2 + b^2}$$

and represents the distance from the origin to the point (a,b).

At this stage, it is important to realise that an Argand diagram only *looks like* an ordinary x, y plane from co-ordinate geometry. As we will see, points on an Argand diagram can be added, subtracted, multiplied and divided in a way that is not possible for points on an x, y plane.

As well as being necessary in the solution of many equations, complex numbers are used in many real life contexts, particularly those where two quantities vary simultaneously. Some examples are radio waves, mobile phone signals and dealing with current, resistance and voltage in alternating currents.

Exercises 33.1

1. State the real and imaginary parts of the following complex numbers:
(i) $7 - 5i$, **(ii)** $8 + 2i$, **(iii)** $-2 - i$, **(iv)** $11i$.

2. State the real and imaginary parts of the following complex numbers:
(i) $-3 - 2i$, **(ii)** $5 - 4i$, **(iii)** 8, **(iv)** $-6i$.

3. Simplify the following:
(i) i^6, **(ii)** i^9, **(iii)** i^{10}.

4. Simplify each of the following:
(i) i^7, (ii) i^{11}, (iii) i^{15}.

5. Represent each of the following complex numbers on an Argand diagram:
(i) $5 + 2i$, (ii) $-2 + i$, (iii) $6i$, (iv) -4.

6. Represent each of the following complex numbers on an Argand diagram:
(i) $-3 + 4i$, (ii) $6 - i$, (iii) $-4i$, (iv) 6.

7. $z_1 = 3 - 5i$, $z_2 = -1 + 6i$ and $z_3 = -4 + 4i$.
(i) Represent these three complex numbers on an Argand diagram.
(ii) By using modulus, determine which of the three complex numbers is furthest from the origin.

8. $z_1 = 2 + 6i$, $z_2 = 4 - 5i$ and $z_3 = -7i$.
(i) Represent these three complex numbers on an Argand diagram.
(ii) By using modulus, determine which of the three complex numbers is furthest from the origin.

33.2 Some Operations with Complex Numbers

1. Equality of Complex Numbers

Two complex numbers are only equal if they are equal in all respects, i.e. if the real parts are equal and the imaginary parts are equal.

Equality of Complex Numbers

$a + bi = c + di$

if and only if

Re: $a = c$

Im: $b = d$

This definition of equality can be used to work out unknown coefficients in equations, sometimes by forming and solving simultaneous equations.

Example 1

Find the values of the real numbers x and y if

$$(2x + 3) + (x + 1)i = (3y + 4) + (4 - y)i,$$

where $i^2 = -1$.

Solution

(We are told that these two complex numbers are equal. So we put 'real = real' and 'imaginary = imaginary'.)

$$(2x + 3) + (x + 1)i = (3y + 4) + (4 - y)i$$

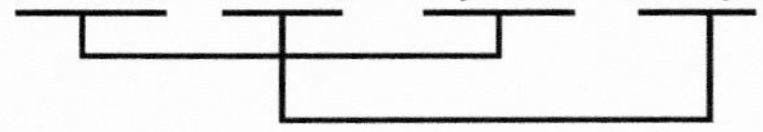

Then:

Re = Re: $2x + 3 = 3y + 4$ ... **1**

Im = Im: $x + 1 = 4 - y$ ... **2**

(Now we solve these equations simultaneously.)

1: $2x - 3y = 1$

2: $x + y = 3$

1: $2x - 3y = 1$

2 × 3: $3x + 3y = 9$

$5x = 10$

$x = 2$

2: $y = 1.$

2. Addition of Complex Numbers

Suppose $z = 2 - 3i$ and $w = 1 + 5i$. Then $z + w$ is also a complex number which can be calculated by using the ordinary laws of algebra, i.e. by adding the real parts and adding the imaginary parts separately, i.e.

$$z + w = (2 - 3i) + (1 + 5i)$$
$$= (2 + 1) + (-3 + 5)i$$
$$= 3 + 2i$$

The addition of complex numbers on an Argand diagram is performed in an interesting way.

If $z = 2 - 3i$, then z is represented by the point (2,–3) on an Argand diagram.

The complex number $w = 1 + 5i$ may be considered to be the **translation** from (0,0) to (1,5), i.e. a change of 1 in the Re direction and a change of 5 in the Im direction.

This translation may be written $\overrightarrow{ow}$.

Adding w to z may be interpreted as finding the image of z under the translation $\overrightarrow{ow}$, i.e.

$$z + w = z + \overrightarrow{ow}.$$

From the diagram opposite, we can see that the image is (3,2) = $3 + 2i$.

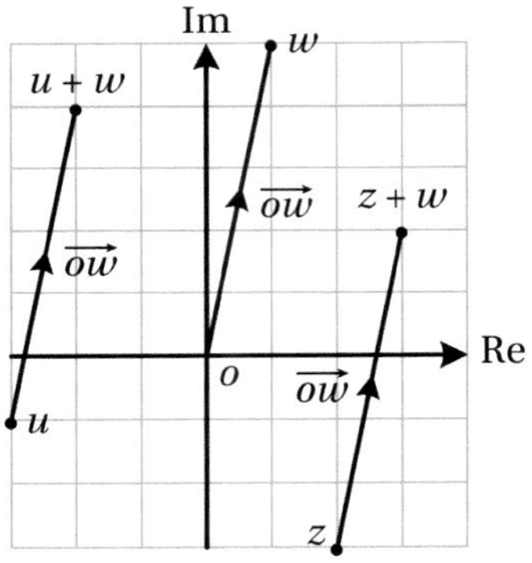

If $w = 1 + 5i$ is added to any other complex number, then that number will undergo the same translation. For example, if $u = -3 - i$, then

$$u + w = (-3 - i) + (1 + 5i)$$
$$= (-3 + 1) + (-1 + 5)i$$
$$= -2 + 4i$$

which we can see from the diagram is the image of u under the translation $\overrightarrow{ow}$.

You should also note that $w + z$ may be interpreted as the image of the point w under the translation $\overrightarrow{oz}$. From the diagram opposite, we can see that

(i) $w + z$ gives the same outcome as $z + w$,

(ii) the points o, w, $z + w$ and z are the vertices of a parallelogram,

(iii) $|z + w|$ is not greater than $|z| + |w|$, because one side of a triangle cannot be longer than the sum of the other two sides.

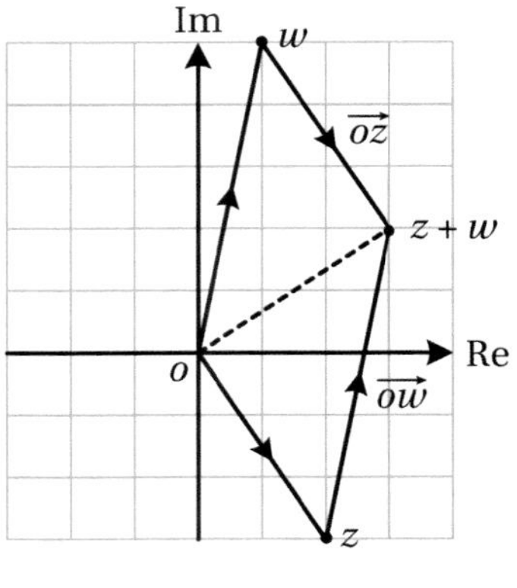

3. Negative of a Complex Number

If $\quad z = 3 - 4i$
then $\quad -z = -(3 - 4i)$
$\quad -z = -3 + 4i,$
i.e. both the real part and the imaginary parts are multiplied by –1.

On an Argand diagram, if z is the translation $\overrightarrow{oz}$, then $-z$ may be considered to be the translation $-\overrightarrow{oz}$, which is the same as the translation from z to o, i.e.

$$-\overrightarrow{oz} = \overrightarrow{zo}.$$

The translation $\overrightarrow{zo}$ is the same length as the translation $\overrightarrow{oz}$, but points in the opposite direction.

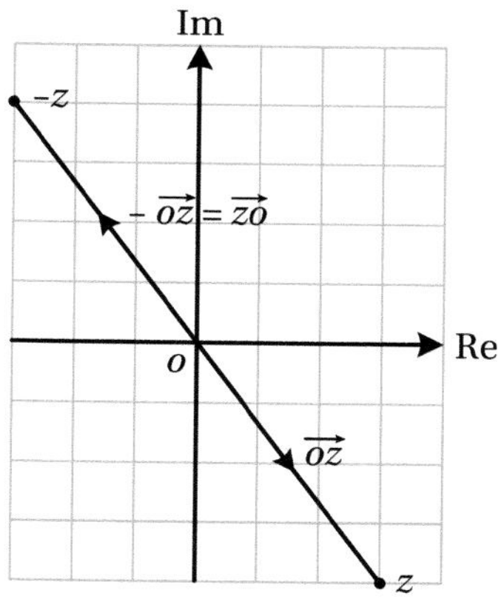

4. Subtraction of Complex Numbers

Suppose $z = 3 + 2i$ and $w = 1 - 3i$, then

$$z - w = (3 + 2i) - (1 - 3i)$$
$$= (3 - 1) + (2 + 3)i$$
$$= 2 + 5i$$

i.e. subtract the real parts and subtract the imaginary parts separately.

On an Argand diagram, $z - w$ means that we start with the point z and translate it by the translation

$$-\overrightarrow{ow} = \overrightarrow{wo},$$

i.e. move z the same distance but in the exact opposite direction to $\overrightarrow{ow}$.

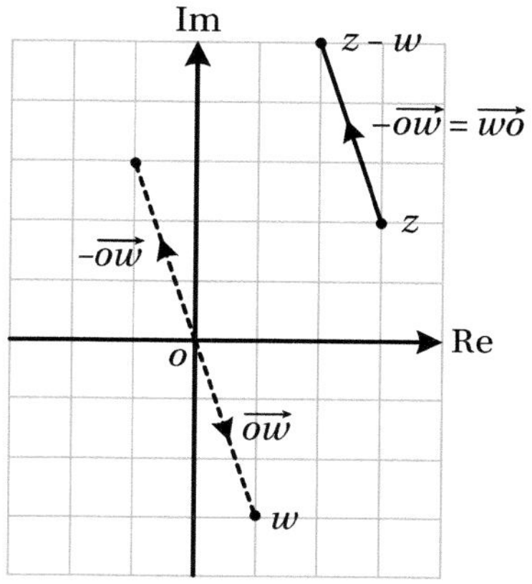

5. Multiplication of a Complex Number by a Real Number

The complex number $z = 8 + 6i$ can be represented by the point (8,6) on an Argand diagram, and

$$|z| = \sqrt{8^2 + 6^2} = \sqrt{100} = 10$$

Below are some examples of what we get when we multiply z by a real number $k \in \mathbb{R}$.

(i) $2z = 2(8 + 6i)$
$\quad = 16 + 12i$

i.e. multiply both the real part and the imaginary part of the complex number by 2.
On an Argand diagram, 2z is represented by the point (16,12) and

$$|2z| = \sqrt{16^2 + 12^2} = \sqrt{400} = 20$$

Thus, the modulus of $2z$ is twice that of z, and so $2z$ is twice as far from the origin as z.
The translation $2\,\overrightarrow{oz}$ is in the same direction as the translation $\overrightarrow{oz}$ but is twice as long.
In this sense, multiplying a complex number by 2 can be considered as an enlargement or stretching of the complex number by a factor of 2.

(ii) $\frac{1}{2}z = \frac{1}{2}(8 + 6i)$
$\quad = 4 + 3i$

i.e. multiply both the real part and the imaginary part of the complex number by $\frac{1}{2}$.
On an Argand diagram, $\frac{1}{2}z$ is represented by the point (4,3) and

$$\left|\frac{1}{2}z\right| = \sqrt{4^2 + 3^2} = \sqrt{25} = 5$$

Thus, the modulus of $\frac{1}{2}z$ is $\frac{1}{2}$ that of z, and so it is half as far from the origin as z.

The translation $\frac{1}{2}\overrightarrow{oz}$ is in the same direction as the translation $\overrightarrow{oz}$ but is half as long.

Hence, multiplying a complex number by $\frac{1}{2}$ can be considered a reduction or contraction of the complex number by a factor of $\frac{1}{2}$.

(iii) $-2z = -2(8 + 6i)$
$= -16 - 12i$

i.e. multiply both the real part and the imaginary part of the complex number by -2.

On an Argand diagram, $-2z$ is represented by the point $(-16,-12)$ and

$$|-2z| = \sqrt{(-16)^2 + (-12)^2}$$
$$= \sqrt{400}$$
$$= 20$$

As $|-2z| = 2|z|$, $-2z$ is twice as far from the origin as z.
The translation $-2\,\overrightarrow{oz}$ is in the opposite direction to the translation $\overrightarrow{oz}$ and is twice as long.

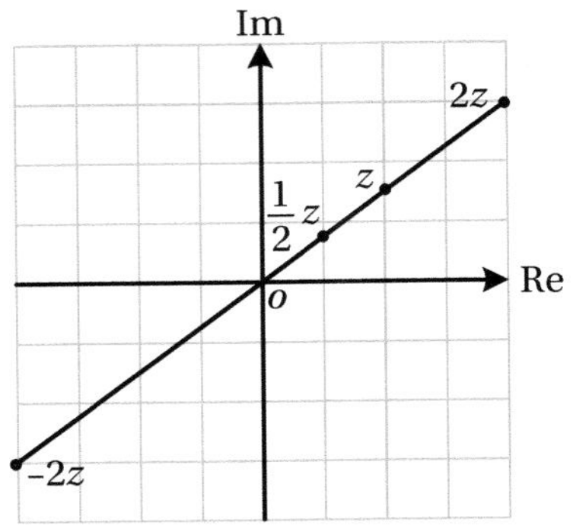

These multiples of z are shown on the diagram opposite.

Example 2

$z = 4 + 5i$ and $w = -3 + 2i$, where $i^2 = -1$.

(i) Calculate $3z - 2w$ in the form $a + bi$.

(ii) Show that

$$|z + 2w| < |z| + 2|w|.$$

Solution

(i) $3z - 2w = 3(4 + 5i) - 2(-3 + 2i)$
$= (12 + 15i) + (6 - 4i)$
$= (12 + 6) + (15 - 4)i$
$= 18 + 11i$

(ii) $|z| = |4 + 5i| = \sqrt{4^2 + 5^2} = \sqrt{41}$ and $|w| = |-3 + 2i| = \sqrt{(-3)^2 + 2^2} = \sqrt{13}$

RHS $= |z| + 2|w|$
$= \sqrt{41} + 2\sqrt{13} \approx 13{\cdot}61$

Also

LHS $= |z + 2w|$
$= |(4 + 5i) + 2(-3 + 2i)|$
$= |-2 + 9i|$
$= \sqrt{(-2)^2 + 9^2}$
$= \sqrt{85} \approx 9{\cdot}22$

As $9{\cdot}22 < 13{\cdot}61$, $|z + 2w| < |z| + 2|w|$.

Example 3

The Argand diagram opposite shows the six complex numbers a, b, c, d, e and f.

If these points represent the complex numbers z, w, $2w$, $-z$, $z + w$ and $z + 3w$, identify which point represents each complex number.

By copying the diagram, explain your reasoning.

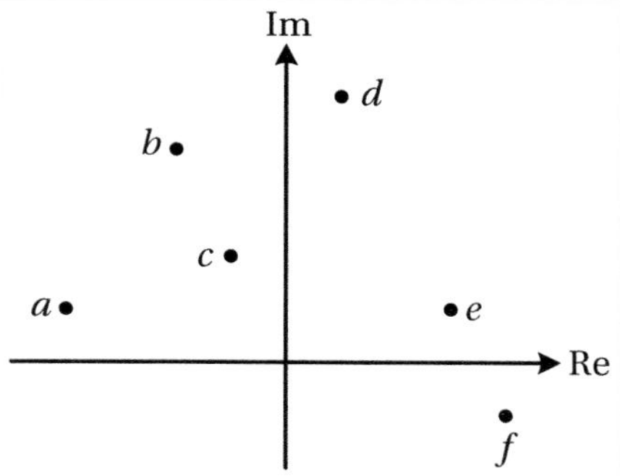

Solution

(i) As the translation from o to b is twice the translation from o to c, we can say that

$c = w$

and $b = 2w$.

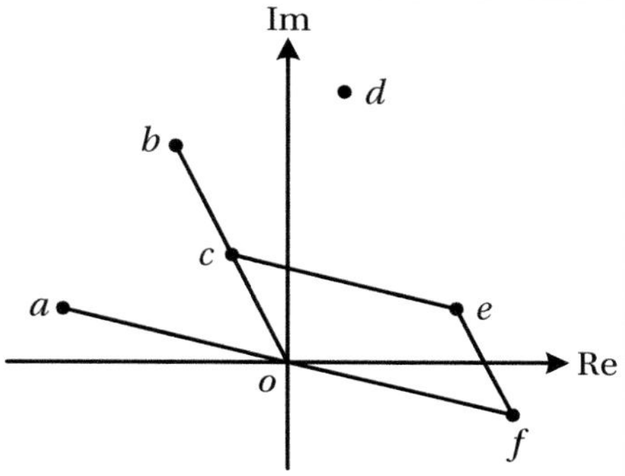

(ii) As the translation o to a is equal in length but opposite in direction to the translation from o to f, one of these points is z and the other is $-z$. As $ocef$ is a parallelogram, f must be z, giving e is $z + w$. Also $a = -z$. Thus,

$f = z$

$a = -z$

$e = z + w$.

(iii) Finally, d must be $z + 3w$.

$d = z + 3w$.

6. Multiplication of a Complex Number by a Complex Number

To multiply one complex number by another, we multiply using the ordinary laws of algebra (just think of i as a letter just like x), ***except*** that whenever we meet i^2, we replace it by (-1).

Example 4

(i) If $z = 1 - 5i$ and $w = 1 + 2i$, express $z.w$ in the form $a + bi$.

(ii) If $u = k - 5i$ and $v = 1 + 2i$, find the value of $k \in \mathbb{R}$ for which $u.v$ lies on the imaginary axis.

Solution

(i)
$$\begin{aligned} z.w &= (1 - 5i)(1 + 2i) \\ &= 1(1 + 2i) - 5i(1 + 2i) \\ &= 1 + 2i - 5i - 10i^2 \\ &= 1 - 3i - 10(-1) \\ &= 1 - 3i + 10 \\ &= 11 - 3i \end{aligned}$$

(ii)
$$\begin{aligned} u.v &= (k - 5i)(1 + 2i) \\ &= k(1 + 2i) - 5i(1 + 2i) \\ &= k + 2ki - 5i - 10i^2 \\ &= k + (2k - 5)i - 10(-1) \\ &= k + (2k - 5)i + 10 \\ &= (k + 10) + (2k - 5)i \end{aligned}$$

If this complex number lies on the Im axis, then its real part must be 0. Thus,

$k + 10 = 0$

$k = -10$.

The interpretation of the multiplication of complex numbers on an Argand diagram will be studied in detail later.

For the moment, we will just state the following result. Suppose the angles that z and w make with the positive sense of the Re axis are α and β respectively. Then the angle that $z.w$ makes with the positive sense of the Re axis is $\alpha + \beta$, i.e. we add the angles.

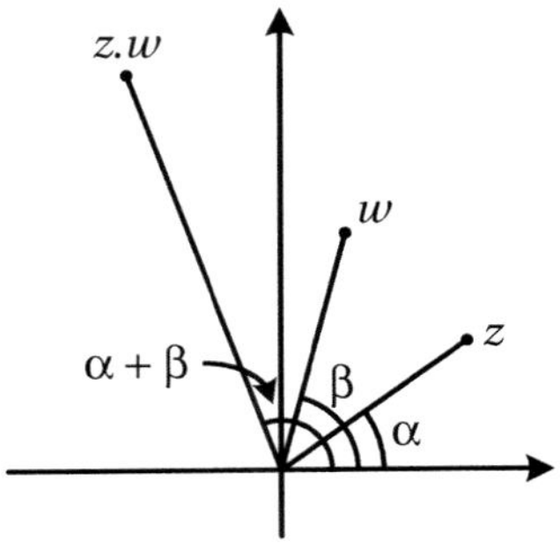

Also, if the lengths of z and w are $|z|$ and $|w|$ respectively, then the length of $z.w$ is given by:

$$|z.w| = |z|.|w|,$$

i.e. we multiply the lengths (the moduli).

Exercises 33.2

1. Find the values of the real numbers x and y if

$$2x + yi = (x + 3) - (x - 1)i, \text{ where } i^2 = -1.$$

2. Find the values of the real numbers p and q if

$$(p + 3) + (p - q)i = q + (q - 5)i, \text{ where } i^2 = -1.$$

3. Find the values of the real numbers x and y if

$$x - 4yi = (y - 2) + (1 - 13x)i, \text{ where } i^2 = -1.$$

4. Find the values of the real numbers x and y if:

$$3x + 2yi = (y + 3) + (2x + 2)i, \text{ where } i^2 = -1.$$

5. $w = 3 - 2i$. Plot w on an Argand diagram. Plot on the same Argand diagram
(i) z_1 and $z_1 + w$, if $z_1 = -1 + 3i$
(ii) z_2 and $z_2 + w$, if $z_2 = 4 + i$
(iii) z_3 and $z_3 + w$, if $z_3 = -3 - i$.

6. $w = -1 + 3i$. Plot w on an Argand diagram. Plot on the same Argand diagram
(i) z_1 and $z_1 + w$, if $z_1 = 4 - i$
(ii) z_2 and $z_2 + w$, if $z_2 = 2 + 5i$
(iii) z_3 and $z_3 + w$, if $z_3 = 6 + 2i$.

7. $z = 5 - i$, $w = -2 + 3i$, $u = 4 + 2i$ and $v = 4i$. Calculate and plot on an Argand diagram
(i) $w - z$ **(ii)** $u - z$ **(iii)** $v - z$.

8. $z = 3 + 3i$, $w = 6 - 2i$, $u = 4$ and $v = 1 - 2i$. Calculate and plot on an Argand diagram
(i) $w - z$ **(ii)** $u - z$ **(iii)** $v - z$.

9. If $z = 4 - i$ and $w = 3 + 2i$, express each of the following in the form $a + bi$:
(i) $z + w$, **(ii)** $2z - w$, **(iii)** zw, **(iv)** z^2.

10. If $z = -2 + i$ and $w = 3 - 4i$, express each of the following in the form $a + bi$:
(i) $z - w$, **(ii)** $3z + 2w$, **(iii)** zw, **(iv)** iz.

11. If $z = 3 + 5i$ and $w = -2 - 3i$, express each of the following in the form $a + bi$:
(i) $2z + w$, **(ii)** $4z - w$, **(iii)** zw, **(iv)** $z(w + 3i)$.

12. If $z = -1 + 4i$ and $w = 4 - 5i$, express each of the following in the form $a + bi$:
(i) $z - 3w$, **(ii)** $2z + 3w$, **(iii)** zw, **(iv)** $(z + w)(z - w)$.

13. If $z = 2 - 3i$, evaluate $2z^2 - 8z$.

14. If $w = -3 + 5i$, evaluate $w^2 + 6w - 10$.

15. $z = 3 + ki$ and $w = t - i$. Find the values of $k, t \in \mathbb{R}$ if $z + w = 8 + i$.

16. If $z = 4 + 3i$, express z^2 in the form $a + bi$.

Find the values of the real numbers t and k if $z^2 + tz = -13 + ki$.

17. The Argand diagram opposite shows the complex numbers a, b, c, d, e and f. If these points represent the complex numbers z, $2z$, w, $-w$, $z + w$ and $z + 4w$, identify which point represents each complex number. By copying the diagram, explain your reasoning.

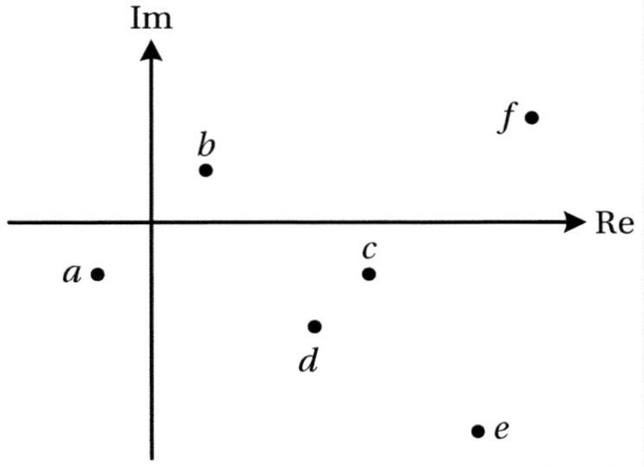

18. The Argand diagram opposite shows the complex numbers a, b, c, d, e and f. If these points represent complex numbers z, $2z$, w, $-w$, $z + w$ and $z - w$, identify which point represents each complex number. By copying the diagram, explain your reasoning.

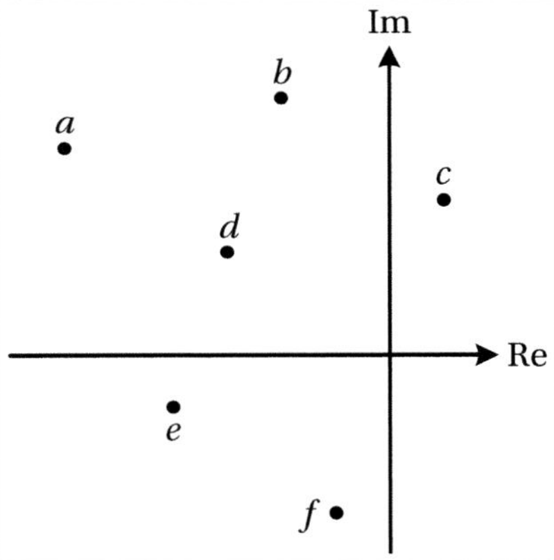

19. The Argand diagram opposite shows points representing the complex numbers z and w. Copy the diagram and show, with construction, how to locate the points representing the complex numbers

(i) $2z$

(ii) $-z$

(iii) $2w$

(iv) $z + w$

(v) $\frac{1}{2}z$

(vi) $2z - w$.

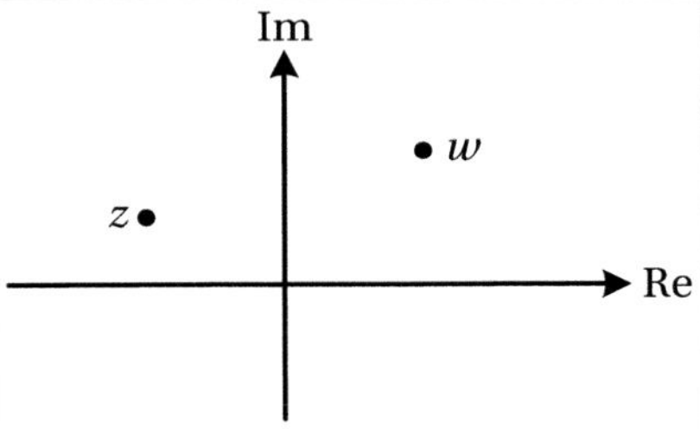

20. The Argand diagram opposite shows points representing the complex numbers z and w. Copy the diagram and show, with construction, how to locate the points representing the complex numbers

(i) $-z$
(ii) $2w$
(iii) $\frac{3}{2}z$
(iv) $z + w$
(v) $z - w$
(vi) u, if $2w + u = z$.

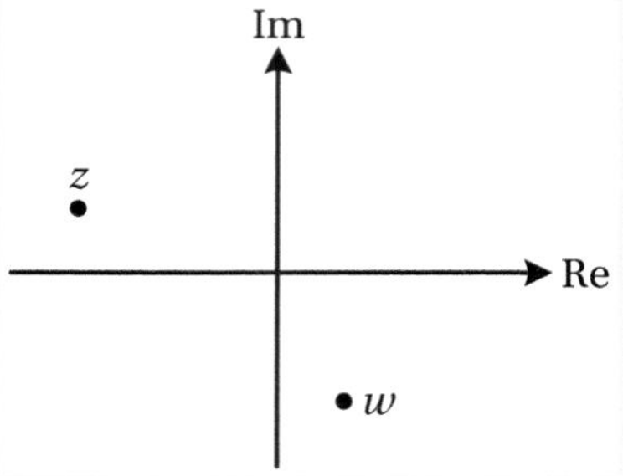

21. The Argand diagram opposite shows points representing the complex numbers z and $z + w$. Copy the diagram and show, with construction, how to locate the points representing the complex numbers

(i) w
(ii) $z - w$
(iii) $2z - w$
(iv) u, if $2u + w = z$.

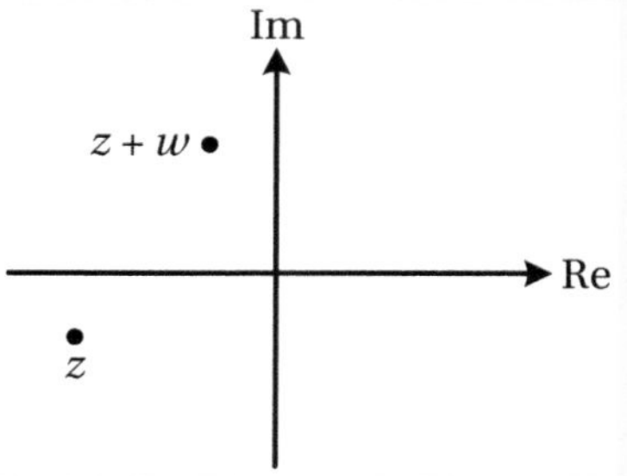

22. If $z = 4 - 2i$ and $w = -1 + 3i$, calculate

(i) $|z|$, **(ii)** $|w|$, **(iii)** $|z + w|$.

Investigate if $|z + w| = |z| + |w|$.

23. If $z = 2 - 3i$ and $w = -3 + i$, calculate

(i) $|z|$, **(ii)** $|w|$, **(iii)** $|2z - w|$.

Investigate if $|2z - w| = 2|z| - |w|$.

24. If $z = 4 - i$, calculate $|2z - 3 + 7i|$.

25. If $z = 2 + i$, calculate $|2z - 1 + 3i|$.

33.3 Conjugates and Division of Complex Numbers

1. Complex Conjugate

The complex conjugate, or just the **conjugate**, of the complex number

$$z = a + bi$$

is written $\bar{z}$ and is given by

$$\bar{z} = a - bi,$$

i.e. we change the sign of the imaginary part of the complex number.

Some examples of complex numbers and their conjugates are given below.

$z =$	$\bar{z} =$
$3 + 2i$	$3 - 2i$
$-1 + 5i$	$-1 - 5i$
$4 - i$	$4 + i$
$7i$	$-7i$
6	6

Complex Conjugates

If $\quad z = a + bi$

then $\quad \overline{z} = a - bi,$

i.e. the conjugate is formed by changing the sign of the imaginary part.

On an Argand diagram,

$$z = a + bi = (a,b)$$

and

$$\overline{z} = a - bi = (a,-b)$$

are images of each other under reflection in the Re axis.

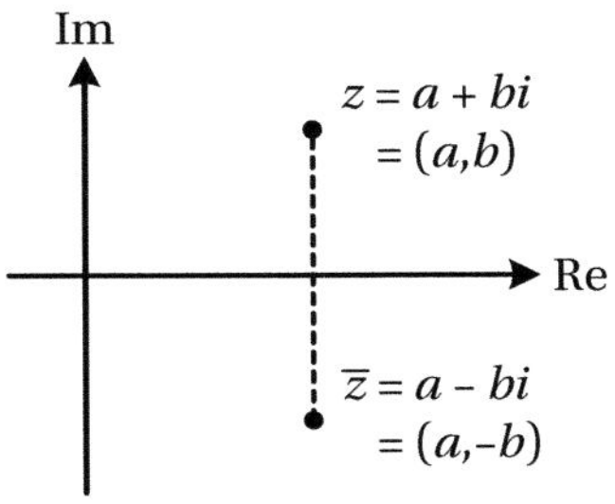

Complex numbers and their conjugates satisfy some interesting and important properties.

Properties of Conjugates

If $\quad z = a + bi \quad$ then

1. $z + \overline{z} = 2\text{Re}(z) = 2a$

2. $z - \overline{z} = 2i\text{Im}(z) = 2bi$

3. $z.z = a^2 + b^2$

i.e. the product of a complex number and its conjugate is always a non-negative real number (no i).

To demonstrate these properties:

1.
$$\begin{aligned} z + \overline{z} &= (a + bi) + (a - bi) \\ &= 2a \\ &= 2\text{Re}(z) \end{aligned}$$

2.
$$\begin{aligned} z - \overline{z} &= (a + bi) - (a - bi) \\ &= 2bi \\ &= 2i\text{Im}(z) \end{aligned}$$

3.
$$\begin{aligned} z.\overline{z} &= (a + bi)(a - bi) \\ &= a(a - bi) + bi(a - bi) \\ &= a^2 - abi + abi - b^2i^2 \\ &= a^2 - b^2(-1) \\ &= a^2 + b^2 \end{aligned}$$

Example 1

If $z = 1 + 2i$, evaluate $z.\overline{z} + 4(z + \overline{z})$.

Solution

If $z = 1 + 2i$, then $\overline{z} = 1 - 2i$ and

$$\begin{aligned} z.\overline{z} + 4(z + \overline{z}) &= (1 + 2i)(1 - 2i) + 4[(1 + 2i) + (1 - 2i)] \\ &= [(1)^2 + (2)^2] + 4[2] \\ &= 5 + 8 = 13. \end{aligned}$$

Two other properties of conjugates involve the conjugates of sums and the conjugate of products.

Properties of Conjugates

4. $\overline{z_1 + z_2} = \bar{z}_1 + \bar{z}_2$
i.e. the conjugate of the sum of two complex numbers is equal to the sum of the conjugates.

5. $\overline{z_1 . z_2} = \bar{z}_1 . \bar{z}_2$
i.e. the conjugate of the product of two complex numbers is equal to the product of the conjugates.

To demonstrate these properties, let $z_1 = a + bi$ and $z_2 = c + di$:

4.
$$\begin{aligned}\overline{z_1 + z_2} &= \overline{(a + bi) + (c + di)} \\ &= \overline{(a + c) + (b + d)i} \\ &= (a + c) - (b + d)i \\ &= (a - bi) + (c - di) \\ &= \overline{z_1} + \overline{z_2}\end{aligned}$$

5.
$$\begin{aligned}\overline{z_1 . z_2} &= \overline{(a + bi)(c + di)} \\ &= \overline{a(c + di) + bi(c + di)} \\ &= \overline{ac + adi + bci + bdi^2} \\ &= \overline{(ac - bd) + (ad + bc)i} \\ &= (ac - bd) - (ad + bc)i \\ \overline{z_1} . \overline{z_2} &= \overline{(a + bi)} . \overline{(c + di)} \\ &= (a - bi).(c - di) \\ &= ac - adi - bci + bdi^2 \\ &= ac - (ad + bc)i - bd \\ &= (ac - bd) - (ad + bc)i \\ &= \overline{z_1 . z_2}\end{aligned}$$

Example 2

If $z = 3 + 2i$ and $w = 4 - i$, verify that $\overline{z.w} = \bar{z}.\bar{w}$, where $\bar{z}$ is the conjugate of z.

Solution

$$\begin{aligned}\overline{z.w} &= \overline{(3 + 2i)(4 - i)} \\ &= \overline{3(4 - i) + 2i(4 - i)} \\ &= \overline{12 - 3i + 8i - 2(-1)} \\ &= \overline{14 + 5i} \\ &= 14 - 5i\end{aligned}$$

$$\begin{aligned}\bar{z}.\bar{w} &= (3 - 2i)(4 + i) \\ &= 3(4 + i) - 2i(4 + i) \\ &= 12 + 3i - 8i - 2i^2 \\ &= 12 - 5i + 2 \\ &= 14 - 5i \\ &= \overline{z.w}\end{aligned}$$

2. Division

Dividing a complex number by a real number is easy, e.g.

$$\frac{12+7i}{4} = \frac{12}{4} + \frac{7}{4}i = 3 + \frac{7}{4}i.$$

However, to divide a complex number by a non-real complex number (i.e. if there is i on the bottom line of the fraction), we must ***multiply above and below by the conjugate of the bottom line***.

The effect of this is to convert the bottom line into a real number, using Property 3 of conjugates. Example 3 shows how this is achieved.

Example 3

If $z = 9 - 7i$ and $w = 1 - 3i$, express $\frac{z}{w}$ in the form $a + bi$, where $i^2 = -1$.

Solution

$$\frac{z}{w} = \frac{9-7i}{1-3i}$$

(The bottom line is 1 – 3i, and its conjugate is 1 + 3i. This is what we multiply above and below by.)

$$\frac{z}{w} = \frac{9-7i}{1-3i} \times \frac{1+3i}{1+3i}$$

$$= \frac{(9-7i)(1+3i)}{(1-3i)(1+3i)}$$

$$= \frac{9+27i-7i-21i^2}{1^2+(-3)^2}$$

$$= \frac{9+20i+21}{10}$$

$$= \frac{30+20i}{10}$$

$$= 3 + 2i.$$

Exercises 33.3

1. If $z = 4 - 2i$, evaluate
   (i) $z + \bar{z}$, **(ii)** $z - \bar{z}$, **(iii)** $z\bar{z}$.
2. If $z = -3 - 5i$, evaluate
   (i) $z + \bar{z}$, **(ii)** $z - \bar{z}$, **(iii)** $z\bar{z}$.
3. If $w = 2 - 7i$, find $w\bar{w} + 2(w + \bar{w})$.
4. If $z = 3 + 4i$, find $z\bar{z} - 4(z + \bar{z})$.
5. Express $\frac{5-i}{1-i}$ in the form $a + bi$.
6. Express $\frac{11+24i}{4+5i}$ in the form $a + bi$.
7. Express $\frac{9+4i}{1+i}$ in the form $a + bi$.
8. Express $\frac{7-5i}{2+3i}$ in the form $a + bi$.
9. Express $\frac{5\sqrt{3}-4i}{2\sqrt{3}-i}$ in the form $a + bi$.

10. Express $\dfrac{5+\sqrt{2}i}{3-\sqrt{2}i}$ in the form $a + bi$.

11. If $z = 1 + i$, express $z + \dfrac{1}{z}$ in the form $a + bi$.

12. If $z = 2 + i$, express $\dfrac{z}{\bar{z}} - \dfrac{\bar{z}}{z}$ in the form $a + bi$, where $\bar{z}$ is the conjugate of z.

13. If $z = 4 + 3i$ and $w = 2 - i$, find the value of $k \in \mathbb{R}$ for which $\dfrac{z}{w} + ki$ is real.

14. If $z = 11 + 10i$ and $w = 2 + 3i$, find the value of $k \in \mathbb{R}$ for which $\dfrac{z}{w} + ki$ is real.

15. Express $\left(\dfrac{3+11i}{1+2i}\right)^2$ in the form $a + bi$.

16. Evaluate $\left(\dfrac{2+3i}{3-2i}\right)^{10}$.

33.4 Square Roots of a Complex Number

The square roots of a complex number are themselves complex numbers.

The following example shows how to find the square roots of a complex number.

Example 1

Find $a, b \in \mathbb{R}$ if $(a + bi)^2 = 21 + 20i$, where $i^2 = -1$.

Solution

(If $(a+bi)^2 = 21 + 20i$, then $a + bi = \sqrt{21+20i}$. So we are being asked to find the square roots of $21 + 20i$.)

$$(a+bi)^2 = 21 + 20i$$
$$a^2 + 2abi + b^2i^2 = 21 + 20i$$
$$a^2 + 2abi - b^2 = 21 + 20i$$
$$(a^2 - b^2) + 2abi = 21 + 20i$$

Re = Re: $a^2 - b^2 = 21$ **... 1**

Im = Im: $2ab = 20$ **... 2**

2: $b = \dfrac{20}{2a} = \dfrac{10}{a}$

1: $a^2 - \left(\dfrac{10}{a}\right)^2 = 21$

$$a^2 - \frac{100}{a^2} = 21$$
$$a^4 - 100 = 21a^2$$
$$a^4 - 21a^2 - 100 = 0 \quad \textit{... quadratic in } a^2$$

$$(a^2 - 25)(a^2 + 4) = 0$$
$$a^2 - 25 = 0 \quad \text{or} \quad a^2 + 4 = 0$$
$$a^2 = 25 \quad \text{or} \quad a^2 = -4 \quad \textit{(not possible, as } a \in \mathbb{R})$$
$$a = \pm 5$$

2: $b = \dfrac{10}{a}$

$a = 5$: $b = 2$

$a = -5$: $b = -2$.

(Thus, $\sqrt{21+20i} = 5 + 2i$ or $-5 - 2i$, i.e. $\sqrt{21+20i} = \pm(5+2i)$.)

Exercises 33.4

1. If $(p + qi)^2 = 24 + 10i$, find the values of the real numbers p and q.
2. If $(s + ti)^2 = -8 - 6i$, find the values of the real numbers s and t.
3. If $(a + bi)^2 = 35 + 12i$, find the values of the real numbers a and b.
4. Express the two possible values of $\sqrt{-5 - 12i}$ in the form $a + bi$, $a, b \in \mathbb{R}$.
5. Express the two possible values of $\sqrt{48 + 14i}$ in the form $a + bi$, $a, b \in \mathbb{R}$.
6. Express the two possible values of $\sqrt{-16 - 30i}$ in the form $a + bi$, $a, b \in \mathbb{R}$.

33.5 Complex Equations

A complex equation is an equation whose solutions are complex numbers. Like real equations, there are many different types of complex equation.

1. **Linear Equations**

A linear equation in z is an equation of the form

$$az = b,$$

or an equation that can be re-arranged into this form.

As with real numbers, we can solve this equation by dividing across by a,

$$z = \frac{b}{a}.$$

However, if a is a non-real complex number, then we will have to multiply above and below by its conjugate to calculate z.

Example 1

Solve the equation

$$\frac{3z}{z - 2i} = 1 + 2i, \qquad \text{where } i^2 = -1,$$

for $z \in \mathbb{C}$. Express your answer in the form $a + bi$.

Solution

(This equation can be re-arranged into linear form.)

$$\frac{3z}{z - 2i} = 1 + 2i$$

$$3z = (1 + 2i)(z - 2i)$$

$$3z = z + 2iz - 2i - 4i^2$$

$$3z - z - 2iz = -2i + 4$$

$$2z - 2iz = 4 - 2i$$

$$z - iz = 2 - i$$

$$z(1 - i) = 2 - i$$

$$z = \frac{2 - i}{1 - i}$$

$$z = \frac{2 - i}{1 - i} \times \frac{1 + i}{1 + i}$$

$$z = \frac{2 + 2i - i - i^2}{1^2 + (-1)^2}$$

$$z = \frac{2 + i + 1}{2}$$

$$z = \frac{3 + i}{2}$$

$$z = \frac{3}{2} + \frac{1}{2}i.$$

2. Quadratic Equations

A ***complex quadratic equation*** is an equation of the form

$$az^2 + bz + c = 0,$$

where a, b, c and $z \in \mathbb{C}$. These equations have many features in common with real quadratic equations (from Algebra), but there are some differences.

The solutions (or roots) can be found using the familiar quadratic formula:

$$z = \frac{-b \pm \sqrt{b^2 - 4ac}}{2a},$$

even if some of the coefficients are not real.

Example 2

Solve the equation

$$z^2 - 4z + 13 = 0$$

for $z \in \mathbb{C}$.

Solution

(We will use the quadratic formula, with a = 1, b = −4 and c = 13.)

$$z = \frac{-(-4) \pm \sqrt{(-4)^2 - 4(1)(13)}}{2(1)}$$

$$z = \frac{4 \pm \sqrt{-36}}{2} \qquad \ldots \sqrt{-36} = \sqrt{(36) \times (-1)} = \sqrt{36} \times \sqrt{-1} = 6i$$

$$z = \frac{4 \pm 6i}{2}$$

$$z = 2 \pm 3i$$

(If we had been asked to solve the equation for $z \in \mathbb{R}$, then there would have been no solution.)

Example 3

(i) Find the real numbers p and q if

$$(p + qi)^2 = -3 + 4i.$$

(ii) Solve the equation

$$z^2 - (3 + 4i)z - 1 + 5i = 0,$$

for $z \in \mathbb{C}$.

Solution

(i)

$$(p + qi)^2 = -3 + 4i$$
$$p^2 + 2pqi - q^2 = -3 + 4i$$
$$(p^2 - q^2) + 2pqi = -3 + 4i$$

Re = Re: $p^2 - q^2 = -3$ **... 1**

Im = Im: $2pq = 4$

$q = \dfrac{2}{p}$ **... 2**

1: $p^2 - \dfrac{4}{p^2} = -3$

$$p^4 - 4 = -3p^2$$
$$p^4 + 3p^2 - 4 = 0$$
$$(p^2 - 1)(p^2 + 4) = 0$$
$$p^2 - 1 = 0 \quad \text{or} \quad p^2 + 4 = 0$$
$$p^2 = 1 \quad \text{or} \quad p^2 = -4$$

(not possible as p is a real number)

$$p = \pm 1$$

2: $q = \frac{2}{p}$

$p = 1$: $q = 2$: $p + qi = 1 + 2i$

$p = -1$: $q = -2$: $p + qi = -1 - 2i$

Thus, $\sqrt{-3 + 4i} = \pm(1 + 2i)$.

(ii) For the equation, $a = 1$, $b = -(3 + 4i)$ and $c = -1 + 5i$.
Then

$$z^2 - (3 + 4i)z - 1 + 5i = 0$$

$$z = \frac{(3 + 4i) \pm \sqrt{[-(3 + 4i)]^2 - 4(1)(-1 + 5i)}}{2}$$

$$z = \frac{(3 + 4i) \pm \sqrt{9 + 24i - 16 + 4 - 20i}}{2}$$

$$z = \frac{(3 + 4i) \pm \sqrt{-3 + 4i}}{2}$$

$$z = \frac{(3 + 4i) \pm (1 + 2i)}{2} \quad \textit{... by part (i)}$$

$$z = \frac{(3 + 4i) + (1 + 2i)}{2} \quad \text{or} \quad z = \frac{(3 + 4i) - (1 + 2i)}{2}$$

$$z = \frac{4 + 6i}{2} \quad \text{or} \quad z = \frac{2 + 2i}{2}$$

$$z = 2 + 3i \quad \text{or} \quad z = 1 + i.$$

3. Equations containing Conjugate or Modulus

If an equation contains the conjugate of z, $\bar{z}$, or the modulus of z, $|z|$, then the preferred approach is to:
let $z = x + yi$.

After simplifying both sides of the equation, we can use the definition of equality to write down, and solve, two simultaneous equations in x and y.

Example 4

Solve for $z \in \mathbb{C}$, the equation

$$2z + (1 + i)\bar{z} = 5 + 3i,$$

where $\bar{z}$ is the complex conjugate of z.

Solution

Let $z = x + yi$. Then $\bar{z} = x - yi$.

Then

$$2z + (1 + i)\bar{z} = 5 + 3i$$

$$2(x + yi) + (1 + i)(x - yi) = 5 + 3i$$

$$[2x + 2yi] + [x - yi + xi + y] = 5 + 3i$$

$$(2x + x + y) + (2yi - yi + xi) = 5 + 3i$$

$$(3x + y) + (x + y)i = 5 + 3i$$

Re = Re: $3x + y = 5$ ... **1**

Im = Im: $x + y = 3$ ... **2**

1: $3x + y = 5$

2 × −1: $-x - y = -3$

$2x = 2$

$x = 1$

2: $y = 2$

Thus $z = x + yi = 1 + 2i$.

Exercises 33.5

1. Solve for $z \in \mathbb{C}$: $3z + 2i = 3 - 10i$.
2. Solve for $z \in \mathbb{C}$: $4z - 15i = 10 - z$.
3. Solve for $z \in \mathbb{C}$: $2z + 6i = iz + 7$.
4. Solve for $z \in \mathbb{C}$: $2iz + 7 - 4i = z$.
5. Solve the equation
$$\frac{z}{z-i} = 2 + i, \quad \text{for } z \in \mathbb{C}.$$
6. Solve the equation
$$\frac{z}{z+1} = 1 + 2i, \quad \text{for } z \in \mathbb{C}.$$
7. Solve for $z \in \mathbb{C}$: $z^2 - 6z + 34 = 0$
8. Solve for $z \in \mathbb{C}$: $z^2 - 8z + 20 = 0$
9. Solve for $z \in \mathbb{C}$: $z^2 + 10z + 41 = 0$
10. Solve for $z \in \mathbb{C}$: $z^2 - 12z + 45 = 0$
11. Solve for $z \in \mathbb{C}$: $z^2 + (-2 + i)z + (1 - i) = 0$
12. Solve for $z \in \mathbb{C}$: $z^2 + (\mathrm{i} - 2)z + (3 - i) = 0$
13. **(i)** Find the real numbers a and b if $(a + bi)^2 = -8i$.
    (ii) Solve the equation $z^2 - (4 + 2i)z + (3 + 6i) = 0$, for $z \in \mathbb{C}$.
14. **(i)** Find the real numbers p and q if $(p + qi)^2 = 3 - 4i$.
    (ii) Solve the equation $z^2 - (4 - 3i)z + (1 - 5i) = 0$, for $z \in \mathbb{C}$.
15. Solve the equation $z^2 - (3 + 2i)z + (5 + 5i) = 0$, for $z \in \mathbb{C}$.
16. Solve the equation $z^2 - (5 + i)z + (6 + 7i) = 0$, for $z \in \mathbb{C}$.
17. Solve, for $z \in \mathbb{C}$, the equation
$$2z + 3\bar{z} = 20 - 3i,$$
where $\bar{z}$ is the complex conjugate of z.
18. Solve, for $z \in \mathbb{C}$, the equation
$$2z - i\bar{z} = 8 - 7i,$$
where $\bar{z}$ is the complex conjugate of z.
19. Solve, for $z \in \mathbb{C}$, the equation
$$z + (3 - i)\,\bar{z} = 7 - 4i,$$
where $\bar{z}$ is the complex conjugate of z.
20. Solve for $z \in \mathbb{C}$:
$$|z| + z - \bar{z} = 5 + 8i.$$
21. Solve for $z \in \mathbb{C}$:
$$|z|^2 + 2z - 3\bar{z} = 3 + 5i.$$
22. Solve for $z \in \mathbb{C}$:
$$|z|^2 + (2 + i)z = 15 - 5i.$$

33.6 Cubic Equations and the Conjugate Roots Theorem

A **complex cubic polynomial** is one of the form

$$f(z) = az^3 + bz^2 + cz + d,$$

where $a, b, c, d, z \in \mathbb{C}$.

The Factor Theorem applies to complex cubic polynomials, just as it does to real cubic polynomials. Thus, $(z - z_1)$ is a factor of $f(z)$ if $f(z_1) = 0$.

We can also use long division to verify that $(z - z_1)$ is a factor of $f(z)$. If we have one root of a complex cubic, we can use the Factor Theorem to solve the cubic equation.

Example 1

$P(z) = z^3 - (3 + i)z^2 + (2 + 3i)z - 2i$, where $i^2 = -1$.

(i) Show that $P(i) = 0$.

(ii) Solve the equation $P(z) = 0$.

Solution

(i)

$$P(i) = (i)^3 - (3 + i)(i)^2 + (2 + 3i)(i) - 2i$$
$$P(i) = -i - (3 + i)(-1) + 2i - 3 - 2i$$
$$P(i) = -i + 3 + i + 2i - 3 - 2i$$
$$P(i) = (3 - 3) + (-i + i + 2i - 2i)$$
$$P(i) = 0$$

(ii) By the Factor Theorem, $(z - i)$ is a factor of $P(z)$.

We find the other factor by using long division.

$$\begin{array}{r|l} & z^2 - 3z + 2 \\ \hline z - i & z^3 - (3+i)z^2 + (2+3i)z - 2i \\ & \underline{z^3 - \quad iz^2} \\ & \quad -3z^2 + (2+3i)z \\ & \quad \underline{-3z^2 + \quad 3iz} \\ & \qquad\qquad 2z - 2i \\ & \qquad\qquad \underline{2z - 2i} \\ & \qquad\qquad\qquad 0 \end{array}$$

The other factor is $z^2 - 3z + 2$ and the equation can be written:

$$(z - i)(z^2 - 3z + 2) = 0$$
$$(z - i)(z - 1)(z - 2) = 0$$
$$z = i \quad \text{or} \quad z = 1 \quad \text{or} \quad z = 2$$

Solutions: $i, 1, 2$.

A theorem that can help us to solve some, but not all, cubic equations is the so called **Conjugate Roots Theorem**.

Conjugate Roots Theorem

If $f(z) = 0$ is an equation with **real coefficients**, and if z_1 is a solution of this equation, i.e. $f(z_1) = 0$, then the conjugate of z_1, $\bar{z}_1$ is also a root of this equation, i.e. $f(\bar{z}_1) = 0$.

It is very important to be aware that the Conjugate Roots Theorem can only be used if all the coefficients are real numbers.

For example, the coefficients in the equation

$$z^3 - z^2 - 7z + 15 = 0$$

are all real. $2 + i$ is a root of this equation. Then the Conjugate Roots Theorem tells us that its conjugate, $2 - i$, is also a root.

However, the coefficients in the equation

$$z^3 - (1 + i)z^2 - 4z + (4 + 4i) = 0$$

are not all real ($-(1 + i)$ and $(4 + 4i)$ are not real). The Conjugate Roots Theorem does **not** apply to this equation. $1 + i$ is a root of this equation, but it is completely false to say that its conjugate, $1 - i$, is another root.

Example 2

Find the values of the real numbers a and b if $2 - 3i$ is a root of the equation

$$z^3 + az^2 + bz - 65 = 0.$$

Find the other roots of this equation.

Solution

$2 - 3i$ is a root. By the Conjugate Roots Theorem, $2 + 3i$ is also a root.

Thus, a quadratic factor is

$$z^2 - (\text{sum})z + (\text{product})$$
$$= z^2 - [(2 - 3i) + (2 + 3i)]z + [(2 - 3i)(2 + 3i)]$$
$$= z^2 - 4z + 13$$

First Method:

Dividing the cubic by $z^2 - 4z + 13$:

$$\begin{array}{r|l}
 & z + (a + 4) \\
z^2 - 4z + 13 & z^3 + az^2 + bz - 65 \\
 & \underline{z^3 - 4z^2 + 13z} \\
 & (a + 4)z^2 + (b - 13)z - 65 \\
 & \underline{(a + 4)z^2 - 4(a + 4)z + 13(a + 4)} \\
 & 0
\end{array}$$

Putting 'like to like':

(i) $13(a + 4) = -65$

$a + 4 = -5$

$a = -9$

(ii) $b - 13 = -4(a + 4)$

$b - 13 = 20$

$b = 33$

The other factor is then

$z + (a + 4) = z - 5.$

Putting this equal to zero, the third root is $z = 5$.

Alternatively:

By observing the first term, z^3, and the last term, -65, in the cubic, we can see that the other factor has to be $(z - 5)$.

Thus,

$$z^3 + az^2 + bz - 65 = (z^2 - 4z + 13)(z - 5)$$
$$= z^3 - 5z^2 - 4z^2 + 20z + 13z - 65$$
$$= z^3 - 9z^2 + 33z - 65$$

Hence, 'putting like to like', $a = -9$ and $b = 33$. The third root is given by

$z - 5 = 0$

$z = 5.$

Exercises 33.6

1. $f(z) = z^3 - (2 + 2i)z^2 - (15 - 4i)z + 30i$, where $i^2 = -1$.
   (i) Show that $f(2i) = 0$.
   (ii) Solve the equation $f(z) = 0$.
2. Show that $3i$ is a root of the equation $z^3 - (2 + 3i)z^2 + (5 + 6i)z - 15i = 0$, and find the other roots of this equation.
3. Show that $-i$ is a root of the equation $z^3 + (-6 + i)z^2 + (8 - 6i)z + 8i = 0$, and find the other roots of this equation.
4. $f(z) = z^3 - (1 + i)z^2 - 4z + (4 + 4i)$.
   (i) Show that $f(1 + i) = 0$.
   (ii) Find all the solutions of the equation $f(z) = 0$.
5. $P(z) = z^3 - iz^2 - (7 + i)z + 6 + 6i$.

   Show that $1 + i$ is a root of $P(z) = 0$, and find the other roots of this equation.
6. If $2 - 3i$ is a root of the equation $z^3 - 2z^2 + 5z + 26 = 0$, find the other two roots of this equation.
7. If $1 - 5i$ is a root of the equation $z^3 - 5z^2 + 32z - 78 = 0$, find the other two roots of this equation.
8. If $1 + i$ is a root of the equation $z^3 - 7z^2 + 12z - 10 = 0$, find the other two roots of this equation.
9. One root of the equation $z^3 - az^2 + bz - 30 = 0$, $a,b \in \mathbb{R}$, $z \in \mathbb{C}$ is $1 + 3i$. Find the value of a and the value of b and the other roots of the equation.
10. $2 + i$ is a root of the equation $z^3 + az^2 + bz - 20 = 0$, $z \in \mathbb{C}$, $a,b \in \mathbb{R}$. Find the value of a, the value of b and the other roots of the equation.

Revision Exercises 33

1. The Argand diagram opposite shows the points a, b, c, d, e and f representing complex numbers. If these complex numbers are $z, \bar{z}, z + \bar{z}, w, z + w$ and $z.w$, determine which point represents each complex number.
   Copy the diagram and use it to explain your reasoning.

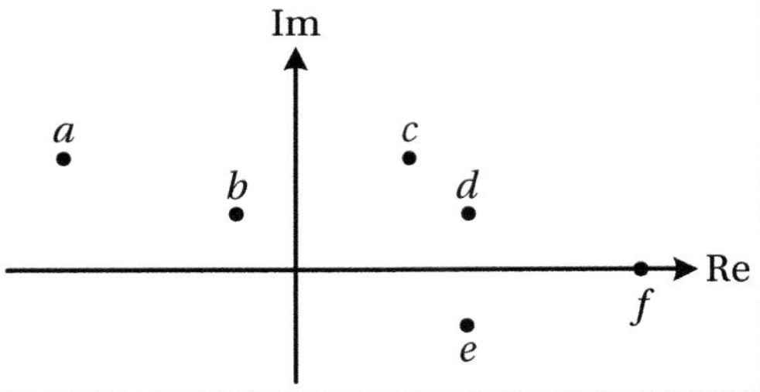

2. The Argand diagram opposite shows the points a, b, c, d, e and f representing complex numbers. If these complex numbers are $z, \bar{z}, w, 2w, z - \bar{z}$ and $z + w$, determine which point represents each complex number.
   Copy the diagram and use it to explain your reasoning.

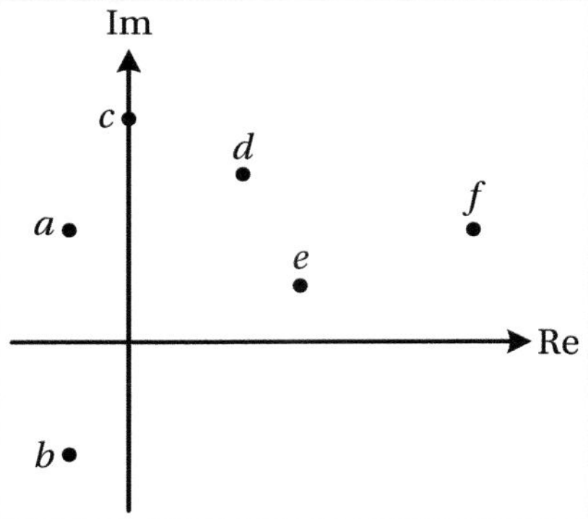

3. If the complex number $z + w$ lies on the real axis, does w have to be the conjugate of z? Give a reason.
4. The complex number $z - w$ lies on the imaginary axis.
   (i) Can we say that w must be the conjugate of z? Give a reason.
   (ii) What can we say about the real parts of z and w?
   (iii) If we also know that $z + w$ lies on the real axis, what can we say about z and w? Give a reason.
5. The Argand diagram opposite shows the two complex numbers z and w.
   Copy the diagram and show, with construction, the location of the following complex numbers:
   (i) $2z$
   (ii) $-w$
   (iii) $\bar{z}$
   (iv) $z + w$
   (v) $z - w$
   (vi) $2z - w$.

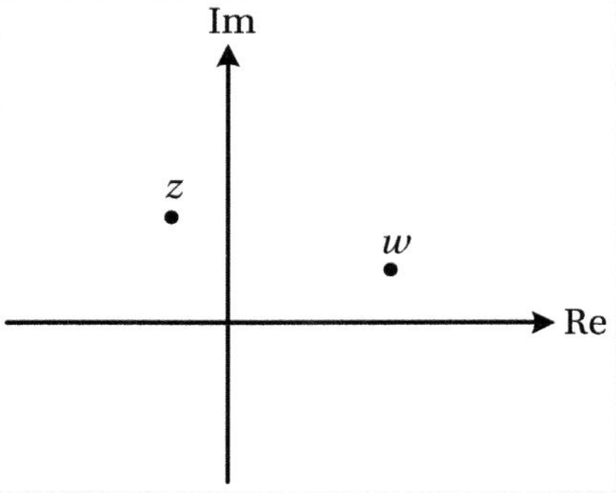

6. Solve the equation
   $$\frac{iz + 3}{z - 2i} = 1 + i, \qquad \text{for } z \in \mathbb{C}.$$
7. Solve the equation
   $$\frac{iz + 4}{z - 3i} = 1 - 2i, \qquad \text{for } z \in \mathbb{C}.$$
8. Let $w_1 = -\frac{1}{2} + \frac{\sqrt{3}}{2}i$ and $w_2 = (w_1)^2$.
   Verify that
   $$x^2 + xy + y^2 = (x - w_1 y)(x - w_2 y), \text{ where } x, y \in \mathbb{R}.$$

9. If $z = x + yi$ and $\bar{z}$ is the conjugate of z, find the value of $x \neq 0$ and $y \neq 0$ such that

$$\frac{1}{z} + \frac{2}{\bar{z}} = 1 + i.$$

10. $z = 5 - ki$, where $k \in \mathbb{R}$ and $i^2 = -1$. If

$$z^2 - 10z = 29,$$

find the possible values of k.

11. $P(z) = z^3 + (2 - 2i)z^2 + (3 - 3i)z - 1 - 4i$.
Find the values of $a, b \in \mathbb{C}$ if

$$P(z) = (z - i)(z^2 + az + b).$$

12. If ki is a root of the equation $3z^3 - z^2 + 12z - 4 = 0$, find the values of $k \in \mathbb{C}$ and the other root of the equation.

13. If $3 - 2i$ and $1 + i$ are two of the roots of the equation

$$z^4 + az^3 + bz^2 + cz + d = 0$$

find the values of $a, b, c, d \in \mathbb{R}$.

14. **(i)** Find the two complex numbers $a + bi$ for which $(a + bi)^2 = 15 + 8i$.
(ii) Solve the equation $iz^2 + (2 - 3i)z + (-5 + 5i) = 0$.

15. Solve the quadratic equation:

$$2iz^2 + (6 + 2i)z + (3 - 6i) = 0, \text{ where } i^2 = -1.$$

16. w is a complex number such that

$$w\bar{w} - 2iw = 7 - 4i,$$

where $\bar{w}$ is the complex conjugate of w.
Find the two possible values of w.
Express each in the form $p + qi$, where $p, q \in \mathbb{R}$.

17. Show that $z^2 - 16$ is a factor of $z^3 + (1 + i)z^2 - 16z - 16(1 + i)$ and hence find the three roots of $z^3 + (1 + i)z^2 - 16z - 16(1 + i) = 0$.

18. $z_1 = a + bi$ and $z_2 = c + di$, where $i^2 = -1$.
Show that $\overline{z_1 + z_2} = \overline{z_1} + \overline{z_2}$, where $\bar{z}$ is the complex conjugate of z.

Complex Numbers 2

In the last chapter, we met complex numbers and investigated their basic properties. In particular, we saw how adding, subtracting and multiplying by a real number could be interpreted as transformations on an Argand diagram. Now we investigate the effect of multiplying, dividing and taking powers of complex numbers on points in an Argand diagram.

This analysis is significantly simplified by changing the view of complex numbers from what is called rectangular form (as met in the last chapter) to what is known as polar form. Then we see how complex numbers and their properties make it easy to mathematically describe how objects can be moved and turned in the plane. This is the approach used to achieve movement in some computer games, although three dimensional games tend to use quaternions, which are the extension of complex numbers to three dimensions.

In this chapter, we also see how the properties of complex numbers written in polar form can help with calculating roots and even proving trigonometric identities.

34.1 Polar Form of a Complex Number

When a complex number is written in the form

$z = x + yi$

then it is said to be given in **rectangular form**. This complex number is represented by the point (x,y) on an Argand diagram.

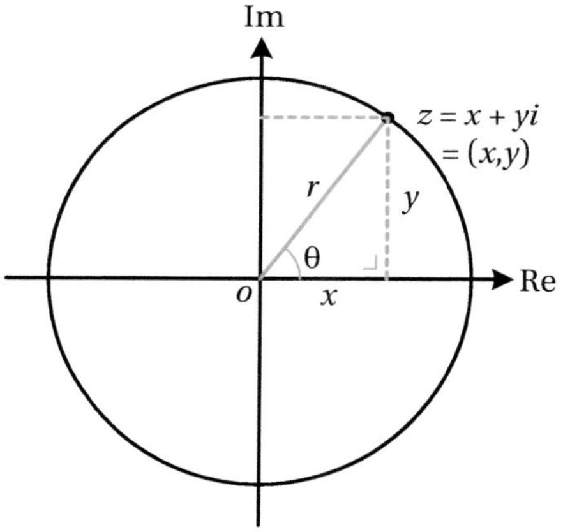

The translation $\overrightarrow{oz}$ involves going a distance of x parallel to the Re axis and a distance y parallel to the Im axis. These are two sides of a rectangle, as shown.

The translation $\overrightarrow{oz}$ can be described in another way, by specifying two other quantities.

1. **Modulus, r**
   The modulus is the distance from o to z, i.e.
   $r = |z| = \sqrt{x^2 + y^2}$

2. **Angle (or argument), θ**
   The angle, θ, is the angle between the positive side of the Re axis and the translation $\overrightarrow{oz}$. The dominant convention is that we take $-180° < \theta \leq 180°$, although other angles are allowed. This angle is sometimes called the argument, and can be written arg(z). How the angle θ is calculated depends on which quadrant the point is in, and will be investigated shortly.

Once r and θ are known, the translation $\overrightarrow{oz}$, i.e. the complex number z, is fully determined.

The link between the two systems is as follows:

(i) $\frac{x}{r} = \cos\theta$

$x = r\cos\theta$

(ii) $\frac{y}{r} = \sin\theta$

$y = r\sin\theta$

Then

$z = x + yi$
$z = (r\cos\theta) + (r\sin\theta)i$
$z = r(\cos\theta + i\sin\theta)$

Once r and θ have been calculated, the complex number $z = x + yi$ can be written directly in the form $z = r(\cos\theta + i\sin\theta)$. This form of a complex number is called **polar form**.

For much work done with complex numbers written in polar form, a convenient and much used abbreviation goes as follows:

$$r(\underline{c}\text{os}\,\theta + \underline{i}\,\underline{s}\text{in}\,\theta) = r\,\text{cis}\,\theta.$$

Now that we have two ways of describing complex numbers, it is necessary to be able to convert from one to the other.

1. Rectangular Form to Polar Form

To convert a complex number from rectangular form to polar form, we draw a rough diagram. r can be found using the definition of modulus, or by using Pythagoras' Theorem. In the 1st quadrant, θ can be calculated directly by using tan. In all other quadrants, we first calculate the acute angle to the nearest horizontal. This angle, R, is called the reference angle, just as in trigonometry. We then use R to calculate θ.

Example 1

Express $z = 1 + \sqrt{3}i$ in polar form, i.e. in the form $r(\cos\theta + i\sin\theta)$.

Solution

(The point which represents z, $(1, \sqrt{3})$, is in the first quadrant. We can calculate θ directly here.)

$$r = \sqrt{1^2 + (\sqrt{3})^2}$$
$$= \sqrt{4} = 2$$

and

$$\tan\theta = \frac{\sqrt{3}}{1} = \sqrt{3}$$
$$\theta = 60° \left(\text{or } \frac{\pi}{3}\right)$$

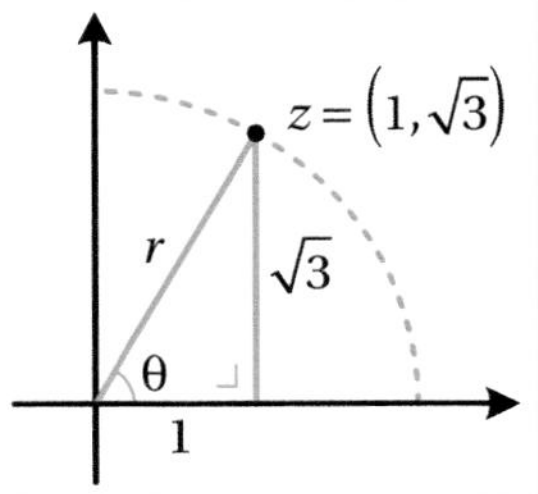

Thus,

$$z = 2(\cos 60° + i\sin 60°) = 2\,\text{cis}\,60°$$

or $z = 2\left(\cos\frac{\pi}{3} + i\sin\frac{\pi}{3}\right) = 2\,\text{cis}\,\frac{\pi}{3}.$

Example 2

Express $z = -3 + 3i$ in the form $r(\cos\theta + i\sin\theta)$.

Solution

(The point representing z is (–3,3) which lies in the second quadrant. Draw a diagram, indicating the lengths of the sides of the triangle (no minus numbers). Show the reference angle, R. Then θ can be found by subtracting R from 180°.)

$$r = \sqrt{3^2 + 3^2}$$
$$= \sqrt{18}$$
$$= 3\sqrt{2}$$

and

$$\tan R = \frac{3}{3} = 1$$
$$R = 45°$$

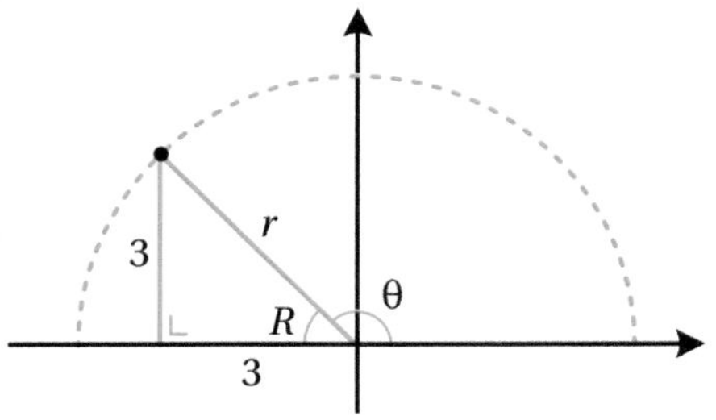

Thus,

$$\theta = 180° - 45° = 135°$$

Hence,

$$z = 3\sqrt{2}\,(\cos 135° + i \sin 135°)$$
$$= 3\sqrt{2} \text{ cis } 135°.$$

Example 3

Express $z = 2\sqrt{3} - 2i$ in the form $r(\cos\theta + i\sin\theta)$, where θ is in radians.

Solution

(z is represented by the point $(2\sqrt{3}, -2)$, which lies in the fourth quadrant. In the fourth quadrant, we take the angle θ to be negative. Calculate the reference angle, R, first. Then $\theta = -R$. Don't forget to write the angle in radians.)

$$r = \sqrt{(2\sqrt{3}^2) + 2^2}$$
$$= \sqrt{16} = 4$$

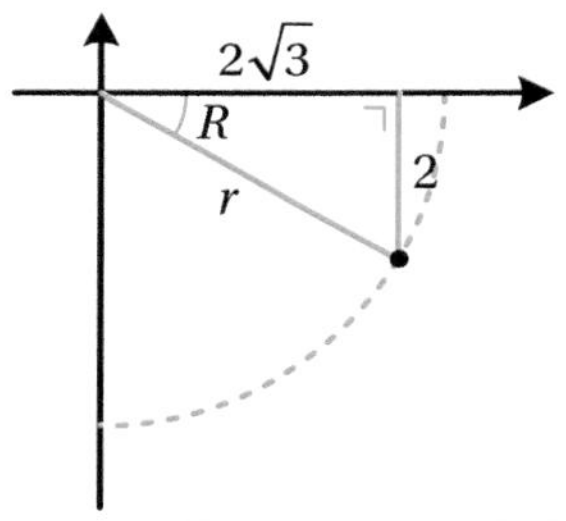

and

$$\tan R = \frac{2}{2\sqrt{3}} = \frac{1}{\sqrt{3}}$$
$$R = \frac{\pi}{6} \quad (30°)$$

Thus,

$$\theta = -\frac{\pi}{6}$$

Hence,

$$z = 4\left(\cos\left(-\frac{\pi}{6}\right) + i\sin\left(-\frac{\pi}{6}\right)\right) = 4 \text{ cis}\left(-\frac{\pi}{6}\right).$$

Example 4

Express $z = -4 - 4i$ in polar form.

Solution

(The point $(-4, -4)$, which represents z, lies in the third quadrant. In this quadrant, we also take the angle to be negative, between $-90°$ and $-180°$. Calculate the reference angle, R, and then $\theta = -(180° - R)$.)

$$r = \sqrt{4^2 + 4^2}$$
$$= \sqrt{32} = 4\sqrt{2}$$

and

$$\tan R = \frac{4}{4} = 1$$

$$R = 45°$$

Thus,

$$\theta = -(180° - 45°) = -135°$$

Hence,

$$z = 4\sqrt{2}\,(\cos(-135°) + i\sin(-135°)) = 4\sqrt{2}\,\text{cis}(-135°).$$

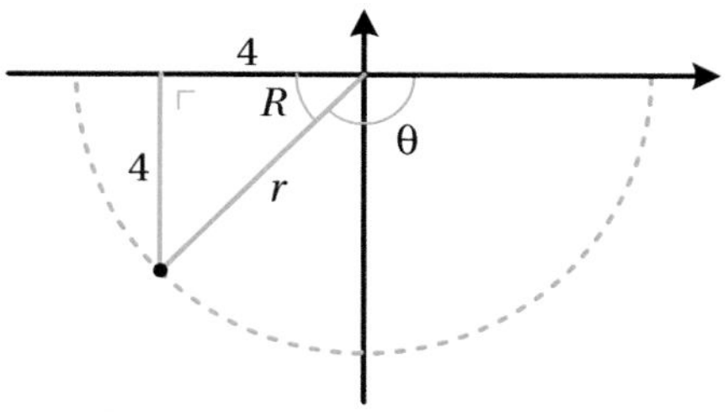

If a complex number is purely real or purely imaginary, then the point which represents the complex number will lie on one of the axes. In this case,

(i) r is the (positive) distance from the origin to the point,
(ii) the angle θ is as shown opposite.

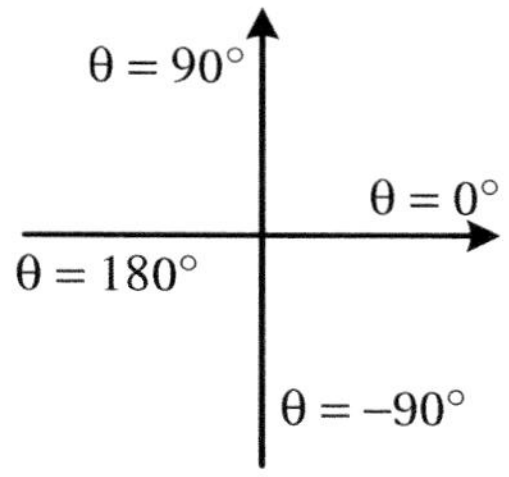

Example 5

Express $z = -4$ in the form $r(\cos\theta + i\sin\theta)$.

Solution

(z is represented by the point (−4, 0), which lies on the negative side of the Re axis.)

$$r = 4$$

and

$$\theta = 180°$$

Hence,

$$z = 4(\cos 180° + i\sin 180°) = 4\,\text{cis}\,180°.$$

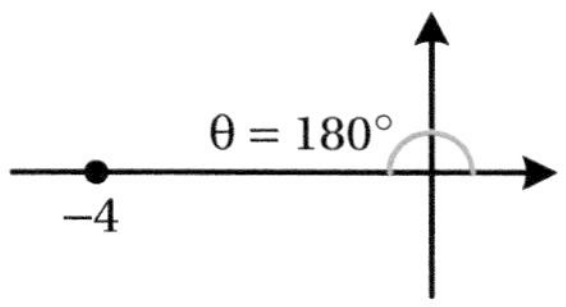

Most scientific calculators can convert complex numbers from rectangular form to polar form. Because different makes and models work very differently, you should learn how your calculator performs this conversion.

For example, to convert $z = -1 - \sqrt{3}i$ to polar form using a Casio fx-83 calculator, we clear the calculator and then press:

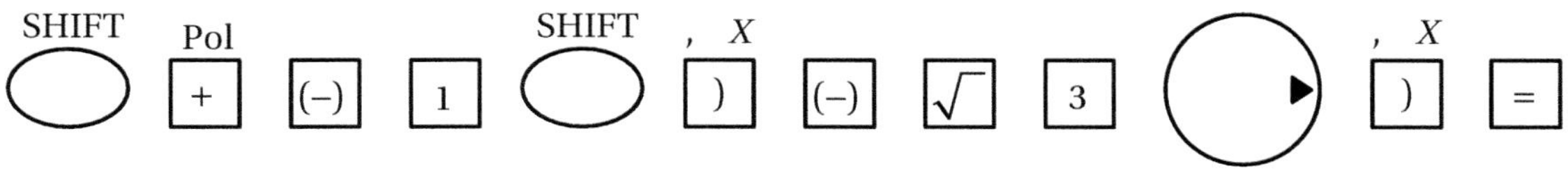

and we will see on the display:

$r = 2$
$\theta = -120$

Note that your calculator has been programmed to use the standard international convention that $-180° < \theta \le 180°$. Also note that if r works out to be a decimal, we can always square it to find r^2 and so write r as a surd.

2. Polar Form to Rectangular Form

To convert a complex number given in polar form to rectangular form, we simply evaluate the trig functions and tidy up. We always tend to use exact values, i.e. no decimals unless specifically instructed. Angles outside (–180°,180°] can occur in calculations.

Example 6

Express in the form $x + yi$:

(i) $z = (4\cos 135° + i\sin 135°)$,

(ii) $z = \sqrt{2}\,(\cos 405° + i\sin 405°)$.

Solution

(i) $z = 4(\cos 135° + i\sin 135°)$

$= 4\left(-\frac{1}{\sqrt{2}} + i\frac{1}{\sqrt{2}}\right)$

$= -\frac{4}{\sqrt{2}} + \frac{4}{\sqrt{2}}i$

$= -2\sqrt{2} + 2\sqrt{2}\,i.$

(ii) $z = \sqrt{2}\,(\cos 405° + i\sin 405°)$

$= \sqrt{2}\left(\frac{1}{\sqrt{2}} + i\frac{1}{\sqrt{2}}\right)$

$= 1 + i.$

Exercises 34.1

Express each of the following in the form $r(\cos\theta + i\sin\theta)$.

1. $z = 1 + i$ **2.** $z = 2\sqrt{3} + 2i$ **3.** $z = 3\sqrt{2} + 3\sqrt{2}i$ **4.** $z = 4 + 4\sqrt{3}i$

5. $z = -1 + i$ **6.** $z = -\sqrt{3} + i$ **7.** $z = -\frac{1}{2} + \frac{\sqrt{3}}{2}i$ **8.** $z = -\sqrt{2} + \sqrt{2}i$

9. $z = 1 - i$ **10.** $z = \sqrt{3} - i$ **11.** $z = -4\sqrt{2} - 4\sqrt{2}i$ **12.** $z = -2 - 2\sqrt{3}i$

13. $z = 4$ **14.** $z = \frac{1}{2}i$ **15.** $z = -6$ **16.** $z = -3i$

Express each of the following in the form $a + bi$.

17. $z = 4(\cos 120° + i\sin 120°)$ **18.** $z = 6(\cos 300° + i\sin 300°)$ **19.** $z = 2(\cos 225° + i\sin 225°)$

20. $z = 8\left(\cos\frac{7\pi}{6} + i\sin\frac{7\pi}{6}\right)$ **21.** $z = 3\left(\cos\frac{9\pi}{4} + i\sin\frac{9\pi}{4}\right)$ **22.** $z = 10(\cos 870° + i\sin 870°)$.

23. The complex number z is shown on the Argand diagram opposite.
(i) Write z in polar form.
(ii) Write z in rectangular form, with the real and imaginary parts correct to two decimal places.

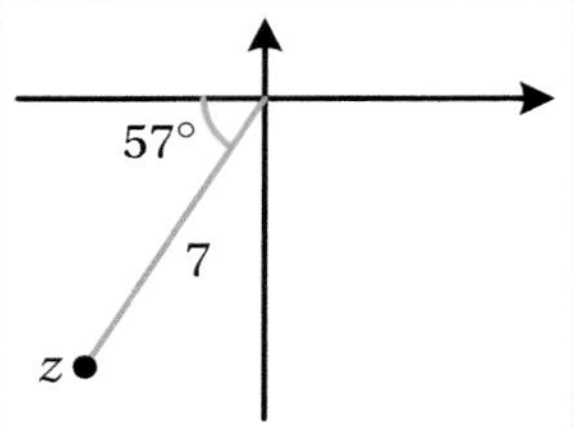

24. The complex number z is shown on the Argand diagram opposite.
(i) Write z in polar form.
(ii) Write z in rectangular form, with the real and imaginary parts correct to two decimal places.

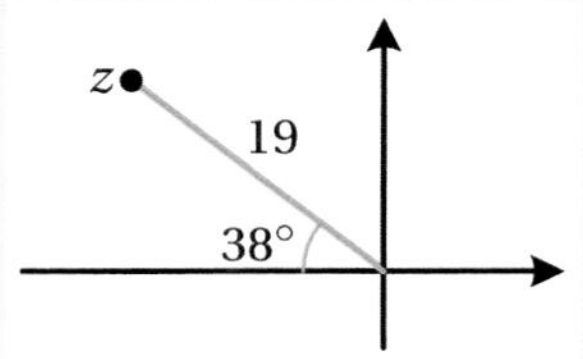

34.2 Properties of cis θ

The main reason for writing complex numbers in polar form is because of the properties of cis $\theta = \cos\theta + i\sin\theta$. In questions based on the properties of cis θ, it is common practice to use the 'cis' notation for the middle sections, but to return to the $\cos A + i\sin A$ notation to finish off.

Property 1

$$(\cos A + i\sin A)(\cos B + i\sin B) = \cos(A+B) + i\sin(A+B)$$

i.e. $\text{cis}\,A\;\text{cis}\,B = \text{cis}(A+B)$

To multiply two cis's, simply add the angles.

Example 1

(i) Show that

$$(\cos A + i\sin A)\,(\cos B + i\sin B) = \cos(A+B) + i\sin(A+B).$$

(ii) Hence, evaluate $(\cos 21° + i\sin 21°)\,(\cos 39° + i\sin 39°)$.

Solution

(i) $(\cos A + i\sin A)\,(\cos B + i\sin B)$

$= \cos A\cos B + i\cos A\sin B + i\sin A\cos B - \sin A\sin B$

$= (\cos A\cos B - \sin A\sin B) + i\,(\sin A\cos B + \cos A\sin B)$

$= \cos(A+B) + i\sin(A+B)$

using the Compound Angle Formulae on page 14 of the *Formulae and Tables*.

(ii) $(\cos 21° + i\sin 21°)\,(\cos 39° + i\sin 39°)$

$= \text{cis}\,21°\,.\,\text{cis}\,39°$

$= \text{cis}(21° + 39°)$

$= \text{cis}\,60°$

$= \cos 60° + i\sin 60°$

$= \dfrac{1}{2} + \dfrac{\sqrt{3}}{2}i.$

Property 2

$$\frac{1}{\cos A + i\sin A} = \cos A - i\sin A = \cos(-A) + i\sin(-A)$$

or $\dfrac{1}{\text{cis}\,A} = \text{cis}(-A) = \cos A - i\sin A$

(i) We can invert a cis by changing the sign of the angle.

(ii) A cosine *minus* i sine can be written as cis of minus the angle.

Example 2

(i) Show that $\dfrac{1}{\cos A + i\sin A} = \cos A - i\sin A = \cos(-A) + i\sin(-A)$.

(ii) Calculate $\dfrac{1}{\cos 45° - i\sin 45°}$.

Solution

(i) $\dfrac{1}{\cos A + i\sin A} = \dfrac{1}{\cos A + i\sin A} \times \dfrac{\cos A - i\sin A}{\cos A - i\sin A}$

$= \dfrac{\cos A - i\sin A}{\cos^2 A + \sin^2 A}$

$= \cos A - i\sin A$ ... as $\cos^2 A + \sin^2 A = 1$

$= \cos(-A) + i\sin(-A)$ ... as $\cos(-A) = \cos A$, $\sin(-A) = -\sin A$

(ii) $\dfrac{1}{\cos 45° - i\sin 45°} = \dfrac{1}{\text{cis}(-45°)}$

$= \text{cis } 45°$

$= \cos 45° + i\sin 45°$

$= \dfrac{1}{\sqrt{2}} + \dfrac{1}{\sqrt{2}}i.$

Property 3

$$\frac{\cos A + i\sin A}{\cos B + i\sin B} = \cos(A - B) + i\sin(A - B)$$

i.e. $\dfrac{\text{cis } A}{\text{cis } B} = \text{cis}(A - B)$

To divide one cis by another, subtract the angle on the bottom from the angle on the top.

Property 3 follows immediately from Properties 1 and 2.

$\dfrac{\cos A + i\sin A}{\cos B + i\sin B} = \dfrac{\text{cis } A}{\text{cis } B}$

$= (\text{cis } A)(\text{cis}(-B))$ ... by Property 2

$= \text{cis}(A - B)$ ... by Property 1

$= \cos(A - B) + i\sin(A - B)$

Alternatively, Property 3 can be derived directly by multiplying top and bottom by the conjugate of the bottom, $\cos B - i\sin B$, and then tidying up. The details are left as an exercise.

Example 3

Express

$$\frac{\cos 5\theta + i\sin 5\theta}{\cos 2\theta + i\sin 2\theta}$$

in the form $\cos\alpha + i\sin\alpha$.

Solution

$\dfrac{\cos 5\theta + i\sin 5\theta}{\cos 2\theta + i\sin 2\theta} = \dfrac{\text{cis } 5\theta}{\text{cis } 2\theta}$

$= \text{cis}(5\theta - 2\theta)$

$= \text{cis } 3\theta$

$= \cos 3\theta + i\sin 3\theta.$

These properties of cis may be interpreted on an Argand diagram.

First of all, if

$$z = \text{cis}\,\theta = \cos\theta + i\sin\theta$$

then $|z| = \sqrt{(\cos\theta)^2 + (\sin\theta)^2}$
$= \sqrt{1}$
$= 1.$

Thus, every cis has a modulus of 1 and so lies on the unit circle on an Argand diagram.

Now suppose

$z = \text{cis}\,A = \cos A + i\sin A$
$w = \text{cis}\,B = \cos B + i\sin B.$

and $u = z.w$ and $v = \frac{1}{z}$.

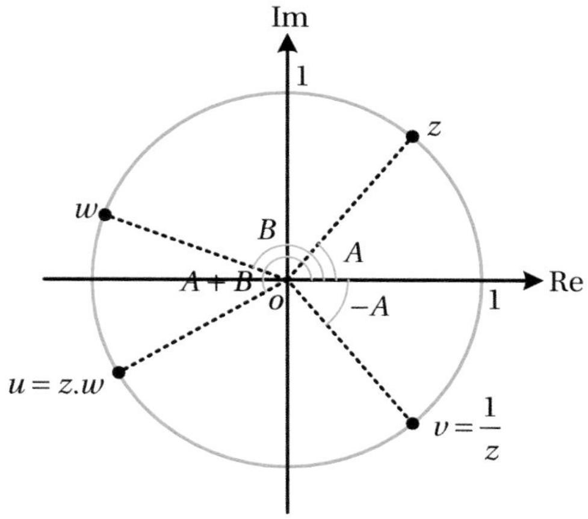

1. $u = z.w$
$= (\text{cis}\,A)\,(\text{cis}\,B)$
$= \text{cis}(A + B)$

Thus, multiplying w by z is a **rotation** of w about the origin in an anticlockwise direction through an angle A, which is the angle of z.

Now suppose $p = r\,(\cos B + i\sin B) = r\,\text{cis}\,B$. Then
$z.p = (\text{cis}\,A)\,(r\,\text{cis}\,B)$
$= r\,\text{cis}(A + B)$

This point is the same distance from the origin as p, but has been rotated through an angle A. Hence, multiplying any complex number by a cis rotates it about the origin, but leaves it the same distance from the origin.

2. $v = \frac{1}{z}$
$= \frac{1}{\text{cis}\,A}$
$= \text{cis}(-A)$
$= \cos A - i\sin A$
$= \bar{z}$

Thus, taking the reciprocal of a cis (one over the cis), has the effect of a **reflection** in the real axis. Also, the reciprocal of a cis is equal to the conjugate of the cis.

3. $\frac{u}{z} = \frac{\text{cis}(A + B)}{\text{cis}\,A}$
$= \text{cis}((A + B) - A)$
$= \text{cis}\,B$
$= w$

Thus, dividing the complex number u by z is a **rotation** of u about the origin through an angle of $-A$ in an anticlockwise direction (or an angle of A in a clockwise direction).

This is true of all complex numbers, no matter what their modulus. If any complex number is divided by a cis with an angle of A, then it is rotated in a clockwise direction of A, but stays the same distance from the origin.

The properties of cis may be used to describe how general multiplication and division affects points on an Argand diagram.

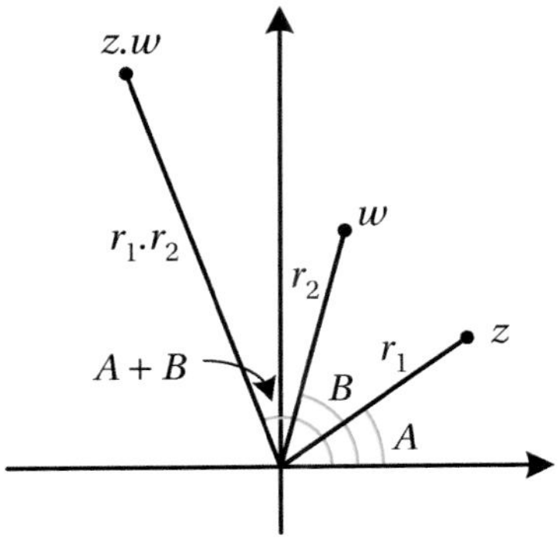

1. Multiplication

If $z = r_1 \text{ cis } A$

and $w = r_2 \text{ cis } B$,

then $z.w = (r_1 \text{ cis } A)(r_2 \text{ cis } B)$

$= r_1\, r_2 \text{ cis}(A + B)$

Thus, to multiply two complex numbers,

(i) multiply the moduli, and

(ii) add the angles.

2. Division

Also $\dfrac{z}{w} = \dfrac{r_1 \text{ cis } A}{r_2 \text{ cis } B}$

$= \dfrac{r_1}{r_2} \text{cis}(A - B)$

Thus, to divide one complex number by another,

(i) divide the moduli, and

(ii) subtract the lower angle from the upper.

Two special cases should be noted.

(i) Multiplying a complex number by i rotates it through 90° in an anticlockwise direction.

(ii) Multiplying a complex number by $-i$ rotates it through 90° in a clockwise direction.

The details are left as an exercise.

The algebraic operations on complex numbers allow us to move objects around the complex plane, changing their location, their orientation and their size. This makes complex numbers a very useful tool for programming animation, e.g. in animated films and computer games.

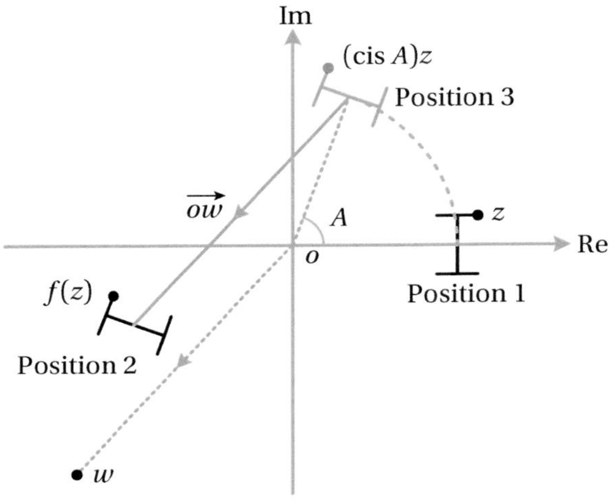

For example, suppose we have the 'I' object located in Position 1 shown and we want to move it to Position 2. This involves a translation and a rotation.

One way of achieving this, using complex numbers, is to find a transformation (function), f, which will map each point z in the object to the corresponding point $f(z)$ in the image. To find such a transformation:

(i) Rotate the object about the origin through an angle A so that the image has the correct orientation (Position 3). To do this:

$z \rightarrow (\text{cis } A)z$

(ii) Translate the object from Position 3 to Position 2 to get $f(z)$. If this translation is $\overrightarrow{ow}$, then

$f : z \rightarrow (\text{cis } A)z + w$

or $f(z) = (\text{cis } A)z + w$.

Exercises 34.2

1. Evaluate $(\cos 105° + i\sin 105°)(\cos 15° + i\sin 15°)$.

2. Evaluate $(\cos 140° + i\sin 140°)(\cos 85° + i\sin 85°)$.

3. Express $(\cos 3\theta + i\sin 3\theta)(\cos 4\theta + i\sin 4\theta)$ in the form $\cos\alpha + i\sin\alpha$.

4. Express $(\cos 7A + i\sin 7A)(\cos 3A + i\sin 3A)$ in the form $\cos\alpha + i\sin\alpha$.

5. Evaluate $\dfrac{1}{\cos 60° + i\sin 60°}$.

6. Evaluate $\dfrac{1}{\cos 150° + i\sin 150°}$.

7. Evaluate $\dfrac{1}{\cos 30° - i\sin 30°}$.

8. Evaluate $\dfrac{1}{\cos 150° - i\sin 150°}$.

9. Evaluate $\dfrac{\cos 72° + i\sin 72°}{\cos 12° + i\sin 12°}$.

10. Evaluate $\left(\cos\frac{2\pi}{3} + i\sin\frac{2\pi}{3}\right)\left(\cos\frac{\pi}{2} - i\sin\frac{\pi}{2}\right)$.

11. Express $\dfrac{\cos 5A + i\sin 5A}{\cos 2A + i\sin 2A}$ in the form $\cos\alpha + i\sin\alpha$.

12. Express $\dfrac{(\cos 2X + i\sin 2X)(\cos 4X + i\sin 4X)}{\cos 3X - i\sin 3X}$ in the form $\cos\alpha + i\sin\alpha$.

13. Express $\dfrac{8\left(\cos\frac{5B}{6} + i\sin\frac{5B}{6}\right)}{4\left(\cos\frac{B}{4} - i\sin\frac{B}{4}\right)}$ in the form $r(\cos\alpha + i\sin\alpha)$.

14. If $z = 2\left(\cos\frac{\pi}{6} + i\sin\frac{\pi}{6}\right)$ and $w = 4\left(\cos\frac{3\pi}{4} + i\sin\frac{3\pi}{4}\right)$, calculate zw in the form $r(\cos\alpha + i\sin\alpha)$, where $i^2 = -1$.

15. $z_1 = 2\left(\cos\frac{\pi}{6} + i\sin\frac{\pi}{6}\right)$ and $z_2 = 3\left(\cos\frac{\pi}{3} + i\sin\frac{\pi}{3}\right)$, where $i^2 = -1$. Calculate $z_1 z_2$ in the form $x + iy$, where $x, y \in \mathbb{R}$.

16. Show that
$$\frac{\cos A + i\sin A}{\cos B + i\sin B} = \cos(A - B) + i\sin(A - B)$$
by multiplying above and below by the conjugate of the bottom line.

17. **(i)** Write i in polar form.
(ii) Explain why iz is the image of z under an anticlockwise rotation about the origin through an angle of 90°.
(iii) Explain why $-iz$ is the image of z under a clockwise rotation about the origin through an angle of 90°.

18. The Argand diagram opposite shows the complex numbers z and $z.w$. z has a modulus of 4.
$z.w$ lies on the negative side of the imaginary axis, a distance of 2 units from the origin.
(i) Write z in polar form.
(ii) Write $z.w$ in polar form.
(iii) Copy the diagram opposite and show on the diagram the position of w. Write w in polar form.

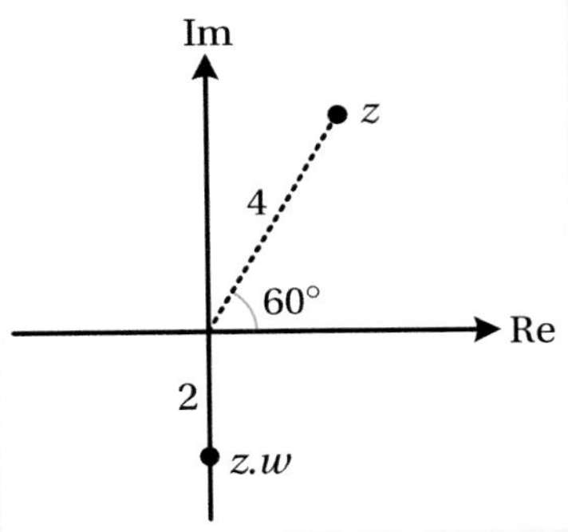

19. The Argand diagram opposite shows the complex numbers z and $z.w$, which are the same distance from the origin.
(i) What can we say about the modulus of w? Give a reason.
(ii) Express w in polar form. Copy the diagram opposite and show w on this diagram if w is the same distance from the origin as z.

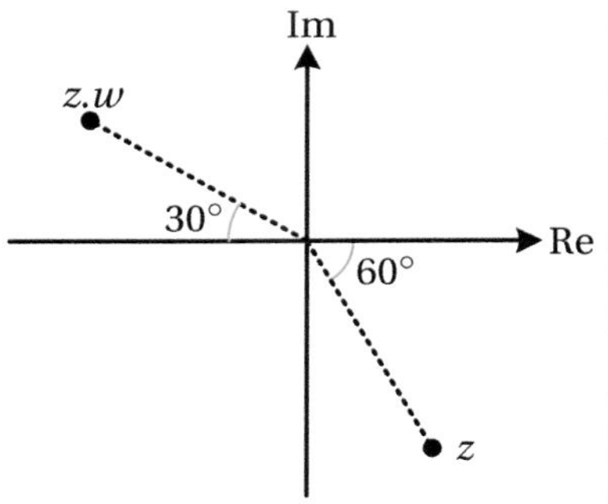

20. The Argand diagram opposite shows the complex numbers z and $\frac{z}{w}$.
(i) Write z and $\frac{z}{w}$ in polar form.
(ii) Write w in polar form. Copy the diagram opposite and show w on this diagram.

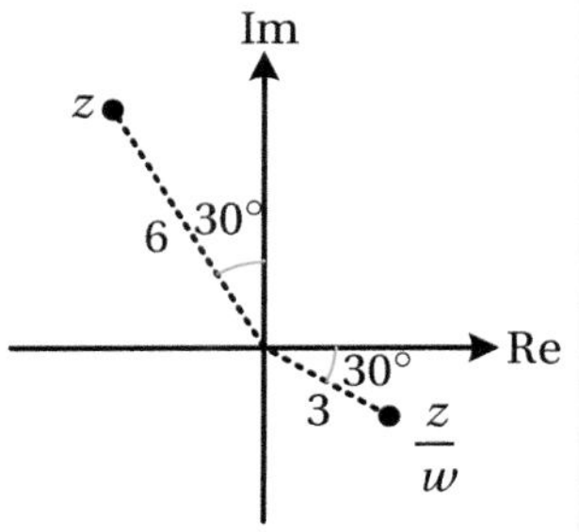

34.3 De Moivre's Theorem

Raising a complex number to a power is also easier when the complex number is written in polar form.

Property 4: De Moivre's Theorem

$(\cos\theta + i\sin\theta)^n = \cos n\theta + i\sin n\theta$

or $(\text{cis}\,\theta)^n = \text{cis}\,n\theta$, for $n \in \mathbb{Q}$,

i.e. we can raise a cis to a power by multiplying the angle by the index.

The proof of De Moivre's Theorem for $n \in \mathbb{N}$ is on our course. This proof makes use of proof by induction.

Proof of De Moivre's Theorem

$P(n)$: $(\cos\theta + i\sin\theta)^n = \cos n\theta + i\sin n\theta$, for $n \in \mathbb{N}$, i.e. $s = 1$

[1] $P(1)$: $(\cos\theta + i\sin\theta)^1 = \cos 1(\theta) + i\sin 1(\theta)$

$\cos\theta + i\sin\theta = \cos\theta + i\sin\theta$ True.

[2] Assume $P(k)$ is true, i.e.

$(\cos\theta + i\sin\theta)^k = \cos k\theta + i\sin k\theta$

To prove $P(k+1)$:

$(\cos\theta + i\sin\theta)^{k+1} = \cos(k+1)\theta + i\sin(k+1)\theta$

$$\begin{aligned}
\text{LHS} &= (\cos\theta + i\sin\theta)^{k+1} \\
&= (\cos\theta + i\sin\theta)^k(\cos\theta + i\sin\theta) \\
&= (\cos k\theta + i\sin k\theta)(\cos\theta + i\sin\theta) \\
&= \cos k\theta\cos\theta + i\cos k\theta\sin\theta + i\sin k\theta\cos\theta - \sin k\theta\sin\theta \\
&= (\cos k\theta\cos\theta - \sin k\theta\sin\theta) + i(\sin k\theta\cos\theta + \cos k\theta\sin\theta) \\
&= \cos(k\theta + \theta) + i\sin(k\theta + \theta) \\
&= \cos(k+1)\theta + i\sin(k+1)\theta \\
&= \text{RHS}
\end{aligned}$$

Conclusion: Hence $P(n)$ is true, for all $n \in \mathbb{N}$. Q.E.D.

Even though we only prove De Moivre's Theorem for $n \in \mathbb{N}$, we can still use it when n is any rational number. Thus, for example,

(i) $(\cos\theta + i\sin\theta)^4 = \cos 4\theta + i\sin 4\theta$

(ii) $(\cos A + i\sin A)^{-2} = \cos(-2A) + i\sin(-2A)$

(iii) $(\cos X + i\sin X)^{\frac{1}{3}} = \cos\left(\frac{1}{3}X\right) + i\sin\left(\frac{1}{3}X\right)$

Example 1

Evaluate $(\cos 45° + i\sin 45°)^8$.

Solution

$$
\begin{aligned}
(\cos 45° + i\sin 45°)^8 &= (\text{cis } 45°)^8 \\
&= \text{cis } (8 \times 45°) \qquad \text{... by De Moivre} \\
&= \text{cis } 360° \\
&= \cos 360° + i\sin 360° \\
&= 1
\end{aligned}
$$

Example 2

Use De Moivre's Theorem to write

$$\frac{(\cos 2\theta + i\sin 2\theta)^3}{(\cos 3\theta - i\sin 3\theta)^4}$$

in the form $\cos\alpha + i\sin\alpha$.

Solution

$$
\begin{aligned}
\frac{(\cos 2\theta + i\sin 2\theta)^3}{(\cos 3\theta - i\sin 3\theta)^4} &= \frac{(\text{cis } 2\theta)^3}{(\text{cis } (-3\theta))^4} \\
&= \frac{\text{cis } 6\theta}{\text{cis } (-12\theta)} \\
&= \text{cis } (6\theta + 12\theta) \\
&= \text{cis } 18\theta \\
&= \cos 18\theta + i\sin 18\theta.
\end{aligned}
$$

On an Argand diagram, successive powers of a complex number z cycle about the origin. If the modulus of z is greater than 1, then the powers spiral away from the origin.

For example, if

$z = 2 \text{ cis } 45°$

then

$z^2 = (2 \text{ cis } 45°)^2 = 4 \text{ cis } 90°$

and $z^3 = (2 \text{ cis } 45°)^3 = 8 \text{ cis } 135°$

and $z^4 = (2 \text{ cis } 45°)^4 = 16 \text{ cis } 180°$.

These points are shown opposite.

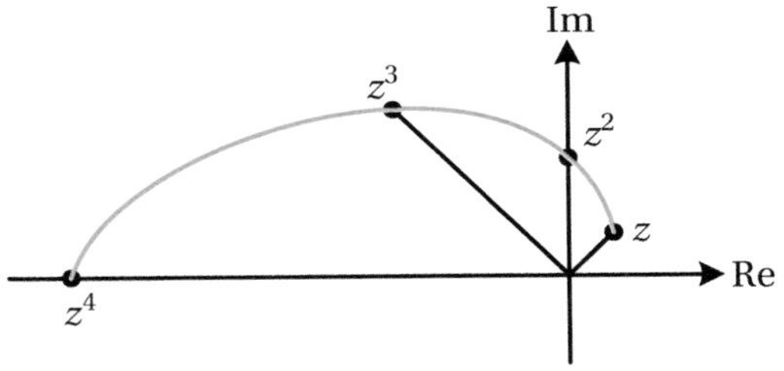

If the modulus of z is less than one, then the successive powers of z spiral in towards the origin. If the modulus of z is 1, then the powers of z rotate about the origin but all lie on the unit circle.

Exercises 34.3

1. Evaluate $(\cos 18° + i\sin 18°)^5$.

2. Evaluate $(\cos 15° + i\sin 15°)^{10}$.

3. Evaluate $(\cos 70° + i\sin 70°)^3$.

4. Evaluate $\left(\cos\frac{\pi}{12} + i\sin\frac{\pi}{12}\right)^4$.

5. Evaluate $\left(\cos\frac{\pi}{9} + i\sin\frac{\pi}{9}\right)^6$.

6. Evaluate $\left(\cos\frac{\pi}{8} - i\sin\frac{\pi}{8}\right)^6$.

7. Evaluate $\left(\cos\frac{\pi}{4} + i\sin\frac{\pi}{4}\right)^{-2}$.

8. Simplify $\left(\cos\frac{\pi}{3} + i\sin\frac{\pi}{3}\right)^2\left(\cos\frac{2\pi}{3} + i\sin\frac{2\pi}{3}\right)^4$.

9. Express $\dfrac{(\cos 2A + i\sin 2A)^3}{(\cos A - i\sin A)^4}$ in the form $\cos\alpha + i\sin\alpha$.

10. Express $\dfrac{(\cos 2\theta + i\sin 2\theta)^6}{(\cos 3\theta - i\sin 3\theta)^3}$ in the form $\cos\alpha + i\sin\alpha$.

11. Express $\dfrac{(\cos 2X - i\sin 2X)^4}{(\cos 4X + i\sin 4X)^{-3}}$ in the form $\cos\alpha + i\sin\alpha$.

12. The diagram opposite shows the three complex numbers z, z^2 and z^3. The modulus of z is greater than 1.
   (i) Copy the diagram and label each of the points shown.
   (ii) Find θ, the argument of z.
   (iii) If $|z^3| = \frac{9}{4}|z|$, express z in polar form.

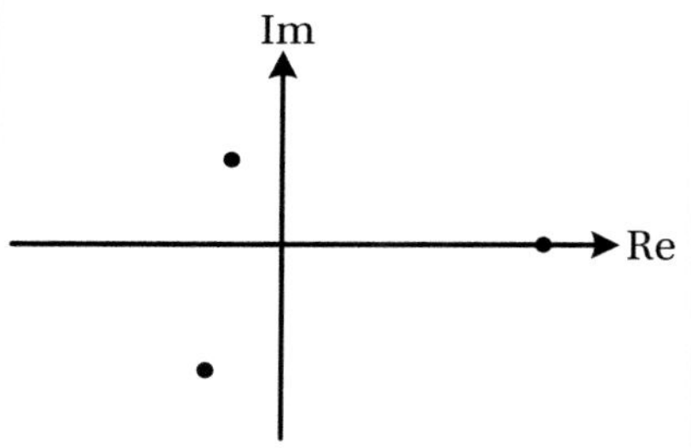

13. The modulus of z is less than 1. The Argand diagram opposite shows the complex numbers z, z^2 and z^3.
   (i) Copy the diagram and label each of the points shown.
   (ii) Find θ, the argument of z.
   (iii) If $|z^3| = \frac{1}{4}|z|$, write z in the form $r(\cos\theta + i\sin\theta)$.

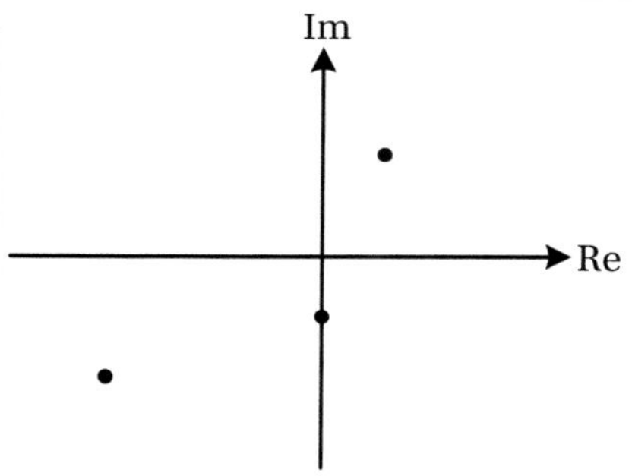

14. z is a non-real complex number, and the argument of z^4 is equal to the argument of z.

Find the two possible values, between $-180°$ and $180°$, of the argument of z.

34.4 Large Powers

De Moivre's Theorem can be used to simplify the calculation of large powers of complex numbers.

Example 1

(i) Express $\frac{1}{2} - \frac{\sqrt{3}}{2}i$ in the form $r(\cos\theta + i\sin\theta)$.

(ii) Hence, express $\left(\frac{1}{2} - \frac{\sqrt{3}}{2}i\right)^{10}$ in the form $a + bi$.

Solution

(i) From the diagram opposite,

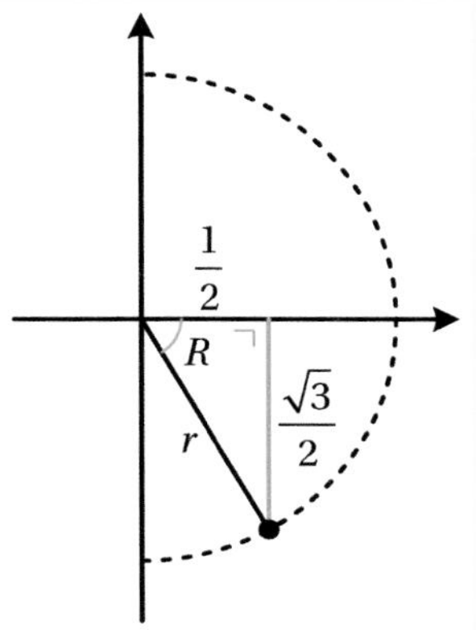

$$r = \sqrt{\left(\frac{1}{2}\right)^2 + \left(\frac{\sqrt{3}}{2}\right)^2}$$

$$= 1$$

and

$$\tan R = \frac{\frac{\sqrt{3}}{2}}{\frac{1}{2}} = \sqrt{3}$$

$$R = 60°$$

Thus,

$$\theta = -60°$$

Hence,

$$\frac{1}{2} - \frac{\sqrt{3}}{2}i = 1(\cos(-60°) + i\sin(-60°)) = \text{cis}(-60°)$$

(ii) $$\left(\frac{1}{2} - \frac{\sqrt{3}}{2}i\right)^{10} = (\text{cis}(-60°))^{10}$$

$$= \text{cis } 10 \times (-60°)$$

$$= \text{cis}(-600°)$$

$$= \cos(-600°) + i\sin(-600°)$$

$$= \cos 600° - i\sin 600°$$

$$= -\frac{1}{2} + \frac{\sqrt{3}}{2}i.$$

Exercises 34.4

1. **(i)** Express $1 - i$ in the form $r(\cos\theta + i\sin\theta)$.

   (ii) Hence, or otherwise, express $(1 - i)^7$ in the form $a + bi$.

2. **(i)** Express $-\sqrt{3} + i$ in the form $r(\cos\theta + i\sin\theta)$.

   (ii) Hence, or otherwise, express $(-\sqrt{3} + i)^5$ in the form $a + bi$.

3. **(i)** Express $-2 - 2i$ in the form $r(\cos\theta + i\sin\theta)$.

   (ii) Hence, or otherwise, express $(-2 - 2i)^6$ in the form $a + bi$.

4. Express $(1 + i)^{10}$ in the form $x + yi$.

5. Express $\left(\frac{1 - \sqrt{3}i}{2}\right)^{15}$ in the form $x + yi$.

6. $(2 + 3i)(a + ib) = -1 + 5i$. Express $a + ib$ in the form $r(\cos\theta + i\sin\theta)$ and hence, or otherwise, calculate $(a + ib)^{11}$.

7. Express $\left(\frac{-4-2i}{1+3i}\right)^5$ in the form $a + bi$.

8. Express $\left(\frac{1-3\sqrt{3}i}{2+\sqrt{3}i}\right)^4$ in the form $a + bi$.

34.5 Roots of a Complex Number

1. General Polar Form

For the next application of De Moivre's Theorem, it is necessary to be able to write a complex number in general polar form. This involves writing the angle (the argument) of the complex number in a more general form.

From trigonometry, we know that we can add any whole number of circles to an angle and the cosine and sine remain unchanged. Likewise, we can subtract any whole number of full circles from an angle and the cosine and sine also remain the same.

Formally:

$$\cos\theta = \cos(\theta + n(360°))$$
$$\sin\theta = \sin(\theta + n(360°)), \qquad \text{for } n \in \mathbb{Z} = \{\ldots, -1, 0, 1, 2, 3, \ldots\}.$$

Thus, if $z = r(\cos\theta + i\sin\theta) = r\,\text{cis}\,\theta$,
then we can also write

$$z = r(\cos(\theta + n(360°)) + i\sin(\theta + n(360°)))$$
$$= r\,\text{cis}\,(\theta + n(360°)) \qquad \text{for } n \in \mathbb{Z}.$$

This is called the ***general polar form*** of the complex number.

To write a complex number in general polar form:

(i) calculate r and θ as usual and write it in polar form,

(ii) add $+n(360°)$, or $+2n\pi$ if using radians, to the angle.

Example 1

Write $z = 1 + i$ in general polar form.

Solution

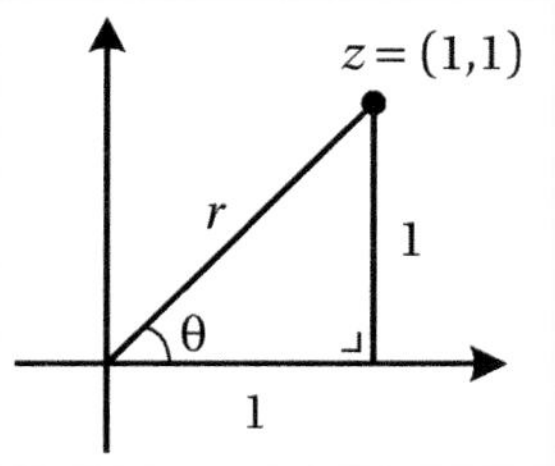

For $z = 1 + i$,

$r = \sqrt{2}$

and $\theta = 45°$.

Then, in polar form,

$$z = \sqrt{2}(\cos 45° + i\sin 45°)$$
$$= \sqrt{2}\,\text{cis}\,45°$$

In general polar form,

$$z = \sqrt{2}(\cos(45° + n(360°)) + i\sin(45° + n(360°)))$$
$$= \sqrt{2}\,\text{cis}(45° + n(360°)), \qquad \text{for } n \in \mathbb{Z}.$$

2. *k*-th Roots of a Complex Number

Consider the equation $z^k = \alpha$, where $\alpha \in \mathbb{C}$ and $k \in \mathbb{N}, k \geq 2$.

By putting both sides of the equation to the power of $\frac{1}{k}$, we can write the equation as

$$z = \alpha^{\frac{1}{k}}.$$

This equation has k individual roots, called the ***k-th roots*** of α. To find all the roots, we **must** write α in general polar form, and use De Moivre's Theorem. Ordinary polar form will only give us one root. The following example show how we find all the roots.

Example 2

Find all the roots of the equation

$$z^3 = -2 + 2i,$$

for $z \in \mathbb{C}$. Write your answers in the form $r(\cos\theta + i\sin\theta)$.

Solution

(Start by writing −2 + 2i in general polar form.)

For $-2 + 2i$,

$$r = \sqrt{(2)^2 + (2)^2} = \sqrt{8} = 2\sqrt{2}$$

and

$$\tan R = \frac{2}{2} = 1$$

$$R = 45°$$

Hence,

$$\theta = 180° - 45° = 135°.$$

In general polar form,

$$-2 + 2i = 2\sqrt{2}\,[\cos(135° + n(360°)) + i\sin(135° + n(360°))]$$
$$= 2\sqrt{2}\text{cis}(135° + n(360°)), \qquad \text{for } n \in \mathbb{Z}$$

(Now we rewrite the equation to get z on its own. Then we use De Moivre's Theorem.)

$$z^3 = -2 + 2i$$
$$z^3 = [2\sqrt{2}\text{cis}(135° + n(360°))]$$
$$z = [2\sqrt{2}\text{cis}(135° + n(360°))]^{\frac{1}{3}}$$
$$z = (2\sqrt{2})^{\frac{1}{3}}(\text{cis}(135° + n(360°)))^{\frac{1}{3}}$$
$$z = \sqrt{2}\text{cis}\,\frac{1}{3}(135° + n(360°))$$
$$z = \sqrt{2}\text{cis}(45° + n(120°))$$

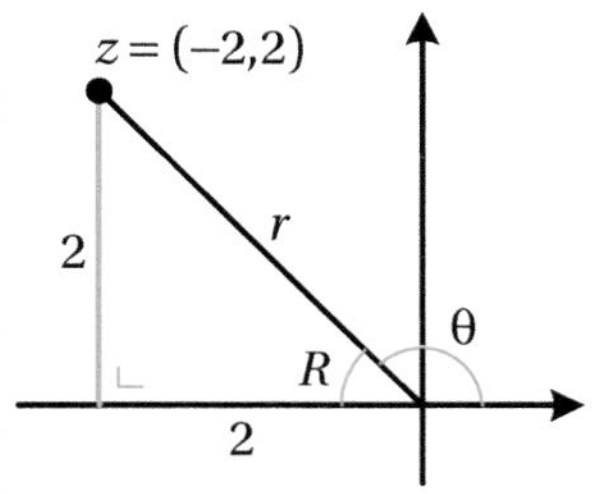

(To find the three individual roots, we put n = 0, 1, 2.)

$n = 0$: $z = \sqrt{2}\text{ cis } 45° = \sqrt{2}(\cos 45° + i\sin 45°)$

$n = 1$: $z = \sqrt{2}\text{ cis } 165° = \sqrt{2}(\cos 165° + i\sin 165°)$

$n = 2$: $z = \sqrt{2}\text{ cis } 285° = \sqrt{2}(\cos 285° + i\sin 285°)$.

In Example 2, putting $n = 3, 4, 5, \ldots$ just repeats the same roots.

The roots in Example 2 are shown on the Argand diagram opposite.

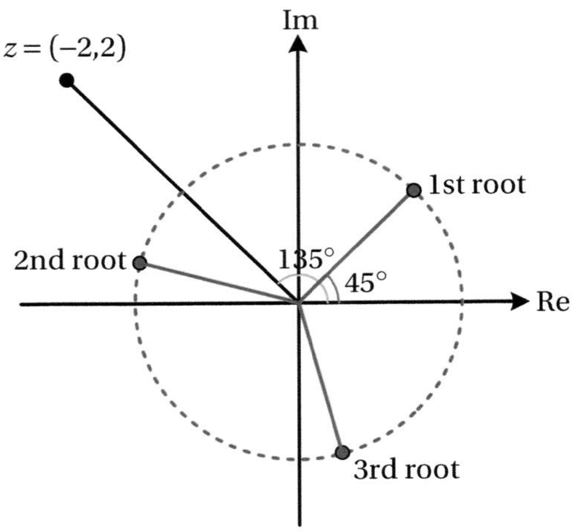

As the roots have the same modulus, they all lie on a circle with centre the origin. The radius of this circle is the cube root of the modulus of z. The first root has an angle one third that of z. Then the other roots divide the circle into three equal parts.

A similar analysis may be made for the roots of any complex number.

3. *k*-th Roots of Unity (One)

The roots of the equation

$$z^k = 1$$

are called the ***k*-th roots of unity (one)**. Although they can be found in the same way as in Example 2, they satisfy some interesting properties. Example 3 outlines and derives some of these properties.

Example 3

Find all the roots of the equation

$$z^k = 1$$

and show that

(i) these roots can be written $1, \omega, \omega^2, \omega^3, \ldots, \omega^{k-1}$

(ii) $\omega^k = 1$

(iii) $1 + \omega + \omega^2 + \omega^3 + \ldots + \omega^{k-1} = 0$.

Solution

(i) $1 = 1 + 0i = (1,0)$

Thus, $r = 1$ and $\theta = 0°$.

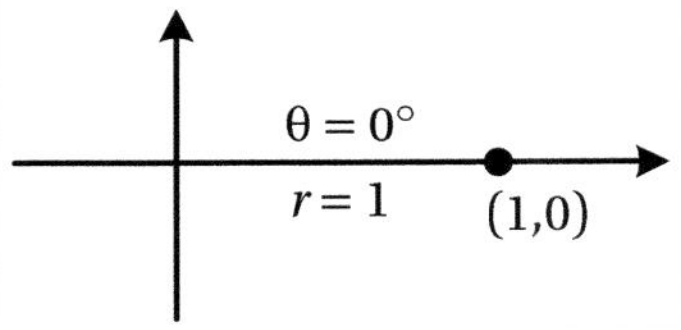

Hence

$$1 = 1\text{ cis}(0° + n(360°))$$

$$1 = \text{cis } n(360°), \quad \text{for } n \in \mathbb{Z}$$

The equation can be written

$$z^k = \text{cis } n(360°)$$

$$z = [\text{cis } n(360°)]^{\frac{1}{k}}$$

$$z = \text{cis}\frac{1}{k} \times n(360°)$$

$$z = \text{cis}\frac{n(360°)}{k}, \quad \text{for } n \in \mathbb{Z}$$

Then the roots are:

$n = 0$: $\quad z = \text{cis } 0° = \cos 0° + i \sin 0° = 1$

$n = 1$: $\quad z = \text{cis}\frac{360°}{k} = \omega$ (say)

$n = 2$: $\quad z = \text{cis}\frac{2(360°)}{k} = \left(\text{cis}\frac{360°}{k}\right)^2 = \omega^2$

$n = 3$: $\quad z = \text{cis}\frac{3(360°)}{k} = \left(\text{cis}\frac{360°}{k}\right)^3 = \omega^3$

.... $\quad$ ....

$n = k - 1$: $\quad z = \text{cis}\frac{(k-1)(360°)}{k} = \left(\text{cis}\frac{360°}{k}\right)^{k-1} = \omega^{k-1}$

(ii) $\omega^k = \text{cis}\frac{k(360°)}{k} = \text{cis } 360° = \cos 360° + i \sin 360° = 1$

or:

As ω is a root of the equation $z^k = 1$, we can substitute ω for z, and so $\omega^k = 1$.

(iii) Let $\quad A = 1 + \omega + \omega^2 + \omega^3 + \ldots + \omega^{k-1}$

Then

$$\begin{aligned}\omega A &= \omega + \omega^2 + \omega^3 + \omega^4 + \ldots + \omega^{k-1} + \omega^k \\ &= \omega + \omega^2 + \omega^3 + \omega^4 + \ldots + \omega^{k-1} + 1 \\ &= A\end{aligned}$$

$\omega A - A = 0$

$(\omega - 1)A = 0$

$A = 0 \qquad \ldots \text{ as } \omega - 1 \neq 0$

On an Argand diagram, the k-th roots of unity lie on the unit circle. The first root has an angle $\frac{360°}{k}$, and from here the roots divide the circle into k equal parts.

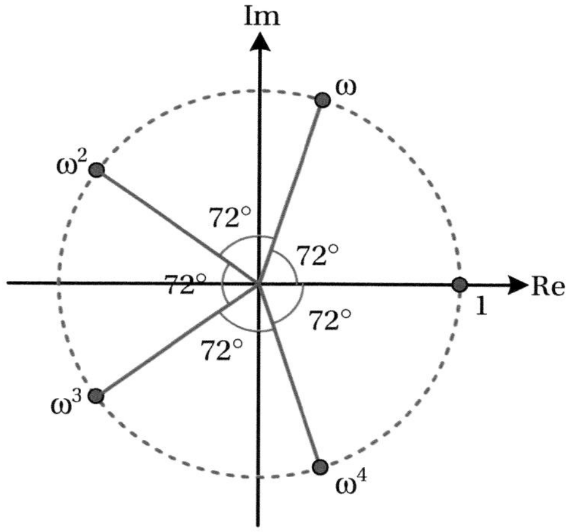

The diagram opposite shows the positions of the roots of the equation

$z^5 = 1$

which are 1, ω, ω^2, ω^3 and ω^4. One of the other properties of the roots of unity is visible on this diagram.

For every non-real root, its conjugate is also a root. Recall that the conjugate of a complex number is the reflection of that number in the real axis. On the diagram, ω and ω^4 are reflections of each other in the real axis and so are conjugates. The same applies to ω^2 and ω^3.

It can also be shown that if ω^p, where $1 \leq p \leq 4$, is a root of the equation, then so is $\frac{1}{\omega^p}$.

This is because

$$\frac{1}{\omega^p} = \frac{\omega^k}{\omega^p} = \omega^{k-p}$$

which is one of the other roots. For example,

$$\frac{1}{\omega^2} = \frac{\omega^5}{\omega^2} = \omega^3.$$

A special case of the k-th roots of unity is the roots of the equation

$z^3 = 1$

which are called the **cube roots of unity**.

In an exercise, you will be asked to show that these roots are 1, $\omega = -\frac{1}{2} + \frac{\sqrt{3}}{2}i$ and $\omega^2 = -\frac{1}{2} - \frac{\sqrt{3}}{2}i$. Then to show that $1 + \omega + \omega^2 = 0$, it is only necessary to add the real terms and add the imaginary terms.

For the cube roots of unity, we can re-arrange

$$1 + \omega + \omega^2 = 0$$

to get $1 + \omega = -\omega^2$

$$1 + \omega^2 = -\omega$$

$$\omega + \omega^2 = -1.$$

Example 4

If ω is a non-real root of the equation $z^3 = 1$, show that

$$(1 + \omega)(1 + 2\omega)(\omega^2 - 1) = 3.$$

Solution

$$\begin{aligned}(1 + \omega)(1 + 2\omega) &= 1 + \omega + 2\omega + 2\omega^2 \\ &= 1 + \omega + 2(\omega + \omega^2) \\ &= 1 + \omega + 2\,(-1) = \omega - 1\end{aligned}$$

Then $(1 + \omega)(1 + 2\omega)(\omega^2 - 1) = (\omega - 1)(\omega^2 - 1)$

$$\begin{aligned}&= \omega^3 - \omega - \omega^2 + 1 \\ &= 1 - (\omega + \omega^2) + 1 \\ &= 2 - (-1) = 3\end{aligned}$$

Exercises 34.5

Write each of the following complex numbers in general polar form.

1. $z = -1 + \sqrt{3}i$ **2.** $z = -2 - 2i$ **3.** $z = -8i$ **4.** $z = 4 - 4i$

5. Find all the solutions of the equation
$z^3 = -27,$ for $z \in \mathbb{C}$.

6. Find all the solutions of the equation
$z^4 = -81,$ for $z \in \mathbb{C}$.

7. Find all the solutions of the equation
$z^2 = -1 - \sqrt{3}i,$ for $z \in \mathbb{C}$.

8. Find all the solutions of the equation
$z^6 = 64,$ for $z \in \mathbb{C}$.

9. Solve the equation $z^6 + 1 = 0$, for $z \in \mathbb{C}$.

10. (i) Find all the solutions of the equation
$z^6 = 1.$

(ii) Show that these roots can be written $1, \omega, \omega^2, \omega^3, \omega^4$ and ω^5, where ω is one of the non-real roots.

(iii) Show that $1 + \omega + \omega^2 + \omega^3 + \omega^4 + \omega^5 = 0$.

(iv) Show that $\omega + \omega^2 + \omega^4 + \omega^5 = 0$.

11. (i) Use De Moivre's Theorem to find, in polar form, the five roots of the equation
$z^5 = 1.$

(ii) Choose one of the roots ω, where $\omega \neq 1$. Prove that $\omega^2 + \omega^3$ is real.

12. The Argand diagram opposite shows all of the roots of the equation

$$z^k = 1.$$

(i) What is the value of k? Give a reason.

(ii) Write the complex numbers represented by the points a, b, c and d in polar form.

(iii) If z is the complex number represented by the point b, determine which of the following are also roots of the equation: $\bar{z}$, $\frac{1}{z}$ and $-z$.

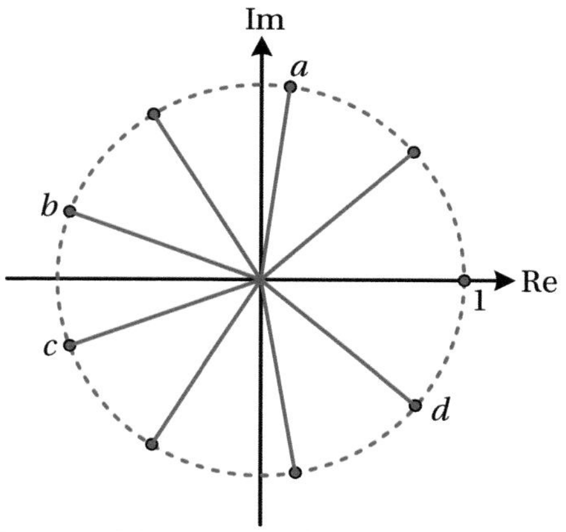

13. If ω is a non-real root of the equation $z^3 = 1$, show that the three roots of this equation can be written $1, \omega, \omega^2$. Show that $(1 + \omega)(1 + \omega^2) = 1$.

14. If ω is a non-real root of the equation $z^3 = 1$, show that

$$(1 - \omega)(1 - \omega^2) = 3.$$

15. If ω is a non-real root of the equation $z^3 = 1$, show that

$$(3 + 2\omega)(6 + 4\omega^2) = 14.$$

16. If ω is a non-real root of the equation $z^3 = 1$, show that

$$(1 + \omega)^2 + (1 + \omega^2)^2 = -1.$$

17. If ω is a non-real root of the equation $z^3 = 1$, show that

$$x^3 + y^3 = (x + \omega y)(x + \omega^2 y)(x + y).$$

18. If ω is a non-real root of the equation $z^3 = 1$, show that

$$\frac{\omega}{x + \omega} + \frac{\omega^2}{x + \omega^2} = \frac{2 - x}{x^2 - x + 1}.$$

34.6 Trigonometric Identities

De Moivre's Theorem may be used to establish certain trigonometric identities, such as to write $\cos n\theta$ and $\sin n\theta$ as polynomials in $\cos\theta$ or $\sin\theta$.

To expand $\cos n\theta$ or $\sin n\theta$ as polynomials in $\cos\theta$ or $\sin\theta$:

(i) write De Moivre's Theorem in this exact form:

$$\cos n\theta + i\sin n\theta = (\cos\theta + i\sin\theta)^n$$
$$= (c + is)^n, \qquad \text{where } c = \cos\theta, \quad s = \sin\theta$$

(ii) using algebra, expand $(c + is)^n$, gathering real terms and imaginary terms,

(iii) if $\cos n\theta + i\sin n\theta = (A) + i(B)$,
then put
Re = Re: $\cos n\theta = A$ if we want to expand $\cos n\theta$, or
Im = Im: $\sin n\theta = B$ if we want to expand $\sin n\theta$

(iv) finish by using $\cos^2\theta + \sin^2\theta = 1$, $(c^2 + s^2 = 1)$.

Example 1

Use De Moivre's Theorem to show that

$$\cos 3\theta = 4\cos^3\theta - 3\cos\theta.$$

Solution

By De Moivre's Theorem, with $n = 3$,

$$\cos 3\theta + i \sin 3\theta = (\cos \theta + i \sin \theta)^3$$
$$= (c + is)^3,$$

where $c = \cos \theta$, $s = \sin \theta$.

Then by algebra, although we can also use the Binomial Theorem:

$$(c + is)^3 = (c + is)(c + is)^2$$
$$= (c + is)(c^2 + 2csi - s^2)$$
$$= c^3 + 2c^2si - cs^2 + c^2si - 2cs^2 - s^3i$$
$$= (c^3 - 3cs^2) + i(3c^2s - s^3)$$

Hence,

$$\cos 3\theta + i \sin 3\theta = (c^3 - 3cs^2) + i(3c^2s - s^3)$$

(As we want to expand $\cos 3\theta$, we put Re = Re.)

$$\cos 3\theta = c^3 - 3cs^2$$
$$= c^3 - 3c(1 - c^2) \qquad \text{... as } s^2 = \sin^2\theta = 1 - \cos^2\theta = 1 - c^2$$
$$= c^3 - 3c + 3c^3$$
$$= 4c^3 - 3c$$
$$= 4\cos^3\theta - 3\cos\theta.$$

Exercises 34.6

1. Use De Moivre's Theorem to show that
   $\sin 3\theta = 3\sin\theta - 4\sin^3\theta.$

2. Use De Moivre's Theorem to show that
   $\cos 4\theta = 8\cos^4\theta - 8\cos^2\theta + 1.$

3. Use De Moivre's Theorem to show that
   $\sin 4\theta = 4\cos^3\theta\sin\theta - 4\cos\theta\sin^3\theta.$

4. Use De Moivre's Theorem to expand $\sin 3\theta$ and $\cos 3\theta$.

   Deduce that $\tan 3\theta = \dfrac{3\tan\theta - \tan^3\theta}{1 - 3\tan^2\theta}.$

Revision Exercises 34

1. **(i)** Write $1 + i$ and $\sqrt{3} - i$ in polar form.

   (ii) Hence, express $z = \dfrac{1+i}{\sqrt{3} - i}$ in polar form.

   (iii) Find the smallest positive integer n such that z^n is a real number. For this value of n, find the value of z^n.

2. **(i)** Find the modulus and the argument of each of the complex numbers z_1 and z_2 where

   $$z_1 = \frac{1+i}{1-i}, \qquad z_2 = \frac{\sqrt{2}}{1-i}.$$

(ii) Plot the points representing z_1, z_2 and $z_1 + z_2$ on an Argand diagram.

(iii) Deduce from your diagram that $\tan \frac{3\pi}{8} = 1 + \sqrt{2}$.

3. Write $\frac{1 + i\tan\theta}{1 - i\tan\theta}$ in the form $\cos\alpha + i\sin\alpha$.

4. Let $z = \cos\theta + i\sin\theta$.

Express $\frac{2}{1+z}$ in the form $1 - i\tan(k\theta)$, $k \in \mathbb{Q}$ and $z \neq -1$.

5. Simplify $\dfrac{\left(\cos\frac{\pi}{4} + i\sin\frac{\pi}{4}\right)^5 \left(\cos\frac{3\pi}{4} + i\sin\frac{3\pi}{4}\right)^3}{\left(\cos\frac{\pi}{4} - i\sin\frac{\pi}{4}\right)^2}$.

6. Use De Moivre's Theorem to find the value of

$$\left\{\frac{\sqrt{-3} - 1}{\sqrt{-3} + 1}\right\}^6.$$

7. Express $\left(\frac{1 + \sqrt{3}i}{1 - \sqrt{3}i}\right)^{10}$ in the form $x + yi$.

8. By using De Moivre's Theorem, find the roots of the equation

$z^4 + 4 = 0$.

Hence, or otherwise, express $z^4 + 4$ as the product of two quadratic polynomials in z with real coefficients.

9. **(i)** Express $-8 - 8\sqrt{3}i$ in the form $r(\cos\theta + i\sin\theta)$.

(ii) Hence, find $(-8 - 8\sqrt{3}i)^3$.

(iii) Find the four complex numbers z such that

$z^4 = -8 - 8\sqrt{3}i$.

Give your answers in the form $a + bi$, with a and b fully evaluated.

10. $1, \omega, \omega^2$ are the three roots of the equation $z^3 - 1 = 0$.

(i) Prove that $1 + \omega + \omega^2 = 0$.

(ii) Hence, find the value of $(1 - \omega - \omega^2)^5$.

11. Find the modulus and the argument of

$$\frac{(2 - i)^2(-1 + 3i)}{3 + i}.$$

12. If ω is a non-real cube root of unity, prove that

(i) $(1 - \omega + \omega^2)(1 + \omega - \omega^2) = 4$

(ii) $(2 + 5\omega + 2\omega^2)^6 = 729$.

35 Integration

As we first meet it, integration is the inverse operation to differentiation. But this is not the reason that we study integration, or integral calculus. The practical applications of integration are as powerful and far reaching as those of differentiation. Integration was first developed, in the late 1600s, by Newton and Leibniz, the mathematicians responsible for the introduction of differentiation.

Like with differentiation, we start integration by examining the concept. Then we investigate the methods of integration. This also involves using standard results and rules.

Once these have been covered, we are in a position to examine a few of the basic applications of integration. On our course, the main application we meet is the use of integration to calculate exactly the area of many irregularly shaped regions, whose areas could only have been approximated without integration. We also meet the idea of the average value of a function over an interval.

35.1 Indefinite Integrals

The inverse operation to differentiation is integration. Because the two processes are so closely linked, we would like the notation for integration to be consistent with that already introduced for differentiation.

For example, if we differentiate x^2, we get $2x$. We can write this as

$$\frac{d(x^2)}{dx} = 2x.$$

Integration should then reverse this process, i.e. if we integrate $2x$, we should get x^2. To develop a notation for this consistent with differentiation, we proceed as follows.

$$\frac{d(x^2)}{dx} = 2x$$

$$d(x^2) = 2x\,dx \qquad \textbf{... 1}$$

We now introduce the symbol $\int$, called the integral sign, to represent the inverse operation to the *d* in differentiation. Thus, $\int$ and *d* have the effect of cancelling each other, i.e.

$$\int dx = x$$

in the same way that $\sin(\sin^{-1}x) = x$ and $(\sqrt{x})^2 = x$.

Then, by **1**,

$$d(x^2) = 2x\,dx$$

$$\int d(x^2) = \int 2x\,dx$$

and $$\int 2x\,dx = x^2.$$

So this is how we indicate that we reverse the operation of differentiation: we place the **integral sign**, $\int$, in front of the $2x$, and the differential, dx, behind it. Both are needed.

The expression $\int 2x\,dx$ is called the **integral** of $2x$ (with respect to x) and represents the function whose derivative is $2x$. For this reason, it may also be referred to as an **anti-derivative**.

However, a problem arises. The integral, or anti-derivative, of a function is not unique, unlike the derivative. Consider the following examples.

(i) $\dfrac{\mathrm{d}(x^2+7)}{\mathrm{d}x} = 2x \quad \Rightarrow \quad \int 2x\,\mathrm{d}x = x^2 + 7$

(ii) $\dfrac{\mathrm{d}(x^2-3)}{\mathrm{d}x} = 2x \quad \Rightarrow \quad \int 2x\,\mathrm{d}x = x^2 - 3$

So what exactly does the expression $\int 2x\,\mathrm{d}x$ stand for?

Once we note that $\dfrac{\mathrm{d}(x^2+c)}{\mathrm{d}x} = 2x$, where c is any constant, we should realise that the integral, or anti-derivative, of $2x$ will be all functions of the form $x^2 + c$, i.e.

$$\int 2x\,\mathrm{d}x = x^2 + c,$$

where c is called the **constant of integration**.

Because of the presence of the unknown constant of integration, this type of integral is called an **indefinite integral**, as distinct from another type of integral to be seen in the next section.

Indefinite Integral

If $\dfrac{\mathrm{d}f(x)}{\mathrm{d}x} = f'(x)$, i.e. $f'(x)$ is the derivative of $f(x)$,

then

$$\int f'(x)\,\mathrm{d}x = f(x) + c$$

is the indefinite integral of $f'(x)$, where c is the constant of integration.

In practice, to calculate integrals, we use a number of standard integrals and a few rules of integration. We now meet the first two standard integrals, which are given on page 26 of the *Formulae and Tables*.

Standard Integrals

1. $\int x^n\,\mathrm{d}x = \dfrac{x^{n+1}}{n+1} + c, \qquad n \neq -1$
2. $\int x^{-1}\,\mathrm{d}x = \int \dfrac{1}{x}\,\mathrm{d}x = \log_e |x| + c = \ln|x| + c, \qquad x \neq 0.$

Each standard integral can be verified by differentiating the answer.

1. $\dfrac{\mathrm{d}}{\mathrm{d}x}\left(\dfrac{1}{n+1}x^{n+1} + c\right) = \dfrac{1}{n+1}\left((n+1)x^n\right)$

$= x^n$

as long as $n \neq -1$, as then the denominator would be zero.

2. **(i)** If $x > 0$, then $\ln|x| = \ln x$. Then

$\dfrac{\mathrm{d}}{\mathrm{d}x}(\ln x + c) = \dfrac{1}{x}$

(ii) If $x < 0$, then $\ln|x| = \ln(-x)$. Then

$\dfrac{\mathrm{d}}{\mathrm{d}x}(\ln(-x) + c) = \dfrac{1}{-x}(-1) = \dfrac{1}{x}.$

To use the first standard integral to integrate powers of x, increase the index by one, and divide by the new index. If the new index is a fraction, invert and multiply. Some examples are:

(i) $\int x^2 dx = \frac{1}{3}x^3 + c,$

(ii) $\int x\, dx = \frac{1}{2}x^2 + c$

(iii) $\int 1\, dx = x + c \quad (\text{as } 1 = x^0)$

(iv) $\int \frac{1}{x^4} dx = \int x^{-4} dx = -\frac{1}{3}x^{-3} + c$

(v) $\int \sqrt{x}\, dx = \int x^{\frac{1}{2}} dx = \frac{2}{3}x^{\frac{3}{2}} + c.$

Example 1

(i) Write down three anti-derivatives of x^4.

(ii) Find $\int x^4\, dx$.

Solution

(i) Three anti-derivatives are $\frac{1}{5}x^5$, $\frac{1}{5}x^5 + 8$ and $\frac{1}{5}x^5 - 12$.

(ii) $\int x^4\, dx = \frac{1}{5}x^5 + c.$

Two rules of integration are given below.

Rules of Integration

Let u and v be functions of x, and c be a constant.

1. $\int c.u\, dx = c\int u\, dx$

2. $\int (u \pm v)\, dx = \int u\, dx \pm \int v\, dx.$

These two rules can be derived from similar rules for differentiation. The first rule says that a constant multiplied by a function of x can be removed outside the integral. The second rule says that a sum or difference can be integrated separately. In each case, we only use one constant of integration.

Example 2

Find **(i)** $\int 4x^2\, dx$

(ii) $\int \left(x^3 - \frac{5}{x} + 3\right) dx$

(iii) $\int (x+1)^2(x-1)\, dx.$

Solution

(i) $\int 4x^2\, dx = 4\int x^2\, dx$

$$= 4\left(\frac{1}{3}x^3\right) + c$$

$$= \frac{4}{3}x^3 + c$$

(ii) $\int\left(x^3 - \frac{5}{x} + 3\right)\mathrm{d}x = \int x^3\,\mathrm{d}x - 5\int\frac{\mathrm{d}x}{x} + 3\int 1\,\mathrm{d}x$

$= \frac{1}{4}x^4 - 5\ln|x| + 3x + c$

(iii) *(Multiply out the brackets first.)*

$\int(x+1)^2(x-1)\,\mathrm{d}x = \int(x^2+2x+1)(x-1)\,\mathrm{d}x$

$= \int(x^3 - x^2 + 2x^2 - 2x + x - 1)\mathrm{d}x$

$= \int(x^3 + x^2 - x - 1)\mathrm{d}x$

$= \frac{1}{4}x^4 + \frac{1}{3}x^3 - \frac{1}{2}x^2 - x + c.$

Exercises 35.1

1. **(i)** List three functions whose anti-derivative is x.

(ii) Find $\int x\,\mathrm{d}x$.

2. **(i)** List three functions whose anti-derivative is x^5.

(ii) Find $\int x^5\,\mathrm{d}x$.

3. **(i)** List three functions whose anti-derivative is $x^2 + 2x$.

(ii) Find $\int(x^2 + 2x)\,\mathrm{d}x$.

4. **(i)** List three functions whose anti-derivative is $x^3 + \frac{1}{x}$.

(ii) Find $\int\left(x^3 + \frac{1}{x}\right)\mathrm{d}x$.

Find each of the following integrals.

5. $\int x^5\,\mathrm{d}x$

6. $\int x^8\,\mathrm{d}x$

7. $\int 4x^3\,\mathrm{d}x$

8. $\int 5x^8\,\mathrm{d}x$

9. $\int(2x^2 + 3x - 1)\,\mathrm{d}x$

10. $\int(8x^3 + 2x^2 - 5x + 1)\,\mathrm{d}x$

11. $\int(4x^5 - 3x^3 + 2x + 7)\,\mathrm{d}x$

12. $\int\left(\frac{1}{x} + 3x - 2\right)\mathrm{d}x$

13. $\int\left(\frac{2}{x^2}\right)\mathrm{d}x$

14. $\int\left(\frac{1}{x^3} + \frac{1}{x^4}\right)\mathrm{d}x$

15. $\int(x+3)^2\,\mathrm{d}x$

16. $\int(2x-1)^2\,\mathrm{d}x$

17. $\int(x+3)(x+4)\,\mathrm{d}x$

18. $\int(2x-1)(2x+1)\,\mathrm{d}x$

19. $\int\left(x - \frac{1}{x}\right)^2\mathrm{d}x$

20. $\int\left(\sqrt{x} - \frac{1}{\sqrt{x}}\right)^2\mathrm{d}x$

35.2 Definite Integrals

A **definite integral** is an integral with limits, e.g.

$$\int_1^3 2x \, dx.$$

The lower number, 1, is called the **lower limit**, while the upper number, 3, is called the **upper limit**.

We study definite integrals because they will be used in applications to be seen in later sections.

To evaluate the definite integral

$$\int_1^3 2x \, dx:$$

(i) integrate $2x$ as usual, leaving out the constant of integration,

$$\int 2x \, dx = x^2$$

(ii) now evaluate the function x^2 at $x = 3$, the upper limit, and subtract the value of the function at the lower limit, $x = 1$, which we write as

$$\begin{aligned}\int_1^3 2x \, dx &= [x^2]_1^3 \\ &= (3)^2 - (1)^2 \\ &= 9 - 1 \\ &= 8\end{aligned}$$

Notice that the outcome of a definite integral is a value (a number), and not a function.

In general, we have the following definition of a definite integral.

Definite Integral

If $\int f(x) \, dx = F(x) + c$

is an indefinite integral, then

$$\begin{aligned}\int_a^b f(x) \, dx &= [F(x)]_a^b \\ &= F(b) - F(a).\end{aligned}$$

Example 1

Evaluate $\int_0^1 (1 - \sqrt{x})^2 dx.$

Solution

$$\begin{aligned}\int_0^1 (1-\sqrt{x})^2\,dx &= \int_0^1 (1-2\sqrt{x}+x)\,dx \\ &= \int_0^1 \left(1-2x^{\frac{1}{2}}+x\right)dx \\ &= \left[x-2.\frac{2}{3}x^{\frac{3}{2}}+\frac{1}{2}x^2\right]_0^1 \\ &= \left[x-\frac{4}{3}x^{\frac{3}{2}}+\frac{1}{2}x^2\right]_0^1 \\ &= \left(1-\frac{4}{3}+\frac{1}{2}\right)-(0) \\ &= \frac{6-8+3}{6}-0 \\ &= \frac{1}{6}.\end{aligned}$$

Exercises 35.2

Evaluate each of the following definite integrals.

1. $\int_1^2 x^2\,dx$

2. $\int_{-1}^3 (3x^2+1)\,dx$

3. $\int_0^1 (x^3+2x+3)\,dx$

4. $\int_2^4 (x^4+2)\,dx$

5. $\int_{-2}^2 (x^2-3x+2)\,dx$

6. $\int_1^5 (1-4x-x^2)\,dx$

7. $\int_1^2 \sqrt{x}\,dx$

8. $\int_0^3 (x-\sqrt{x})\,dx$

9. $\int_1^3 (3x-1)(3x+1)\,dx$

10. $\int_0^2 (x^2+1)(4x-3)\,dx$

11. $\int_1^2 \left(\frac{2}{x}+4x\right)dx$

12. $\int_1^3 \left(\frac{1}{x^2}-\frac{1}{x}\right)dx$

13. If $\int_0^p (x+2)\,dx = \frac{5}{2}$, find the value of $p > 0$.

14. Show that $\int_{\frac{1}{e}}^1 \frac{dx}{x} = \int_1^e \frac{dx}{x}$.

15. Show that $\int_{1-k}^1 (x-1)^2\,dx = \int_1^{1+k} (x-1)^2\,dx$.

35.3 Integrals of Exponential and Trigonometric Functions

1. Integrals of Exponential Functions

From differentiation, we know that

(i) $\frac{d(e^x)}{dx} = e^x$, **(ii)** $\frac{d(e^{ax})}{dx} = ae^{ax}$, **(iii)** $\frac{d(a^x)}{dx} = a^x \ln a$.

From these, we can derive the following standard integrals for exponential functions.

Standard Integrals

3. $\int e^x \, dx = e^x + c$

4. $\int e^{ax} \, dx = \frac{1}{a} e^{ax} + c$

5. $\int a^x \, dx = \frac{a^x}{\ln a} + c$

These integrals are given on page 26 of the *Formulae and Tables*.

Again, each of these standard integrals can be verified by differentiating the answer. Standard integral **3** is obvious.

4. $\frac{d}{dx}\left(\frac{1}{a} e^{ax} + c\right) = \frac{1}{a}(a\, e^{ax}) = e^{ax}$

5. $\frac{d}{dx}\left(\frac{1}{\ln a} a^x + c\right) = \frac{1}{\ln a}(a^x \ln a) = a^x$.

Example 1

Evaluate each of the following integrals, correct to two decimal places.

(i) $\int_2^3 e^{-0 \cdot 1x} \, dx$

(ii) $\int_1^4 2(3^x) \, dx$.

Solution

(i) $\int_2^3 e^{-0 \cdot 1x} \, dx = \left[\frac{1}{-0 \cdot 1} e^{-0 \cdot 1x}\right]_2^3$

$= \left(-10e^{-0 \cdot 1(3)}\right) - \left(-10e^{-0 \cdot 1(2)}\right)$

$= \frac{-10}{e^{0 \cdot 3}} - \frac{-10}{e^{0 \cdot 2}}$

$= -7 \cdot 4082 + 8 \cdot 1873$

$= 0 \cdot 78$, correct to two decimal places.

(ii) $\int_1^4 2(3^x)\,dx = 2\left[\frac{3^x}{\ln 3}\right]_1^4$

$= 2\left(\frac{3^4}{\ln 3}\right) - 2\left(\frac{3^1}{\ln 3}\right)$

$= 147{\cdot}4588 - 5{\cdot}4614$

$= 142{\cdot}00$, correct to two decimal places.

2. Integrals of Trigonometric Functions

From differentiation, we know that

(i) $\frac{d(\sin x)}{dx} = \cos x$ **(ii)** $\frac{d(\cos x)}{dx} = -\sin x.$

From these, we can derive the following standard integrals for trig functions.

Standard Integrals

6. $\int \cos x\,dx = \sin x + c$

7. $\int \sin x\,dx = -\cos x + c$

8. $\int \cos ax\,dx = \frac{1}{a}\sin ax + c$

9. $\int \sin ax\,dx = -\frac{1}{a}\cos ax + c$

To establish these standard integrals, we differentiate the answers.

6. $\frac{d}{dx}(\sin x + c) = \cos x$

7. $\frac{d}{dx}(-\cos x + c) = -(-\sin x) = \sin x$

8. $\frac{d}{dx}\left(\frac{1}{a}\sin ax + c\right) = \frac{1}{a}(a\cos ax) = \cos ax$

9. $\frac{d}{dx}\left(-\frac{1}{a}\cos ax + c\right) = -\frac{1}{a}(-a\sin ax) = \sin ax.$

Standard integrals **6** and **7** are on page 26 of the *Formulae and Tables*. Standard integrals **8** and **9** are not, and will have to be memorised.

Example 2

Find $\int \cos 7x\,dx$.

Solution

$\int \cos 7x\,dx = \frac{1}{7}\sin 7x + c$

Example 3

Evaluate $\int_0^{\frac{\pi}{4}} \sin 3x \, dx$.

Solution

$$\int_0^{\frac{\pi}{4}} \sin 3x \, dx = \left[-\frac{1}{3}\cos 3x\right]_0^{\frac{\pi}{4}}$$

$$= -\frac{1}{3}\left[-\frac{1}{\sqrt{2}} - 1\right]$$

$$= \frac{1+\sqrt{2}}{3\sqrt{2}}.$$

It may be necessary to use some of the trigonometric identities on pages 13 to 15 of the *Formulae and Tables* before being in a position to integrate certain trig functions.

Example 4

Evaluate $\int_0^{\frac{\pi}{4}} (\cos x + \sin x)^2 dx$.

Solution

(After expanding, we will need to use the identities $\cos^2 A + \sin^2 A = 1$ and $\sin 2A = 2 \sin A \cos A$ before integrating.)

$$\int_0^{\frac{\pi}{4}} (\cos x + \sin x)^2 \, dx$$

$$= \int_0^{\frac{\pi}{4}} (\cos^2 x + \sin^2 x + 2 \sin x \cos x) \, dx$$

$$= \int_0^{\frac{\pi}{4}} (1 + \sin 2x) \, dx$$

$$= \left[x - \frac{1}{2}\cos 2x\right]_0^{\frac{\pi}{4}}$$

$$= \left(\frac{\pi}{4} - 0\right) - \left(0 - \frac{1}{2}\right)$$

$$= \frac{\pi}{4} + \frac{1}{2}.$$

To integrate the product of two sines, two cosines or a sine and a cosine, we can use the trig identities on page 15 of the *Formulae and Tables*, to express the product as a sum or a difference.

It is a good idea to write the product with the larger angle first, to avoid negative angles when the product is written as a sum or a difference.

Example 5

Evaluate $\int_0^{\frac{\pi}{8}} \sin 3x \cos 5x \, dx$.

Solution

(Switch the sin 3x and the cos 5x and use

2 cos A sin B = sin(A + B) – sin(A – B).)

$$\int_0^{\frac{\pi}{8}} \sin 3x \cos 5x \, dx$$

$$= \int_0^{\frac{\pi}{8}} \cos 5x \sin 3x \, dx$$

$$= \frac{1}{2}\int_0^{\frac{\pi}{8}} (\sin 8x - \sin 2x) \, dx$$

$$= \frac{1}{2}\left[-\frac{1}{8}\cos 8x + \frac{1}{2}\cos 2x\right]_0^{\frac{\pi}{8}}$$

$$= \frac{1}{2}\left[\left(-\frac{1}{8}\cos \pi + \frac{1}{2}\cos \frac{\pi}{4}\right) - \left(-\frac{1}{8}\cos 0 + \frac{1}{2}\cos 0\right)\right]$$

$$= \frac{1}{2}\left[\left(\frac{1}{8} + \frac{1}{2\sqrt{2}}\right) - \left(-\frac{1}{8} + \frac{1}{2}\right)\right]$$

$$= \frac{1}{2}\left[\frac{1}{2\sqrt{2}} - \frac{1}{4}\right]$$

$$= \frac{1}{2} \times \frac{2-\sqrt{2}}{4\sqrt{2}} = \frac{2-\sqrt{2}}{8\sqrt{2}}.$$

To integrate a cosine squared or a sine squared, we can use the identities

$$\cos^2 A = \frac{1}{2}(1 + \cos 2A) \text{ and } \sin^2 A = \frac{1}{2}(1 - \cos 2A)$$

on page 14 of the *Formulae and Tables*.

Example 6

Evaluate $\int_0^{\frac{\pi}{8}} \cos^2 4x \, dx$.

Solution

From $\cos^2 A = \frac{1}{2}(1 + \cos 2A)$,

$$\cos^2 4x = \frac{1}{2}(1 + \cos 8x).$$

Then $\int_0^{\frac{\pi}{8}} \cos^2 4x \, dx = \frac{1}{2}\int_0^{\frac{\pi}{8}} (1 + \cos 8x) \, dx$

$$= \frac{1}{2}\left[x + \frac{1}{8}\sin 8x\right]_0^{\frac{\pi}{8}}$$

$$= \frac{1}{2}\left[\left(\frac{\pi}{8} + \frac{1}{8}\sin \pi\right) - \left(0 + \frac{1}{8}\sin 0\right)\right]$$

$$= \frac{\pi}{16}.$$

Exercises 35.3

Evaluate each of the following.

1. $\int_0^2 e^x \, dx$

2. $\int_1^{\sqrt{3}} e^x \, dx$

3. $\int_{0\cdot 5}^{1\cdot 5} e^{2x} \, dx$

4. $\int_{-1}^2 e^{4x} \, dx$

5. $\int_0^4 e^{-x} \, dx$

6. $\int_{0\cdot 1}^{0\cdot 8} e^{7x} \, dx$

7. $\int_1^3 (e^x + 2) \, dx$

8. $\int_0^2 (e^x + 1)^2 \, dx$

9. $\int_1^4 (e^{2x} + e^x) \, dx$

10. $\int_0^3 (e^{2x} + 3x^2 - 4x + 7) \, dx$

11. $\int_1^3 \left(\frac{1}{x} + e^{2x}\right) dx$

12. $\int_1^2 \left(e^{3x} + x^2 - 5x - \frac{2}{x}\right) dx$

13. $\int_0^1 2^x \, dx$

14. $\int_{0\cdot 2}^{0\cdot 7} 5^x \, dx$

15. $\int_{0\cdot 1}^{1\cdot 3} 3(4)^x \, dx$

16. $\int_0^1 \left(4(1\cdot 5)^x + 3x^2\right) dx$

17. $\int_{1\cdot 2}^{1\cdot 8} 5(1\cdot 2)^x \, dx$

18. $\int_0^2 (3(2\cdot 1)^x - 2(1\cdot 8)^x) \, dx$

19. (i) Write 2^{2x} in the form a^x.
    (ii) Evaluate $\int_0^1 2^{2x} \, dx$.

20. (i) Write 3^{4x} in the form a^x.
    (ii) Evaluate $\int_0^1 3^{4x} \, dx$.

Evaluate the following integrals.

21. $\int_0^{\frac{\pi}{4}} \cos 4x \, dx$

22. $\int_0^{\frac{\pi}{3}} \sin 2x \, dx$

23. $\int_{\frac{\pi}{6}}^{\frac{\pi}{3}} \cos 6x \, dx$

24. $\int_{\frac{\pi}{6}}^{\frac{\pi}{3}} \sin 3x \, dx$

25. Evaluate $\int_0^{\frac{\pi}{4}} (\cos x - \sin x)^2 \, dx$.

26. Evaluate $\int_0^{\frac{\pi}{8}} (\cos 2x + \sin 2x)^2 \, dx$.

27. Evaluate $\int_0^{\frac{\pi}{3}} \cos 3x \cos x \, dx$.

28. Evaluate $\int_{\frac{\pi}{3}}^{\frac{2\pi}{3}} \sin 4x \cos 2x \, dx$.

29. Evaluate $\int_0^{\frac{\pi}{3}} \sin 2\theta \cos \theta \, d\theta$.

30. Evaluate $\int_0^{\frac{\pi}{6}} \cos x \cos 3x \, dx$.

31. Evaluate $\int_0^{\frac{\pi}{4}} \cos^2 x \, dx$.

32. Evaluate $\int_0^{\frac{\pi}{3}} \sin^2 x \, dx$.

33. Evaluate $\int_0^{\frac{\pi}{6}} 2 \sin^2 3x \, dx$.

34. Evaluate $\int_0^{\frac{\pi}{4}} 2 \cos^2 4x \, dx$.

35.4 Area to the *x*-Axis

The definite integral $\int_a^b f(x)\, dx$ represents the **signed area** between the curve $y = f(x)$ and the x-axis, for $a \le x \le b$.

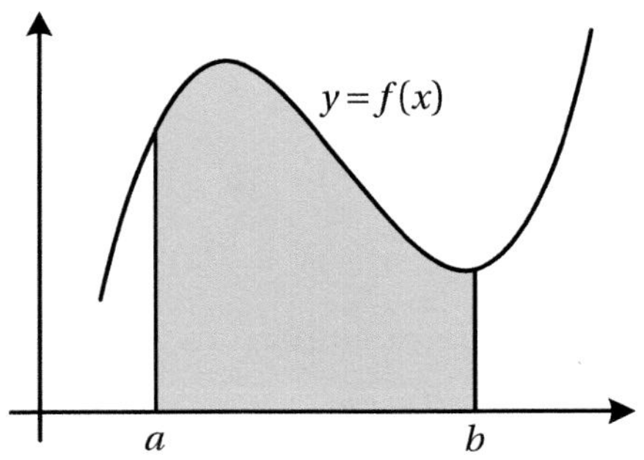

The idea of 'signed area' is that the integral treats area above the x-axis as positive and area below the x-axis as negative.

Once we establish that this is correct, we can use integration to calculate the areas of regions that before could only have been approximated.

We can explain the connection between area and integrals in two ways: one giving the link between areas and definite integrals and the other explaining the choice of integral notation.

Method 1

Let $y = f(x)$ be a function such that

$$\int f(x)\, dx = F(x) + c.$$

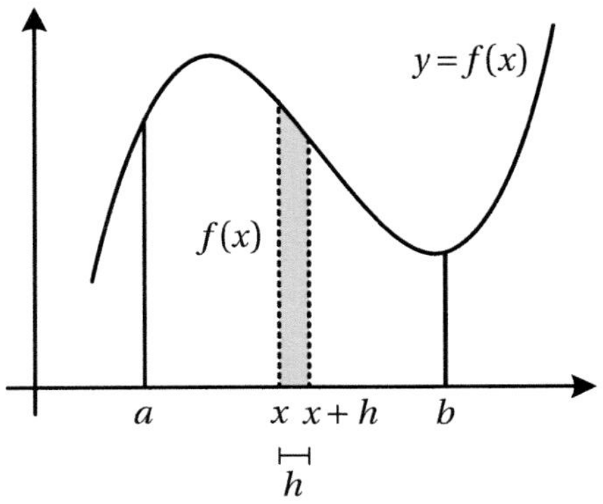

Let $A(x)$ be the area between the curve $y = f(x)$ and the x-axis for $a \le x \le x$, where $x \ge a$.

The area of the strip shown opposite can then be considered to be the area under the curve from $x = a$ to $x = x + h$ minus the area under the curve from $x = a$ to $x = x$, i.e. the area of the strip shown is

$$A(x+h) - A(x).$$

We may also consider the strip shown to be approximately rectangular, with area given by base by height, i.e. $f(x).h$. Thus,

$$A(x+h) - A(x) \approx f(x).h$$

or $$\frac{A(x+h) - A(x)}{h} \approx f(x).$$

As h gets closer to 0, the strip becomes more like a rectangle. In the limit, as $h \to 0$, we can treat the strip as exactly rectangular. Thus,

$$\lim_{h \to 0} \frac{A(x+h) - A(x)}{h} = f(x)$$

$$\frac{\mathrm{d}A}{\mathrm{d}x} = f(x)$$

$$\mathrm{d}A = f(x)\,\mathrm{d}x$$

$$A(x) = \int f(x)\,\mathrm{d}x$$

$$A(x) = F(x) + c$$

As $A(a) = 0$, because the area under the curve between $x = a$ and $x = a$ is zero, we get

$$A(a) = F(a) + c$$
$$0 = F(a) + c$$
$$c = -F(a)$$

Hence, $A(x) = F(x) - F(a)$.

We want $A(b)$, i.e. the area under the curve between $x = a$ and $x = b$.

Thus,

$$A(b) = F(b) - F(a)$$

$$A(b) = \int_a^b f(x)\,\mathrm{d}x$$

by the definition of a definite integral. Thus, the area between the curve shown and the x-axis, for $a \le x \le b$, is $\int_a^b f(x)\,\mathrm{d}x$.

Method 2

The area between the curve and the x-axis, for $a \le x \le b$, can be found by dividing the region up into a very large number of vertical strips, starting at $x = a$ and ending at $x = b$. Then the area of the region can be got by summing the areas of the strips.

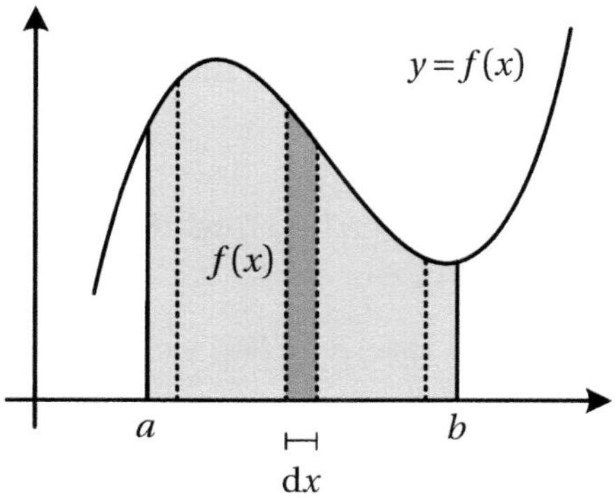

If the width of a typical strip is $\mathrm{d}x$, and its height is $f(x)$, then the area of the strip is $f(x)\,\mathrm{d}x$, treating the strip as a rectangle, because in theory it is so narrow.

Thus, when the number of strips tends to infinity:

$$\text{area of region} = \sum f(x)\,\mathrm{d}x$$

The integral sign, $\int$, came from an elongated S meaning 'sum'. Hence,

$$\text{area of region} = \int_a^b f(x)\,dx,$$

putting in the limits of integration.

In both explanations, you should note that the height of the strip is given as $f(x)$. If the curve lies below the x-axis, then $f(x)$ is negative, and so the resulting integral will be negative. This is what we mean when we say that the definite integral gives the 'signed area' between the curve and the x-axis.

Area between a curve and the x-axis

The definite integral

$$\int_a^b y\,dx = \int_a^b f(x)\,dx$$

gives the area between the curve $y = f(x)$ and the x-axis, for $a \le x \le b$.
If the area lies below the x-axis, then this integral is negative.

To find the area between a curve and the x-axis, it is important to sketch a graph in the required region, in particular noting the position of the curve relative to the x-axis. To find where a curve crosses the x-axis, we let $y = 0$ in the equation of the curve.

Then:

1. If the curve lies **completely above** the x-axis, then the integral

$$\int_a^b y\,dx = \int_a^b f(x)\,dx$$

is **positive**, and gives the area.

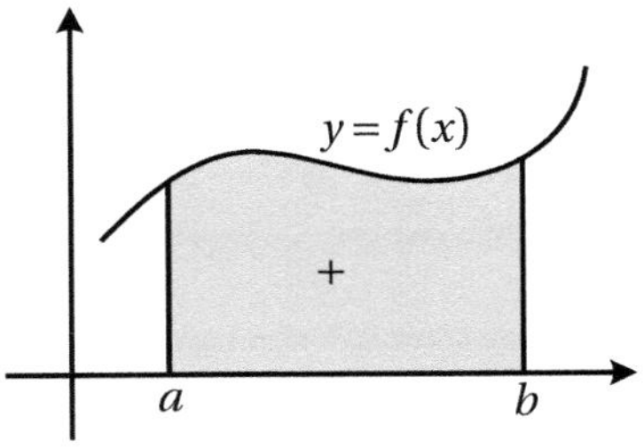

2. If the curve lies **completely below** the x-axis, then the integral

$$\int_a^b y\,dx = \int_a^b f(x)\,dx$$

is **negative**, and we have to change its sign to get the area.

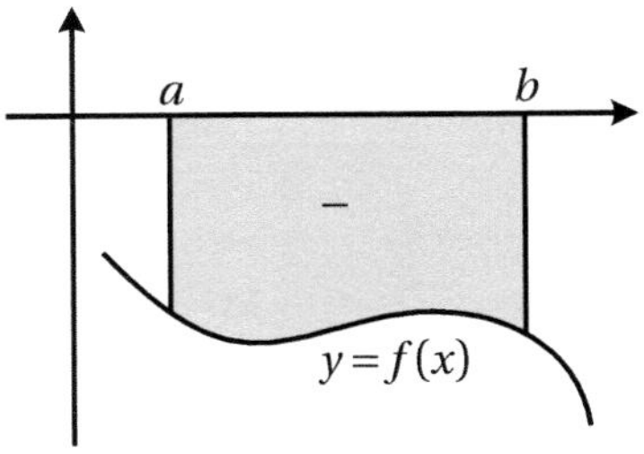

3. If the curve lies **partially above and partially below**, then we must find areas above and below separately. Then we add these to get the total area.

In practice, we get the areas between a and c, and between c and b separately.

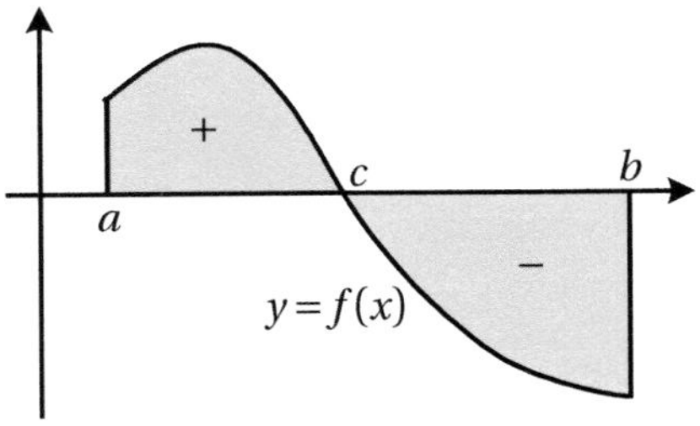

Example 1

Find the area of the region bounded by the curve $y = 3x^2 + 1$, the x-axis and the lines $x = 1$ and $x = 3$.

Solution

(To find if and where the curve crosses the x-axis, let y = 0.)

$$y = 0: \quad 3x^2 + 1 = 0$$
$$3x^2 = -1$$

As this has no real solution, the curve does not cross the x-axis. As

$$3x^2 + 1 > 0$$

for all $x \in \mathbb{R}$, the curve lies completely above the x-axis.

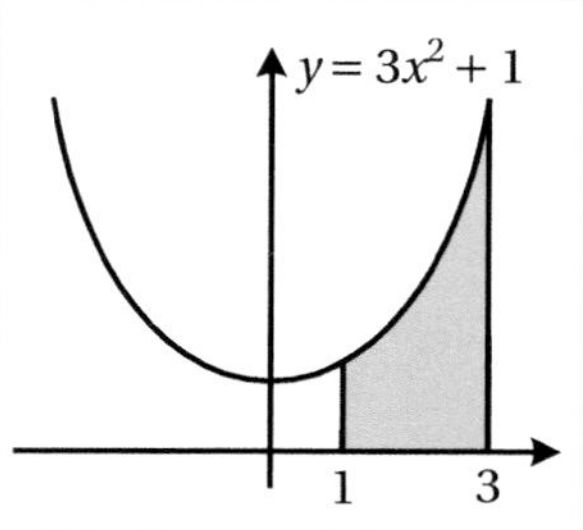

$$\text{Area} = \int_1^3 y\, dx$$
$$= \int_1^3 (3x^2 + 1)\, dx$$
$$= [x^3 + x]_1^3$$
$$= (3^3 + 3) - (1^3 + 1)$$
$$= 30 - 2$$
$$= 28.$$

Example 2

Let $f(x) = x^3 - 4x^2 - x + 4$.

(i) Show that $f(1) = 0$ and find the three roots of the equation $f(x) = 0$.

(ii) Find the area of the region bounded by the curve $y = f(x)$ and the x-axis.

Solution

(i) $f(x) = x^3 - 4x^2 - x + 4$.

$f(1) = 1 - 4 - 1 + 4 = 0$.

Thus, $(x - 1)$ is a factor of $f(x)$.

$$\begin{array}{r} x^2 - 3x - 4 \\ x - 1 \overline{)\, x^3 - 4x^2 - x + 4} \\ x^3 - x^2 \qquad\qquad \\ \hline -3x^2 - x \qquad \\ -3x^2 + 3x \qquad \\ \hline -4x + 4 \\ -4x + 4 \\ \hline \end{array}$$

Thus, $f(x) = 0$

$$(x - 1)(x^2 - 3x - 4) = 0$$
$$(x - 1)(x + 1)(x - 4) = 0$$
$$x = 1 \text{ or } x = -1 \text{ or } x = 4$$

are the roots of the equation $f(x) = 0$.

(ii) The curve $y = f(x)$ crosses the x-axis at –1, 1 and 4.

Let A_1 be the area above the x-axis, and A_2 be the area below the x-axis.

$$\int_{-1}^{1} y\,dx = \int_{-1}^{1} [x^3 - 4x^2 - x + 4]\,dx$$

$$= \left[\frac{1}{4}x^4 - \frac{4}{3}x^3 - \frac{1}{2}x^2 + 4x\right]_{-1}^{1}$$

$$= \left(\frac{1}{4} - \frac{4}{3} - \frac{1}{2} + 4\right) - \left(\frac{1}{4} + \frac{4}{3} - \frac{1}{2} - 4\right)$$

$$= -\frac{8}{3} + 8$$

$$= \frac{16}{3}$$

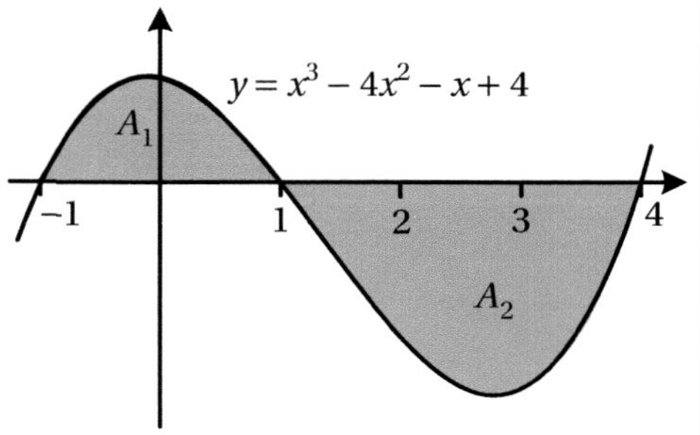

Thus, $A_1 = \frac{16}{3}$

$$\int_{1}^{4} y\,dx = \int_{1}^{4} [x^3 - 4x^2 - x + 4]\,dx$$

$$= \left[\frac{1}{4}x^4 - \frac{4}{3}x^3 - \frac{1}{2}x^2 + 4x\right]_{1}^{4}$$

$$= \left(64 - \frac{256}{3} - 8 + 16\right) - \left(\frac{1}{4} - \frac{4}{3} - \frac{1}{2} + 4\right)$$

$$= -\frac{63}{4}$$

Thus, $A_2 = \frac{63}{4}$

Then, the required area is

$$A_1 + A_2 = \frac{16}{3} + \frac{63}{4} = \frac{253}{12}.$$

Exercises 35.4

1. Find the area bounded by the curve $y = x^2 + 8$, the x-axis, and the lines $x = 1$ and $x = 3$.
2. Find the area lying above the x-axis and under the curve $y = 4x - x^2$.
3. Find the area bounded by the curve $y = x^2 - 16$, the x-axis and the lines $x = 2$ and $x = 5$.

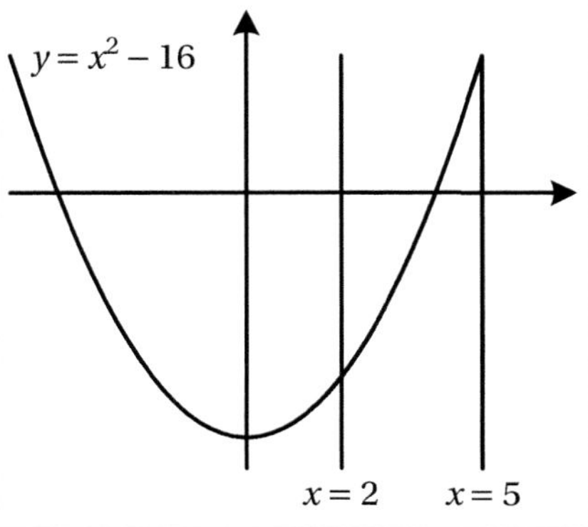

4. Find the area bounded by the curve $y = x^2 - 6x + 5$, the x-axis and the lines $x = 0$ and $x = 4$.
5. Find the area bounded by the curve $y = x^3 - 6x^2 + 8x$ and the x-axis.
6. Find the area bounded by the curve $y = x^3 - 9x$ and the x-axis.
7. Find the area bounded by the curve $y = e^x$ and the x-axis, for $0 \le x \le \ln 5$.
8. Find the area bounded by the curve $y = e^x - e^{2x}$ and the x-axis, for $0 \le x \le \ln 10$.
9. Find the area between the curve $y = 2^x$ and the x-axis, for $1 \le x \le 4$.
10. Find the area bounded by the curve $y = 3^x$ and the x-axis, for $0 \le x \le 3$.

35.5 Area to the y-Axis

In similar fashion, the signed area between the curve $x = g(y)$ and the y-axis, for $c \le y \le d$, is given by

$$\int_c^d x \, dy = \int_c^d g(y) \, dy.$$

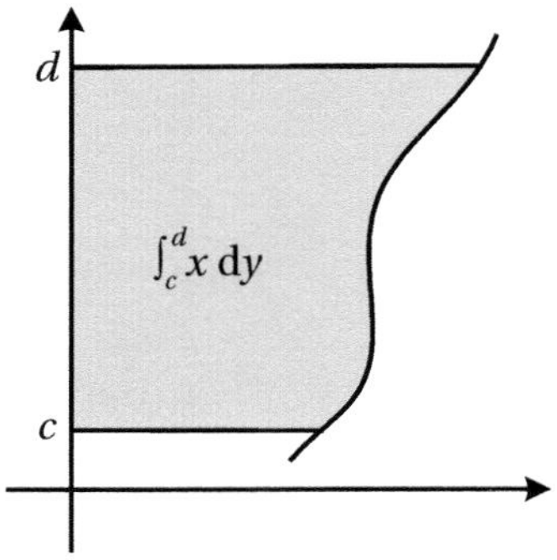

This means that area to the right of the y-axis is positive, while area to the left of the y-axis is negative.

Again, it is important to find where the curve crosses the y-axis.
To find where the curve crosses the y-axis, we let $x = 0$.

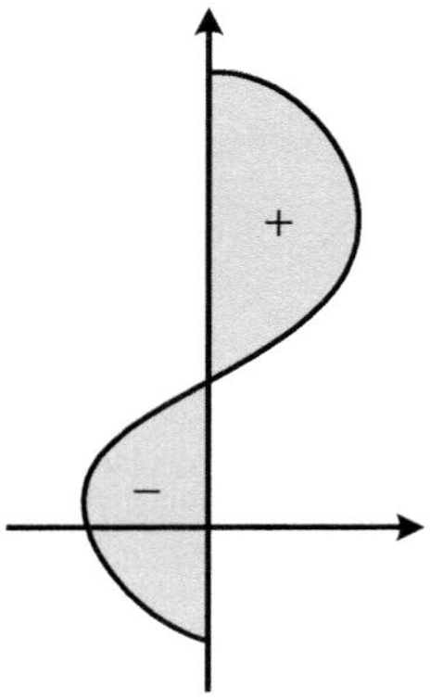

Area between a curve and the y-axis

The definite integral

$$\int_c^d x \, dy = \int_c^d g(y) \, dy$$

gives the area between the curve $x = g(y)$ and the y-axis, for $c \le y \le d$.

If the area lies to the left of the y-axis, then this integral is negative.

Example 1

Find the area bounded by the curve $x = y^2 + 1$, the y-axis and the lines $y = 0$ and $y = 1$.

Solution

Putting $x = 0$, we see that the curve does not cross the y-axis.

Indeed, it lies completely to the right, as shown opposite.

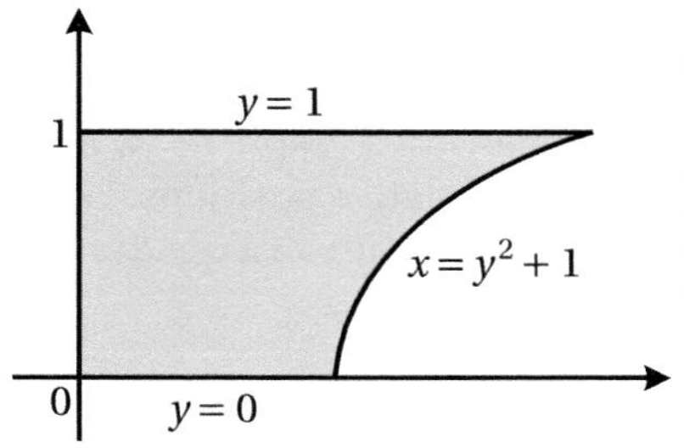

Thus:

$$\begin{aligned}\text{Area} &= \int_0^1 x \, dy \\ &= \int_0^1 (y^2 + 1) \, dy \\ &= \left[\frac{1}{3}y^3 + y\right]_0^1 \\ &= \frac{1}{3} + 1 = \frac{4}{3}.\end{aligned}$$

Exercises 35.5

1. Find the area to the right of the y-axis bounded by the curve $x = 4 - y^2$.
2. Find the area to the left of the y-axis bounded by the curve $x = y^2 - 2y - 3$.
3. Find the area bounded by the curve $x = 3y^2 - 9$, the y-axis, for $0 \le y \le 1$.
4. Find the area bounded by the curve $x = y^2 + 4y$ and the y-axis.

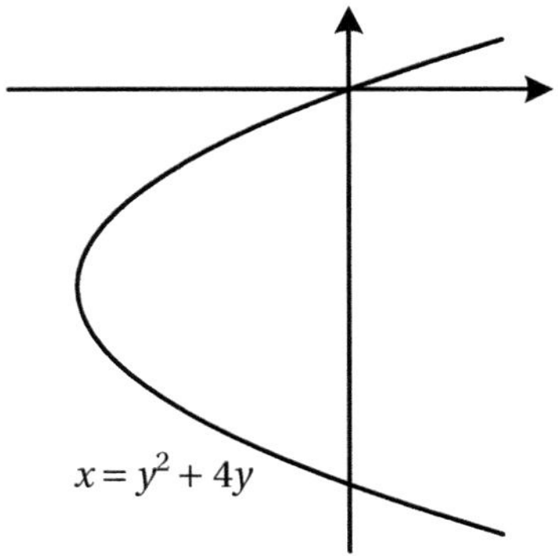

5. Find the area bounded by the y-axis and the curve $x = y^2 - 4y + 3$, for $1 \le y \le 4$.
6. Find the area between the curve $x = 1 + e^{2y}$ and the y-axis, for $0 \le y \le 2$.

35.6 Area between Two Curves

There are a number of different methods for using integration to find the area between two curves. But the methods share a number of common features.

(i) Start by finding the **points of intersection of the two curves**. This is essential as it gives the limits of integration. It also provides us with useful information for drawing the curves.

(ii) If we are not supplied with a graph, **draw a rough sketch** of the two curves. This is because it is important to see their relative positions. We use whatever information we can get, e.g. points on the curve, knowledge of the shape of a quadratic curve, maximum and minimum points, to help draw the two curves on the same graph.

1. Addition and Subtraction of Areas

To find the area between two curves, we can calculate the area between each curve and the x-axis or the y-axis, being careful with the positions of the curves relative to the axes. Then we can calculate the required area by addition or subtraction. Don't forget that we are allowed to calculate regular areas, e.g. rectangles, triangles, by using the well-known formulae for these areas.

Example 1

Find the area bounded by the curves $y = x^2 + 2$ and $y = 4 - x^2$.

Solution

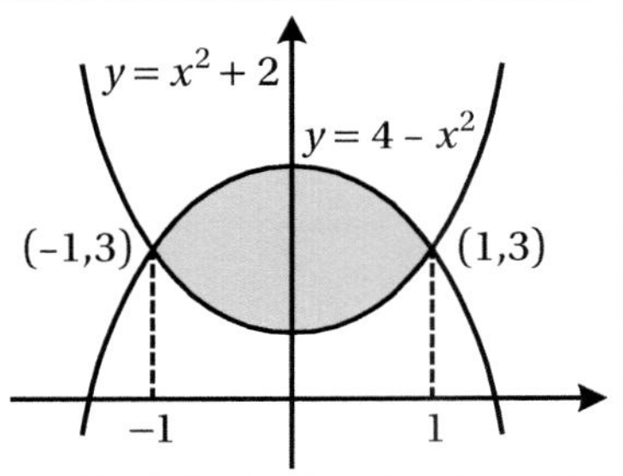

To find the points of intersection of the curves, we equate the y expressions.

$$x^2 + 2 = 4 - x^2$$
$$2x^2 = 2$$
$$x^2 = 1$$
$$x = \pm 1$$

When $x = \pm 1$, $y = (\pm 1)^2 + 2 = 3$.
Thus, the points of intersection are $(-1,3)$ and $(1,3)$.
The curves are quadratic: $y = x^2 + 2$ is $\cup$-shaped, while $y = 4 - x^2$ is $\cap$-shaped.

Let A_1 be the area between $y = 4 - x^2$ and the x-axis, for $-1 \le x \le 1$. Then

$$\begin{aligned} A_1 &= \int_{-1}^{1} y \, \mathrm{d}x \\ &= \int_{-1}^{1} (4 - x^2) \, \mathrm{d}x \\ &= \left[4x - \frac{1}{3}x^3\right]_{-1}^{1} \\ &= \left(4 - \frac{1}{3}\right) - \left(-4 + \frac{1}{3}\right) \\ &= 8 - \frac{2}{3} = \frac{22}{3} \end{aligned}$$

Let A_2 be the area between $y = x^2 + 2$ and the x-axis, for $-1 \le x \le 1$. Then

$$\begin{aligned} A_2 &= \int_{-1}^{1} y \, \mathrm{d}x \\ &= \int_{-1}^{1} (x^2 + 2) \, \mathrm{d}x \end{aligned}$$

$$= \left[\frac{1}{3}x^3 + 2x\right]_{-1}^{1}$$
$$= \left(\frac{1}{3} + 2\right) - \left(-\frac{1}{3} - 2\right)$$
$$= \frac{2}{3} + 4 = \frac{14}{3}$$

Then the shaded area is

$$A_1 - A_2 = \frac{22}{3} - \frac{14}{3} = \frac{8}{3}.$$

2. Vertical and Horizontal Translation of Curves

Finding the area between two curves can sometimes be simplified by translating both curves vertically or horizontally. This is especially true when finding the area between a curve and a horizontal or vertical line. Then we can translate both curves vertically or horizontally so that the horizontal line becomes the x-axis, or the vertical line becomes the y-axis. Example 2 shows how this is done.

Example 2

Find the area bounded by the curve $y = -x^2 + 5x - 1$ and the line $y = 3$.

Solution

(We start by finding the points of intersection.)

From $\quad y = -x^2 + 5x - 1$

and $\quad y = 3,$

we get

$$-x^2 + 5x - 1 = 3$$
$$-x^2 + 5x - 4 = 0$$
$$x^2 - 5x + 4 = 0$$
$$(x - 1)(x - 4) = 0$$
$$x = 1 \quad \text{or} \quad x = 4$$

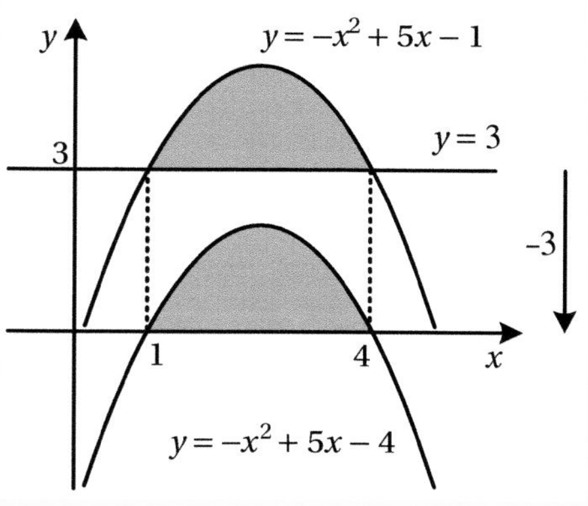

The points of intersection are (1,3) and (4,3).

Method 1

(The area between the curve $y = -x^2 + 5x - 1$ and the line $y = 3$ is the area between the curve and the x-axis, for $1 \le x \le 4$, minus the area of the rectangle with vertices (1,0), (4,0), (4,3) and (1,3).)

$$\text{Area} = \int_1^4 (-x^2 + 5x - 1)\,dx - (3 \times 3)$$
$$= \left[-\frac{1}{3}x^3 + \frac{5}{2}x^2 - x\right]_1^4 - 9$$
$$= \left(-\frac{64}{3} + 40 - 4\right) - \left(-\frac{1}{3} + \frac{5}{2} - 1\right) - 9$$
$$= \frac{9}{2}$$

Method 2

(If we translate the line $y = 3$ vertically by -3, this line is mapped to the x-axis. We need to find the image of the curve under the same vertical translation.)

Under the vertical translation of –3, the image of the curve is

$$y = (-x^2 + 5x - 1) - 3$$
$$y = -x^2 + 5x - 4$$

Then

$$\text{Area} = \int_1^4 (-x^2 + 5x - 4)\,dx$$
$$= \left[-\frac{1}{3}x^3 + \frac{5}{2}x^2 - 4x\right]_1^4$$
$$= \left(-\frac{64}{3} + 40 - 16\right) - \left(-\frac{1}{3} + \frac{5}{2} - 4\right)$$
$$= \frac{9}{2}, \quad \text{as before.}$$

3. Vertical Strip Method

Sometimes, the region whose area has to be found must be divided into many sub-regions in order to use integration. In some such cases, a more convenient approach exists.

For example, suppose we want to find the shaded area shown below.

In theory, we can divide this region up into a very large number of narrow vertical strips, and then sum the areas of all these strips to find the shaded area.

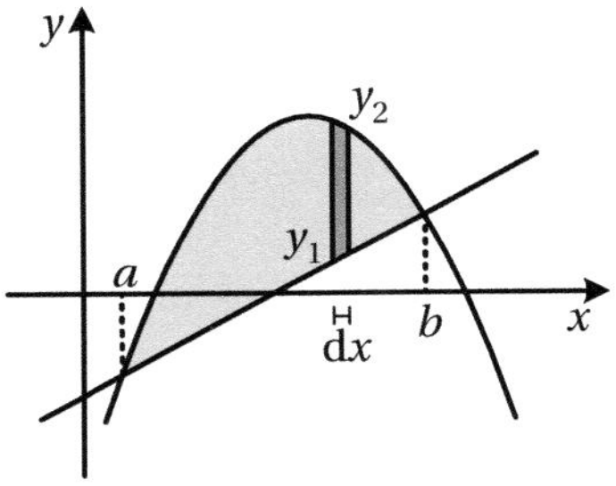

Consider the typical strip shown. Its width is dx. If y_1 is the lower curve and y_2 is the upper curve, then the height of the strip is $y_2 - y_1$, taking the strip to be approximately rectangular.

Then, as the number of strips tends to infinity,

$$\text{area} = \sum (y_2 - y_1)\,dx$$
$$= \int_a^b (y_2 - y_1)\,dx$$

In practice, we substitute for y_2 and y_1 in terms of x before integrating. The limits of integration, a and b, are from the left most strip to the right most strip.

This method has a number of advantages for this type of question.

- We don't have to divide the area up into pieces.
- It doesn't matter whether the area is above or below the x-axis.
- If it is more convenient, we can draw a horizontal line (strip) and use

  $$\text{Area} = \int_c^d (x_2 - x_1)\,dy$$

  where x_2 is on the right, x_1 is on the left and c and d are the limits on the y-axis.

However, there are a couple of points to remember.

- We must still start by finding the points of intersection, or at least the relevant co-ordinate of each, and draw a rough sketch.
- For a vertical line (strip), the region must have one curve for its entire upper boundary and a single different curve for its entire lower boundary.

Area between two curves: Strip Method

The area of the region bounded below by the curve $y_1 = f(x)$ and bounded above by the curve $y_2 = g(x)$, for $a \le x \le b$, is

$$\text{area} = \int_a^b (y_2 - y_1)\,\mathrm{d}x$$
$$= \int_a^b (g(x) - f(x))\,\mathrm{d}x$$

Example 3

Find the area of the enclosed region bounded by the curve $y = x^2 - 6$ and the line $y = x$.

Solution

The curve $y = x^2 - 6$ is a ∪-shaped quadratic curve with local minimum (0,–6).
This can be verified by a table of values, translating the curve $y = x^2$ vertically by –6 or by using differentiation. The line $y = x$ contains the points (0,0), (1,1), etc.

To find the points of intersection:

$y = x^2 - 6$

and $y = x$

giving

$x^2 - 6 = x$

$x^2 - x - 6 = 0$

$(x - 3)(x + 2) = 0$

$x = 3$ or $x = -2$

$y = 3$ or $y = -2$

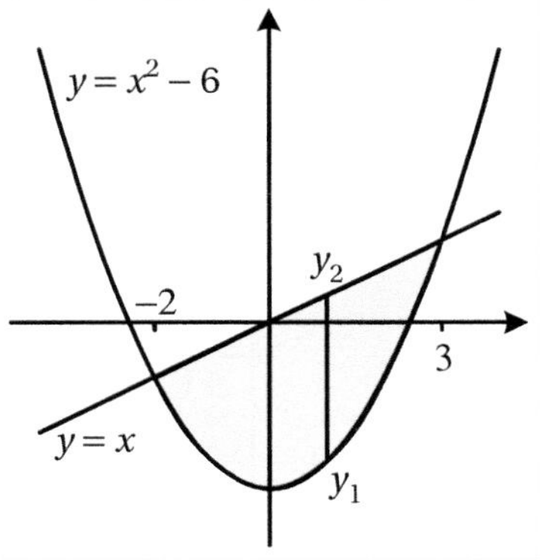

The points of intersection are (–2,–2) and (3,3).

Consider the vertical strip shown, of width dx.

As $y = x$ is the upper curve, $y_2 = x$, and as $y = x^2 - 6$ is the lower curve, $y_1 = x^2 - 6$.

Then

$$\text{area} = \int_{-2}^{3} (y_2 - y_1)\,\mathrm{d}x$$
$$= \int_{-2}^{3} [(x) - (x^2 - 6)]\,\mathrm{d}x$$
$$= \int_{-2}^{3} (x + 6 - x^2)\,\mathrm{d}x$$
$$= \left[\frac{1}{2}x^2 + 6x - \frac{1}{3}x^3\right]_{-2}^{3}$$
$$= \left(\frac{9}{2} + 18 - 9\right) - \left(2 - 12 + \frac{8}{3}\right)$$
$$= \frac{125}{6}.$$

Exercises 35.6

1. Determine the area enclosed by the curve $y = x^2 + 1$ and the line $y = 5$.

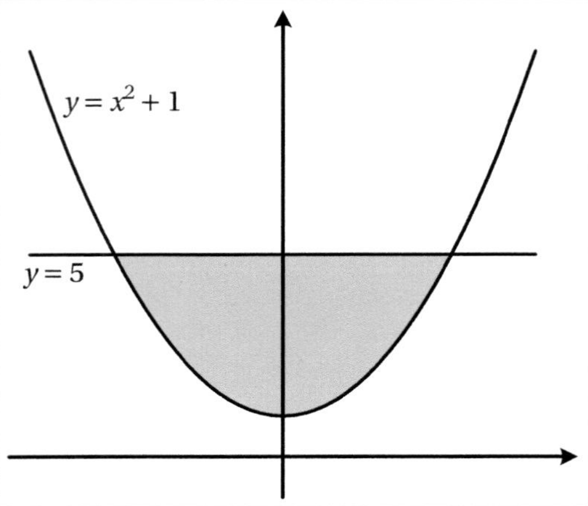

2. Find the area of the region bounded by the curve $x = 1 + y^2$ and the line $x = 10$.

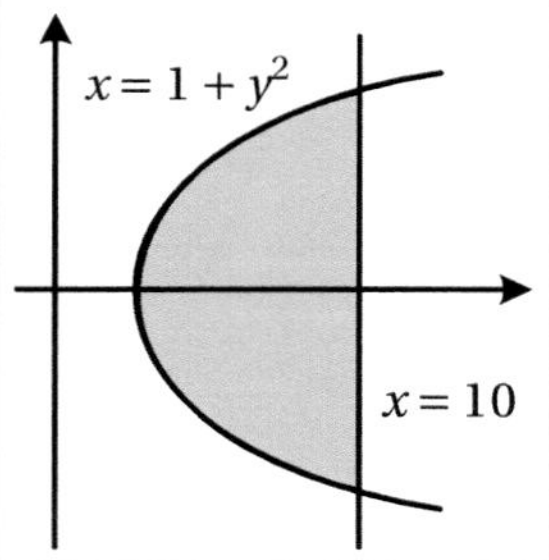

3. Find the area of the region enclosed by the curves $y = x^2 - 4$ and $y = 8 - 2x^2$.

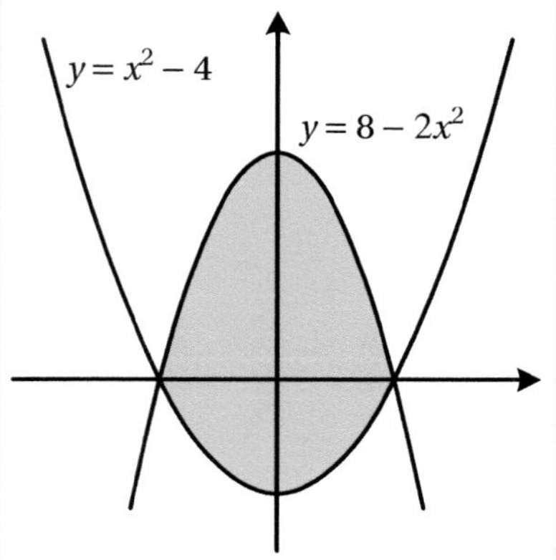

4. Find the area of the region enclosed by the curves $y = 2x^2$ and $y = x^2 + 2x + 3$.

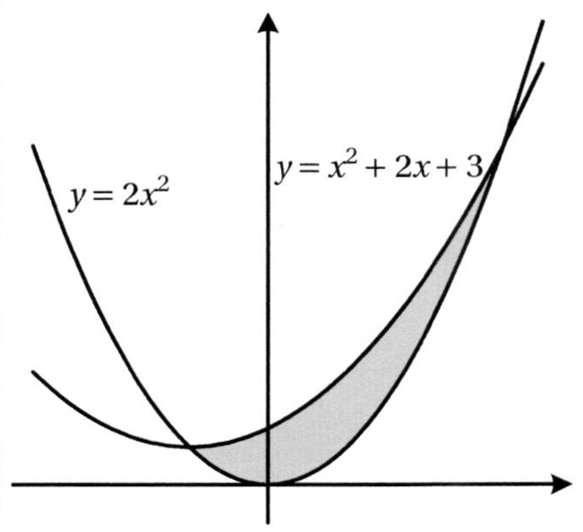

5. Find the area of the region bounded by the curves $y = x^2$ and $y = -x^2 + 6x$.

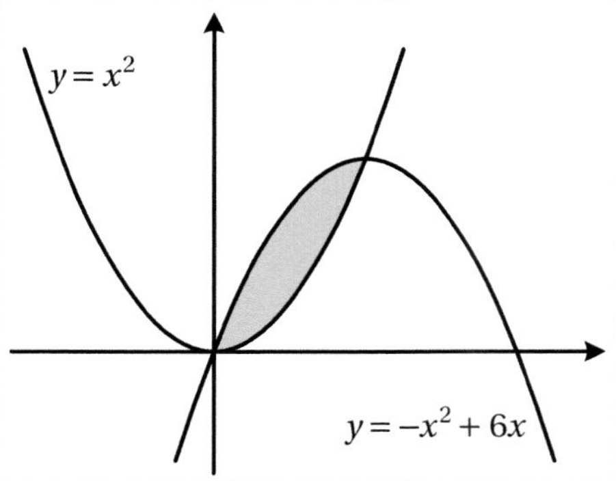

6. Find the area of the region bounded by the curve $y^2 = 4x$ and the line $y = 2x - 4$.

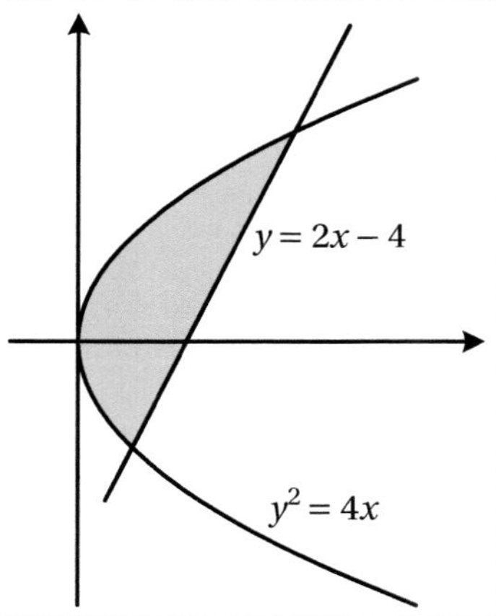

7. Find the area of the region bounded by the line $y = 2x - 3$ and the curve $y = x^2 - 2x - 3$.

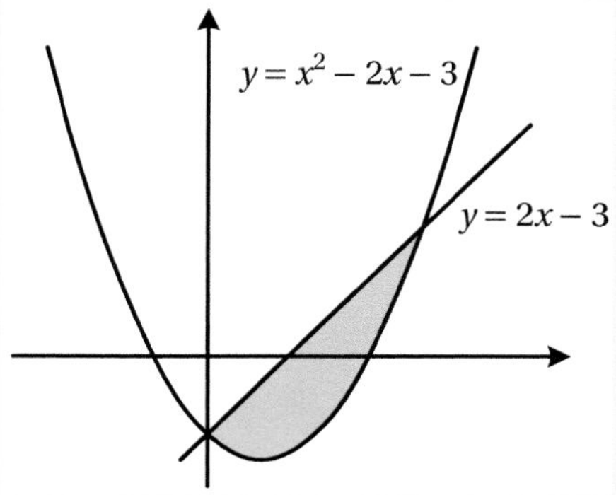

8. The line $y = 2x - 5$ is a tangent to the curve $y = x^2 - 4$. The shaded region is bounded by the curve, the line and the x-axis. Calculate the area of this region.

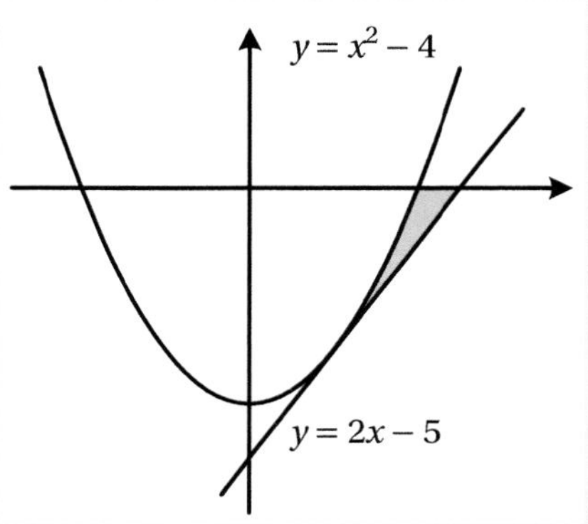

9. Find the area of the region bounded by the line $y = \frac{1}{2}x + 1$ and the curve $y = -\frac{1}{4}x^2 + x + 3$.

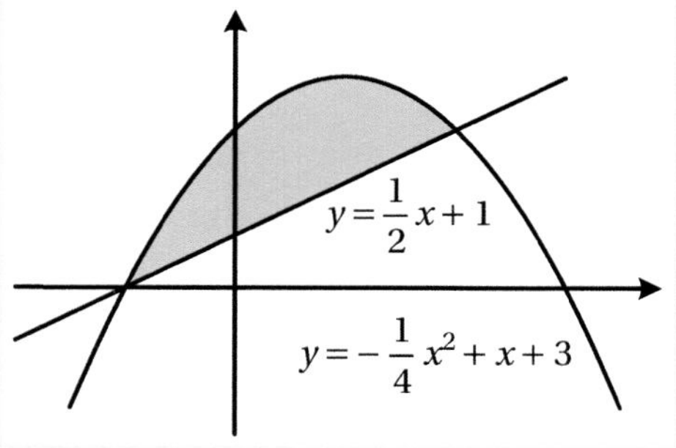

10. Find the area of the region bounded by the curve $y = x^2 + x$ and the curve $y = 2x^2 - 2$.

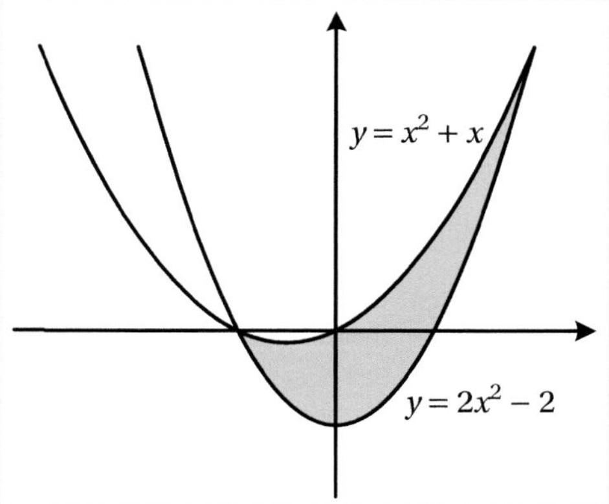

11. Find the area of the region bounded by the curves $y = e^{2x}$, $y = e^x$ and the line $x = 2$. Give your answer correct to two decimal places.

12. Find the area of the region bounded by the curves $y = 4^x$, $y = 2^x$ and the line $x = 4$. Give your answer correct to two decimal places.

35.7 Average Value of a Function

The **average value** of a continuous function, $y = f(x)$, over a closed interval $[a,b]$ is the height, c, of a rectangle with the interval $[a,b]$ as base, which has an area equal to the area between the curve and the x-axis, over the same interval.

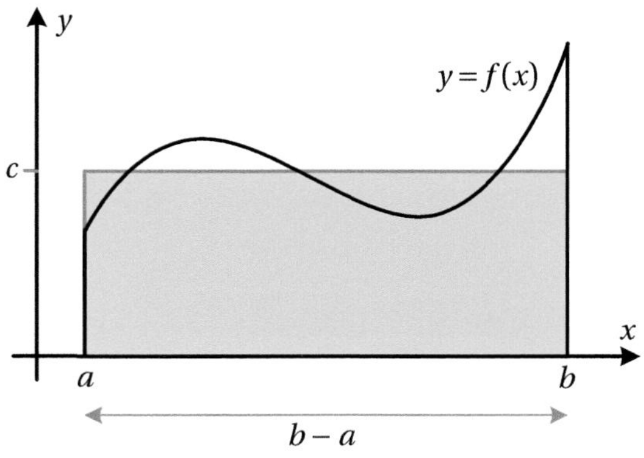

The value c is shown in the diagram opposite.

From the diagram,

area of rectangle $= (b - a)(c)$

and area under curve $= \int_a^b f(x)\,dx$.

Thus, $(b-a)(c) = \int_a^b f(x)\,\mathrm{d}x$

giving $c = \dfrac{\int_a^b f(x)\,\mathrm{d}x}{b-a}$

as the average value of the function $y = f(x)$ over the interval $[a,b]$.

Average Value of a Function over an Interval

The average value of the function $y = f(x)$ over the interval $[a,b]$

is $\dfrac{\int_a^b f(x)\,\mathrm{d}x}{b-a}$.

Example 1

Find the average value of the function $f(x) = x^2 - 2x + 3$ over the interval $[0,3]$.

Solution

$$\begin{aligned}
\text{Average value} &= \frac{\int_a^b f(x)\,\mathrm{d}x}{b-a} \\
&= \frac{\int_0^3 (x^2 - 2x + 3)\,\mathrm{d}x}{3-0} \\
&= \frac{1}{3}\left[\frac{1}{3}x^3 - x^2 + 3x\right]_0^3 \\
&= \frac{1}{3}[(9 - 9 + 9) - (0 - 0 + 0)] \\
&= 3.
\end{aligned}$$

Example 2

The volume, V cm^3, of liquid in a hemispherical bowl is given by

$$V = \frac{1}{3}\pi(30h^2 - h^3)$$

where h cm is the depth of the liquid. Find the average volume of liquid in the bowl as the depth increases from 0 cm to 4 cm.

Solution

$$\begin{aligned}
\text{Average volume} &= \frac{\int_0^4 V\,\mathrm{d}h}{4-0} \\
&= \frac{1}{4}\int_0^4 \frac{1}{3}\pi(30h^2 - h^3)\,\mathrm{d}h \\
&= \frac{\pi}{12}\left[10h^3 - \frac{1}{4}h^4\right]_0^4 \\
&= \frac{\pi}{12}[(640 - 64) - (0 - 0)] \\
&= \frac{576\pi}{12} \\
&= 48\pi \text{ cm}^3.
\end{aligned}$$

Example 2 shows that the idea of average value can be applied to many real life situations. One of the most important is the idea of average speed over a period of time.

From our previous work, we know that

$$\text{average speed} = \frac{\text{total distance}}{\text{total time}}.$$

But what if we are given speed, v, as a function of time, i.e. $v = v(t)$ over the interval from $t = a$ to $t = b$? Consider the so-called **speed-time graph** shown below.

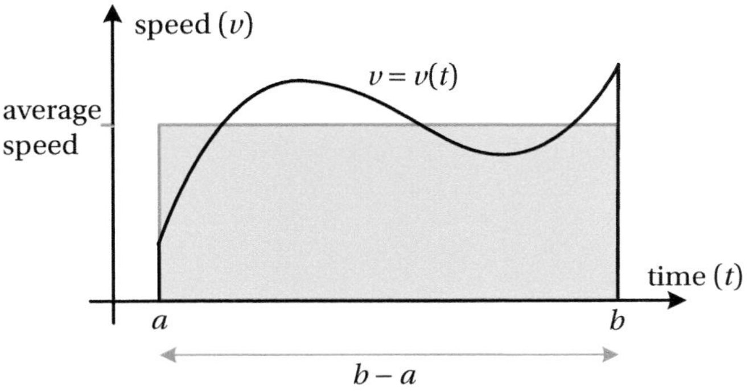

Thus, we have:

(i) total time $= b - a$,

(ii) total distance travelled is represented on a speed-time graph by the area under the curve.

From the definition of the average of a function, we then have

$$\text{average speed} = \frac{\int_a^b v(t)\,\mathrm{d}t}{b-a}.$$

Example 3

The speed, v ms^{-1}, of a particle is given in terms of time t seconds by

$v = 4 \sin 3t$.

(i) Find the total distance travelled in the time from $t = 0$ to $t = \frac{\pi}{3}$.

(ii) Find the average speed of the particle over this time.

Solution

(i) The total distance is the area under the speed-time graph.

$$\begin{aligned}\text{total distance} &= \int_0^{\frac{\pi}{3}} v\,\mathrm{d}t \\ &= \int_0^{\frac{\pi}{3}} 4\sin 3t\,\mathrm{d}t \\ &= -\frac{4}{3}\Big[\cos 3t\Big]_0^{\frac{\pi}{3}} \\ &= -\frac{4}{3}[\cos\pi - \cos 0] \\ &= -\frac{4}{3}[(-1) - (1)] \\ &= \frac{8}{3}\text{ m.}\end{aligned}$$

(ii) Average speed $= \dfrac{\text{total distance}}{\text{total time}}$

$$= \frac{\frac{8}{3}}{\frac{\pi}{3} - 0} = \frac{8}{\pi}\text{ ms}^{-1}.$$

Exercises 35.7

1. Find the average value of the function $f(x) = 2x^2 - 4x + 5$ over the interval $[0,3]$.
2. Find the average value of the function $f(x) = x^3 - 3x^2 + x - 4$ over the interval $[2,4]$.
3. Find the average value of the function $f(x) = 3x + \frac{2}{x}$ over the interval $[1,5]$. Give your answer correct to three decimal places.
4. Find the average value of the function $f(x) = 6 + 2\cos 3x$ over the interval $[0,\pi]$.
5. Find the average value of the function $f(x) = 7 - 3\sin 2x$ over the interval $[0,\pi]$.
6. Find the average value of the function $f(x) = 2e^{3x}$ over the interval $[0,2]$.
7. Find the average value of the function $f(x) = 3e^{4x}$ over the interval $[0,1]$.
8. Find the average value of the function $f(x) = 4^x$ over the interval $[1,3]$.
9. The pressure p of a mass of gas is related to its volume by

   $p = 60v^{-\frac{3}{4}}$.

   Find the average pressure as the gas expands from $v = 1$ to $v = 16$.
10. The volume, $V\text{ cm}^3$, of liquid in a conical vessel is given by

    $V = \frac{\pi}{12}h^3$

    where h cm is the depth of the water. Find the average volume of water in the bowl as the depth increases from 2 cm to 12 cm.
11. The population, p, in millions, of a certain country is modelled by the equation

    $p = 2{\cdot}5e^{0{\cdot}005t}$,

    where t is the number of years after 1900. Find the average population of the country between 1900 and 2000.
12. A particle is moving in a straight line such that after t seconds its velocity, $v\text{ ms}^{-1}$, is given by

    $v = 6t + 12t^2$.

    Find the average velocity during the first two seconds of motion.
13. A particle is moving in a straight line such that after t seconds its velocity, $v\text{ ms}^{-1}$, is given by

    $v = 2t + 5t^2$.

    Find the average velocity during the first two seconds of motion.
14. The speed, $v\text{ ms}^{-1}$, of a particle is given as

    $v = 8\sin 2t + 3\cos 2t$

    where t is in seconds.

    (i) Find the total distance travelled in the time interval $0 \le t \le 1$.

    (ii) Find the average speed over this interval.

    Give your answers correct to two decimal places.

Revision Exercises 35

1. By finding factors, evaluate $\int_2^3 \frac{x^3 - 1}{x - 1}\,dx$.

2. f is a function such that $f'(x) = 6 - \sin x$ and $f\left(\frac{\pi}{3}\right) = 2\pi$. Find $f(x)$.

3. Evaluate $\int_0^1 e^x(2e^x - 1)\,dx$.

4. Evaluate $\int_0^2 4^x(2^x + 1)\,dx$.

5. Evaluate $\int_0^{\frac{\pi}{4}} 2\cos 5x \cos x\,dx$.

6. Evaluate $\int_0^{\frac{\pi}{6}} 2\sin 7x \sin 5x\,dx$.

7. Find the area between the curve $y = 2 - e^x$ and the x-axis, for $0 \le x \le \ln 5$.

8. Let A_1 be the area between the curve $y = x^2$ and the line $y = a^2$, where $a > 0$.

   Let A_2 be the area between the curve $y = x^2$ and the line $y = b^2$, where $b > 0$.

   Show that $A_1 : A_2 = a^3 : b^3$.

9. The graph of the function $f(x) = ax^2 + bx + c$ from $x = -h$ to $x = h$ is shown in the diagram.
   (i) Show that the area of the shaded region is $\frac{h}{3}[2ah^2 + 6c]$.
   (ii) Given that $f(-h) = y_1$, $f(0) = y_2$ and $f(h) = y_3$, express the area of the shaded region in terms of y_1, y_2, y_3 and h.

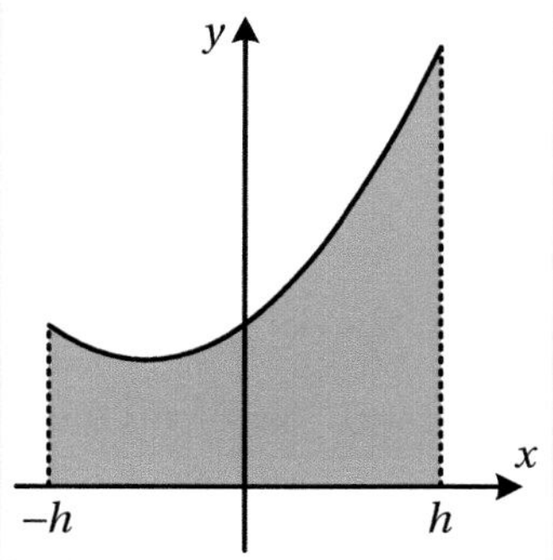

10. The diagram shows the curve $y = 4 - x^2$ and the line $2x + y - 1 = 0$.

    Calculate the area of the shaded region enclosed by the curve and the line.

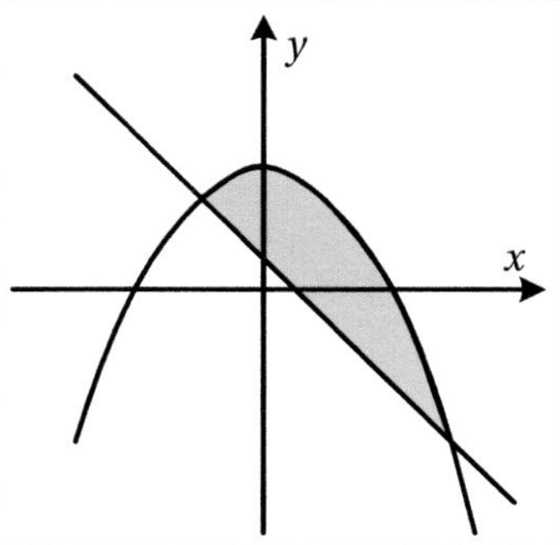

11. Show that the average value of the function $f(x) = ax + b$ over the interval $[c,d]$ is $\frac{f(c) + f(d)}{2}$.

12. Show that the average value of the function $f(x) = x^2$ over the interval $[0,a]$ is $\frac{1}{3}f(a)$.

13. Show that over the range $0 \le x \le 6$, the average value of the function $f(x) = 9x(6 - x)$ is two thirds of the maximum value of the function.

14. The area between the curve $y = x^2 + 2x$ and the x-axis, for $0 \le x \le 3$, is equal to the area of a rectangle of base 3 and height k. Find the value of k.

36

Introduction to Statistics

Statistics are of great importance in modern life. It is hard to read a serious newspaper or listen to a news broadcast without encountering statistics in some shape or form. Major decisions at international, national and corporate level are made based on data collected and analysed using statistical methods.

The key to reliable statistics is the professional gathering of appropriate data. This is the topic of discussion in this chapter. We examine the main types of statistical studies, including surveys, opinion polls, controlled experiments and observational studies. There are many possible pitfalls in the designs of these studies, from incorrectly identifying the relevant population, through badly chosen samples, inappropriate or confusing questions in a questionnaire to badly matched control groups for controlled experiments and observational studies.

In summary, the greatest of care must be taken to avoid bias, confounding variables and any other feature which could lead to unreliable data.

36.1 Data Types

Statistics is all about collecting, presenting, analysing and interpreting data. We start by investigating the different possible types of data.

1. **Categorical Data**
   In simple terms, **categorical data** is data that is not numerical, e.g. the models of car in a car-park, your favourite film, the countries you have visited. Numbers, e.g. hotel room numbers, can be categorical if they are just being used as tags. Categorical data can be either nominal or ordinal.

   (a) **Nominal Data**
   Categorical data is said to be **nominal** if it consists of names with no order implied, i.e. if there is no idea of better and worse, or bigger and smaller, etc. Examples are the first names of students in your class, the types of cheese being sold in a delicatessen, the candidates standing in an election.

   (b) **Ordinal Data**
   Categorical data is said to be **ordinal** if there is a clear idea of order, e.g. from better to worse, or larger to smaller. For example, the grades (A, B, C, ...) that a student achieves in the Junior Cert. is an example of ordinal data. Another example is the possible answers to a survey question, where respondents are invited to tick one of the boxes 'strongly agree', 'agree', 'disagree' and 'strongly disagree'.

2. **Numeric Data**
   Data which consists of real numbers is called **numeric** data. Immediately, we can say that all numeric data is ordered. Numeric data can be either discrete or continuous.

   (a) **Discrete Data**
   Numeric data is said to be **discrete** if the possible numbers can be clearly separated from each other, e.g. the number of siblings in a family. Discrete data is typically counted, as distinct from being measured. For example, the number of heads obtained when a coin is tossed 100 times, the number of occupants in cars which pass a certain Garda checkpoint and the number of votes gained by each contestant in a talent contest are all discrete, numeric data.

   When there is a large number of possible values, it is usual practice to group them into intervals. For example, the prices paid for houses in a particular town or neighbourhood would, in practice, be grouped into intervals such as €150,000 to €200,000, etc. The price of a house is discrete, because it cannot be €167,326·754.

(b) Continuous Data
Numeric data is said to be **continuous** if the numbers obtained can (theoretically) take on any value in an interval of the real line. If given any two different numbers, no matter how close, there could always be a number in between, then the data is continuous. For example, the weights of new-born babies is continuous data. If two babies weigh 3859 g and 3860 g, respectively, at birth, in theory a third baby could weigh 3859·723... g at birth. Continuous data is usually grouped into intervals, just like discrete data with many possible values.

There is another way of classifying data. This is as either univariate data or bivariate data.

1. **Univariate Data (Single Variable Data)**
When observations are made and only one value is recorded, then the data obtained is called **univariate** (think of one variable) or **single variable data**. For example, measuring the height of a student in your class, recording their favourite colour, or recording the prices of properties for sale are all univariate data.

2. **Bivariate Data (Paired Data)**
Sometimes, we are interested in taking two measurements when observations are being made. For example, if we measure the height and shoe size of students in your class. This type of data is called **bivariate** (bi means two: think of two variables) or **paired data**. The reason for taking paired data is usually to see if there is a relationship between the two values recorded. We will do exactly that in a later chapter.

In practice, to fully describe the data type we use the format shown below.

Categorical Discrete Continuous	+	Single variable Paired

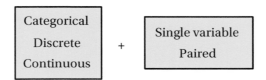

You should note the following.

1. When dealing with single variable data, it is usually not necessary to specify 'single variable data', unless there is possible uncertainty between single variable data and paired data. The default is single variable data. So, for example, the data obtained when a die is thrown repeatedly is just called 'discrete data'.

2. When dealing with categorical paired data, we usually don't bother to distinguish between nominal and ordinal. We just use 'categorical' for both. Also, for paired data, if the types of the individual values are the same, we only use the name of the type once. For example, age in years and number of visits to the doctor in the last year would be called 'discrete paired data'. On the other hand, if the data types for the individual values are different, then we give them both. For example, nationality and age in years would be 'categorical and discrete paired data'. If a question asks us to be more specific, then we can state whether the categorical data is nominal or ordinal.

Another way of describing data is with reference to the source of the data.

1. **Primary Data**
Data collected by the researcher who is going to use it is called primary data.

2. **Secondary Data**
Data which is not collected by the researcher, but rather is obtained from sources such as the internet, newspapers and databases is referred to as secondary data. Secondary data must be treated more carefully than primary data, as the reliability of the source has to be questioned.

Example 1

A number of people were asked which political party they supported and what their annual income was.

(i) Consider the question about the political party. Describe the type of data obtained.

(ii) Is the data resulting from the question about annual income categorical or numeric? Describe the data type more accurately.

(iii) Consider together the two facts asked of each person. Give a full description of the type of data under consideration.

Solution

(i) The data obtained about the political parties supported by those asked is categorical data, because each political party is a category. It is also nominal data as there is no idea of order.

(ii) The data obtained about annual income is numeric, e.g. €22,000 or €37,500. This data is discrete, because even though a person's income may be €31,435·67, it cannot be €31,435·67915...

(iii) If we take the two facts together for each person, i.e. record them in the form (political party, annual income), then the data is paired. The first element is categorical and the second is discrete. So, a full description of the data would be 'categorical and discrete paired data'.

Exercises 36.1

1. At an antiques auction where the top price paid was €960, the amount spent by each of the bidders was recorded.
(i) What type of data is the amount spent by the bidders?
(ii) Would you consider it a good idea to group the data? If so, suggest possible groups.

2. As part of cost savings, Seatofyourpants Airways, a budget airline, decides to charge passengers by their own weight. So, each intending passenger has to stand on a scales and pay according to their weight.
(i) In theory, what type of data is the weight of the passengers?
(ii) If the scales measures weight to the nearest gram, what type of data do we now have?
(iii) If the pricing structure classifies passengers as 'Under 40 kg', '40 to 60 kg', '60 to 80 kg', '80 to 100 kg' and 'Over 100 kg', what type of data do we now have?

3. From a large DVD catalogue, films are selected and their running times are noted.
(i) What type of data is the running time of a film?
(ii) The running time on a DVD cover gives the running time correct to the nearest minute. Taking this running time, what type of data do we have?
(iii) Given that the shortest and longest films selected are 72 minutes and 212 minutes, respectively, can you suggest how this data may be grouped?

4. Students in a class are asked to name their favourite subject, and the percentage mark they achieved in last summer's exam in this subject.
(i) What type of data is 'favourite subject'?
(ii) If their mark is given as a percentage correct to the nearest unit, what type of data is 'percentage mark'?
(iii) Considering favourite subject and percentage mark together, give a full description of the type of data.

5. A farmer has three fields, A, B and C, in which potatoes are growing. Potatoes are selected, and the name of the field and the weight of the potato are recorded.
   (i) What type of data is the name of the field?
   (ii) Give a full description of the type of data when the name of the field and the weight of the potato are taken together.

6. The number of goals scored by a football team is recorded for each match it plays in a season, as is its league position after that match.
   (i) What type of data is the number of goals scored?
   (ii) Taking the number of goals scored and league position together, give a full description of the type of data involved.

7. At the beginning of each working day, the exchange rate of sterling against the euro, i.e. the value of £1 in euro, was recorded, along with the day of the week on which the measurement was taken.
   (i) What type of data is the exchange rate?
   (ii) Taking the exchange rate and the day of the week together, give a full description of the type of data involved.

8. A hurling league contains a large number of teams, and each team plays each other team twice, once at home and once away. In a particular year, none of the matches in the league ended in a draw. As the matches are played, the team that scores first and the winning team are recorded.
   (i) What type of data is the first team to score?
   (ii) Taking the first team to score and the winning team together, give a full description of the type of data involved.

9. Peter wants to determine the rate of heart attacks in the county where he lives.
   (i) He designs a survey to query a number of individuals around his county. Explain why the data he obtains is primary data.
   (ii) Instead, he decides to consult official records from health sources. Explain why this data is secondary data.
   (iii) In this case, which set of data is likely to be more reliable? Explain your answer.

10. Una wants to determine the most popular confectionary in her local area.
   (i) She designs a survey to query people chosen at random in her local area. Explain why the data she obtains is primary data.
   (ii) Alternatively, she decides to conduct research on the internet and obtained data from ACNielsen and other market analysts. Explain why this data is secondary data.
   (iii) In this case, which set of data is more likely to be reliable? Explain your answer.
   (iv) What other way could Una have obtained reliable data for the sales of different confectionery brands in her area?

36.2 Statistical Information and Data Based Statements

The term ‘statistics’ has a number of different possible interpretations.

1. ‘Statistics’ is a subject, with a large bank of knowledge, which is both studied and practised. In fact, you are studying statistics right now!
2. The term ‘statistics’ can refer to the methods used to gather and interpret data. This is the interpretation that will concern us for the rest of the topic of statistics.
3. Another meaning of ‘statistics’ is the collections of data obtained. For example, a recent news story reported that “statistics show that the number of road deaths in Ireland was 10% lower in 2008 than in 1959, in spite of the fact that the number of vehicles was 8 times greater”.
4. A ‘statistic’ is a summary of a set of data, e.g. the mean. ‘Statistics’ is then just the plural of this.

Populations, Sampling Frames and Samples

Suppose you want to determine the average height of all the students in your school. You have a couple of options.

1. You could measure the height of each student in your school and calculate the average height. The set of the heights of all the students in your school is called a **population**, i.e. the set of all possible measurements that can be taken. Collecting all the measurements is called taking a **census**. The average height you calculate is called a **parameter** of the population.

2. The **sampling frame** is that part of the population that you can get access to. For example, suppose five students are out of school on the day you take your measurements. The sampling frame would be all the students in school on that day. (In another example, suppose you wished to poll all the adults in Ireland. The population is all adults in Ireland, but the sampling frame might be those in telephone books or on an electoral register.) The closer the sampling frame is to the entire population, the better.

   You could select a number of students at random from the sampling frame and take the average of their heights. The heights of the students you select is called a **sample**. The average height of the students in your sample is called a **statistic**. This sample statistic is just an estimate of the population parameter.

In the real world, many populations are too large to consider taking all possible measurements, and others are infinite. In these cases, we are forced to rely on samples and statistics. The key to statistics is try to make the sample as reflective as possible of the population, so that any statistic obtained from the sample is as accurate an estimate as possible of the population parameter.

Descriptive and Inferential Statistics

As statistics refers to the methods used to gather and interpret data, it can be broken down under two headings: **descriptive statistics** and **inferential statistics**.

1. **Descriptive Statistics**

   Descriptive statistics is where we graphically represent and analyse data that we have obtained. We can represent the data by pie charts, histograms, etc. We can calculate statistics such as the mean, mode, and later on other statistics such as standard deviation. The key idea is that we are dealing with 'known data'. We are not trying to move 'outside the box'.

   For example, you could measure the height of every student in third year in your school. You could then calculate the mean height of all third years in your school. This is descriptive statistics. However, the minute you use your result to try to say something about the mean height of all third years in your county, or Ireland, or the world, you move away from descriptive statistics and into inferential statistics.

2. **Inferential Statistics**

   Inferential statistics is where we use the data obtained to make estimates or predictions, i.e. we try to say (infer) something about a situation that has not yet been observed. Inferential statistics tries to make statements about 'unknown data'. This is a much more involved and complicated area, and one where it is very easy to make statements which, mathematically, are not backed up by the known facts.

   For example, suppose you arrive very early in school one morning, and you ask the next ten students who arrive what their favourite colour is. Suppose the most frequent answer is 'green'. Would you feel that you had enough evidence to say that the most popular colour among people in your school, or in Ireland, is green?

Problems with Statistics and Data Based Statements

Misleading statistics are commonplace in real life. This can be due to incorrect methods used in their collection or in their interpretation. The same observation applies to many data based statements we encounter in the media and elsewhere.

Percentages are a classical example. You should always ask: a percentage of what? The following example is a typical case.

Example 1

Consider the following extract from a newspaper article:

"In the Leaving Cert of 2009, 23·6% of students sitting higher level Applied Maths achieved an 'A' grade, whereas only 10·2% of those sitting higher level English got an 'A' grade. This shows an unfair bias towards the sciences and against English."

(i) At face value, do you think the conclusion is valid? Explain.

(ii) On further research, you find that 1333 students took higher level Applied Maths in 2009, while 32863 students took higher level English in 2009.
What is your opinion of the conclusion in the article now?

Solution

(i) On first reading, it appears as if there is a bias in favour of Applied Maths (not sciences in general) over English.

(ii) Using a calculator, the number of 'A's in higher level Applied Maths is 315, while the number of 'A's in higher level English is 3352. So there were more than 10 times as many 'A's in English than in Applied Maths. This in no way supports the conclusion drawn in the article.

Exercises 36.2

1. Paraic wants to determine the average age of all passengers who take the train from Cork to Dublin on a certain date.
- **(i)** What is the population?
- **(ii)** Describe how the population parameter could be obtained.
- **(iii)** Paraic decides to select a sample of train passengers taking the train from Cork to Dublin on the date in question. Describe how he calculates the sample statistic.
- **(iv)** He then uses this data to make statements about all passengers from Cork to Dublin on all dates. What type of statistics is this?

2. Sorcha wants to determine the average amount spent on mobile phones per year by all the people in Ireland.
- **(i)** Describe the population and the population parameter.
- **(ii)** She decides to interview a sample of people and determine the average amount spent on mobile phones from her sample. What is the sample statistic?
- **(iii)** She then uses the data from her sample to draw conclusions about the mobile phone expenses of the entire population of Ireland. What type of statistics is this?

3. Stephen wants to determine the average speed of all vehicles as they drive past the front gates of his school.
- **(i)** What is the population and the population parameter?
- **(ii)** Is it practical to measure the population parameter? Give a reason.
- **(iii)** Stephen decides to stand outside one morning and measure the speeds of all vehicles passing the front gates of the school during a one hour period. He then calculates the average speed of all these vehicles. What name would apply to the data he obtains and the average speed he calculates?

4. Louise conducts an experiment which consists of repeatedly throwing a die. She wants to estimate the average number of throws necessary until a '6' turns up for the third time.
   (i) Describe the population. Explain why the population is infinite.
   (ii) What is the population parameter?
   (iii) Louise decides to throw a die until a '6' appears for the third time. She records the number of throws required. She then repeats this experiment 100 times. She uses her data to calculate the average number of throws needed to have a '6' appear for the third time. How would you describe the value she obtains?

5. "Almost everybody in the world has more than the average number of feet."
   (i) At first glance, do you think this statement is correct?
   (ii) Now consider the statement carefully. Do you think it is correct? Explain.

6. "300,000 deaths occur each year through inactivity, while only 7 deaths a year result from extreme skiing. So you should play it safe and take up extreme skiing."
   Comment on this data-based argument.

7. "The number of students who achieved five or more honours grades (A, B or C) in their Leaving Cert. exam has increased by 12% in the last 4 years. This proves that the government's education policy is working."
   Comment on this data-based argument.

8. A large financial firm discovered that of the sick days taken by their employees, 40% occurred on a Friday or a Monday. They immediately clamped down on sick days.
   (i) Do you know what the firm imagined that the statistics revealed? Explain.
   (ii) Now analyse the figures more closely. Can you determine any other explanation? Give a reason.

36.3 Reliable Samples and Sampling Techniques

With sampling, the key is to try to make the sample as close as possible to a miniature version of the population, although it is unreasonable to expect a sample to be an exact replica of the population. Some of the key issues in choosing a reliable sample are discussed below.

1. **The Population should be clearly understood**

   Suppose a sports organisation wants to gauge the reaction to a proposed rule change. Then the population (called the target population) is not the public at large, but rather those involved in playing that particular sport. Any sample chosen should be taken from those involved in that sport.

2. **The Sampling Frame should be as close as possible to the entire Population**

   Every possible element of the population should be able to belong to the sample. This sounds simple, but it's not. For example, if you are trying to conduct a survey of all the homeless people in Dublin, you will have great difficulty in compiling a list of the entire population. Nevertheless, by contacting all the agencies working with the homeless in Dublin, Dublin Simon, Focus Ireland, etc, you can build a sampling frame that is very close to the entire population.

3. **The Sample Size should be Large Enough**

   It is very important to make sure that the size of the sample is large enough to be reasonably confident about the results obtained. For example, if you wanted to poll voters about their voting intentions in an upcoming referendum, it should be clear that asking 3 or even 10 people is going to be nowhere near enough to have any confidence in the data obtained.

No sample, unless it covers the entire population, can be guaranteed to give the same result as the population. There will always be a 'margin of error', e.g. a margin of error of 4%. The smaller the margin of error, the more confident we can be that the result for the sample is a good estimate for the corresponding result for the population. Margin of error will be discussed in more detail later.

4. **The Sample should be Random**

   In theory, a sample is said to be **random**, if every element of the population has an equal probability of being selected for the sample. It might seem straightforward to pick a sample randomly from a population, but in the real world it is harder than it seems. This is because it is extremely easy to have bias in choosing a sample. This is the next point.

5. **There should be no Bias in selecting the Sample**

   Bias is systematically favouring one or more groups within the population, whether consciously or unconsciously. If the sample you choose is biased, then you will get unreliable results. Here are two examples where bias enters the choice of sample.

   (i) Suppose you want to survey people about their attitudes to sport. You choose to interview selected people in a shopping centre. But there is a very important match on at the same time. There will be a bias against a huge number of people interested in sport, because they will be sitting in front of the television watching the match.

   (ii) Suppose you want to survey people's attitude to the performance of the government. So you place yourself on a street corner and ask people at random. This sounds unbiased, but on closer examination there is bias. You are more likely to stop people who look approachable, you will avoid grumpy looking people, and ignore people who refuse to answer. These people may be more inclined to have a negative view, and so, by ignoring them, you may end up with a sample that is more positive than the population.

   There are other possible sources of bias, e.g. badly worded questions, untruthful answers, which we will discuss in later sections.

Now we turn our attention to some of the more important types of sampling techniques in use, i.e. methods of obtaining data which we can then analyse.

Sampling Techniques

1. **Simple Random Sampling (SRS)**

   In simple random sampling (SRS), each individual in the target population has an equal chance of being chosen. And if you are choosing a sample of size n, then all possible combinations of n individuals are equally likely. In practice, we settle for each individual in the sampling frame having an equal probability of being chosen.

   Suppose you want to choose a simple random sample of 50 from all the students in your school. One way is to write the names of all the students on slips of paper which we then place in a drum. Then the required 50 can be chosen by drawing from the drum. For larger samples, e.g. choosing from a population of 10,000, we may need to number all the elements of the population and use a calculator, computer or random number tables to make our selection.

   SRS minimises bias and makes analysing results easy. Also, the variability within the sample gives a good estimate of the variability within the population.

2. **Systematic Sampling**

   Systematic sampling is similar to SRS except that instead of picking the individuals to be sampled by using random numbers, the individuals are placed in a list and then every tenth (or fifteenth, etc) individual is sampled. The first individual to be sampled is chosen at random.

Suppose we want to choose a sample of 100 from a population of 2000. We can start by dividing: $\frac{2000}{100} = 20$. Then we should start by choosing the first individual at random from the first 20 on our list, and then take every 20th individual after that. This ensures that every individual in the population has an equal chance of being selected.

This method is often used instead of SRS as it is cheaper and just as good, provided there is no hidden order in the list.

3. Stratified Sampling

However, SRS and systematic sampling can be vulnerable to bias if there are distinct groups within the population whose reactions are known to differ. For example, suppose we want to find the reaction of the public to a new romantic comedy film. Men and women react differently to romantic comedy. If we take a random sample of size 10 from the entire population, would could, quite legitimately, get a sample containing 8 women and 2 men (or 8 men and 2 women). Either way, we will get results which differ greatly from those of the entire population. The problem here is that the sample does not reflect the whole population, which is roughly 50% male and 50% female.

Stratified sampling addresses this issue. To perform stratified sampling what we should do is as follows.

(i) Decide on the different strata (groups). Each element of the population must belong to exactly one of the strata.
(ii) Decide, even roughly, what percentage of the overall population belongs to each stratum.
(iii) Use the overall size of the sample you intend to take, along with the percentages from (ii), to calculate how many measurements (sample points) are to be taken in each stratum. (This is called proportionate allocation and is the main way of performing stratified sampling. There are other, more involved, ways.)
(iv) Choose *randomly* from each stratum the required number of sample points.
(v) Use all the gathered data to calculate the required statistic, e.g. the mean, for the sample.

Stratified sampling has certain advantages over other sampling methods.
(i) It betters reflects a population that contains distinct groupings, which are considered may have different reactions.
(ii) It allows analysis of each stratum individually.
(iii) Where necessary, it allows for different sampling techniques to be used within each stratum.

The main disadvantages are that it requires detailed information about the population, and that it can be costly to implement.

4. Cluster Sampling

In cluster sampling, the entire population is divided into (very often a large number of) groups, called clusters. Each element of the population belongs to exactly one cluster. Then a number of clusters are selected at random. So, for example, 20 clusters might be picked out of 1000. Cluster sampling works best when the clusters are of the same, or similar, size.

Then, either all the population elements in a cluster are sampled or a random selection of a number of population elements in each cluster is taken. The first case is called **one-stage cluster sampling** and the second is called **two-stage cluster sampling**. Opinion polls of voter intentions are generally two-stage cluster samples.

Cluster sampling is less accurate than SRS or stratified sampling, but it is cheaper. It works particularly well when the population is widely spread geographically. If SRS is used, it might involve a huge amount of travel for interviewers. This can be very expensive. By forming clusters based on location, it is only necessary to visit a relatively small number of locations, thereby cutting down on costs.

5. Quota Sampling

Quota sampling is very similar to stratified sampling. However, it is far less accurate, but cheaper to implement. Like stratified sampling, we start by dividing the entire population into groups (strata). The elements of each group are likely to have similar reactions to the question posed. We also use the relative sizes of the groups to decide how many sample points we want in each group.

The key difference arises in how the sample points are chosen within each group. In stratified sampling, the sample points are chosen at random. In quota sampling, the interviewer is given a quota for each group. He, or she, can then take sample points (interviews) from the different groups until the quota for that group is filled. Then they stop taking sample points from that group.

Although very cheap, this method is subject to the problems of bias discussed earlier. In theory, quota sampling is not random sampling because every population element does not have a chance of being chosen. Quota sampling tends to be used when time is short or money is tight.

6. Convenience Sampling

In a convenience sample, sample points are chosen because of their ease of access. For example, a student wants to obtain data on the opinion of adults to bullying in the workplace.

She decides to ask her family members, neighbours and friends. A convenience sample is a non-probability sampling method and is among the least reliable of the methods listed here. However, it can be useful for getting an initial estimate before obtaining a more reliable sample using other methods.

7. Respondent Driven Sampling

In this scenario, a very large number of people are invited to respond to the questions. Typically only a small percentage actually take the trouble to reply. Examples are:

(i) sending a questionnaire by post or email to a very large number of recipients not chosen at random,

(ii) posting a questionnaire online,

(iii) inviting listeners or viewers to vote on a question put on a radio or TV programme, or inviting readers of a newspaper to respond to a printed question.

The data obtained by these methods are notoriously unreliable, as there can be huge bias. In all cases there is a serious risk of a large proportion of the respondents being those with an agenda. Although cheap (and even profitable in some cases), this method should not be used when a reliable set of data is required.

Example 1

A large university wants to gauge the reaction to a proposal to ban the use of laptop computers in lectures. The university has 10000 students and a teaching staff of 2000. It is felt that the teaching staff would be more in favour of the proposal than the student body.

(i) The university decides to obtain a sample of size 300. It chooses these at random from the 12000 students and staff. What type of sampling is involved here? What is the disadvantage of such a sampling type?

(ii) Suggest a more appropriate sampling model to take into account the views of the different groups within the target population.

Instead, the university decides to place an interviewer at the front gate to the university. It asks her to obtain the views of the first x students and y members of the teaching staff she encounters.

(iii) What sampling model is involved here?

(iv) If the sample is to reflect the target population, what are the values of x and y?

Solution

(i) This type of sample is called a simple random sample.
There may be a disproportionate number of students or members of the teaching staff in the sample chosen at random, and so the result may not accurately reflect the population.

(ii) A more appropriate sampling model would be stratified sampling, with

$$300 \times \frac{10000}{12000} = 250$$

students and 300 – 250 = 50 members of the teaching staff chosen at random for interview.

(iii) This is quota sampling.

(iv) As with stratified sampling, $x = 250$ and $y = 50$.

Exercises 36.3

The following table shows the breakdown of boys and girls in a secondary school. The number of classes in each year is also indicated. The class sizes are all roughly the same, each having between 25 and 30 students.

	Number of classes	Boys	Girls
1st Year	3	40	50
2nd Year	3	50	40
3rd Year	3	45	40
4th Year	3	20	60
5th Year	3	25	50
6th Year	3	20	60
Totals	18	200	300

It is proposed to conduct a number of surveys to determine the attitudes of students to a number of proposals. The school authorities are not in favour of a census, i.e. polling all students. They suggest a sample, of no more than 30 students. In the following questions, we are concerned only with the choice and design of a suitable sample, and the choice of sample points (students to poll). It is assumed that we have an accurate list of the sampling frame, i.e. the list of all the students in the school.

1. One survey questions whether students would prefer to keep the existing school hours, or start and finish a half an hour earlier each day. There is no reason to suppose that there will different responses between boys and girls, or between students from different years, as groups.

(i) What type of sample would you recommend, bearing in mind a sample size of 30?
Explain why.

(ii) How should you go about choosing the sample points (students to poll)?

(iii) What would be the problem with going out into the school-yard at break and asking the first 30 students you see?

(iv) If you describe your proposal for collecting the sample to the vice-principal, and he says he wants as few classes as possible disturbed, what other sample design can you come up with? Explain.

(v) Describe how you would now choose the students to be polled.

(vi) If, on reflection, you think that there might be two different groups whose responses will not be the same, i.e. those who live near the school and those who live further away, how could you accommodate this in your sample design? What further information would you need from the school?

2. Another survey questions the attitude of students to a proposal to paint all the corridors pink. It is considered that the reactions of the boys and the girls, as groups, to this proposal will be different.
(i) What type of sample would you recommend, bearing in mind a sample size of 30? Explain why.
(ii) How many boys should be polled? How many girls should be polled?
(iii) How should the boys and the girls be chosen?
(iv) Why would it not be appropriate to have 1st year, 2nd year and so on up to 6th year as the strata in stratified sampling?
(v) Suppose you only wanted a rough answer and were willing to use quota sampling. Suppose you had five helpers who were willing to go out into the yard and poll students as they meet them. Each helper is told to ask x boys and y girls. What is the value of x and the value of y?

3. Another survey questions whether more time should be allocated to sports, or physical education, in the timetable. It is considered that the responses of students in the exam years, 3rd year and 6th year, as groups, will be different from students in other years.
(i) Explain how you would design a sample to take this into account.
(ii) To the nearest whole number, how many students from the exam years should be polled, and how many students from other years should be polled?
(iii) How would you select the students to be polled in each group?

4. For another survey, it is determined that the responses of students in different years will vary, sometimes significantly. Bear in mind the overall limit of 30 on the sample size.
(i) Explain why simple random sampling (SRS) is not the most appropriate sample design.
(ii) Explain the advantages of stratified sampling over SRS in this case. What strata would you choose? Calculate, to the nearest unit, how many samples should be taken in each stratum.
(iii) Suppose it is further decided to cluster sample, by choosing at random one class within each stratum. Ignoring the small differences in size between the strata and the small differences in class sizes, how many students in each chosen class should be polled so as not to have more than 30 sample points overall?

In each of the following questions, state what type of sampling plan was used. Comment on how appropriate it is and state any problems as regards bias.

5. To gather the opinions of its customers, an airline company made a list of all its flights and randomly selected 25 flights. All the passengers on those flights were asked to fill out a survey.

6. To gauge how its employees felt about proposed higher college fees, a university divided its employees into three categories, teaching staff, non-teaching staff and student employees. A random sample was selected from each group and they were telephoned and asked for their opinion.

7. A polling company wants to find the reaction of the public in Ireland to a controversial television programme. It chooses five counties in Ireland at random. Then, in each of the selected counties, it divides the population into a number of groups. It selects five groups at random in each of the chosen counties. It then interviews forty people at random in each of these groups.

8. A large department store wants to know if consumers would be willing to pay slightly higher prices to have computers available throughout the store to help them locate items. The store positions an interviewer at the door and tells her to collect a sample of 100 views, by asking the next person who comes in the door directly after finishing the previous interview.

9. A mobile phone company wants to gauge the reactions of its customers to a proposed new payment plan. It posts a questionnaire on its website, and invites visitors to complete the questionnaire, offering those who do the chance of winning a cash amount.

10. Tomas wants to conduct a survey for a school project. He wants to assess the reaction of students to a new points system for access to third level education. He decides to ask his schoolmates, his cousins and his friends on his hurling team.

36.4 Sample Surveys (including Opinion Polls)

A **statistical (sample) survey** is used to gather quantitative information about items in a population. Surveys may try to gather information about facts (e.g. household income) or about opinions (e.g. voting intentions). The latter are usually referred to as **opinion polls**.

Great care must be taken in the design of the survey or opinion poll and the questionnaire that goes with it.

1. Clarify the Objectives of the Survey

When deciding to conduct a statistical survey, it is important to first clarify your goals. To help you do this, imagine that you are writing your report at the end of the survey. What issues do you want to be in a position to comment on? Often just stating the problem clearly will be enough to identify what you want to study, but in more complex situations, you may need to break the problem down into a number of clear objectives.

2. Define the Target Population and the Sampling Frame

Before a study is to be conducted, it is obviously necessary to get a clear idea of what we want to measure, and for what population. For example, if you want to determine if fifth year students prefer watching sport or reality TV, what fifth year students are you taking about: those in your school, your county or the whole country? Remember, you will not be able to make reliable statements about a population different from that used in your survey.

It is also necessary to be clear about the sampling frame, i.e. those elements of the population that you can identify and have access to. You should do whatever you can, within reason, to make the sampling frame as close to the population as possible.

3. Design the Questionnaire

When designing a questionnaire, you should bear the following points in mind.

(a) All questions should be **relevant** to your survey. For example, do not ask for a respondent's age unless it is going to be used for something.

(b) All questions should be phrased in **clear, unambiguous and succinct language**. The purpose of this is to eliminate the possibility that a question will mean different things to different people.

(c) **Closed format questions** (e.g. those with multiple choice answers) **are easier** for the respondent to answer and the researcher to analyse than open format questions (those which are answered by expressing an opinion).

(d) With closed format questions, **all possible answers should be accommodated**. You should also note that if asking how often a person watches the news on television, the following list of options:
- Very often
- Often
- Sometimes
- Rarely
- Never

is poor because many of these terms mean different things to different people. A better list of options would be
- Once a day or more often
- 2 to 6 times a week
- About once a week
- About once a month
- Never.

(e) The list of possible answers to closed format questions should be **equally distributed throughout the range** of possible answers. For example, supplying the following list of options when questioning a respondent's opinion of a new fashion shop:
- Fabulous
- Excellent
- Great
- Good
- Fair
- Not so good

is poor as it contains bias.

(f) **Clear instructions for answering** should be given, e.g. "tick one box" or "tick all boxes that apply".

(g) There should be **no leading questions**. A leading question, such as "Don't you think that we should all pay more taxes to help the poor?" allows the respondent to see what answer the researcher wants. In a well constructed survey it should not be possible to tell what answer the researcher wants.

(h) Each question should **query a single topic only**, i.e. ideas should not be linked in a question. For example, consider the question

"Do you agree that Joe Blogs is the best player ever and should be given a huge pay rise?"

It is quite possible for a respondent to agree with one part of this question and disagree with the other part.

(i) **Do not ask embarrassing questions**, unless absolutely essential. It is common practice for respondents not to tell the truth in answer to embarrassing questions, such as those about personal or private matters.

4. Determine a Delivery Method for your Questionnaire

There are different methods of delivering your questionnaire to your selected respondents. Each of these has its advantages and its disadvantages.

(i) Face to face interview.

Conducting a face to face interview allows the interviewer to assess the truthfulness of responses and explain any doubts about questions. However, they can be expensive to carry out, and depending on the questions to be asked, can cause embarrassment.

(ii) Telephone interview.

Conducting interviews by telephone is more anonymous than face to face interviews, and so respondents can feel more at ease in answering awkward questions. Clarifications can also be given, but it can be less obvious to the interviewer when the respondent is giving an untruthful answer. They can also be expensive to carry out.

In both (i) and (ii), it is important that the interviewers are well trained and ask the questions in a professional manner.

(iii) Postal or email questionnaire.

Sending out the questionnaire to selected respondents by post or email is relatively inexpensive, and may elicit more accurate responses due to the private nature of the answering process. However, to obtain reliable data, people who do not respond must be followed up. Unless a very high response rate is obtained, it is likely that those with an agenda will dominate the responses obtained. Sometimes, an incentive, such as being placed in a draw for a prize, is offered to encourage responses.

Example 1

Comment on the following questions from a questionnaire. If necessary, suggest a better way of asking the question.

(i) What is your favourite colour?

Blue	Red	Green	Black	White
☐	☐	☐	☐	☐

(ii) How much do you spend on computer games?

An awful lot ☐

A lot ☐

Not much ☐

Nothing ☐

(iii) The government does not spend enough on overseas aid. Do you agree?

Solution

(i) The list given does not cover all possible answers. By including one further tick box called 'Other', we cover all possibilities.

(ii) The possible answers are too vague, and may mean different things to different people. An improved question might be:

On average, how much do you spend per month on computer games?

€100 or more ☐

€50 – €100 ☐

€10 – €50 ☐

€0 – €10 ☐

(iii) This is a leading question, as it is clear that the question is looking for the respondent to agree. A better wording would be:

In your opinion, the amount the government spends on overseas aid is:

Too much ☐

Just right ☐

Not enough ☐

Exercises 36.4

Comment on each of the following questions as put on a questionnaire. If necessary suggest a better way of asking the question.

1. Have you stopped eating chocolate?

   Yes ☐

   No ☐

2. What is your annual income?

   €10000 – €20000 ☐

   €20000 – €40000 ☐

   €40000 – €60000 ☐

3. What is your favourite subject?

   Irish ☐

   English ☐

   Maths ☐

   Other ☐

4. What is your opinion of our new hi-grade oil?
5. The new government appears to be dealing very well with the current crisis. Do you agree?
6. How often do you pick your nose?
7. How would you rate the service in our department store?

   Excellent ☐

   Very good ☐

   Above average ☐

   Average ☐

   Below average ☐

8. How often do you take a sun holiday?

9. Siobhan wants to use a questionnaire to determine the favourite type of television show of students in her mixed school. She guesses that boys and girls will have different opinions, as will students from different years. Suggest three questions that she could include in her questionnaire.

10. Eabha wants to use a questionnaire to determine which of three supermarkets X, Y and Z in her local town is favoured by those living in her neighbourhood. She expects that men and women will have different opinions, as will people of different ages. She is also interested in how often they shop in the supermarkets and how much they spend there.
    Noting that respondents may shop in more than one supermarket, design a list of questions for her questionnaire.

11. David wants to survey the boys, between ages 8 and 18, in his neighbourhood about their favourite sports. He estimates that boys of different ages will have different opinions, and those with family members involved in certain sports will favour those sports.
    (i) Describe how David should clearly define the population.
    (ii) Suggest how David can make his sampling frame as close as possible to the population.
    (iii) Design a list of questions that David should include in his questionnaire.
    (iv) Having picked his sample from his sampling frame, suggest how David should deliver his questionnaire to the people in his sample.

12. Eamonn wants to determine what countries are the most popular as holiday destinations for adults in his neighbourhood. He suspects that single people, married people with no children and married people with children will have different preferences. He also suspects that the age of the adults in his neighbourhood will be a factor in their choice of destination.
    (i) Describe how Eamonn should clearly define the population.
    (ii) Suggest how Eamonn can make his sampling frame as close as possible to the population.
    (iii) Design a list of questions that Eamonn should include in his questionnaire.
    (iv) Having picked his sample from his sampling frame, suggest how Eamonn should deliver his questionnaire to the people in his sample.

36.5 Designed (Controlled) Experiments and Observational Studies

A Designed Experiment (Controlled Experiment)

In statistics, an experiment is designed differently, and works differently, to a survey or opinion poll. The purpose of an experiment is to investigate whether varying the value of one variable (called the **independent variable** or **explanatory variable**) causes a variation in another variable (called the **dependent variable** or **response variable**). All the other variables are controlled, i.e. held constant. This is what is called a **controlled experiment**, or **designed experiment**.

An example of a controlled experiment is investigating if a new medicine is more effective in clearing up the common cold. Here the explanatory variable is getting, or not getting, the new medicine, and the response variable is if a subject's cold clears up more quickly than otherwise.

In general, a controlled experiment assigns subjects *randomly* to two groups, one called the **experimental group** and the other called the **control group**. The environments for the two groups are kept exactly the same, except for the one quantity in which they differ (the explanatory variable). Then the response variable is measured for each group. The purpose is to see if there is a significant difference in the response variable between the two groups.

One common example is that of a **clinical trial**. Suppose we want to test a new tablet to help ward off colds. We would give the subjects in the control group a placebo (e.g. a sugar tablet), and the subjects in the experimental group get the new tablet. We can then measure over a period of time, the number of colds picked up by the subjects in each group.

To make sure that a controlled experiment is reliable, there are a number of aspects that we should pay careful attention to.

1. **Eliminating Bias**

   To minimise bias, it is essential that the control group and the experimental group are as similar as possible. For large groups assigned randomly, we can be reasonably sure that the groups have a similar distribution.

However, for small groups there is a large risk of bias, even if subjects are assigned randomly. For example, one group might be 70% female while the other might be 40% female. To overcome this, we can stratify the groups, so that they match as closely as possible.

Another way of doing this is to take 'paired data', i.e. take two subjects who are very similar and assign one to each group at random.

2. **Avoiding Confounding Variables**

   Holding all variables, other than the explanatory variable, constant is an essential part of a controlled experiment, and these other variables often have to be monitored very closely to make sure that no variation occurs. A **confounding variable** is a variable that is not controlled in the study, but can have an influence on the results. In designing an experiment, it is absolutely essential to consider all the controlled variables, and to keep them constant, because if a confounding variable is found, it will render your results meaningless.

3. **Control Group**

   It is vital that the control group is as carefully monitored as the experimental group. Don't forget that, at the end of the day, you will only be able to draw conclusions about the *difference* in the responses of the two groups. So, if the responses from the control group are not accurate, then any attempt to interpret the difference will be meaningless.

4. **Ethical Issues**

   Ethical issues, which are concerns about moral justification or simply fairness, occur frequently when designing controlled experiments. If these issues are too large, then a controlled experiment has to be abandoned in favour of one or more observational studies (see below), which are far less reliable. Two important issues are the **informed consent** of the participants in the study and the maintenance of **confidentiality**.

   One obvious example where a huge ethical issue arises is trying to determine if smoking increases the likelihood of lung cancer. On no moral ground can you select two groups and ask one to smoke and the other not to. In a case like this, we would set up an observational study.

   Another example is where a new drug being tested has clearly improved benefits over existing treatments. Is it ethical to deny those in the control group, who are probably being given the previous best treatment, the benefits of the new drug? In practice, the experiment is usually concluded as soon as reliable data is obtained and the new drug is also administered to those in the control group.

   There are many other ethical issues besides medical ones. For example, suppose a school decides to test the benefits of small class sizes. It proposes to form two fifth year classes, one of size 40 and the other of size 10, with students chosen at random for each class. How would you feel if you were in the class of 40?

B Observational Study

Like a controlled experiment, an observational study tries to establish if there is a link between two states which may be termed **exposure** and **condition**, e.g. the exposure might be smoking and the condition might be lung cancer. However, unlike in a controlled experiment, in an observational study, the researcher merely observes and takes measurements. No treatment is given to any of the subjects.

There are a number of different types of observational study.

1. **Cross-sectional Study**

   A cross-sectional study involves the gathering of data at some point in time or over a short period. It only involves one group, the sample, taken from the population at large. The elements of the sample are then queried as to whether they have the exposure and/or the condition. Many will have neither.

A cross-sectional study is very like a survey, but it may be used to suggest a causal link, however not to prove one. It can also be used to determine the prevalence of a condition among the population at large.

For example, a sample of the whole population might be taken and each person might be asked if they smoke and if they have lung cancer.

Other observational studies can give stronger evidence for a causal link. These involve two groups, called the 'experimental group' and the 'control group'. Depending on the type of study, these may be based on those with and without the exposure, or on those with and without the condition.

2. Cohort Studies

In cohort studies, the experimental group is drawn from those exposed and the matched control group from those not exposed. Then both groups are tracked forward from the time of selection. There are two types of cohort studies: retrospective and prospective.

In retrospective cohort studies, the two groups are chosen at some moment in the past and are tracked forward to now. For example, if there was an accident at a chemical factory a number of years ago, the experimental group might be chosen from those exposed, and the control group might be a matched group or the population at large. Then both are tracked forward for the incidence of disease (condition).

In prospective cohort studies, the two groups are chosen now, and tracked forward. For example, if an accident occurs today at a chemical factory, the experimental group is chosen from those exposed, and the control group, if not the population at large, is taken from those not exposed. Then both are tracked forward for the incidence of disease (condition).

Cohort studies are useful when it is possible to accurately identify those exposed, e.g. rare exposure.

3. Case-Control Studies

In case-control studies, the experimental group is chosen from those with the condition, e.g. the disease. The control group is then a matched group without the condition. Then both groups are researched backwards as to their exposure. For example, to investigate the link between smoking and lung cancer, the experimental group could be a number of people with lung cancer, and the control group would be a matched group of individuals without lung cancer. Both groups would be investigated as to their history of smoking.

Case-control studies are useful when it is easy to identify those who have the condition e.g. rare condition (disease).

In both cohort studies and case-control studies, the researcher does not have control over which subjects are assigned to which group: having or not having the exposure or condition determines which group a subject is in. For example, in a case-control study investigating a link between eating fast-food and diabetes, those with diabetes would be assigned to the experimental group and those without diabetes would be assigned to the control group. This is unlike a controlled experiment, where the researcher has complete control over the groups.

Both cohort studies and case-control studies are called **longitudinal studies** as they track subjects over a period of time. This makes them more reliable than cross-sectional studies, as they are better able to deal with bias and confounding variables. Of the two, cohort studies are more reliable than case-control studies, but are not appropriate when the condition is rare.

On our course, we do not need to go into detail about the different types of observational studies. We just need to be aware that there are a number of varieties, which all share the idea that the researcher observes but does not treat. Also, where two groups are employed, the researcher does not control which subjects belong to which group. Both of these distinguish an observational study from a controlled experiment.

All in all, to demonstrate a causal relationship between variables, a controlled experiment is more powerful (convincing) than an observational study. But for ethical reasons, or reasons of cost or time, it might not be possible or practical to conduct a controlled experiment. Then one or other of the different types of observational study may be the best option.

Example 1

Identify the type of survey involved in the following cases. Comment on what should be done to avoid bias, any ethical issues that may exist and the cost of each survey.

(i) To investigate if eating vegetables helps to avoid sickness, we form two groups. We ask one group to eat a significant number of vegetables on a regular basis, and the other group to avoid eating vegetables as much as possible. We then track the health of the members of the two groups over a period of time.

(ii) To investigate if eating vegetables helps to avoid sickness, we form two groups. One group is composed of those who are regularly sick and the other of those who are rarely sick. We interview the members of each group to determine their consumption of vegetables over the previous number of years.

(iii) To investigate if eating vegetables helps to avoid sickness, we form two groups. One group is composed of those who regularly eat vegetables and the other of those who rarely if ever eat vegetables. Then we track the members of each group forward to determine their level of sickness.

Solution

(i) Because we are treating one group (asking them to eat vegetables), this is a controlled experiment. To avoid bias, we should match the members of the two groups on the basis of age, gender, etc as much as possible. An ethical issue could be asking the elements of the control group not to eat vegetables, if it can be shown that this has an adverse effect on their health. Because the survey is to be conducted over a period of time and health checks have to be repeatedly taken, it is likely to be expensive.

(ii) Because no treatment is involved and we are investigating causality, this is an observational study. To avoid bias, the members of the two groups should be matched as closely as possible. Because we are only observing, there are no ethical issues. As we are conducting a once-off series of interviews, this survey is likely to be relatively inexpensive.

(iii) Because no treatment is involved and we are investigating causality, this is an observational study. To avoid bias, the members of the two groups should be matched as closely as possible. Because we are only observing, there are no ethical issues. Because the survey is to be conducted over a period of time and health checks have to be repeatedly taken, it is likely to be expensive.

In general, a statistical investigation starts with one or more questions, and proceeds to collecting data. This data is then analysed and the results interpreted. The results are then compared with the original questions to see if the objectives of the survey have been achieved. If the objective has not been achieved, we start again.

This process is called the **data handling cycle**.

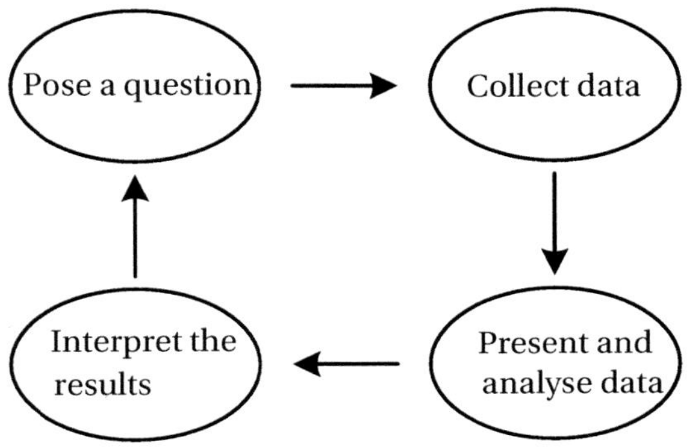

Exercises 36.5

1. Suppose you want to find the average household income in your county. Take it that you do not have the resources to conduct a census (determine all household incomes in your county).
   (i) Explain why a survey is the most appropriate type of study to conduct.
   (ii) Explain the reasons for choosing a researcher-conducted study. Are there any drawbacks to this type of approach? Discuss.
   (iii) Explain the reasons for choosing a questionnaire delivered by post. Are there any drawbacks to this approach? Explain.
   (iv) Why is a controlled experiment not appropriate to this study? Explain.
   (v) Why is an observational study not appropriate to this study? Explain.

2. A referendum is a few weeks away. Voters will be asked a yes/no question about a proposed change to the constitution. You want to estimate the percentage of the voting population who intend to vote 'yes', 'no' and those who don't know.
   (i) Explain why a survey is the most appropriate type of study to conduct.
   (ii) Explain the reasons for choosing a researcher-administered study. Are there any drawbacks to this type of approach? Discuss.
   (iii) Explain the reasons for choosing a postal questionnaire. Are there any drawbacks to this approach? Explain.
   (iv) Why is a controlled experiment not appropriate to this study? Explain.
   (v) Why is an observational study not appropriate? Explain.

3. You have heard it stated that taking an aspirin tablet once a day reduces the risk of a heart attack. You want to conduct a study to test this theory.
   (i) Explain why a survey is not the appropriate type of study to undertake.
   (ii) Assuming that taking a small dose of aspirin once a day does not cause a health risk, are there any ethical issues involved in this study? Discuss.
   (iii) Explain why a controlled experiment is the most reliable approach for this type of study.
   (iv) Detail exactly how you would go about designing the controlled experiment.
   (v) What issues could cause bias in the results, and how could you deal with them?

4. A new drug, called XPY, has been developed to treat a very rare condition (less than 0·01% of the population have this condition). Untreated, this condition can lead to death in a relatively short period of time. There is a current drug, KZR, being used to control the condition, but it only works in 60% of cases. It is claimed that XPY works in 95% of cases and controls the condition much better than KZR. We want to test these claims about XPY.
   (i) Explain why it would be unethical to conduct a controlled experiment, at least in the long run.
   (ii) Outline the stages that should be followed to conduct this study. Mention what treatment should be given to the control group, and when the experiment should stop.
   (iii) Why is a survey not appropriate here?
   (iv) Why is an observational study not appropriate here?

5. You want to investigate if patients who undergo a certain rare medical procedure in hospital are more likely to suffer from bowel cancer at a later date.
   (i) Why is a survey not appropriate?
   (ii) Why would a controlled experiment be unethical?
   (iii) Describe an observational study that you might design to investigate if there is a link.
   (iv) Are there any ethical issues associated with this observational study? Explain.

6. Doctors are concerned that a certain rare disease could be more common among workers exposed to wood shavings in their workplace.
   (i) Why is a survey not appropriate?
   (ii) Why would a controlled experiment be unethical?
   (iii) Describe an observational study that you might conduct.

7. A study in 2009 concluded that people with a thigh measurement of more than 46·5 cm have a smaller risk of heart problems or an early death than those with a thigh measurement less than this (yes really!). Suppose you wish to conduct your own study to see whether or not this is valid.
   (i) Why is a survey or a controlled experiment not appropriate? Give reasons.
   (ii) What type of observational study would you suggest? Give reasons.

8. You want to conduct a study to determine if there is any link between the performance of students in the Leaving Cert and whether or not they eat breakfast each morning. You can assume that you are not in a position to conduct a census of all Leaving Cert students.
   (i) Describe an ideal study you could perform to investigate a possible connection. Are there any ethical issues associated with this type of study? Explain.
   (ii) Because of these ethical issues, describe another suitable type of study.

Revision Exercises 36

Comment on the following questions that are proposed for a questionnaire. If necessary or possible, suggest an improved question.

1. How do you feel today?
2. How much undeclared income did you earn last year?
3. How would you rate your English teacher? ☐ Excellent ☐ Very good.
4. Friday is the best day of the week. Don't you agree?
5. Maths is a very important subject for developing problem-solving skills.
   Don't you think that maths is the most important subject in school?
6. Two wrongs don't make a right. Don't you agree?
7. How many rooms are there in your home?
8. TDs in the Dail are too concerned with local issues to make sure that they are re-elected at the next General Election. Don't you agree?

9. Brian wants to survey his classmates to determine their favourite type of music.
   Construct a question he could ask to obtain data he could analyse.
10. Mary wants to conduct a survey to determine the recreational activities of her classmates. Describe how she could design a series of questions for this purpose.
11. Paul wants to survey the students in his school about how long they spend playing computer games each week, and which games they play. Design a questionnaire that he could present to his fellow students.
12. A company has conducted an advertising campaign for a new product. It has not seen any rise in sales of the product. It wants to conduct a survey to see what went wrong. It wants to know about the penetration of the ad, i.e. how many people saw the ad, and what their reaction was to the ad. Design a questionnaire to gather data that the company can use to analyse the problem.
13. A bicycle manufacturer has the option of increasing the number of gears on a bike from 21 to 35, but it will mean an increase of €50 in the retail cost of the bike. You have been asked to conduct a study to determine how the market would react to this change.
    (i) What is the precise goal of the study?
    (ii) What is the target population?

(iii) Describe a possible study design that would suit this situation.
(iv) What questions would you ask?

14. A suggestion has been made that eating fast-food on a regular basis increases the incidence of requiring an appendectomy (surgical removal of the appendix). You want to conduct a study to test this suggestion.
(i) What is the precise goal of the study?
(ii) What is the target population?
(iii) Explain why a controlled experiment is not appropriate in this case.
(iv) Describe what type of observational study you would conduct.
(v) How would you gather your data?

15. A new theory suggests that for people between 20 and 40 years of age with back pain, cycling for 15 minutes at least four days a week substantially reduces the back pain. You decide to conduct a study to test this theory.
(i) What is the target population? How would you go about finding the members of this population?
(ii) Describe what precise information you would need, and how you would determine a 'substantial reduction' in back pain.
(iii) What type of study would you recommend?
(iv) What groups would you select?
(v) How would you collect your data?

16. A televised debate takes place between the two presidential candidates a short while before a presidential election. The candidates are A from party X and B from party Y. There are also voters who have no allegiance to either party. You want to study what effect the debate has had on the electorate in general. You choose a sample of voters and determine their voting intentions immediately before the debate. Then you poll the same sample for their voting intentions immediately after the debate.
(i) What sampling plan would you design? In what way should you stratify the sample so as to be as representative as possible of the electorate at large?
(ii) What question should be asked of each person before and after the debate? What answers should be allowed?
(iii) How would you collect the data? Explain the options.
(iv) Describe how you could present the results in a fair way.
(v) Describe how you could present the results in a sensationalist way.

17. A manufacturing company makes a large number of precisely engineered components which are meant to be identical and of a uniform high standard. There is concern over the quality of a particular large batch. The customer will reject the entire batch if over 5% of the components prove to be sub-standard. 40% of the batch were produced by machine A, 40% by machine B and 20% by machine C. The serial number on each component identifies which machine produced it.

The company is not sure if there is a problem with one or more of the machines, or if the problem occurred at another stage of the production. It is proposed to sample the batch and test those components chosen.
(i) What is the population from which the sample is to be taken?
(ii) Describe a suitable sampling technique to decide whether or not to test the whole batch before sending it to the customer. It should take into account the issues raised above.
(iii) How would your sampling technique also help to identify if there was a problem with a particular machine?

18. A large polytechnic (third level institution specialising in science and engineering) has 12,000 male students and 8,000 female students. It wants to conduct a survey to determine student satisfaction with the bathroom facilities on campus. It is proposed to ask a sample of students for their opinions.
(i) One possibility is to pick 100 students at random from the student body in a simple random sample. Discuss the advantages and disadvantages of this model.

(ii) Another suggestion is to form a stratified sample. If 100 students are to be asked, how many male and female students should be asked? What are the advantages of this sampling method over a simple random sample?

(iii) A third suggestion is to get an interviewer to go to the student restaurant and ask 30 male students and 20 female students, chosen by the interviewer, for their opinions. What type of sampling technique is this? Discuss the advantages and disadvantages of this technique.

19. To investigate the relationship between egg consumption and heart disease, a group of patients admitted to hospital after suffering heart attacks were questioned about their egg consumption. A group of age and gender matched patients admitted to hospital after suffering fractures were also questioned, in an identical way, about their egg consumption.

(i) Describe the type of study that is involved here.

(ii) Is there any possible bias present? Explain.

20. A leading child psychologist has made the claim that 'children in stepfamilies are more likely to be bullies', without providing any evidence. You want to design a study to test this claim.

(i) What parts of this claim need to be clarified and quantified?

(ii) Why is it not possible to conduct a controlled experiment here?

(iii) Describe what type of study you would conduct.

37

Representing and Analysing Data

In statistics, once data has been obtained, the next task is to represent it graphically and to analyse its important features. Of course, bad data can also be represented graphically and analysed, but the outcome will be of little use. However, if the advice from the last chapter is followed, then it will be a case of dealing with reliable data.

Data can be represented graphically using a number of different display types, e.g. pie charts, line plots, bar charts, stem plots. For continuous data, histograms and frequency curves tend to be used.

Our analysis of data focuses on describing, both by calculation and graphically, the average (middle or central tendency) of the data, and its dispersion (spread or variability). The different measures of central tendency that we meet are the mean, the median and the mode, and also discussed is the issue of when each is used. The interquartile range and the standard deviation describe the spread of data.

37.1 Graphical Methods 1

At Junior Cert, a number of different graphical methods were used to present statistical information, and so make it easier to comprehend. We quickly review these methods here.

1. Pie Chart

A pie chart (or circular graph) is a circle divided into sectors which represent frequencies or proportions taken from a set of data. Pie charts are generally used to show the frequencies or proportions of categorical or discrete numeric data. They are used when we are primarily interested in what fraction each is of the whole set of data. Thus, a pie chart cannot be constructed until all the data has been obtained.

Example 1

A large car salesroom recorded over a one month period the colours of the new cars it sold to customers. The data is given in the frequency table below.

Colour	Black	White	Red	Blue	Silver	Other
No. of cars	24	15	9	5	12	7

You want to show this information on a pie chart.

(i) Describe precisely the data type when the colour of each car sold is recorded.

(ii) Calculate the fraction of all cars sold for each colour, and determine the angle at the centre of the sector for that colour on a pie chart.

(iii) Construct a pie chart, showing a title and labels.

Solution

(i) When the colour of a new car which is sold is recorded, the data is

univariate *(one value recorded)*

categorical *(colour is not numeric)*

nominal *(we cannot arrange the colours in any kind of order).*

(ii) We can construct the following table to calculate the fractions and angles at the centres of the sectors. The total number of cars sold is

$24 + 15 + 9 + 5 + 12 + 7 = 72.$

(To find the fractions for each colour, divide the number for that colour by 72, the total sold. To find the angle at the centre of each sector, multiply each fraction by 360°.)

Colour	No. of Cars	Fraction	Angle
Black	24	$\frac{1}{3}$	$\frac{1}{3} \times 360° = 120°$
White	15	$\frac{5}{24}$	$\frac{5}{24} \times 360° = 75°$
Red	9	$\frac{1}{8}$	$\frac{1}{8} \times 360° = 45°$
Blue	5	$\frac{5}{72}$	$\frac{5}{72} \times 360° = 25°$
Silver	12	$\frac{1}{6}$	$\frac{1}{6} \times 360° = 60°$
Other	7	$\frac{7}{72}$	$\frac{7}{72} \times 360° = 35°$
Totals	72	1	360°

(iii) The pie chart is shown below.

Colour of Cars Sold

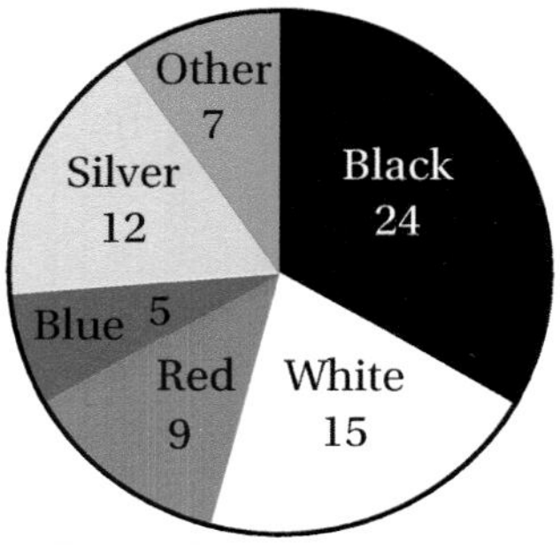

Pie charts are useful when we want to get an idea what fraction each part is of the whole. They are used frequently in business and the mass media, but are rarely used in scientific work. This is because it is often difficult to compare different pie charts.

2. Line Plots

A line plot is a very basic method of graphing a small amount of discrete data. It is closely related to a bar chart, which is a more professional method of presentation.

For example, suppose the ages (in years) of twenty members of a youth club are recorded as follows.

13 11 13 14 12 13 11 15 13 12 11 13 14 16
12 13 14 12 13 15.

We can now construct the line plot by placing an 'X' over each age for each occurrence of that age in the data.

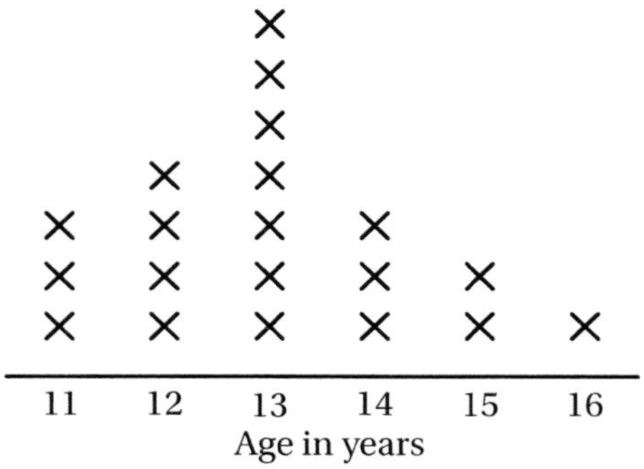

3. Bar Charts

A bar chart (or bar graph) is a chart with rectangular bars, whose lengths are proportional to the frequencies or proportions of the data they represent. Bar charts are used for categorical or discrete numeric data. In a bar chart, the widths of the rectangles should all be the same and there should be space between the rectangles. The rectangles can be plotted vertically or horizontally.

Example 2

The sales achieved by a saleswoman (to the nearest €1,000) in the six-month period from January to June are given in the table below.

Month	Jan	Feb	Mar	Apr	May	Jun
Sales in €1000	9	12	15	10	17	9

(i) What type of data is represented by the months?

(ii) Show the data on a bar chart.

(iii) If she gets a bonus of €100 for each month in which her sales are above €11,000, what bonus does she get for the six-month period shown?

Solution

(i) The months are categorical ordinal data.

(ii) The bar chart is shown opposite.

(iii) *(She earned more than €11,000 in February, March and May.)* Her bonus for the period is 3 × €100 = €300.

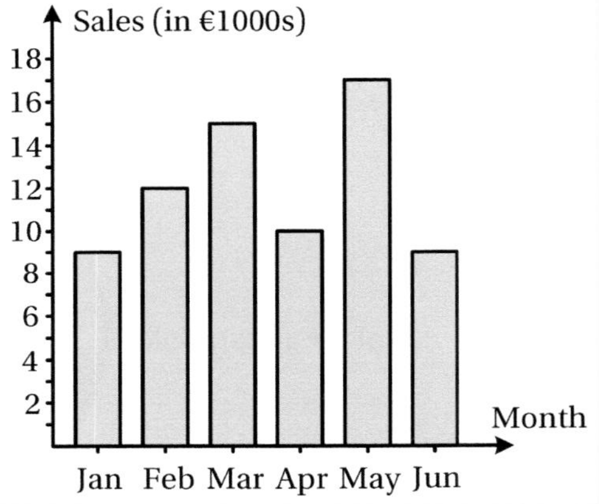

There are many variations possible on the basic bar chart. Two of the more common are multiple (or combined) bar charts and stacked bar charts. Example 3 illustrates their use.

Example 3

The sales figures (to the nearest €10,000) of the salespeople in a company over a three-month period are given in the table below.

Sales Figures (in €10,000s)

	Jan	**Feb**	**Mar**
Peter	8	11	14
Susan	12	8	6
Helen	10	15	7
Cian	6	3	8
Anne	14	12	5

(i) Show this data on a multiple bar chart, with the salespeople listed on the horizontal axis and the sales represented by vertical rectangles. What is the purpose of displaying the data in this way?

(ii) In what other way could the bar chart have been presented with vertical rectangles? What different effect would this give when compared to the bar chart in part (i)?

(iii) The company is interested in the total sales month on month and on the proportion of sales achieved by each salesperson. Use a stacked bar chart to present the information in this way. State an advantage and a disadvantage of this type of presentation.

Solution

(i)

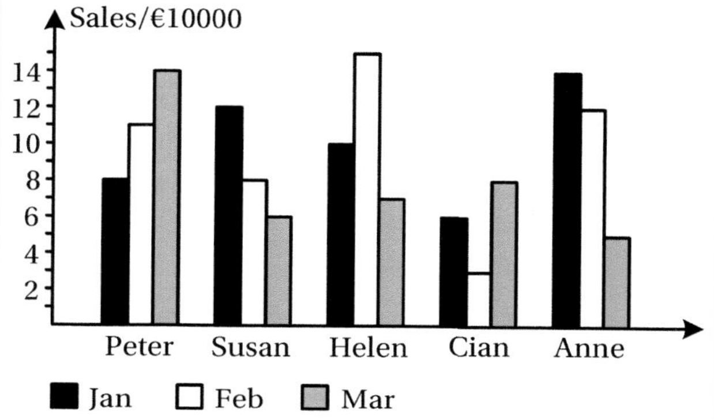

The purpose of showing the data in this way is to display how each salesperson has progressed over the three month period. (Note the importance of an explanatory key below the bar chart.)

(ii) The vertical rectangles could have been grouped by month rather than by salesperson. This would have allowed comparison of the salespeople with each other on a month by month basis.

(iii) *(In a stacked bar chart, each rectangle is broken down into its component parts, in this case the sales of each salesperson. Because there are only three months, we will draw the monthly rectangles horizontally. First, we need to calculate the total sales for each month. These are, in €10000, 50, 49 and 40 for January, February and March respectively.)*

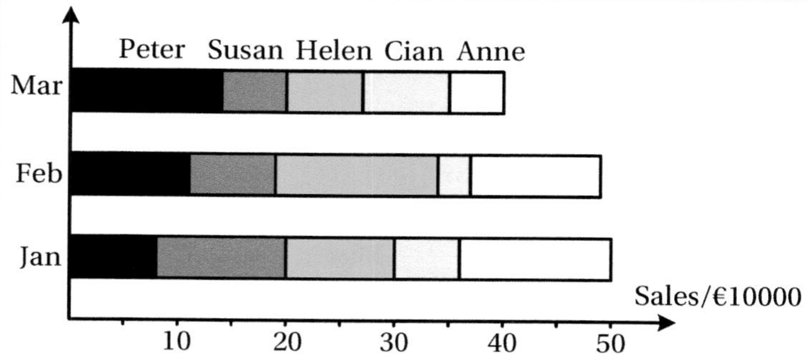

The advantage of this type of display over the multiple bar chart is that it allows observers to see the development of the total sales on a month by month basis, as well as what proportion of these sales is achieved by each salesperson.

The disadvantage of this type of display is that it can be difficult to compare the month by month sales of all the salespeople besides Peter.

4. Histograms

The following table is an example of a grouped frequency distribution. It represents the results of 50 students in an exam. Note that '40–60' means 40 is included but 60 is not.

Result (%)	0–40	40–60	60–80	80–100
No. of students	8	21	18	3

This type of data can be represented by a **histogram**, which is similar to a bar chart, but in theory each frequency is represented by the area of a rectangle. So that frequencies are translated into heights, we need each of the intervals to be of equal width. In the table above, the first interval is twice the others. Therefore, we divide the 8 results in this interval into two 4s, one for the interval 0–20 and the other for the interval 20–40. This gives us the adjusted table below, which now has all intervals of equal width.

Result (%)	0–20	20–40	40–60	60–80	80–100
No. of students	4	4	21	18	3

When representing this data in a histogram (of frequency),

(i) the rectangles must stand over the intervals they represent,

(ii) the rectangles must be touching, unless a frequency is zero,

(iii) with all intervals of equal width, the frequencies are represented by the heights of the rectangles.

The histogram for the grouped frequency table above is shown opposite.

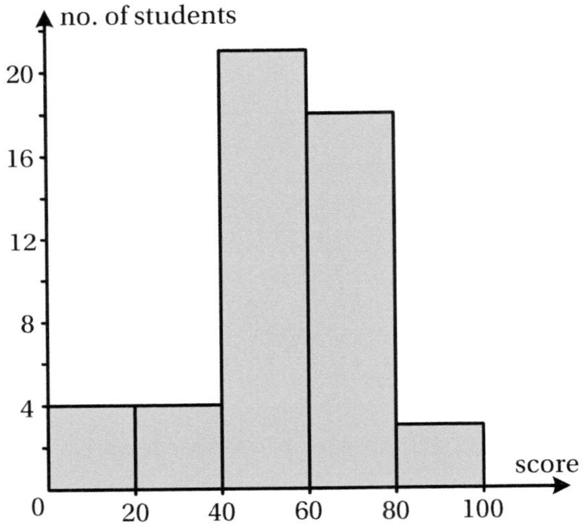

It is also possible to construct a histogram of proportion by first calculating the proportion of the data in each interval. These are calculated by dividing the individual frequencies by the total (50).

Result (%)	0–20	20–40	40–60	60–80	80–100
No. of students	4	4	21	18	3
Proportion	0·08	0·08	0·42	0·36	0·06

The histogram of proportion then looks identical to the one above, except that the proportion values are indicated on the vertical axis instead of the frequencies.

Note: If we are given raw data, we can group them into intervals by using a **tally**. For example, the following data gives the length of time, in minutes to one decimal place, a number of students take to answer a question:

1·7, 3·1, 2·3, 1·5, 0·9, 1·1, 3·5, 1·4, 2·1, 1·7, 1·9, 0·8,
3·6, 2·5, 1·8, 1·1, 2·1, 3·1, 1·7, 3·2, 2·3, 1·4, 1·8, 2·1.

For this data, we can construct the following tally, which allows us to determine the frequency of each interval 0–1, 1–2, 2–3 and 3–4.

Notice the way the tallies are grouped into fives for easy counting.

0–1	ǀǀ	2
1–2	卌 卌 ǀ	11
2–3	卌 ǀ	6
3–4	卌	5

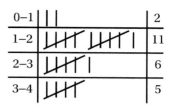

Exercises 37.1

1. The numbers of siblings (brothers and sisters) of the students in a primary school class were recorded as follows:

   2, 1, 3, 0, 1, 2, 1, 1, 0, 2, 1, 3, 4, 1, 4, 3, 1, 5, 2, 1, 2, 1, 0, 1, 1, 2, 1, 0, 1, 2.

   (i) How many students were in the class?
   (ii) Represent this data by a frequency table.
   (iii) Show this data on a pie chart.
   (iv) What other type of graphical display might be suitable for this data? Construct this type of display.

2. The number of goals scored in 24 matches was recorded as follows.

   2, 2, 5, 1, 3, 2, 1, 4, 4, 0, 1, 6, 4, 2, 3, 2, 1, 0, 3, 5, 4, 2, 3, 3.

   (i) Represent this data by a frequency table.
   (ii) Show this data on a bar chart.
   (iii) Show this data on another suitable type of display.

3. The shares in a company are owned by Mr Black, Ms White, Ms Green and Mr Brown according to:

Mr Black	Ms White	Ms Green	Mr Brown
20%	15%	55%	10%

   (i) Represent this data on a pie chart.
   (ii) Represent this data on a bar chart.
   (iii) Why is a histogram not suitable as a means of displaying this data?

4. The pie chart opposite shows the number of goals scored by four members of a soccer team. Joe scored 12 goals.

   (i) How many goals were scored in total by these four players?
   (ii) How many goals did Larry score?
   (iii) Who was the top scorer of these four players and how many goals did he score?

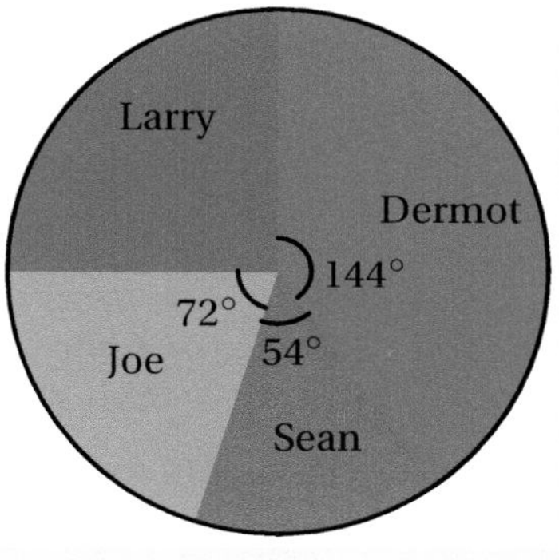

5. There are 540 pupils in a school. Their usual means of transport to school are shown on a pie chart for which the sector angles are as follows.

Bus	Car	Bicycle	Walk
144°	100°		80°

   (i) How many pupils generally cycle to school?
   (ii) Show this information on a pie chart.
   (iii) Show this information on a bar chart.

6. A pie chart is drawn to represent the numbers x, $x + 2$ and 8. If the angle at the centre of the sector representing $x + 2$ is 120°, find the value of x.

7. A pie chart is drawn to represent the numbers x, $2x$ and $x + 4$. If the angle at the centre of the sector representing x is 75°, find the value of x.

8. A company records the number of sick days taken by their employees in different departments in the past month. This is given below.

Accounts: 2, 3, 0, 0, 1, 3, 1, 2, 1, 1, 0
Sales: 3, 0, 2, 3, 1, 0, 1, 2, 1, 0, 1, 1, 3
Manufacturing: 2, 1, 1, 0, 3, 2, 2, 1, 0, 3, 3, 3, 2, 1, 0, 1, 1, 2, 1, 3

(i) Using a tally, form a frequency table of the number of sick days taken by employees from all departments. Represent this data by a bar chart.
(ii) Use a vertical multiple bar chart to show the number of sick days taken by each department separately. Label the departments on the vertical axis.
(iii) What other way could the data be grouped on a vertical multiple bar chart?

9. The number of computer games bought by students in two first year classes in two different schools over a six-month period is given in the following table.

Class A: 1, 3, 0, 0, 2, 4, 1, 3, 1, 2, 0, 0, 4, 3, 1, 2, 1, 0, 3, 2, 1, 0, 1, 0, 2
Class B: 0, 3, 2, 2, 1, 0, 1, 1, 1, 3, 3, 2, 3, 4, 3, 2, 2, 0, 3, 2, 2, 1, 1, 0, 3

(i) Use a tally to form a frequency table for each class.
(ii) Display the information using a vertical multiple bar chart.
(iii) Display the information using a stacked bar chart with each bar showing the number of games bought.

10. In a large office, the number of phone calls made at different extensions on a given day was recorded and is shown in the table below.

No. of calls	0–5	5–10	10–15	15–20	20–25
No. of extensions	12	20	32	18	10

(Note: '5–10' includes 5 calls but not 10.)

(i) Explain why a histogram is the most suitable type of graphical display for this set of data.
(ii) Construct a histogram to show this data.
(iii) What is the greatest possible number of extensions that could have made more than 18 calls on that day?

11. The time taken by the students in a class to answer a test question is recorded in the table below.

No. of minutes	0–2	2–4	4–6	6–8	8–10
No. of students	9	8	7	6	4

(Note: '2–4' includes 2 minutes but not 4 minutes.)

(i) How many students are in the class?
(ii) Explain why a histogram is the most suitable type of graphical display for this set of data.
(iii) Construct a histogram to show this data.

12. The ages of a number of children in a playground were recorded in the table below.

Ages (in years)	0–2	2–4	4–6	6–8	8–10
No. of children	4	7	11	6	6

(Note: '2–4' includes exactly 2 but not exactly 4 years of age.)

(i) Explain why a histogram is the most suitable type of graphical display for this set of data.
(ii) Construct a histogram to show this data.
(iii) All children under 7 years of age are given an ice-cream. What is the greatest number of ice-creams that could have been given out?

13. The histogram below shows the amounts saved in a given month by a number of members of a credit union.

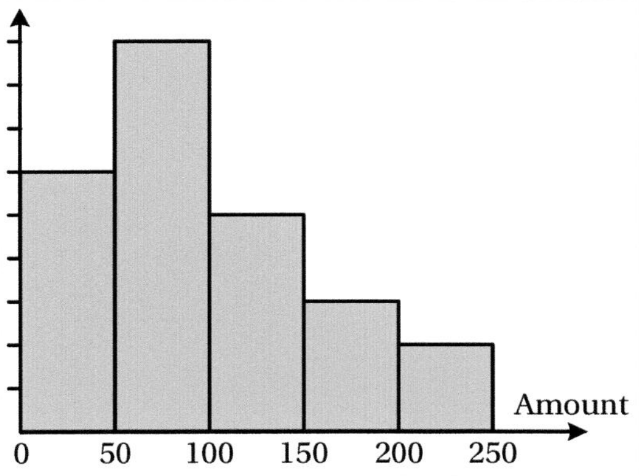

(i) Copy the histogram, and divide the rectangles into blocks of equal size. By counting the total number of blocks, determine what proportion (percentage) is represented by an individual block.

(ii) Complete the table below, showing the percentage of members who saved the varying amounts.

Amount (€)	0–50	50–100	100–150	150–200	200–250
% of members					

(iii) If 12 members saved between €0 and €50, complete the following table.

Amount (€)	0–50	50–100	100–150	150–200	200–250
Number of members	12				

37.2 Graphical Methods 2

5. Stem and Leaf Plots

A **stem and leaf plot** (sometimes called a **stemplot**) is a quick way of presenting discrete or continuous data to help with visualising the shape of the distribution. A stem and leaf plot is only suitable for samples of size between about 8 and 150. A stem and leaf plot is similar to a histogram. However, unlike a histogram, a stem and leaf plot retains the individual data elements, at least to a certain level of accuracy.

To consider how to construct a stem and leaf plot, consider the following raw data, which is the number of correct answers obtained by 10 students in a multiple choice test with 30 questions: 6, 8, 11, 14, 17, 17, 19, 21, 24, 26. Note that this data has already been ranked (placed in order). We can represent this as follows:

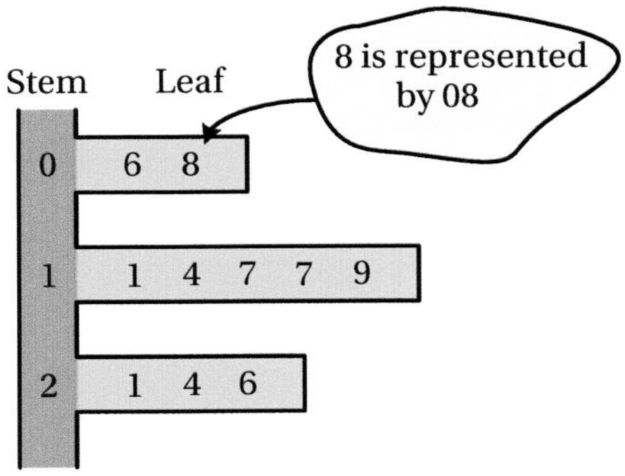

Number of correct answers

Stem	Leaf
0	6 8
1	1 4 7 7 9
2	1 4 6

Key: 2 | 1 stands for 21

In the diagram, the idea of the stem of a tree, and its leaves, is shown on the left, and the stemplot on the right. The stem is all digits besides the last digit. For example, the stem of 218 is 21, the stem of 11·23 is 11·2 and the stem of –2·4 is –2. The leaf is then the last digit.

To construct a stemplot:

(i) List the stems vertically in order from smallest to largest, and include any missing stems. Call the column 'Stem'.
(ii) Draw a vertical line to the right of the stem and a horizontal line under the heading 'Stem'.
(iii) Write the leaves opposite the corresponding stems. Call the column 'Leaf'.
(iv) Include a 'Key' to explain what each symbol stands for.
(v) Include a title for the stemplot.

It may be convenient to construct an unordered stemplot before producing the final ordered stemplot. A stemplot makes it easy to identify outliers. An **outlier** is a result that is far removed from the rest of the data. We will return to outliers later.

Example 1

The following data represents the times (measured to one tenth of a second) taken by a number of students to run a certain distance:

12·4	10·0	11·1	9·3	11·5	10·7	11·1	14·8
9·3	12·7	9·2	11·1	10·8	10·4	10·7	11·9

(i) Construct an unordered stemplot to show this data.
(ii) Construct a stemplot to show this data.
(iii) What time is an outlier?

Solution

(i) & **(ii)** *(The smallest number is 9·2 and the largest number is 14·8. Thus, the stems will be 9, 10, 11, 12, 13, 14. The unordered stemplot is shown on the left and the (ordered) stemplot is shown on the right.)*

Stem	Leaf
9	3 3 2
10	0 7 8 4 7
11	1 5 1 1 9
12	4 7
13	
14	8

Time (in seconds)

Stem	Leaf
9	2 3 3
10	0 4 7 7 8
11	1 1 1 5 9
12	4 7
13	
14	8

Key: 11|6 stands for 11·6

(iii) The outlier is 14·8 seconds.

If the data from a stemplot is turned on its side, we get a histogram, but one which retains the exact information from the data.

Consider the following scores, out of 20, obtained by a number of students in a French exam:
8, 12, 6, 9, 14, 19, 16, 13, 5, 3, 7, 7, 17, 12, 14, 8, 9, 10, 5, 16, 10, 12, 14, 8.

If we construct a stemplot with just two stems '0' and '1', the outcome would not be very informative. Instead, we can construct a stemplot with two '0' stems, the first representing scores from 0 to 4 and the second representing 5 to 9. Likewise, we could have two '1' stems, the first representing 10 to 14 and the second representing 15 to 19. Then the stemplot below could be constructed.

0	3
0	5 5 6 7 7 8 8 8 9 9
1	0 0 2 2 2 3 4 4 4
1	6 6 7 9

Key: 0 | 6 stands for 6

6. Back to Back Stem and Leaf Plots

To compare two similar sets of numeric data we can construct a **back to back stem and leaf plot**, sometimes called a back to back stemplot. In a back to back stemplot, the stem is located in the middle of the graph. The leaves from one set of data are shown on the left of the stem, while the leaves from the other set of data are shown on the right.

One advantage of a back to back stem plot is the ability to see the similarities and the differences between the two sets of data.

Example 2

The percentage scores obtained by the boys and girls of a class in a maths test were recorded as follows:

Boys: 72 64 90 58 51 67 82 71 65 84 48 67

Girls: 53 77 77 72 93 84 61 62 74 78 83 72

(i) Construct a back to back stemplot to show this data.

(ii) On quick examination of the back to back stemplot, would you consider that the boys had a higher average mark than the girls? Give a reason.

Solution

(i) *(We will order the data as a list before we construct the back to back stemplot.)*

Boys: 48 51 58 64 65 67 67 71 72 82 84 90

Girls: 53 61 62 72 72 74 77 77 78 83 84 93

The back to back stemplot is drawn below.

Boys		Girls
8	4	
8 1	5	3
7 7 5 4	6	1 2
2 1	7	2 2 4 7 7 8
4 2	8	3 4
0	9	3

6 | 5 stands for 65

(ii) On quick examination, it appears as if the girls have a higher average than the boys. This is because the boys results are clustered about the 60s, while the girls results are clustered about the 70s.

Exercises 37.2

1. The ages of a number of paying customers in a fast food restaurant one afternoon was recorded as follows:

12	35	17	9	23	15	15	15	18	21	19	25	12	30	14
27	14	22	37	18	8	51	20	10	23	15	18	20	24	11

(i) Use a stem and leaf plot to represent this data.
(ii) Construct a histogram from the stem and leaf plot.

2. A post-office recorded the weights of 22 parcels (in kg) as follows:

2·6	3·1	7·2	0·4	5·8	3·7	4·2	1·9	2·9	5·3	2·1
2·9	8·7	4·4	1·4	5·2	2·1	9·6	3·2	0·2	3·7	4·7

(i) Use a stem and leaf plot to represent this data.
(ii) Construct a histogram from the stem and leaf plot.

3. The IQs of a number of university students were measured and the data below obtained.

121	115	108	119	127	122	138	141	109	111	120	138
116	133	105	128	144	115	120	131	140	113	128	116
108	116	122	131	117	119	128	127	134	115	138	122

(i) Construct an unordered stem and leaf plot.
(ii) Construct a proper (ordered) stem and leaf plot.
(iii) Construct a histogram from the stem and leaf plot.

4. A number of people in a rural area were surveyed about the distance (in km) to their nearest supermarket. The following data was obtained.

1·2	1·5	3·2	0·3	2·4	5·7	2·6	1·8	4·0	1·3
0·9	1·8	4·5	2·7	0·5	1·8	1·5	2·1	2·7	2·0
1·5	4·2	1·6	1·9	2·1	0·7	2·2	1·3	1·1	2·4

(i) Construct an unordered stem and leaf plot.
(ii) Construct a proper (ordered) stem and leaf plot.
(iii) Construct a histogram from the stem and leaf plot.

5. The air temperature (in degrees centigrade) at a particular place was recorded for a number of consecutive nights in February, and the following data was obtained.

1·6	−0·3	−2·4	−1·3	2·4	0·7	−0·5	3·1	−1·7	−0·6
−2·5	2·6	1·3	1·7	−1·4	−1·9	0·7	0·2	−0·8	2·3

(i) Construct an unordered stem and leaf plot, noting that the stem should contain both 0 and −0.
(ii) Construct a proper (ordered) stem and leaf plot.
(iii) Construct a histogram from the stem and leaf plot.

6. The heights (in cm) of the students in a class were measured and the following data obtained.

165	132	168	159	124	138	145	122	167	173
164	131	130	128	166	159	162	160	142	136
139	159	130	142						

(i) Construct an unordered stem and leaf plot.
(ii) Construct a proper (ordered) stem and leaf plot.
(iii) Construct a histogram from the stem and leaf plot.
(iv) The data appears to be clustered in two regions. Give one possible explanation for this.

7. The IQs of the students in a certain third level course were measured and the following data obtained.

117	124	119	122	123	117	123	114	112	128
132	122	110	115	125	132	118	124	126	113
122	125	122	130						

(i) Using the stems 11 (for 110 to 114), 11 (for 115 to 119), 12 (for 120 to 124), 12 (for 125 to 129) and 13 (for 130 to 134), construct an unordered stem and leaf plot.

(ii) Construct a proper (ordered) stem and leaf plot.
(iii) Construct a histogram from the stem and leaf plot.

8. In a sports competition, the ages of the team members of two teams A and B are given below.

Team A:	18	25	31	19	23	18	32	21	23	34	19	20	19	31	21
Team B:	24	31	18	23	25	29	19	30	26	27	26	31	19	20	24

(i) Draw a back to back stemplot to represent this data.
(ii) From this stem plot, what can you comment about the age distribution of the two teams?

9. A rugby team, the Autumn Box, plays twelve matches each season. The numbers of points it scored in each of its matches in the 2008 and 2009 seasons are given in the list below.

2008:	25	6	15	18	34	12	21	8	13	42	9	12
2009:	10	28	25	3	45	33	22	27	15	24	13	22

(i) Draw a back to back stem plot to represent this data.
(ii) Without knowing anything about the numbers of points conceded, in which season would you estimate that the Autumn Box finished higher up the league? Give a reason.

10. Twelve sample employees were chosen from each of two large companies, A and B. On a given day, the time taken (in minutes) by each employee to arrive at their place of work, measured from the moment they left their accommodation, was recorded.

A:	10	2	17	25	12	18	14	12	10	6	32	11
B:	8	17	25	16	24	33	32	7	29	36	45	22

(i) Draw a back to back stem plot to represent this data.
(ii) If one of these companies is based in a county town and the other in a large city such as Cork or Dublin, could you guess which is which? Give a reason.

11. In a university, there are 10 students in each of final year physics and final year maths. Each student undertook an IQ test, and the results are recorded below.

Physics:	138	142	133	148	141	133	120	155	128	137
Maths:	124	137	158	142	149	151	133	145	142	147

(i) Draw a back to back stem plot to represent this data.
(ii) Which faculty can claim to have the more intelligent final year students? Give a reason.

12. Customers who bought new cars at two car salesrooms, A and B, were queried as to the amount of the loan they had taken out to buy their new car. The results, to the nearest €1000, are given in the list below.

A:	8	25	33	48	22	17	56	9	15	44	35	52
B:	12	7	6	10	15	22	9	15	14	23	8	13

(i) Draw a back to back stem plot to represent this data.
(ii) One of these car salesrooms specialised in luxury cars. Can you guess which one? Give a reason.

37.3 Measures of Central Tendency

John, who is in Fifth Year, arrives home from school one day and tells his mother that he got 65% in an English test. She is not quite sure if this is a good result or not.

What she would really like to know is the average of all the results in the class. This would allow her to assess more accurately John's position. There are three different types of average, or measure of central tendency, namely the mean, the median and the mode.

1. The Mean

To calculate the **mean** of a set of numbers, we simply add up all the numbers and divide by the number of numbers. From this, we can see that the mean, which is represented by the symbol μ or $\bar{x}$, is only suitable for numeric data.

For example, the mean of 3, 5, 8, 2 is $\frac{3+5+8+2}{4} = 4{\cdot}5$. Notice that the mean does not have to be one of the elements of the dataset.

The Mean

The mean, μ or $\bar{x}$, of the dataset

$$x_1,\ x_2,\ x_3,\ \ldots,\ x_n$$

with n elements is given by

$$\mu = \bar{x} = \frac{x_1 + x_2 + x_3 + \ldots + x_n}{n}.$$

From the definition of the mean,

$$x_1 + x_2 + x_3 + \ldots. + x_n = n\bar{x},$$

i.e. the sum of all the numbers in the dataset is just the number of numbers multiplied by the mean. For example, if we know that the mean of 7 numbers is 8, then we know that the sum of the 7 numbers is $7 \times 8 = 56$.

Example 1

A dataset of seven numbers contains the numbers 14, 3, 10, 11 and 8. The mean of the dataset is 9. The two other numbers are also positive integers.

(i) What is the sum of the two other numbers?

(ii) Is it possible for the other two numbers to be equal? Explain.

(iii) What is the largest possible difference in the values of the other two numbers?

(iv) If one of the two other numbers is 7 greater than the other, find the other two numbers.

Solution

(i) The mean of the 7 numbers is 9. Thus the sum of all 7 numbers is $7 \times 9 = 63$.

The sum of the 5 known numbers is

$$14 + 3 + 10 + 11 + 8 = 46.$$

Thus, the sum of the other two numbers is

$$63 - 46 = 17.$$

(ii) If the other two numbers are equal, then each would have to be $\frac{17}{2} = 8{\cdot}5$. But because we are told that all numbers are positive integers, this is not possible.

(iii) Because both of the other numbers are positive integers, the least possible value for one of these numbers is 1. Then the other number has to be 16. This gives the greatest possible difference, which is 16 – 1 = 15.

(iv) Let x be one of the two numbers. Then $x + 7$ is the other number. The sum of these two numbers is 17. Thus,

$$x + (x + 7) = 17$$

$$2x = 10$$

$$x = 5$$

The other two numbers are 5 and 5 + 7 = 12.

The mean of a frequency distribution can be calculated by constructing a table designed for the purpose.

Mean of a Frequency Distribution

The mean, $\bar{x}$, of the frequency distribution

Result	x_1	x_2	...	x_n
Frequency	f_1	f_2	...	f_n

is $$\bar{x} = \frac{x_1 f_1 + x_2 f_2 + \dots x_n f_n}{f_1 + f_2 + \dots + f_n} = \frac{\Sigma xf}{\Sigma f}$$

The symbol Σxf stands for the 'sum of all terms of the form x by f' and Σf stands for the sum of all the fs. The symbol Σ is called 'sigma'.

The mean of a grouped frequency distribution is found in exactly the same way as for a frequency distribution, except that 'x' stands for the mid-interval value. For example, the interval '5–10' would be represented by its mid-interval value, i.e. the value half way between 5 and 10. Thus, for this interval,

$$x = \frac{5 + 10}{2} = 7{\cdot}5.$$

Example 2

The number of marks, out of 20, achieved by a group of students in a test is recorded in the table below.

Marks	0–4	4–8	8–12	12–16	16–20
Number of students	3	5	12	6	2

Estimate, correct to two decimal places, the mean mark achieved by the students in the group.

Solution

Interval	x	f	xf
0–4	2	3	6
4–8	6	5	30
8–12	10	12	120
12–16	14	6	84
16–20	18	2	36
	Totals	28	276

Then $\bar{x} = \dfrac{\sum xf}{\sum f} = \dfrac{276}{28} = 9{\cdot}86.$

The mean mark of all the students is 9·86.

Suppose that the mean of the four numbers, a, b, c, d is $\bar{x}$. Then

(i) the mean of $3a, 3b, 3c, 3d$ is $3\bar{x}$,

(ii) the mean of $a + 2, b + 2, c + 2, d + 2$ is $\bar{x} + 2$,

(iii) the mean of $5 - 2a, 5 - 2b, 5 - 2c, 5 - 2d$ is $5 - 2\bar{x}$.

These can easily be checked. The details form one of the exercises.

2. The Median

Another measure of the central tendency of a dataset is the **median**. The median is the middle value when the data are arranged in order.

For example, consider the data 5, 2, 13, 8, 9, 3, 10. Arranging this dataset in order:

$$2,\ 3,\ 5,\ \boxed{8},\ 9,\ 10,\ 13,$$

the middle result is 8. This is the median of this dataset.

The above dataset has an odd number of elements, making it easy to identify the median. If the number of elements in the dataset is even, then the median is the average of the two middle numbers.

For example, the median of the data 8, 4, 1, 5, 2, 9 can again be found by ordering the numbers: 1, 2, 4, 5, 8, 9. Now, because there is an even number of data elements, the median is the average of the middle two, i.e.

$$\text{median } = \frac{4+5}{2} = 4{\cdot}5.$$

Example 3

A dataset contains seven numbers and has a median of 11. Two more numbers are added, and the median is still 11. Suggest two ways by which this could be the case.

Solution

(With seven numbers, the median is the fourth number when the numbers are arranged in order. When two extra numbers are added, the median is the fifth number. This must also be 11.)

Method 1: One of the numbers is less than 11 and the other number is greater than 11.

Method 2: At least one of the two added numbers is 11.

3. The Mode

The **mode** is possibly the easiest measure of central tendency to understand. Given a list of data, the mode is the result which occurs most frequently.

For example, the dataset 3, 3, 4, 4, 4, 4, 5, 5, 6, 7, 9, 9, 10 has a mode of 4, as this is the result that occurs most frequently.

It is possible that a set of data might have more than one mode. For example, the dataset 4, 4, 4, 5, 7, 8, 9, 9, 9, 10, 10 has two modes, 4 and 9, because they both occur three times. This dataset is said to be bimodal. If there are three or more modes, then the dataset is called multimodal. If each result occurs an equal number of times, e.g. once, then there is no mode.

For a grouped frequency distribution, the interval with the highest frequency is called the **modal class**. For example, the grouped frequency distribution

Interval	0–20	20–40	40–60	60–80	80–100
Frequency	6	14	25	15	8

has a modal class of '40–60', because this is the interval with the greatest frequency.

The mode is the only one of the three measures of central tendency that can be used with nominal data, e.g. the first names of all the students in your school.

For some datasets, the mean, median and mode are the same. But for many they are not. The following example shows how this can arise.

Example 4

The monthly salaries of the eight people working in a small company are given in the table below.

Staff member	Ann	Sue	John	Colm	Ben	Ian	Ciara	Pat
Salary (in €)	2000	2000	2000	3000	4000	4000	5000	10000

(i) State the mode. Give a reason.

(ii) Calculate the median salary.

(iii) Calculate the mean salary.

(iv) The owner of the company is Laura, who decides to put herself on the payroll with a monthly salary of €40000. What affect will this have on the mode, the median and the mean? Which measure of central tendency is most affected?

Solution

(i) The mode is €2000, as this is the most common monthly salary.

(ii) *(As there is an even number of results, the median is the average of the middle two.)*

The median salary is $\frac{3000 + 4000}{2} = €3500$.

(iii) Mean: $\bar{x} = \frac{2000 + 2000 + 2000 + 3000 + 4000 + 4000 + 5000 + 10000}{8}$

$\bar{x} = €4000$

(iv) If we have an extra result of €40000:

1. the mode is still €2000
2. the median is now the fifth result, i.e. €4000.
3. the new mean is

$$\bar{x} = \frac{2000 + 2000 + 2000 + 3000 + 4000 + 4000 + 5000 + 10000 + 40000}{9}$$

$\bar{x} = €8000.$

The measure of central tendency that has been most affected by the new data element is the mean.

Uses, Advantages and Disadvantages of Mean, Median and Mode

1. Mean

Use: We can use the mean to describe the middle of a set of numeric data that does not have an outlier.

Advantages:
- It is the most commonly used measure of central tendency in science, business and engineering.
- The mean is useful for further mathematical development.
- It is unique: there is only one answer.
- It is useful when comparing sets of data.

Disadvantages:
- The mean is affected by extreme values (outliers).
- Because the mean does not have to be one of the actual outcomes, it can sometimes give a value that is of little use, e.g. a developer will not build houses for families with a mean of 2·1 children.

2. Median

Use: We can use the median to describe the middle of a set of data that does have an outlier.

Advantages:
- Outliers do not affect the median to anything like the same extent as they do the mean.
- The median is unique: there is only one answer.
- It is useful when comparing sets of data.

Disadvantages:
- The median is not as popular as the mean.
- The median is less suitable than the mean for further mathematical development.

3. Mode

Use: We can use the mode when the data is non-numeric, or when we are asked to find the most frequently occurring result.

Advantages:
- The mode is not affected by outliers.
- The mode is easy to obtain.

Disadvantages:
- The mode is not as popular as the mean or the median.
- The mode is not suitable for further mathematical development.
- The mode is not necessarily unique.
- When there is more than one mode, it is difficult to interpret and compare different datasets.
- If all frequencies are the same, then every value is the mode, and so the mode is useless.

Exercises 37.3

1. **(i)** Calculate the mean of the dataset: 4, 7, 2, 10, 8, 7, 12, 5, 6, 11.
(ii) How many elements of the dataset are less than the mean?
(iii) If one more number is added to the dataset, and the new mean is 8, find the value of the number added.

2. **(i)** Calculate $\bar{x}$, the mean of the following numbers: 8, 12, 4, 20, 10, 12.
(ii) If each of the numbers is divided by 2, show that the mean of the new data is $\frac{\bar{x}}{2}$.
(iii) If each of the original numbers is multiplied by 3, show that the mean of the new data is $3\bar{x}$.

3. **(i)** A dataset contains the numbers 4, 7, 8, 10, 16. Calculate the mean of this dataset.
(ii) An extra number is added to the dataset. The effect of this number is to reduce the mean of the dataset by 1. What is this extra number?
(iii) A second extra number is also added and returns the mean of the dataset to its original value. What is this second number?

4. If the mean of the four numbers a, b, c, d is $\bar{x}$, express in terms of $\bar{x}$ the mean of
(i) $2a,\ 2b,\ 2c,\ 2d$, **(ii)** $5-a,\ 5-b,\ 5-c,\ 5-d$,
(iii) $4+3a,\ 4+3b,\ 4+3c,\ 4+3d$.

5. A number of people were asked to count the number of text messages they sent over a six-hour period. The results are recorded in the table below.

Number of texts	0	1	2	3	4	5	6
Number of people	4	6	10	15	12	8	2

Calculate the mean number of texts sent over the six hour period.

6. The ages of the children in a crèche are recorded in the table below.

Age (in years)	1	2	3	4	5
Number of children	4	10	12	x	5

If the mean age of the children in the crèche is 3 years, find the value of x.

7. The number of new cars in various price ranges sold by a retailer in one month is recorded in the following table:

Price (€1000's)	10–15	15–20	20–25	25–30	30–35
Number sold	5	15	25	15	10

[Note: 10–20 means at least 10 but less than 20, etc.]

By taking the data at the mid-interval values, calculate the mean price per car.

8. Estimate the mean of the grouped frequency distribution which represents the length of time, in hours, taken by a number of university students to complete an assignment.

Time (in hours)	0–2	2–4	4–6	6–8	8–10
Number of students	3	8	11	6	4

9. A dataset contains the positive whole numbers 4, 7, 2, 6, x.

(i) If the median is 5, what is the value of x?
(ii) If the median is 4, what are the possible values of x?
(iii) If the median is 6, what are the possible values of x?

10. A dataset contains the different whole numbers 8, 12, 9, 3, x, y, where $x < y$.

(i) If the median is 8·5, what are the possible values of x and y?
(ii) If the median is 10, what is the value of x, and what are the possible values of y?
(iii) If $x = 14$, what is the median of the data?

11. If a dataset contains 35 elements, when they are arranged in order, which element is the median? The results of 35 students in a multiple choice test with six questions are given below.

Number correct	0	1	2	3	4	5	6
Number of students	5	3	3	4	7	10	3

(i) What is the median result?
(ii) What is the mode, i.e. the modal number of correct answers?
(iii) Calculate the mean number of correct answers.
(iv) Place the median, the mode and the mean in ascending order.

12. The number of attempts required by a number of sixth year students to pass a driving test is given in the table below.

Number of attempts	1	2	3	4	5	6
Number of students	8	5	4	2	2	1

(i) What is the median number of attempts?
(ii) What is the modal number of attempts?
(iii) Calculate the mean number of attempts.
(iv) Place the median, the mode and the mean in ascending order.

13. A dataset contains the numbers 5, 6, 2, 8, 9, 5, 23.
    (i) Identify the outlier in this dataset.
    (ii) Which measure of central tendency is most appropriate for this dataset?
    (iii) Explain why the mean is not the appropriate measure of central tendency for this dataset.

14. A dataset contains the numbers 12, 4, 15, 7, 8, 11, x.
    (i) If $x > 30$, what is the most appropriate measure of central tendency? Give a reason.
    (ii) If $0 \leq x \leq 18$, what is the most appropriate measure of central tendency? Give a reason.

15. A school bus contains eight children under five years old and their teacher who is driving the bus. Explain why the mean is not the appropriate measure of central tendency when measuring the weights of all the occupants of the bus.

16. A studio audience was asked to select their favourite act from six acts in a talent show. What is the appropriate measure of central tendency for the results?

17. Consider the number of fingers that everybody in the world has on their right hand.
    (i) What would you say the median number is?
    (ii) What would you say the mode is?
    (iii) Give a description of roughly what value the mean would be. Do you think this value is useful?

18. The birth-months of all the students in a school are recorded. What is the most appropriate measure of central tendency? Give a reason.

37.4 Range, Percentiles and Interquartile Range (IQR)

The mean, median and mode give an idea of the middle of a dataset. But another important feature is the spread, or **variability**, of a dataset. One reason why this is important is that it helps us to determine the relative standing of a result.

For example, suppose you obtain a score of 70% in a test and the class average is 60%. How well did you do, besides scoring above the average? If many students achieved above 80% , then a score of 70% is just a little above average. On the other hand, if the highest score in the class is 73%, then 70% is a very good score, very near the top of the class. In the second case, the score of 70% has a much higher relative standing than in the first.

1. **Range**

There are different ways of measuring the variability, or spread, of a dataset. The first we consider is the **range**, which can be found by subtracting the lowest value from the highest value in the data set. The range is a crude measure of variability as it ignores the bulk of the data and can be distorted by outliers.

For example, consider the ages of people in an internet cafe on a particular evening: 23, 18, 32, 43, 24, 31, 27, 38, 20, 32, 30, 76, 26, 19, 38, 22. The first thing to do is to **rank** this data, i.e. write the data in ascending order. Doing so, we get:

18, 19, 20, 22, 23, 24, 26, 27, 30, 31, 32, 32, 38, 38, 43, 76.

The lowest value is 18 and the highest is 76. Thus, the range is 76 – 18 = 58. However, the dataset contains an outlier: 76. If this value is removed, the range is 43 – 18 = 25, a very different result.

2. **Percentiles**

One way of establishing relative standing is to use what are called **percentiles.** Not to be confused with percentages, percentiles are comparison scores. Percentiles divide the data in a set into 100 equal parts.

If a data element is in the 80th percentile, written P_{80}, it means that 80% of the data in the set lies below the data element.

There are two calculations we can be asked to make with percentiles, given a list of data.

(i) Calculate the percentile ranking of an individual result.

(ii) Calculate the value of P_n, i.e. the value that corresponds to the nth percentile.

The following example shows one way by which these can be calculated.

Example 1

20 students in a class sat a maths exam and their ranked scores were:

14, 18, 27, 35, 43, 48, 57, 58, 60, 63, 63, 65, 67, 71, 73, 76, 79, 81, 84, 92.

(i) Sarah obtained 71 in this test. What is her percentile ranking?

(ii) What is the 35th percentile, i.e. P_{35}?

(iii) What is the 78th percentile, i.e. P_{78}?

Solution

(i) Counting, we find that 13 students scored less than Sarah in the test. Thus, her percentile ranking is

$$\frac{13}{20} \times 100 = 65$$

Hence, Sarah's score is in the 65th percentile.

(ii) Calculate c, the raw number which is 35% of the way through the list of 20.

$$c = \frac{35}{100} \times 20 = 7$$

As c is a whole number, the required percentile is the average of results numbered c and $c + 1$, i.e. we require the average of the 7th and 8th results, 57 and 58. The required percentile is

$$P_{35} = \frac{57 + 58}{2} = 57{\cdot}5.$$

(iii) Again calculate c, the raw number that is 78% of the way through the list.

$$c = \frac{78}{100} \times 20 = 15{\cdot}6$$

As this is not a whole number, round 15·6 up to the nearest whole number 16, and take the 16th result, 76. Thus,

$$P_{78} = 76.$$

This method of determining relative standing is suitable for a dataset with a small number of elements. For large datasets, we are better off using z-scores, which will be seen in Chapter 39.

3. Quartiles and Interquartile Range (IQR)

Some percentiles have special names. For example, the 25th, 50th and 75th percentiles are called **quartiles**, because they divide the data in quarters. These are named as below.

25th percentile: lower quartile (Q_1)

50th percentile: median (Q_2)

75th percentile: upper quartile (Q_3).

There is no single accepted definition of how to calculate quartiles (one widely used statistical software package gives users a choice of five methods). We will use the following method which is consistent with the definitions of the median and percentiles seen earlier.

Having calculated Q_1 and Q_3, the lower and upper quartiles respectively, we can then obtain the next measure of variability (spread), called the **interquartile range**, or **IQR**. This is the difference between Q_1 and Q_3, i.e.

$$\text{IQR} = Q_3 - Q_1.$$

The IQR is a better measure of variability than the range, as it is not distorted by outliers.

Example 2

Eleven students attempt a test which consists of 50 short multiple choice questions. The number of correct answers they scored is given in the following ordered (ranked) list.

12, 15, 21, 23, 28, 29, 33, 35, 38, 42, 45.

(i) Find the median score.

(ii) Find the lower and upper quartiles.

(iii) Calculate the interquartile range.

Solution

(i) As there are 11 scores, the middle score is the 6th, i.e.

median = 29

(ii) [$Q_1 = P_{25}$. $c = \frac{25}{100} \times 11 = \frac{1}{4} \times 11 = 2{\cdot}75$. So we take the 3rd score.]

$Q_1 = 21$

[$Q_3 = P_{75}$. $c = \frac{75}{100} \times 11 = \frac{3}{4} \times 11 = 8{\cdot}25$. So we take the 9th score.]

$Q_3 = 38$.

(iii) $\text{IQR} = Q_3 - Q_1$

$= 38 - 21$

$= 17$.

The interquartile range can also be calculated from a stem plot, which just allows us to more easily count through the ordered data.

Exercises 37.4

1. **(i)** Calculate the range of the data: 4, 8, 11, 13, 19, 23.

(ii) If another number is added to the data, could there be a reduction in the range?

(iii) If with the inclusion of another number, the range is increased by 2, state the possible values of the other number.

2. **(i)** Calculate the range of the data: 25, 27, 32, 33, 40, 45, 46, 48, 49.

(ii) If one of these numbers is removed and the range is reduced by 1, what is the value of the number removed?

(iii) If each of the numbers in the dataset is doubled, what would the range be?

3. **(i)** Calculate the range of the data: 3, 5, 8, 8, 9, 11, 13, 16, 27.

(ii) Give a subset of five of these numbers which has a range of 11.

(iii) Is it possible to find a subset of these numbers which has a range of 12?

4. (i) A is the dataset: 11, 5, 15, 13, 8, 2, 9, 10.
Find the range of A.
(ii) Three more numbers are added to A, and the range stays the same. What can you say about the three numbers?
(iii) If two numbers are removed from A, what is the greatest possible reduction in the range?

5. The ages of the children attending the accident and emergency department in a children's hospital on a particular morning are listed below in ranked form.
1, 1, 2, 5, 5, 6, 7, 8, 8, 9, 10, 10, 10, 11, 11, 12
(i) Stephen is aged 7. In what percentile is his age?
(ii) Calculate the 27th percentile.
(iii) Calculate the 64th percentile.

6. The number of cars sold by a car dealership over a number of weeks is recorded below.
6, 8, 5, 9, 4, 10, 7, 8, 11, 3, 5, 1, 7, 9, 6, 10, 5, 2.
(i) Rank the data in ascending order.
(ii) In the second week in March, the car dealership sold 3 cars. Determine the percentile ranking for this week's sales.
(iii) Calculate the 80th percentile.

7. A is the dataset listed below. It represents the ages, in years, of people hiring DVDs from a DVD rental shop in a particular period.
23 12 16 34 32 28 25 19 17 46 25 32 18 23 41
30 24 14 38 22 23 44 20 18 21 37 32 27 33 15.
(i) Use a stemplot to arrange the data in ascending order.
(ii) Calculate the 50th percentile. What is the 50th percentile called?
(iii) Calculate the 25th percentile. What is the 25th percentile called?
(iv) Calculate the 75th percentile. What is the 75th percentile called?

8. The weights of a number of children, to the nearest kilogram, are given below.
32 38 41 40 45 29 36 35 38 39 41 45 32 33 47
41 30 40 39 43 45 29 33 35 32 37 38 42 31 36.
(i) Use a stemplot to arrange the data in ascending order.
(ii) Calculate the median.
(iii) Calculate the weight required to be in the 75th percentile or higher.
(iv) Sheila, one of the children, weighs 30 kg. Does her weight lie in the lowest quarter of the weights?

9. In a class test, the percentage marks of a number of students are given below.
45 68 65 72 39 77 56 64 89 44 67 72 68 48
61 90 78 52 82 43 45 70 59 81 41 42 88 79.
(i) Use a stemplot to arrange the data in ascending order.
(ii) Calculate the interquartile range.
(iii) If Sean says that he is in the top 25% of the class, what is the least score that he could have achieved?

10. In a class test, Caoimhe scores 50%, but is told that her score is in the 60th percentile.
The score of her friend, Helen, is in the 85th percentile.
(i) Does this mean that Caoimhe really scored 60%? Explain your answer.
(ii) If Helen scored 65% in the test, what percentage of the class scored between Caoimhe and Helen?
(iii) Another friend states that half the class got less than 50%. Is this possible? Give a reason.

11. In a class test, Paraic scores 75% and his friend Niall scores 65%.
(i) If Niall's score is in the 54th percentile, in what percentiles could Paraic's score lie? Explain your answer.
(ii) Paraic's score is actually in the 80th percentile. Is it true to say that over a quarter of the class scored between 65% and 75% in the test? Explain your answer.

12. At a Garda speed checkpoint, the speeds of a number of vehicles, in kmh^{-1}, were recorded as they passed a certain point. The data is given below.

57 59 64 48 52 58 67 54 53 58 72 61 55 60 57
58 73 66 59 56 53 61 54 59 68 85 57 84 58 60.

(i) Show this data on a stem plot.
(ii) Calculate the lower quartile and the upper quartile.
(iii) Calculate the interquartile range.

13. The ages, in years, of the guests at a wedding are recorded below.

33 22 45 44 70 34 72 75 28 27 29 31 34 44 68 25
21 28 27 29 64 25 28 49 70 26 30 29 43 23 26 28.

(i) Show this data on a stem plot.
(ii) Calculate the lower quartile and the upper quartile.
(iii) Calculate the interquartile range.
(iv) Is the median closer to the lower quartile or the upper quartile? What does this tell you about the grouping of the data?

14. The times taken, in seconds, by a number of students to complete a short maths problem are recorded below.

65 78 85 63 48 68 95 76 70 62 63 84 72 58 69
64 83 51 72 65 62 64 78 52 59 70 85 65 67 70.

(i) Show this data on a stem plot.
(ii) Calculate the lower quartile and the upper quartile.
(iii) Calculate the interquartile range.
(iv) Is the median closer to the lower quartile or the upper quartile? What does this tell you about the grouping of the data?

37.5 Standard Deviation

The most commonly used measure of variability is the **standard deviation**, which is denoted by s or the Greek letter σ (small sigma). The standard deviation gives the average deviation (difference) of each result from the mean. Thus, the more widely spread out the data is, the larger the standard deviation will be.

For example, consider the data: 1, 2, 3, 4, 5, which has a mean $\bar{x} = 3$. The deviation of each data element x, from the mean is defined to be $x - \bar{x}$. Thus the deviations for 1, 2, 3, 4, 5 are respectively −2, −1, 0, 1, 2. The average (mean) of these deviations is 0, as the positive deviations are cancelled by the negative deviations. This always happens.

To overcome this problem, we square each deviation (this will remove any negatives) and then get the average squared deviation.

The average squared deviation is then

$$\frac{(1-3)^2 + (2-3)^2 + (3-3)^2 + (4-3)^2 + (5-3)^2}{5}$$

$$= \frac{4+1+0+1+4}{5} = 2$$

To find the average deviation (not the average squared deviation), we can just take the square root of this value. The result is the standard deviation, σ. Thus, $\sigma = \sqrt{2} = 1{\cdot}41$, correct to two decimal places. σ is small sigma, not to be confused with $\sum$, capital sigma, met earlier.

Standard Deviation

Let $\bar{x}$ be the mean of the data $x_1, x_2, ..., x_n$. Then the standard deviation, σ, is given by

$$\sigma = \sqrt{\frac{(x_1 - \bar{x})^2 + (x_2 - \bar{x})^2 + ... + (x_n - \bar{x})^2}{n}}.$$

Example 1

A: 9, 10, 11 and B: 5, 10, 15 are two datasets, each having a mean of 10.

(i) In your estimation, which dataset has the greater standard deviation? Give a reason.

(ii) Find the standard deviation of A and the standard deviation of B, correct to two decimal places. Comment on the two values.

Solution

(i) The elements of B are more widely spread about the mean than are the elements of A. Thus, we would expect B to have the greater standard deviation.

(ii) For A: $\sigma = \sqrt{\frac{(9-10)^2 + (10-10)^2 + (11-10)^2}{3}}$

$$= \sqrt{\frac{1+0+1}{3}} = \sqrt{\frac{2}{3}} = 0{\cdot}82.$$

For B: $\sigma = \sqrt{\frac{(5-10)^2 + (10-10)^2 + (15-10)^2}{3}}$

$$= \sqrt{\frac{25+0+25}{3}} = \sqrt{\frac{50}{3}} = 4{\cdot}08.$$

As expected, the standard deviation of B is greater than the standard deviation of A.

The standard deviation of the frequency distribution

Result	x_1	x_2	...	x_n
Frequency	f_1	f_2	...	f_n

is defined by

$$\sigma = \sqrt{\frac{f_1(x_1 - \bar{x})^2 + f_2(x_2 - \bar{x})^2 + ... + f_n(x_n - \bar{x})^2}{f_1 + f_2 + ... + f_n}} = \sqrt{\frac{\sum_{i=1}^{n} f_i(x_i - \bar{x})^2}{\sum_{i=1}^{n} f_i}}.$$

This is actually the same definition of the standard deviation for a data list, and is only given in this form for convenience. In practice, the calculation can be laid out in the form of a table, which is just an extension of that used to calculate the mean.

The standard deviation of a grouped frequency distribution (a table with intervals on the top line) can be found by using the same approach, but here the *x*s are the mid-interval values.

Example 2

The lengths, in cm, of a number of fish which were captured and tagged in a lake are recorded in the table below.

Length (in cm)	0–10	10–20	20–30	30–40	40–50
Number of fish	4	16	20	12	6

(i) Calculate the mean length of the fish.

(ii) Calculate the standard deviation, correct to two decimal places.

Solution

(We will set up a table to calculate both the mean and the standard deviation.)

Interval	x	f	xf	$x-\bar{x}$	$(x-\bar{x})^2$	$f\times(x-\bar{x})^2$
0–10	5	4	20	–20	400	1600
10–20	15	16	240	–10	100	1600
20–30	25	20	500	0	0	0
30–40	35	12	420	10	100	1200
40–50	45	6	270	20	400	2400
Totals		58	1450			6800

(i) $\bar{x} = \dfrac{\sum xf}{\sum f} = \dfrac{1450}{58} = 25$ cm.

(ii) $\sigma = \sqrt{\dfrac{\sum f\times(x-\bar{x})^2}{\sum f}} = \sqrt{\dfrac{6800}{58}} = 10{\cdot}83$ cm.

Most scientific calculators allow data to be entered, either as a list or as frequencies, and can calculate their mean and the standard deviation. Two of the most popular modern calculators are the Casio fx-83ES (Natural Display) and the Sharp EL-W531 (WriteView), and both have the capability of calculating the mean and standard deviation directly.

Exercises 37.5

1. Calculate the mean and the standard deviation of the numbers 1, 2, 3, 4, 5.
2. Calculate the mean and the standard deviation of the numbers 6, 7, 10, 12, 15.
3. Calculate the mean and the standard deviation of the numbers 8, 10, 15, 17, 20.
4. Calculate the mean and the standard deviation of the numbers 21, 28, 35, 42, 53, 61.
5. The mean of the numbers 5, 7, 10, x, 15 is 10. Find the value of x. Calculate the standard deviation of these numbers.
6. The mean of the numbers 4, x, 13, 17, 27 is 14. Find the value of x. Calculate the standard deviation of these numbers.
7. Calculate the mean and the standard deviation of the distribution:

Result	0	1	2	3	4
Frequency	6	10	16	12	5

8. Calculate the mean and the standard deviation of the distribution:

Result	3	4	5	6	7	8
Frequency	2	4	10	18	14	5

9. Calculate the mean and the standard deviation of the distribution:

Result	2	3	4	5	6	7
Frequency	8	10	15	12	4	2

10. Calculate the mean and the standard deviation of the distribution:

Result	1	2	3	4	5	6
Frequency	12	18	16	14	8	4

11. The number of goals scored in 60 games of football is recorded in the table below.

Number of goals	0	1	2	3	4	5
Number of games	8	16	17	9	7	3

Calculate the mean number of goals scored, and find the standard deviation correct to two decimal places.

12. The number of films watched by a group of people in a given week is recorded in the table below.

Number of films	0	1	2	3	4	5
Number of people	2	6	10	16	12	8

Calculate the mean number of films watched, and find the standard deviation correct to two decimal places.

13. The length of time a number of students spent watching television over a weekend was recorded and the results are given below.

Time (in hours)	0–2	2–4	4–6	6–8	8–10
Number of students	4	7	15	5	5

Calculate the mean time and the standard deviation, correct to the nearest minute.

14. The share price of a company at the end of each trading day was recorded over a period of time. The results are given in the table below.

Share price (in cents)	10–20	20–30	30–40	40–50	50–60
Number of days	2	7	15	28	6

Calculate the mean share price and the standard deviation, correct to the nearest cent.

15. The ages, in years, of the members of the audience at a music recital were recorded, and the results are given below.

Age (in years)	10–20	20–30	30–40	40–50	50–60	60–70
Number of people	2	15	22	27	32	13

Calculate the mean age and the standard deviation, correct to the nearest integer.

16. The weights, in kg, of the fish caught in an angling competition were recorded, and the results are given below.

Weight (in kg)	0–1	1–2	2–3	3–4	4–5
Number of fish	4	8	10	28	10

Calculate the mean weight and the standard deviation, correct to two decimal places.

37.6 Analysis of Graphs

When a frequency or grouped frequency distribution has a large number of intervals, then the corresponding histogram has many vertical columns. In such a case, we often find that the histogram is replaced by the corresponding **frequency curve**. This can be formed by drawing a curve going through the midpoint of the top of each rectangle, and often down to the horizontal axis at each end. An example of a histogram and the corresponding frequency curve is shown below.

The frequency curve maintains the idea that frequencies are represented by areas under the graph, just like a histogram. Also, comments on statistical graphs apply to both histograms and frequency curves.

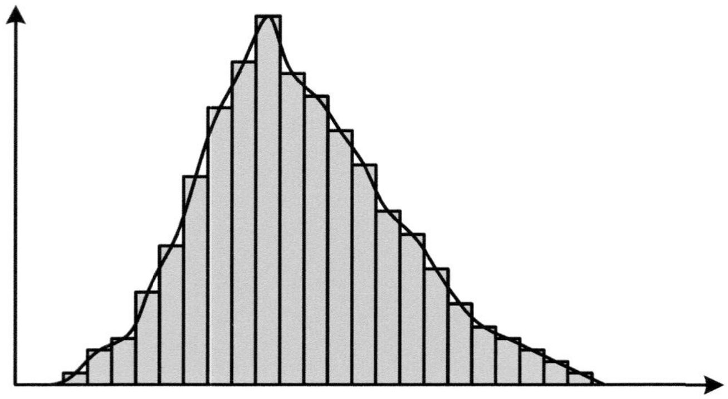

1. Positions of the Mode, Median and Mean on a Statistical Graph

We can interpret the positions of the mode, the median and the mean of a distribution on its statistical graph (histogram or frequency curve).

(i) The Mode

The position of the mode on a graph is at the highest point. The mode, like all measures of central tendency, must be a value on the horizontal axis.

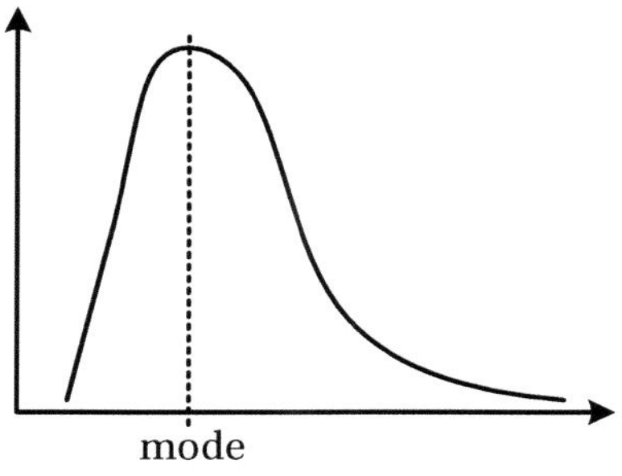

Recall that the mode of a distribution does not have to be unique. There could be two or more modes. A distribution, and its graph, which has two modes is called bimodal. An example of a bimodal graph is shown opposite.

If a distribution, and its graph has many modes, it is called multimodal. A distribution with a single mode is sometimes called unimodal.

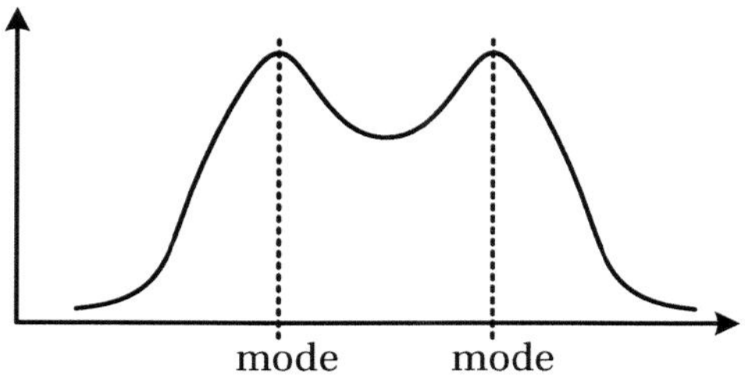

(ii) The Median

The median is at the point where the area under the graph is divided in two, 50% on each side.

By comparing this graph with the unimodal graph shown above, we can see that the median does not have to be in the same place as the mode.

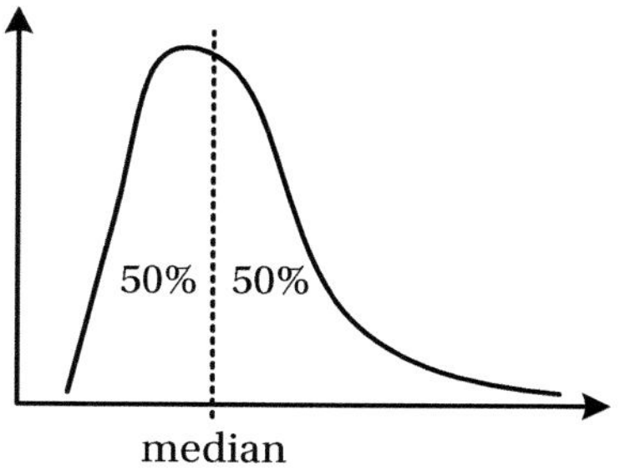

(iii) The Mean

The mean is the point upon which the whole graph would balance, if we consider it to be a block of uniform density.

The mean is shown opposite as a pivot, or fulcrum, under the graph.

Unlike the mode and the median, the mean is affected by the distance of areas from the middle.

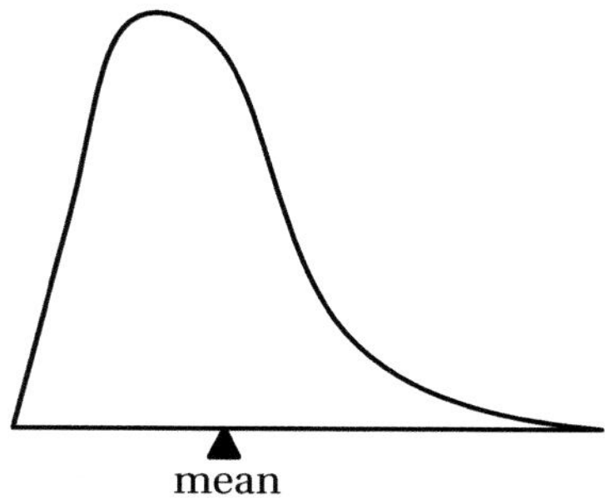

2. Shapes of Graphs and Positions of the Mode, the Median and the Mean

(i) Symmetric Graph

A graph is said to be symmetric if it has a vertical axis of symmetry through the middle.

For a symmetric, unimodal, graph, the mode, the median and the mean are in the same place, going through the highest point of the graph.

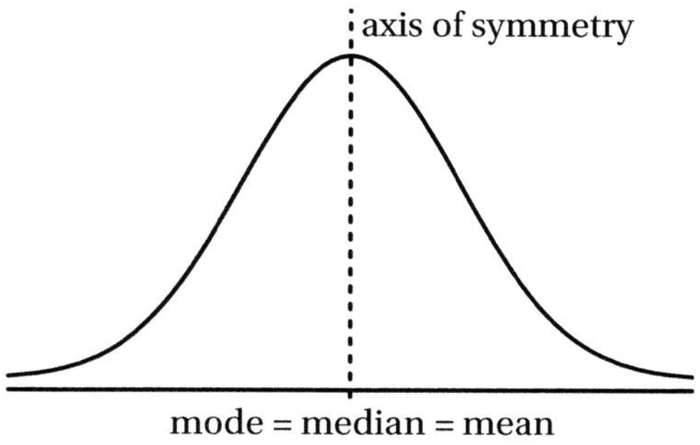

(ii) Positively Skewed (Skewed to the Right)

A graph is positively skewed, or skewed to the right, if the high point is to the left of the graph and there is a significant tail to the right.

If a graph is positively skewed, then the mode is less than the median, which in turn is less than the mean.

In symbols,
mode < median < mean.

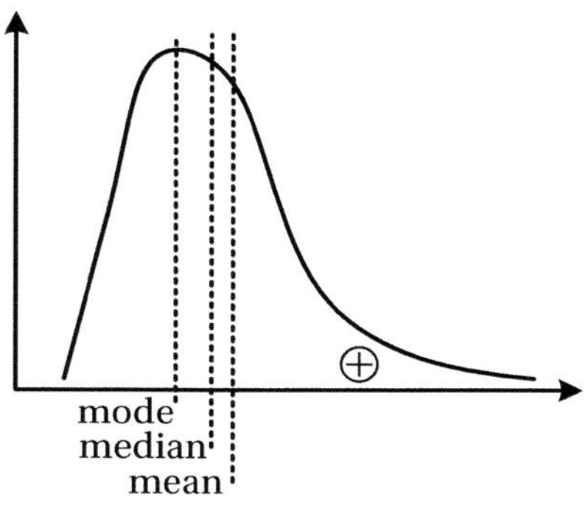

(iii) Negatively Skewed (Skewed to the Left)

A graph is negatively skewed, or skewed to the left, if the high point is to the right of the graph and there is a significant tail to the left.

If a graph is negatively skewed, then the mode is greater than the median, which in turn is greater than the mean.

In symbols,
mean < median < mode.

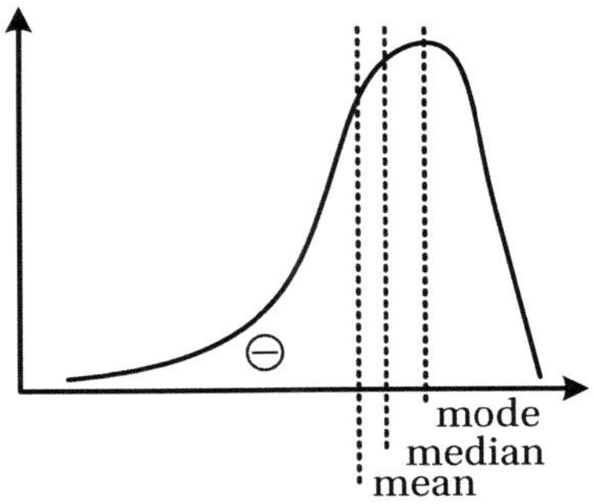

When a graph is skewed, the mode is at the highest point, the mean is dragged into the tail, and the median is in between the two.

Example 1

A large grouped frequency distribution has a mean of 28 and a mode of 34. The distribution is moderately skewed.

(i) Sketch a frequency curve to represent this data.

(ii) Explain where the median of the data lies.

Solution

(i) *(Because there is only one mode mentioned, the distribution is unimodal. Because the mean is less than the mode, the frequency curve is negatively skewed. This is shown opposite.)*

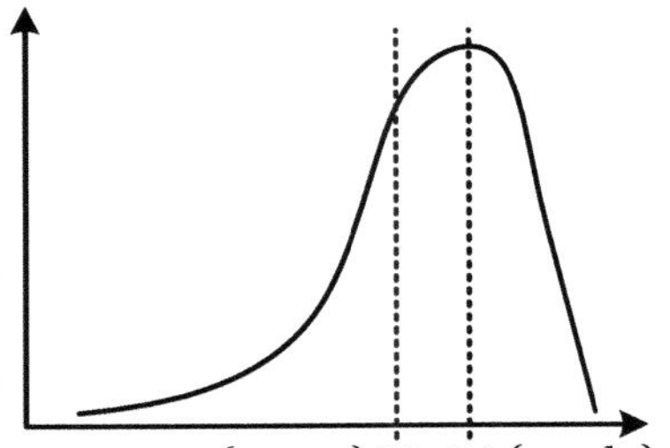

(ii) As the median lies between the mode and the mean, the median will lie between 28 and 34.

3. Interpretation of Standard Deviation on a Graph

The diagram opposite shows the effect that the standard deviation can have on the shape of a statistical graph. In the diagram, we show the graphs of two distributions, *A* and *B*, which have the same mean μ.

But because the graph of *A* is more widely spread about the mean than that of *B*, *A* has a greater standard deviation than *B*.

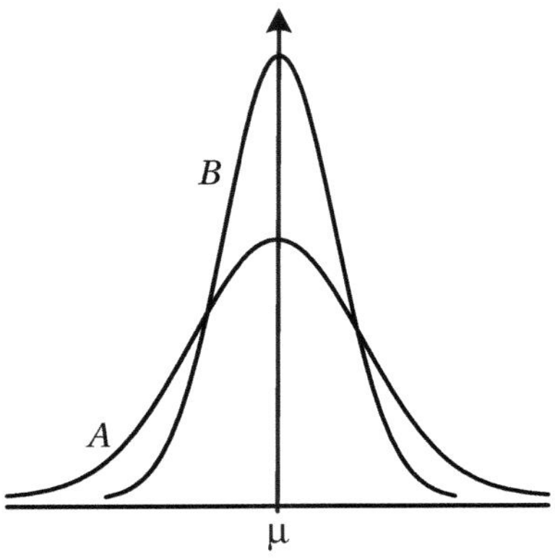

Example 2

The diagram shows histograms representing four distributions, *A*, *B*, *C* and *D*, all of which have a mean of 2·5. Consider the following statements.

(i) *A* has the smallest standard deviation.

(ii) *D* has the largest standard deviation.

(iii) No two of the distributions have the same standard deviation.

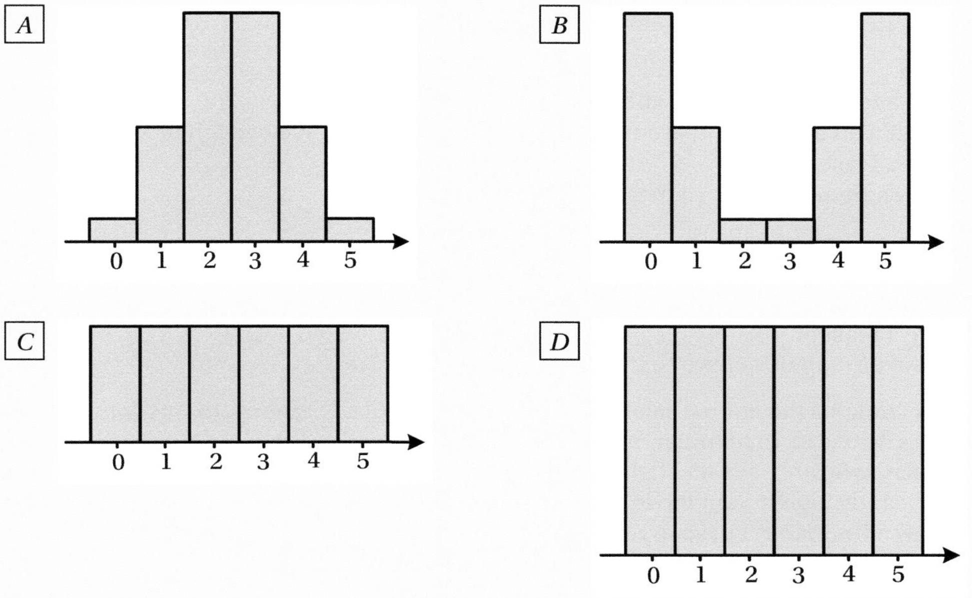

Answer:

1. if (i) only is true,

2. if (i) and (ii) are true,

3. if (ii) and (iii) are true,

4. if (i) and (iii) are true,

5. if all three statements are true.

Solution

(We must first decide which of the statements are true.)

(i) is true, as it has the greatest proportion of its area close to its mean.

(ii) is not true, because *B* has the greatest standard deviation, with a huge proportion of its area near the edge.

(iii) is not true, because *C* and *D* have an equal spread about the mean.

Hence, the answer is 1.

Exercises 37.6

1. A histogram representing a frequency distribution has a mode of 6 and a mean of 6.
   (i) What is the median of the distribution?
   (ii) Would you describe the histogram as symmetric, skewed left or skewed right?

2. A histogram representing a frequency distribution has a median of 10 and a mode of 12.
   (i) Would you consider that the distribution is symmetric? Give a reason.
   (ii) Is the histogram skewed to the left or to the right? Give a reason.
   (iii) Give an estimate of the mean of the distribution.

3. A frequency curve has a mode of 7·5 and a mean of 9.
   (i) Give a rough estimate of where the median should lie.
   (ii) Would you describe the frequency curve as symmetric, skewed left or skewed right? Give a reason.
   (iii) Draw a frequency curve that fits the information given.

4. A frequency curve has a mode of 15 and a median of 13.
   (i) Give a rough estimate of where the mean should lie.
   (ii) Would you describe the frequency curve as symmetric, skewed left or skewed right? Give a reason.
   (iii) Draw a frequency curve that fits the information given.

5. A dataset contains the annual salaries of the employees of a company. In this company there are many employees who work in manufacturing. These are paid roughly the same amount. There are also a number of managers, who are paid at a slightly higher rate. Finally, there are two company executives whose salaries are significantly higher than those of the managers. The dataset is represented by a frequency curve.
   (i) Draw a frequency curve to represent the dataset.
   (ii) Is the frequency curve symmetric or skewed? Give a reason.
   (iii) Are there any outliers? Give a reason.

6. Which of the following distributions do you think would be (a) symmetric, (b) skewed to the right, (c) skewed to the left? Give a reason for your answer in each case.
   (i) The ages of all the people in Ireland.
   (ii) The prices of all new cars sold in Ireland last year.
   (iii) The number of fingers on the left hand of everybody in the world.
   (iv) The heights of all the students in your class.

7. The histograms for two grouped frequency distributions, A and B, are shown below.

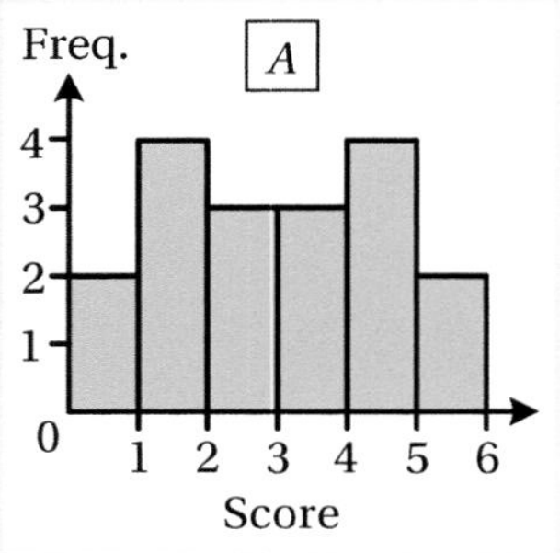

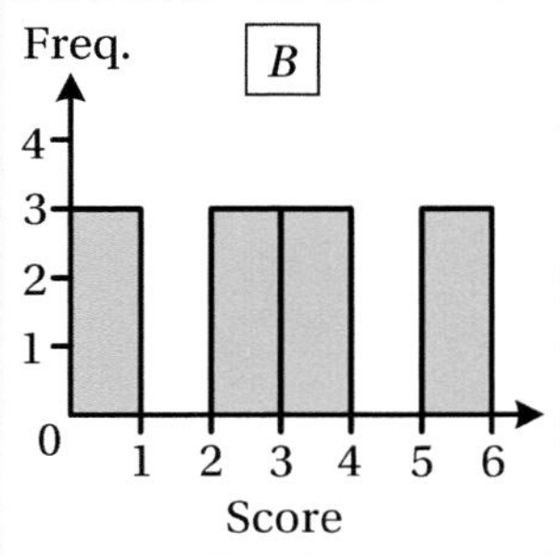

   (i) From initial inspection, what would you estimate the mean of each distribution to be? Give a reason.
   (ii) Again from initial inspection, which distribution would you expect to have the greater standard deviation, or do you think that they are roughly the same?
   (iii) Using the mid-interval values, calculate the mean of each distribution.
   (iv) Using the mid-interval values, calculate the standard deviation of each distribution. How does the result compare with your estimate in part (ii)?

8. The histograms for two grouped frequency distributions, *A* and *B*, are shown below.

(i) From initial inspection, what would you estimate the mean of each distribution to be? Give a reason.

(ii) Again from initial inspection, which distribution would you expect to have the greater standard deviation, or do you think that they are roughly the same?

(iii) Using the mid-interval values, calculate the mean of each distribution.

(iv) Using the mid-interval values, calculate the standard deviation of each distribution. How does the result compare with your estimate in part (ii)?

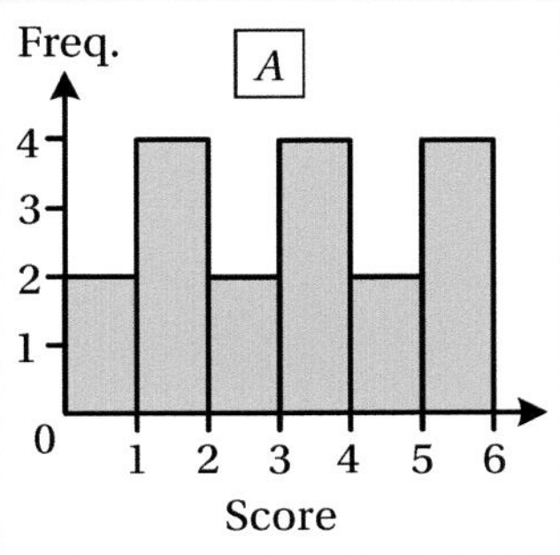

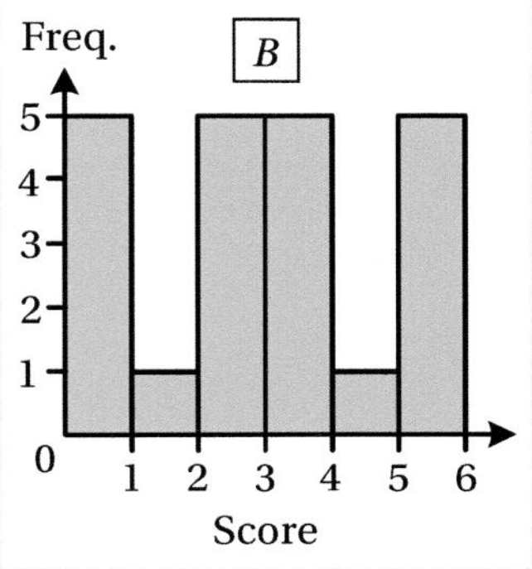

9. The histograms for two grouped frequency distributions *A* and *B*, are shown below.

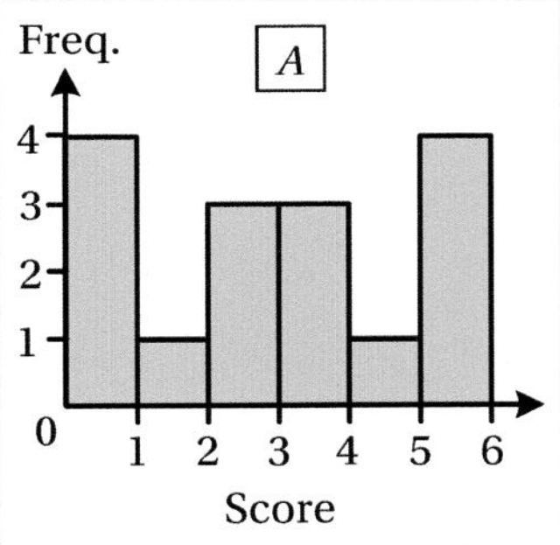

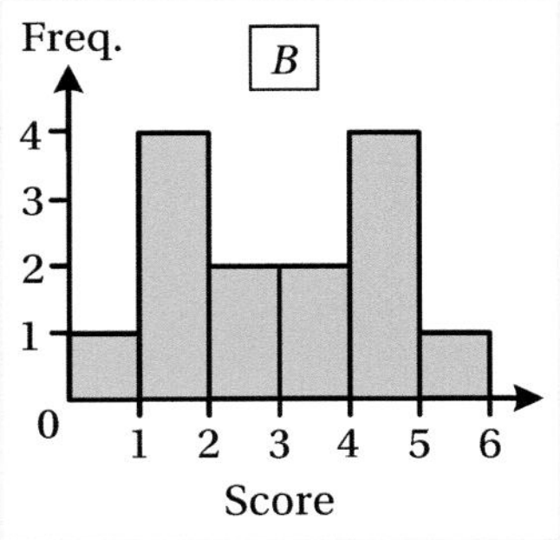

(i) From initial inspection, what would you estimate the mean of each distribution to be? Give a reason.

(ii) Again from initial inspection, which distribution would you expect to have the greater standard deviation, or do you think that they are roughly the same?

(iii) Using the mid-interval values, calculate the mean of each distribution.

(iv) Using the mid-interval values, calculate the standard deviation of each distribution. How does the result compare with your estimate in part (ii)?

10. A frequency curve is moderately skewed to the right. Its mean is 24. Its standard deviation is 4.

(i) Describe where you think its median and mode are, assuming that it is unimodal.

(ii) A similarly skewed curve has the same mean and a standard deviation of 8. Describe the positions of its median and mode, relative to those of the first curve.

Revision Exercises 37

1. The makes of car in the employee carpark of a small factory are listed below.

Make	Number of cars
Ford	6
Toyota	8
Nissan	5
Peugeot	2
Volkswagen	10
Opel	x

   (i) When this data is represented on a pie chart, the angle at the centre of the sector representing Ford cars is 60°. Calculate the value of x.
   (ii) What type of data is the makes of car?
   (iii) Show this data on a pie chart.
   (iv) Show this data on a line plot and on a bar chart.
   (v) The following day, all these cars are present, along with two extra Nissans, belonging to two new employees. When a new pie chart is constructed, what is the reduction in the angle at the centre of the sector representing Ford cars?

2. In a short maths test, the marks achieved by the students in a class are recorded in the following table.

Marks	Number of students
0–10	1
10–20	0
20–30	1
30–40	1
40–50	2
50–60	2
60–70	3
70–80	7
80–90	6
90–100	3

   (i) Would a pie chart be a useful way of displaying this data? Explain.
   (ii) Represent this data on a histogram. Is the distribution symmetric, skewed to the right or skewed to the left?
   (iii) Determine the modal class, the median and the mean (using the mid-interval values). State whether this agrees with your expectation from your answer to part (ii).
   (iv) Calculate the standard deviation, using your calculator.
   (v) Does this set of data have an outlier? Explain.

3. Draw a frequency curve that has the following properties.
   (i) Symmetric, bimodal and a range of [10,20].
   (ii) Symmetric, unimodal and a range of [0,40].
   (iii) Skewed to the right, mode of 10 and mean of 14.
   (iv) Skewed to the left, mode of 20 and range of [0,30].

4. The students in a class are divided into two groups, A and B, each with twelve students. All the students are given a spelling test consisting of 50 words. The number of right answers given by each student in each group is listed below.

Group A:	31 17 42 23 27 15 27 38 25 20 28 33
Group B:	18 35 26 22 14 44 33 19 20 47 21 39

(i) Represent this data on a back to back stemplot. On first inspection, which group, if any, do you think performed better?
(ii) Which group has the greater range?
(iii) Calculate the median for each group. How do the groups compare?
(iv) Calculate the mean for each group. Comment on the difference between the median and the mean for each group.
(v) Calculate the interquartile range for each group. What do you think this tells us about the distribution of scores in each group?
(vi) Calculate the standard deviation for each group. How do the standard deviation and the interquartile range compare for each group?

5. The histograms for two grouped frequency distributions are shown below.

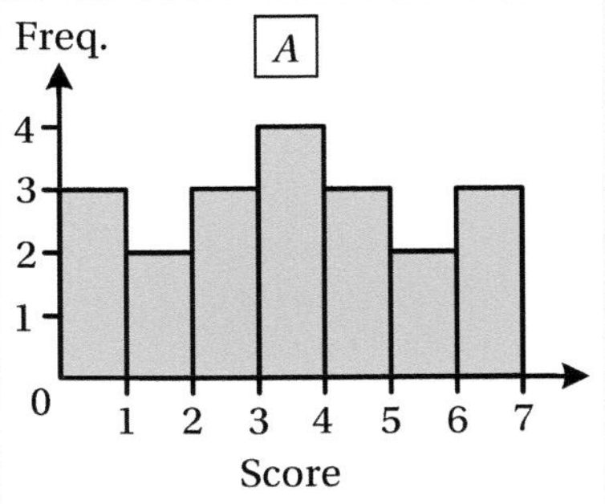

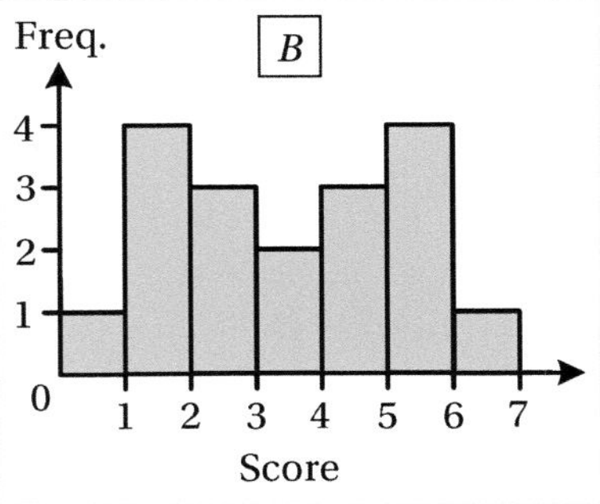

(i) From initial inspection, what would you estimate the mean of each distribution to be? Give a reason.
(ii) Again from initial inspection, which distribution would you expect to have the greater standard deviation, or do you think that they are roughly the same?
(iii) Using the mid-interval values, calculate the mean of each distribution.
(iv) Using the mid-interval values, calculate the standard deviation of each distribution. How does the result compare with your estimate in part (ii)?
(v) Which one of these two distributions is bimodal? How would you describe the other distribution?

6. If σ is the standard deviation of a, b, c, d, express in terms of σ the standard deviation of
(i) $2a, 2b, 2c, 2d$
(ii) $3a + 1, 3b + 1, 3c + 1, 3d + 1$.

Correlation

38

In statistics, as in real life, there is often a relationship between two random variables, or two sets of data. For example, there is the relationship between a person's average intake of food and their weight, or between the outside temperature in cold weather and the energy consumption in the form of electricity and gas. Correlation is the branch of statistics that determines the strength of the relationship between two sets of data, and what that relationship is. This analysis can be used to make predictions using hypothetical values of one unknown.

In the first example above, there is a positive correlation between food intake and weight, i.e. as one increases, so does the other. In the second example, there is a negative correlation between temperature and energy consumption, i.e. as one goes down, the other goes up. In both cases, however, the link is not an exact cause and effect: there are other factors to be considered.

When linear correlation does exist between paired data, we will be interested in finding the so-called line of best fit, which will in turn allow us to make estimates.

38.1 Drawing Scatterplots

One of the main uses of statistics is to investigate if two quantities are related, for example, the heights and weights of students in your class. **Correlation** is the branch of statistics which investigates if two quantities are related, and if so, how strong the relationship is between them. Correlation is investigated for bivariate, numerical data, e.g. the heights and weights of people in a group.

If we let the variable X represent one of the values measured and Y represent the other value measured, then each pair of values can be represented as a couple (x,y). For example, if Paul's height is 1·72 m and his weight is 73 kg, this would be recorded as the couple (1·72,73).

If there is no obvious cause and effect between the two variables, then it does not matter which we call X and which we call Y. On the other hand, if either

(i) we have control over one variable and just want to observe the other, e.g. the amount of fertiliser applied to plants and their heights, or

(ii) one variable is suspected to cause a change in the other, e.g. the amount of rainfall and the time taken to make a car journey, or

(iii) we want to use one variable to estimate the value of the other variable, e.g. to predict weight given height,

then we should let X (the independent or explanatory variable) be the first variable, and Y (the dependent or response variable) be the second variable.

The data in the form of couples can be plotted as a set of points on a **scatterplot**. This is just a region of the x, y plane familiar from co-ordinate geometry. For a scatterplot, it is not necessary to begin each axis at 0, but we should begin each axis below the lowest value for that variable.

Example 1

A physics teacher in a secondary school is curious about a possible correlation between higher maths results and physics results for her Leaving Cert students. So after the Leaving Cert results are published one year, she records the results in both subjects for the 16 students in her physics class. Because she needs numeric data, she converts each grade to the corresponding CAO points, e.g. an A1 is 100 points, and A2 is 90 points etc.

The results she obtained for her students are listed below.

Student	Maths	Physics
Emma	75	85
Helen	70	75
Susan	85	65
Rachel	40	50
Aoife	60	60
Sarah	70	65
Ciara	100	100
Chloe	90	80
Aisling	50	45
Louise	75	90
Emer	55	60
Orla	80	65
Siobhan	70	80
Anne	90	75
Eibhlin	65	70
Nora	85	80

(i) If she thinks that a good maths ability might improve a student's performance in physics, which variable should be X and which should be Y?

(ii) Represent the data on a scatterplot.

Solution

(i) X should be the maths result and Y should be the physics result. Thus, for example Emma's scores should be plotted as the point (75,85).

(ii)

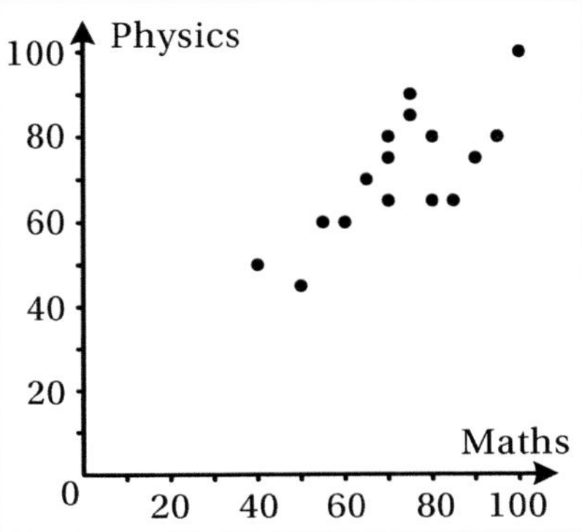

Exercises 38.1

1. The heights, in metres, and the weights, in kg, of the twelve members of a boys soccer panel were recorded, and the data is given below.

Sean:	1·67 m, 62·5 kg	Alan:	1·52 m, 57·3 kg
Jason:	1·77 m, 68·2 kg	David:	1·54 m, 54·0 kg
Hugh:	1·55 m, 65·0 kg	Darren:	1·63 m, 60·7 kg
Steve:	1·82 m, 71·3 kg	Larry:	1·74 m, 65·2 kg
Mark:	1·58 m, 53·5 kg	Eoin:	1·70 m, 82·5 kg
Trevor:	1·84 m, 75·3 kg	Andy:	1·69 m, 64·3 kg

   (i) For a scatterplot showing (height, weight), suggest suitable starting values and scales on each axis.
   (ii) Construct a scatterplot showing (height, weight).

2. A number of students sat a multiple choice test which consisted of 20 questions. Each student was also asked to express their attitude to the test on a scale of 1 to 10, 1 being very much against and 10 being very much in favour of the test. The results are given below in the form (x,y), where x is the number of correct answers and y is the attitude of the student to the test.

   (17,7), (15,4), (18,6), (14,5), (19,8), (10,3), (17,9), (18,8), (13,5), (18,9)

   Construct a scatterplot showing (number correct, attitude).

3. The IQ levels of 10 Leaving Cert students and the points they achieved in the Leaving Cert are recorded below.

A:	IQ: 122, Points: 450	B:	IQ: 110, Points: 470
C:	IQ: 135, Points: 540	D:	IQ: 140, Points: 380
E:	IQ: 128, Points: 570	F:	IQ: 108, Points: 310
G:	IQ: 115, Points: 430	H:	IQ: 120, Points: 510
I:	IQ: 124, Points: 555	J:	IQ: 130, Points: 470

   (i) Which quantity, IQ level or Leaving Cert points, should be X? Give a reason.
   (ii) Construct a scatterplot showing this data.

4. A maths exam was held on a Monday. The percentages achieved by a number of students in this exam, along with the number of hours they spent watching television the previous weekend, are recorded below in the form (percentage, number of hours).

   (45,10), (64,3), (58,7), (70,9), (85,2), (32,10),
   (94,9), (90,3), (52,5), (75,4), (95,0), (62,6)

   (i) If the data is to be used to see if watching more TV before an exam affects students' exam performance, which quantity should be X?
   (ii) Construct a scatterplot showing this data.

38.2 Correlation

When bivariate data is drawn on a scatterplot, the closer the points are to a straight line, the greater the (linear) correlation between the two variables. If the two variables are perfectly correlated, then the points will all lie on a straight line. But this is very rare in statistical investigations. In almost all cases, the points are scattered.

We need a way of quantifying how closely the points on a scatterplot are approximated by a straight line, called the **line of best fit**. This job is done by a quantity known as the **correlation coefficient**, denoted by r.

r is always a value between –1 and 1. The ***sign*** of r has to do with whether the line approximating the data, the line of best fit, is increasing or decreasing. The ***value*** of r has to do with how close the points lie to the line of best fit. The closer the points are to the line of best fit, the closer the value of r is to 1 or –1. If the data is very scattered, then the value of r will be close to 0.

(i) Positive correlation

If, in general, the values of Y increase as X increases, then there is said to be positive correlation, i.e. the value of r is positive.
In this case the line of best fit will be increasing from left to right.

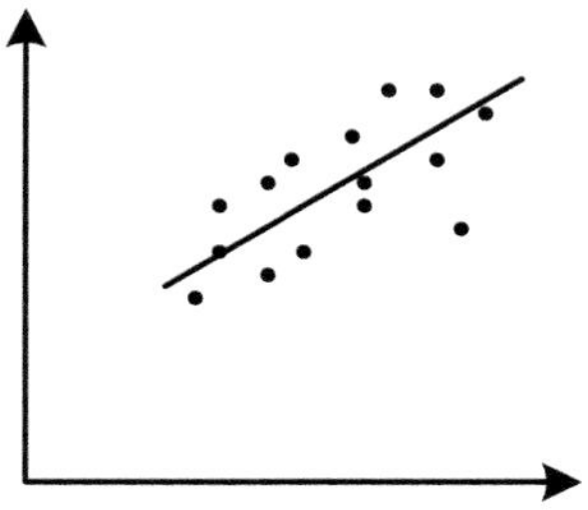

In the scatterplot shown opposite, the line of best fit is increasing as we go from left to right. Thus, $r > 0$.

(ii) Negative correlation

If, in general, the values of Y decrease as X increases, then there is said to be negative correlation, i.e. the value of r is negative.
In this case the line of best fit will be decreasing from left to right.
Thus, $r < 0$.

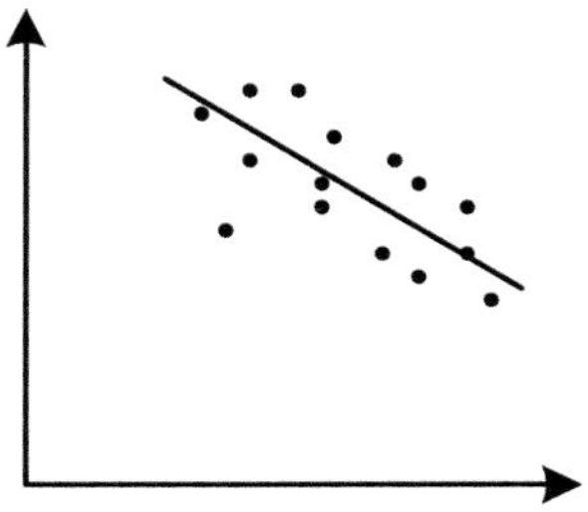

(iii) No correlation

If the points are scattered at random then there is no correlation between the two variables, and the value of r is zero, or close to zero.

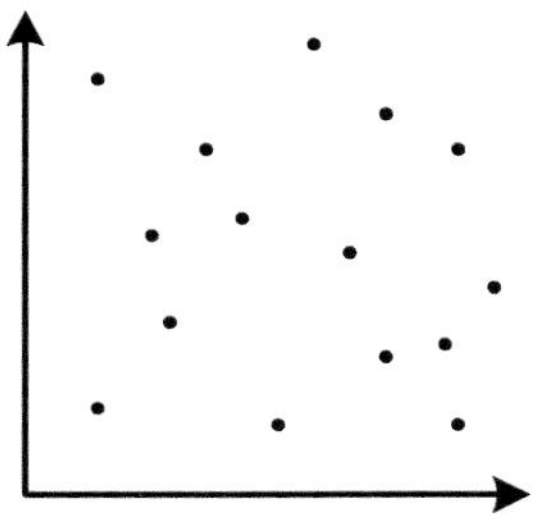

Some examples of scatterplots, their lines of best fit (where applicable) and the corresponding values of the correlation coefficient, r, are shown below.

The line of best fit is the line that goes through the middle of the data. In theory, it is the line where the distances from the points on both sides of the line to the line balance each other.

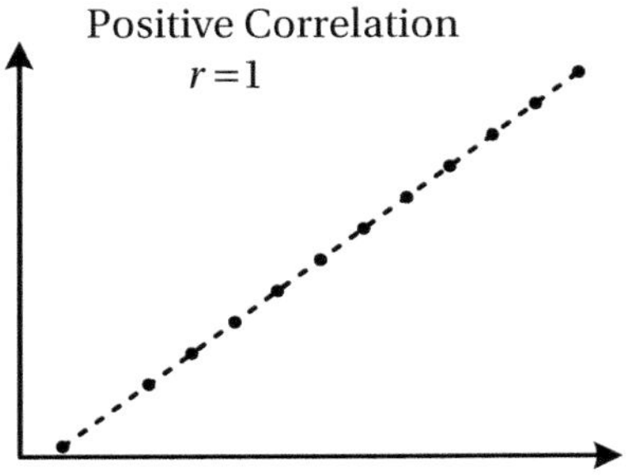

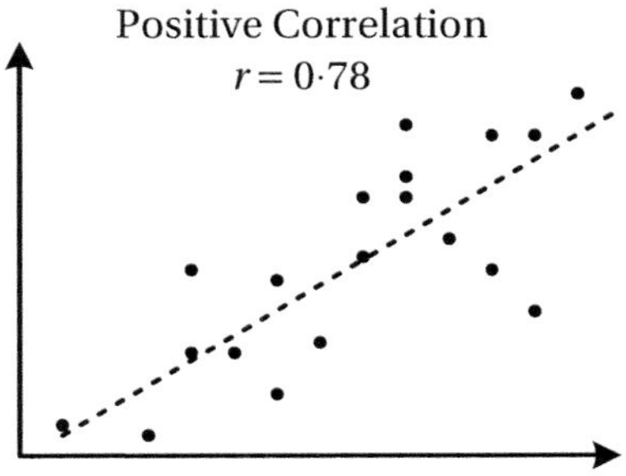

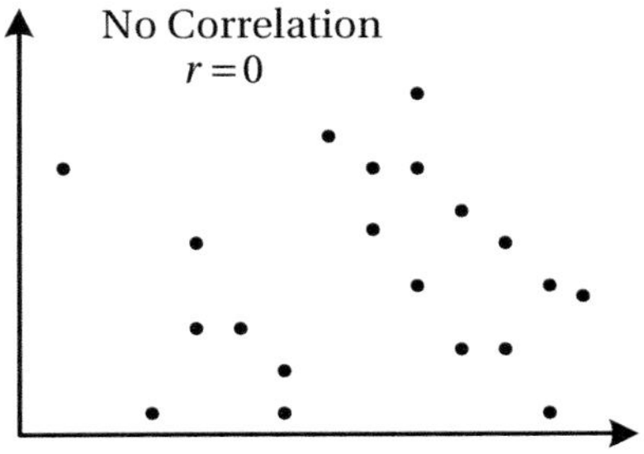

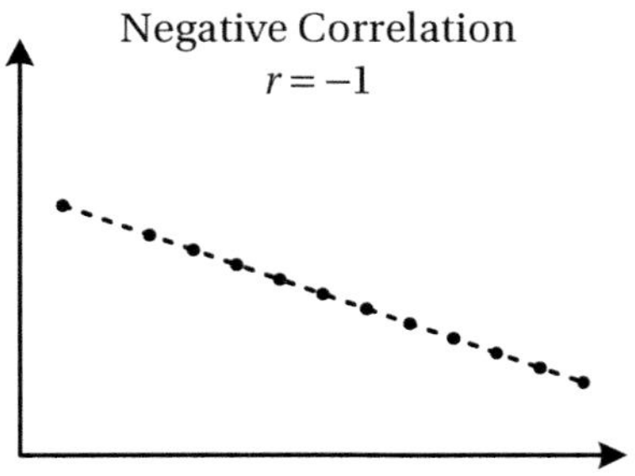

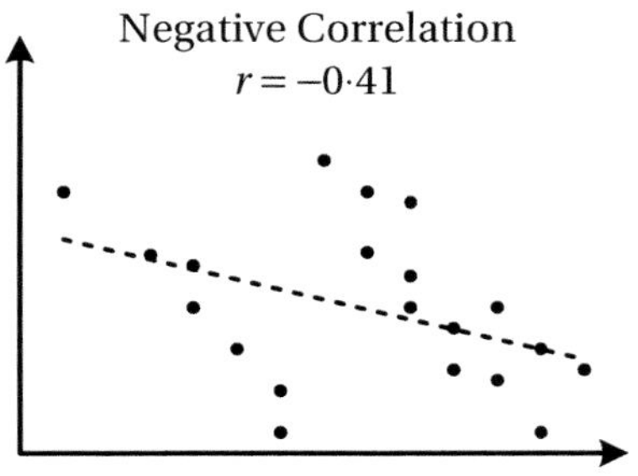

In general, correlation is divided into strong, moderate and weak, based on the value of r. The following diagram gives a commonly used scale for these, but depending on the circumstances, small variations in these are possible.

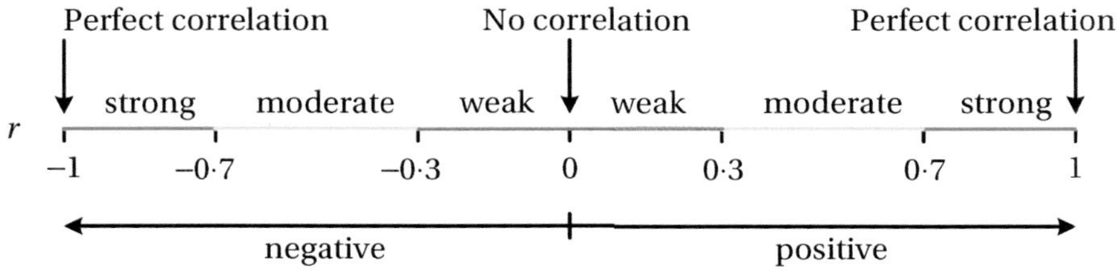

Notes:

1. The correlation coefficient, r, has no units. Thus the value of r will not be altered by changing units from, say, metres to centimetres when measuring height.

2. If all the points on a scatterplot lie on a horizontal line or they all lie on a vertical line, then we can either say that the correlation coefficient is not defined, or is equal to zero.

3. The data should be as representative as possible of the population about which we want to determine a possible correlation. For example, if we are investigating the link between time spent playing sport and annual income, it would not be representative to only consider university graduates in their twenties.

The Effect of Outliers on the Correlation Coefficient

Outliers can have a very big effect on the value of r, the correlation coefficient. This can occur either by hiding a strong correlation, or making a weak correlation look strong.

(i) Outlier(s) hiding a strong correlation

Consider the two sets of data shown below, A and B. They are the same except that B contains one extra point, the outlier labelled P. However, the difference in the values of r is very significant. The data represented in A shows strong correlation, while that in B shows weak correlation.

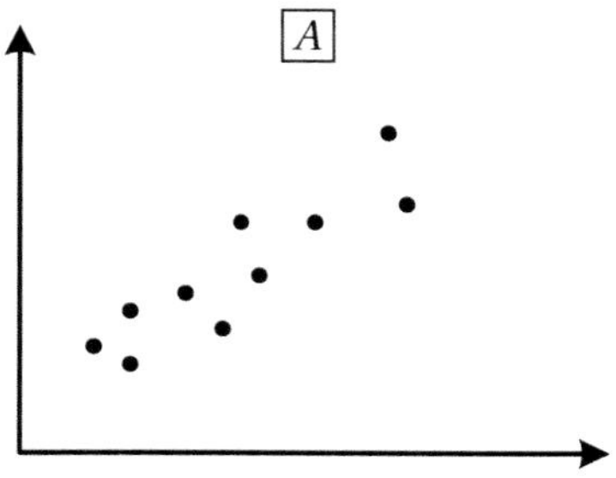

$r = 0{\cdot}89$

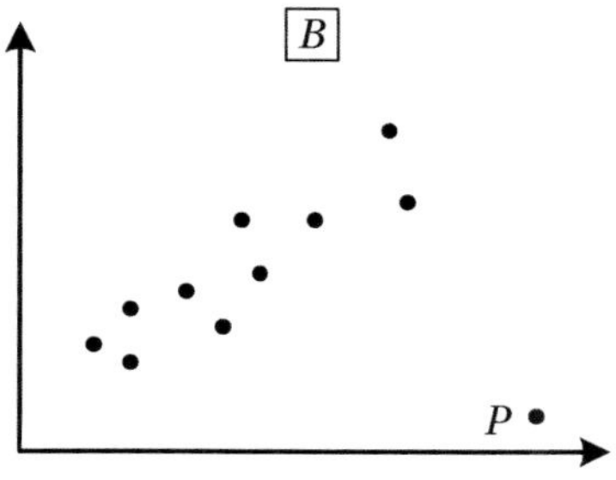

$r = 0{\cdot}21$

(ii) Outlier(s) making a weak correlation look strong

Consider the two sets of data shown below, *C* and *D*. Again they are the same except that *D* contains one extra point, the outlier labelled *P*. Again the difference in the *r* values is very significant. The data in *C* shows very weak positive correlation, but the extra point *P* causes the correlation to become very strong.

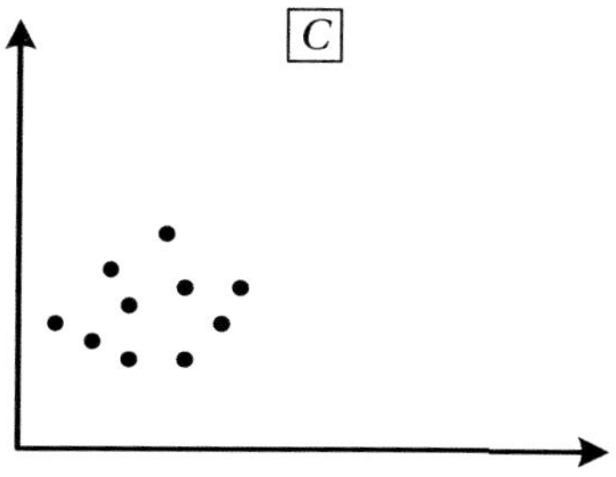

$r = 0{\cdot}18$

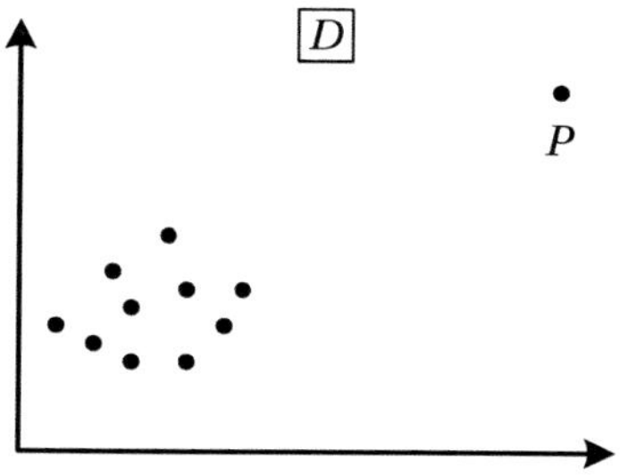

$r = 0{\cdot}82$

Outliers can have a big effect on the correlation, but they don't have to. If for example, there is a very strong correlation, and the outlier lies close to the line of best fit of the data minus the outlier, then the outlier will have little or no effect on the correlation.

How to deal with outliers is the subject of much debate. All seem to agree that if the outlier is as a result of some error, then it should be removed. However, if the outlier legitimately belongs to the data, then most feel that it should not be removed, even if this appears to distort the analysis of the rest of the data.

Exercises 38.2

1. The scatterplot shown opposite represents bivariate data.

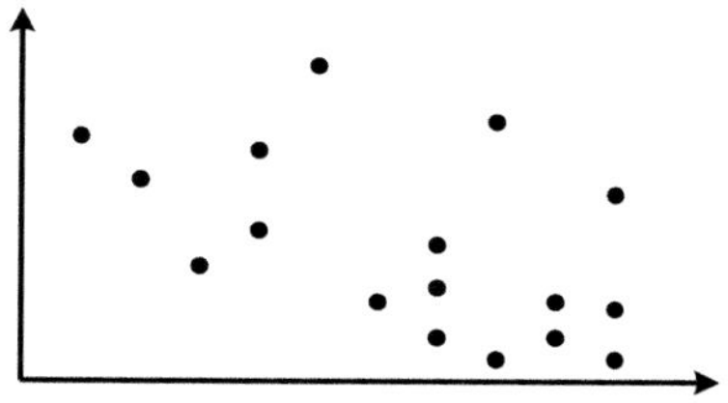

(i) Is there positive or negative correlation between the variables represented on the two axes?

(ii) Would you say that the correlation between the two variables is strong, moderate or weak?

(iii) The correlation coefficient, *r*, is one of the following values:

$0{\cdot}91,\ 0{\cdot}57,\ 0{\cdot}13,\ 0,\ -0{\cdot}26,\ -0{\cdot}53,\ -0{\cdot}87.$

Which do you think is the correct value of *r*? Give a reason.

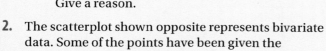

2. The scatterplot shown opposite represents bivariate data. Some of the points have been given the names *A*, *B*, *C*, *D*, *E* and *F*.

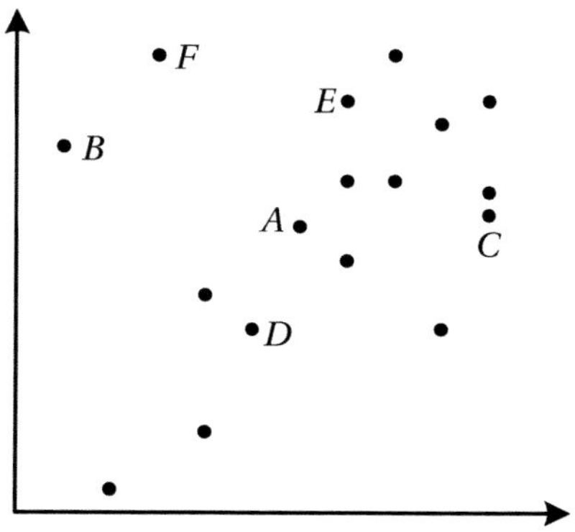

(i) Is there a positive or negative correlation between the variables represented on the two axes?

(ii) Would you say that the correlation is strong, moderate or weak? Give a reason.

(iii) The correlation is one of the following values:

$0{\cdot}88,\ 0{\cdot}75,\ 0{\cdot}34,\ 0{\cdot}02,\ -0{\cdot}48,\ -0{\cdot}79.$

Which do you think is the correct value of *r*? Give a reason.

(iv) One of the named points lies almost exactly on the line of best fit. Which one do you think it is?

(v) If two of the named points are removed, the value of *r*, the correlation coefficient, changes to 0·72. Which two named points are removed?

3. The ages in years (X) and the scores (Y) in a computer game are recorded as couples (x,y) for twelve students A to L, and the data is given below.

A: (7,22)	B: (8,36)	C: (9,20)
D: (9,34)	E: (10,38)	F: (10,54)
G: (11,50)	H: (12,36)	I: (12,50)
J: (13,46)	K: (14,56)	L: (15,44)

(i) Draw a scatterplot to represent this data.
(ii) Is there a positive or negative correlation between X and Y? Give a reason.
(iii) Would you say that the correlation is strong, moderate or weak? Give a reason.
(iv) The correlation coefficient is one of the following values:
0·92, 0·66, 0·28, 0, –0·35, –0·74.
Which do you think is the correct value of r? Give a reason.
(v) Which student do you think performed the best, relative to age? Give a reason.
(vi) If the units of age were changed to months, what would the effect be on the value of the correlation coefficient?

4. The nominal engine capacity, in cubic centimetres, which we call X, and the time taken, to the nearest second, to travel from rest to 100 km/h, which we call Y, are noted for a number of different models of car, which we call A to O. The data is given as couples (x,y) in the following table.

A: (1100,16)	B: (1100,18)	C: (1200,15)
D: (1200,15)	E: (1400,12)	F: (1400,13)
G: (1400,15)	H: (1600,11)	I: (1600,12)
J: (1600,10)	K: (1800,14)	L: (2000,12)
M: (2000,11)	N: (2000,10)	O: (2000,9)

(i) Draw a scatterplot to represent this data.
(ii) Is there a positive or negative correlation between X and Y? Give a reason.
(iii) Would you say that the correlation is strong, moderate or weak? Give a reason.
(iv) The correlation coefficient is one of the following values:
0·87, 0·56, 0·32, 0·04, –0·32, –0·51, –0·76, –0·93.
Which do you think is the correct value of r? Give a reason.
(v) Which model do you think had the slowest time to 100 km/h, relative to its engine capacity? Give a reason.
(vi) If the units of engine capacity were changed to litres, what would be the effect on the correlation coefficient?

5.

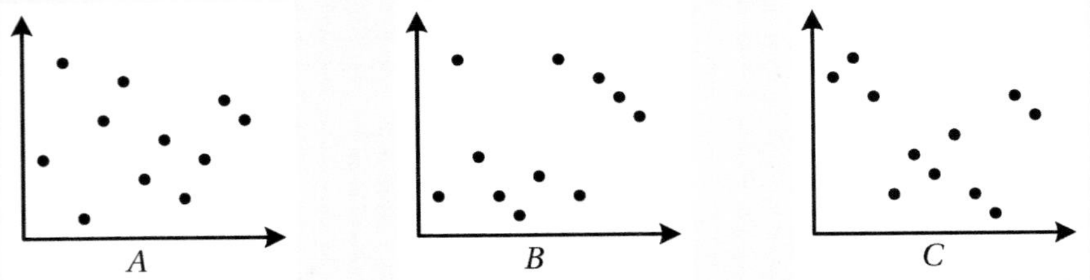

The diagram above shows three scatterplots, A, B and C. The correlation coefficients, in no particular order, are –0·39, 0 and 0·32.
(i) Match the scatterplots with the correlation coefficients.
(ii) Which of the scatterplots shows no correlation between the variables on the two axes?
(iii) For the two scatterplots with non-zero correlation coefficients, is the correlation between the variables strong, moderate or weak? Give a reason.

6.

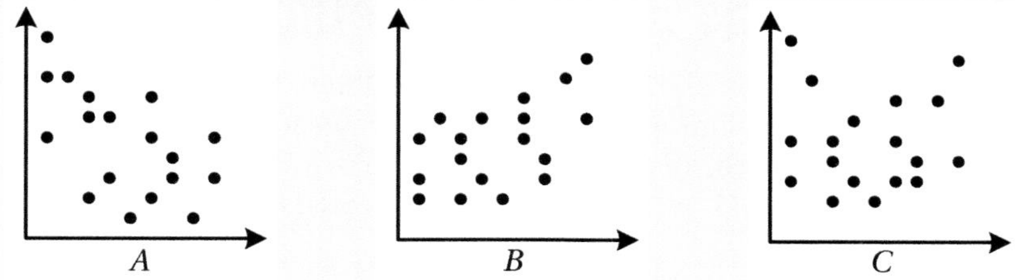

The diagram above shows three scatterplots A, B and C. The correlation coefficients, in no particular order, are 0, 0·54 and −0·58.

(i) Match the scatterplots with the correlation coefficients.

(ii) Which of the scatterplots shows no correlation between the variables on the two axes?

(iii) For the two scatterplots with non-zero correlation coefficients, is the correlation between the variables strong, moderate or weak? Give a reason.

For each of the following pairs of variables, is the correlation likely to be positive, negative or zero? If non-zero, is it likely to be strong, moderate or weak?

7. The length of time spent by children eating their dinner and the outside temperature.

8. The engine capacity of a car and its petrol consumption.

9. The number of goals scored by a team in the Premier League and the number of goals it concedes.

10. The number of fast food meals eaten by children in a month and their weight.

11. The height of a person and the number of siblings he or she has.

12. The number of countries that a person has visited and their age.

13. A person's annual income and the number of years they spent in full time education.

14. The number of years spent by a prisoner in jail and the number of years of full time education.

15. The age of a car and the distance it takes to stop from a speed of 60 km/h.

16. The reading age of a child in primary school and the number of hours of television he or she watches per week.

17. Which of the following correlation coefficients shows the strongest correlation:

−0·52, 0·34, 0·78, −0·83?

For this correlation coefficient, state whether the correlation is positive or negative, and whether it is strong, moderate or weak.

18. Which of the following correlation coefficients shows the (i) strongest, (ii) weakest, correlation:

0·72, 0·51, −0·38, −0·85, −0·42, 0·23, −0·67?

In each case state whether the correlation is weak, moderate or strong.

38.3 Calculating and Interpreting the Correlation Coefficient

The main method of calculating the correlation coefficient is to use the Pearson correlation coefficient formula. There is a whole host of different versions of this. Some are suitable for populations, others for samples. Among those that are suitable for both, all of which give the same answer, some have simpler formulae, but more complicated calculations. Others have more complicated formulae but simpler calculations.

Suppose we have n pairs of bivariate data of the variables X and Y. Let's suppose these are

$(x_1,y_1), (x_2,y_2), (x_3,y_3), \ldots, (x_n,y_n)$.

One formula for the correlation coefficient, r, is then

$$r = \frac{n\sum XY - \sum X \sum Y}{\sqrt{n\sum X^2 - \left(\sum X\right)^2}\sqrt{n\sum Y^2 - \left(\sum Y\right)^2}}$$

Although it looks very complicated, it can be calculated relatively easily by constructing a table of values. However, in practice, we will use a calculator to calculate the correlation coefficient. Here we show the required key strokes for the Casio fx-83ES, one of the most popular makes of calculator.

For the Casio fx-83ES, we start by pressing

MODE 2 2

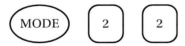

This will display two columns, called X and Y, and waits for you to enter your data. After entering each number press " = ". It is easier to enter the X values first and then use the arrow keys to go back to the top and enter the Y values. When all values have been entered and checked, you can press "ON", which will clear the display.

To retrieve the value of r, the correlation coefficient, press

SHIFT 1 7 3 =

The value of r for the entered data will be displayed.

Example 1

A number of Junior Certificate students sat exams in maths and science. Each exam was marked out of 20. The scores of these students are listed in the table below.

Student	Maths (X)	Science (Y)
Aine	12	15
Brendan	18	16
Colm	11	14
Dermot	9	7
Ella	5	10
Freda	17	12
Gary	14	15
Hannah	12	19

(i) Calculate r, the correlation coefficient, for this data, correct to two decimal places.

(ii) Does the value of r indicate a positive or negative correlation between the maths and science scores of these students? Give a reason.

(iii) Would you say that the correlation is strong, moderate or weak? Give a reason.

Solution

(i) Entering the data in a calculator, we get

$r = 0{\cdot}4908$

$r = 0{\cdot}49$, correct to two decimal places.

(ii) As $r > 0$, there is positive correlation between the maths and science scores for these students.

(iii) As r lies between 0·3 and 0·7, we would say that the correlation between the scores is moderate.

Correlation does not mean Causality

It is important to realise that just because there is a high correlation (either positive or negative) between two variables, it does not mean that a change in one variable causes a change in the other. For example, there is probably a strong correlation between the number of ice-creams and beach balls sold in a seaside shop. But neither causes the other; they are both influenced by the weather and the temperature. This is called a **lurking variable**.

Sometimes there may be a strong cause and effect, but in one direction only. For example, there is a strong correlation between smoking and lung cancer. But anyone who suggests that lung cancer causes smoking would be laughed at.

The key phrase to remember is that correlation does not imply causality. There is very often a number of underlying factors that affect both variables. Thus you should be very wary of media sources suggesting that just because there is a high correlation between two quantities, that one causes the other.

On the other hand, if we are trying to show causality, we need to first show correlation. If there is no correlation, then there cannot be any causality. So correlation is not irrelevant when it comes to deciding if one variable has a causal effect on the other. Just be careful not to go too far with the conclusions.

Exercises 38.3

1. The final points total of the ten teams in a league, and the number of red cards picked up by each team during the season are given below in the form (x,y), where X is the number of points and Y is the number of red cards.

(43,8), (42,5), (39,4), (38,7), (33,10), (31,1), (24,2), (19,4), (17,4), (16,6)

(i) Using a calculator, calculate the correlation coefficient.

(ii) Describe the type of correlation, if any, between the points total and the number of red cards picked up.

2. Over the period of a week, a department store counted the number of people who entered the store (X) and the amount taken in sales (Y), in €. The data is recorded in the form of couples (x,y), and is given below.

Monday:	(800,12000)	Tuesday:	(1200,10000)
Wednesday:	(1100,9000)	Thursday:	(1000,13000)
Friday:	(1400,16000)	Saturday:	(2200,20000)
Sunday:	(1800,32000)		

(i) Calculate the correlation coefficient.

(ii) Describe the type of correlation between the number of visitors and the value of sales.

(iii) Can you suggest a reason why there is not perfect correlation between the number of visitors and the value of sales?

(iv) Suppose the table had given the number of visitors in hundreds, i.e. as 8, 12, etc, and the sales in thousands of euro, i.e. 12, 10 etc. Would this have affected the value of the correlation coefficient? Perform a calculation to check.

3. A small study is conducted to determine if there is a link between the height of adults and their self-esteem. Height is measured in metres and self-esteem is measured on a scale of 0 to 5, with 5 being the highest level of self-esteem. The data is recorded in the table below, which also shows whether the subjects are male or female.

Gender	Height (X)	Self-esteem (Y)
Male	1.93	4.2
Male	1.6	2.1
Male	1.68	3.7
Male	1.73	4.8
Male	1.78	3.2
Male	1.85	4.7
Female	1.83	3.8
Female	1.78	4.2
Female	1.6	4.1
Female	1.7	3.9
Female	1.75	2.6
Female	1.57	4.6

(i) Calculate the correlation coefficient of all the data.
(ii) Describe the type of correlation between height and self-esteem for all the subjects. Would you feel safe in saying that there is a definite link between height and self-esteem based on the value of the correlation coefficient? Give a reason.
(iii) Now calculate the correlation coefficient for the male subjects. Does this differ significantly from that of the whole group? Suggest a reason why.
(iv) Calculate the correlation coefficient for the female subjects. Does this differ significantly from the whole sample or from the male subjects? Suggest reasons why.
(v) Assuming this is only a pilot study, would you feel confident to take only male subjects or only female subjects if asked to perform a larger study to determine if there is a link between height and self-esteem among the general population? Give a reason.

4. For a number of patients undergoing kidney dialysis, measurements of heart rate (X) and blood pressure (Y) were taken. The data is given below in the form of couples (x,y).
(83,141), (86,162), (88,161), (92,154), (94,171)
(98,174), (101,184), (114,190), (117,187), (121,191)
(i) Represent the data on a scatterplot.
(ii) Use the scatterplot to estimate the correlation coefficient.
(iii) Calculate the correlation coefficient.
(iv) How accurate was your estimate from the scatterplot?

5. It has been shown that there is a strong positive correlation between the amount of diet food consumed and the weights of the consumers. Do you think that this means that eating diet food causes an increase in weight? Explain.

6. A study showed that there was a moderate positive correlation between the level of carbon dioxide in the air in a particular area, and the crime level in that area. Do you think this provides evidence that higher levels of carbon dioxide in the air cause an increase in crime levels? Can you think of any other reason why a correlation between carbon dioxide levels and crime levels might exist?

7. A strong positive correlation exists between ice cream sales and the number of drownings. Does this suggest that a high volume of ice cream sales causes more drownings? Can you think of any other factor that might cause the correlation between ice cream sales and drownings?

8. A study has shown that a strong positive correlation exists between young children sleeping with the light on and the incidence of short-sightedness of these children in later life. Do you think that sleeping with the light on causes short-sightedness in later life? What other factor could explain the correlation? (*Hint: who leaves the light on in bedrooms of young children, and why?*)

9. A survey has shown that among adults in their twenties and thirties there is a strong positive correlation between going to bed with their shoes on and waking up with a headache. Do you think that this suggests that going to bed with your shoes on causes you to wake up with a headache? Can you suggest any other reason why a person who goes to bed with their shoes on might wake up with a headache?

38.4 The Line of Best Fit and Making Predictions

As long as the correlation coefficient is not near zero, a line can be drawn that serves as the best approximation to the data. This line is called the **line of best fit**, or the **linear regression line**, and is the line to which the data points are closest.

The formula for the equation of the line of best fit is quite involved and we are not required to deal with it. Instead, what we can be asked to do is as follows.

1. Draw the line of best fit by eye.
2. Find the slope and the equation of the line of best fit, using co-ordinate geometry.
3. Obtain the equation of the line of best fit by calculator.
4. Use the line of best fit to make predictions.

1. Drawing the Line of Best Fit by Eye

The following points should be remembered in order to draw the line of best fit by eye.

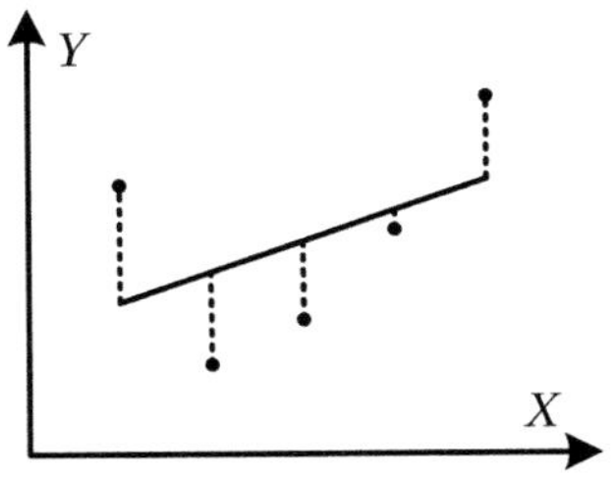

(i) Technically, the line of best fit (of Y on X) is the line that minimises the dotted distances shown opposite. By eye, the distances above should roughly be equal to the distances below.

(ii) There should roughly be the same number of points on both sides of the line, unless there are outliers that lie far from the line.

(iii) The line of best fit does not have to contain any of the individual data points, or the origin.

(iv) If $\bar{x}$ is the mean of the X values, and $\bar{y}$ is the mean of the Y values, one point that is always on the line of best fit is $(\bar{x}, \bar{y})$. So if we have numerical data, we can calculate and plot this point. Then by rotating a clear ruler about this point, we can try to pick out the line of best fit. If we are given a scatterplot without numerical data, this will not be possible.

2. Finding the Slope and Equation of the Line of Best Fit

Once the line of best fit has been drawn, we can set about finding its slope and its equation, using co-ordinate geometry.

(i) Find two points on the line, which should be reasonably far apart, and preferably not data points.

(ii) If we call the two points (x_1,y_1) and (x_2,y_2), then the slope of the line of best fit is given by

$$m = \frac{y_2 - y_1}{x_2 - x_1}.$$

The slope of the line of best fit can be interpreted as the 'rate of change' of Y as X changes. For example if the slope of the line of best fit is –2, then for every 1 unit increase in X, Y decreases by 2 units.

(iii) If we also want the equation of the line of best fit, we can use the formula

$$(y - y_1) = m(x - x_1)$$

again taken from co-ordinate geometry.

3. Using a Calculator to Find the Equation of the Line of Best Fit

The same data entry sequence that was used with a calculator to find the correlation coefficient can also be used to obtain the equation of the line of best fit.

The Casio fx-83ES assumes that the equation of the line of best fit is $y = A + Bx$, where A is the y-intercept (i.e. where the line cuts the Y axis) and B is the slope. After entering the paired data, we can press

SHIFT 1 7

and 1 = for A, and 2 = for B.

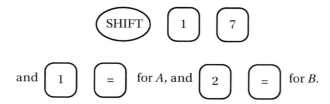

We can then check these against the values we have calculated manually.

4. Using the Line of Best Fit to Make Predictions

After drawing the line of best fit, we can use it to estimate values of Y for given values of X. The value of Y we get from a line of best fit should be regarded as just a best estimate, and could be subject to substantial error.

If the value of X lies within the horizontal range of the data points, then estimating the value of Y is called **interpolation**. If the value of X lies outside the horizontal range of the data points, then estimating the value of Y is called **extrapolation**. Extrapolation is far less reliable than interpolation.

Example 1

The heights (in metres) and the arm spans (in metres) of a sample of adults were measured. If X is the height and Y is the arm span, the data is recorded as a number of couples (x,y), which are given below.

(1·72,1·68), (1·65,1·66), (1·85,1·75), (1·62,1·58), (1·70,1·60), (1·83,1·85)

(1·58,1·64), (1·92,1·85), (1·75,1·64), (1·72,1·74), (1·63,1·60), (1·84,1·76)

(i) Show this data on a scatterplot.

(ii) Describe the type of correlation that exists between height and arm span for the data obtained.

(iii) Calculate the mean of the heights, $\bar{x}$, and the mean of the arm spans, $\bar{y}$. Give your answers correct to three decimal places.

(iv) Draw the line of best fit for the data.

(v) Use the line of best fit to predict the arm span of a person of height 1·87 m.

(vi) By choosing two points on the line of best fit, find the slope and the equation of the line of best fit.

(vii) Use a calculator to find the exact equation of the line of best fit.

(viii) What does the slope of the line of best fit tell us about the data?

(ix) If a very tall person of height 2·02 m is measured, use the line of best fit to predict their arm span. Is this interpolation or extrapolation? Give a reason.

Solution

(i) The scatterplot is shown below.

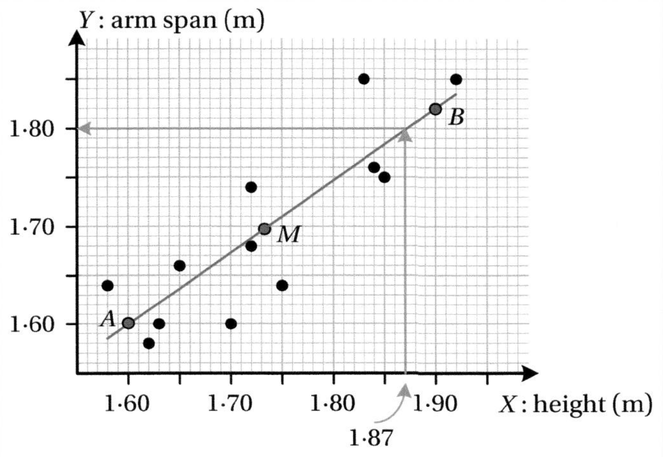

(ii) From the positions of the data points, there is a strong positive correlation between X and Y.

(iii) Let $\bar{x}$ be the mean of the X values. Then

$$\bar{x} = \frac{1{\cdot}72 + 1{\cdot}65 + \ldots + 1{\cdot}63 + 1{\cdot}84}{12} = \frac{20{\cdot}81}{12} = 1{\cdot}734$$

Let $\bar{y}$ be the mean of the Y values. Then

$$\bar{y} = \frac{1{\cdot}68 + 1{\cdot}66 + \ldots. + 1{\cdot}60 + 1{\cdot}76}{12} = \frac{20{\cdot}35}{12} = 1{\cdot}696.$$

(iv) *(The point $(\bar{x},\bar{y}) = (1{\cdot}734, 1{\cdot}696)$ must lie on the line of best fit. This is shown on the scatterplot as the point M. By considering all lines through this point, and trying to have roughly equal distances to the line for points on both sides, we can draw the line of best fit as the blue line on the scatterplot.)*

(v) *(To use the scatterplot to estimate the arm span (Y) of a person with height (X) of 1·87, we go vertically up from 1·87 to the line of best fit, and then horizontally across to the Y axis. This is shown on the scatterplot.)*

Predicted arm span of a person of height 1·87 m is 1·80 m.

(vi) *(We will take the points labelled A and B on the line of best fit because they are far apart and they can be easily read off the scatterplot. Then we can calculate the slope and the equation of the line of best fit.)*

Points: $A = (1{\cdot}6, 1{\cdot}6) = (x_1, y_1)$

$B = (1{\cdot}9, 1{\cdot}82) = (x_2, y_2)$

Slope: $m = \frac{y_2 - y_1}{x_2 - x_1} = \frac{1.82 - 1.6}{1.9 - 1.6} = 0.733$

Equation: $(y - y_1) = m(x - x_1)$

$(y - 1.6) = 0.733(x - 1.6)$

$y - 1.6 = 0.733x - 1.1728$

$y = 0.733x + 0.4272$

(vii) Entering the data into a calculator, we get $A = 0.4002$ and $B = 0.7471$. Thus the equation of the line of best fit is

$$y = 0.4002 + 0.7471x.$$

(viii) The slope of the line of best fit tells us the rate of change of Y as X changes. In this case, for every centimetre that X increases, we would predict Y to increase by 0·7471 centimetres, using the calculated value.

(ix) If $x = 2.02$, we can use the equation of the line of best fit to predict the value of y.

$x = 2.02$: $y = 0.733\,(2.02) + 0.4272 = 1.91$

Thus we would expect a person of height 2·02 m to have an arm span of 1·91 m.

As 2·02 lies outside the range of the height data given in the table (1·58 to 1·92), predicting the arm span of a person of height 2·02 m is extrapolation.

It is important to realise that the points on a scatterplot may not be modelled best by a line, i.e. they may not be linearly correlated.

Some sets of data are better modelled by quadratic or other polynomial curves, or by an exponential curve.

For example, the data shown on the scatterplot opposite has an r value of 0·10, demonstrating a very weak linear correlation. But this does not mean that the data is not correlated. In fact it shows a strong correlation with a quadratic curve. We call this quadratic correlation.

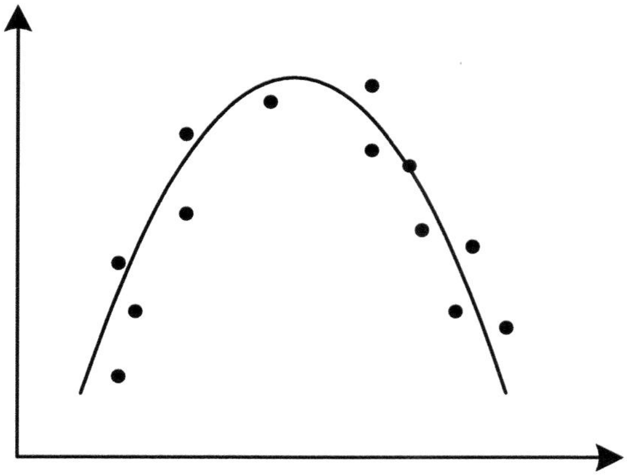

On our course, we do not have to be able to work with quadratic, or other, correlations. It is sufficient to know that they exist. When we talk about 'correlation' on our course, we mean linear correlation.

Exercises 38.4

1. In a survey, a number of people were questioned as to their annual income (Y) and the number of years they spent in full time education (X). The data is given below as couples in the form (x,y).

(19,125000), (20,100000), (16,40000), (16,35000), (18,41000), (12,29000), (14,35000), (12,24000), (16,50000), (17,60000).

(i) Show this data on a scatterplot.
(ii) Describe the correlation that exists between the number of years in education and the annual income.
(iii) Calculate the mean of the number of years in education and the mean of the income values.
(iv) Draw the line of best fit for the data.

(v) If a person has spent 15 years in education, use the line of best fit to predict that person's annual income.
(vi) By choosing two points on the line of best fit, find the slope and the equation of the line of best fit.
(vii) What does the slope of the line of best fit tell us about the data?

2. To determine if the age of a car affects the stopping distance when the brakes are applied, a survey is conducted of ten cars of the same make and model. The ages of the cars and their minimum stopping distances from a speed of 40 km/h are recorded. The results are given in the table below.

Car age (months)	Minimum stopping distance (metres)
9	28·4
15	29·3
24	37·6
30	36·2
38	36·5
46	35·3
53	36·2
60	44·1
64	44·8
76	47·2

(i) Represent this data on a scatterplot, with X being the age of the car and Y being the minimum stopping distance.
(ii) Describe the correlation that exists between the age of the car and the minimum stopping distance.
(iii) Calculate the correlation coefficient, using a calculator.
(iv) Draw the line of best fit of the data.
(v) Use the line of best fit to predict the minimum stopping distance for a 4 year old car.
(vi) Find the equation of your line of best fit, without using a calculator.
(vii) Use your equation of the line of best fit to estimate the minimum stopping distance of a car of the same make and model which is 7 years old.
(viii) What does the slope of the line of best fit tell us?
(ix) Use a calculator to determine the equation of the line of best fit.

3. For a number of runners in a marathon, the average number of kilometres run in training each week in the run up to the marathon (X), and their finishing time, in minutes, (Y), for the marathon were recorded. The data is given below as a set of couples of the form (x,y).

(50,148), (45,168), (53,145), (42,138), (52,132),
(48,153), (40,170), (45,161), (55,132), (38,165).

(i) Represent this data on a scatterplot, with X being the average number of kilometres run and Y being the finishing time.
(ii) Describe the correlation that exists between the average number of kilometres run in training and the time taken to complete the marathon.
(iii) Draw the line of best fit of the data.
(iv) Use the line of best fit to predict the finishing time for a runner whose average distance run in training is 46 kilometres.

(v) By choosing two points on the line, find the equation of your line of best fit.
(vi) What does the slope of the line of best fit tell us?
(vii) Use a calculator to find the equation of the line of best fit.
(viii) Use the equation of the line of best fit to estimate the finishing time of a runner whose average training distance per week is 60 kilometres.

4. A number of students volunteered for a medical test. The lung capacity, in cm^3, (X) of each student and the length of time, in seconds, (Y) for which they could hold their breath were measured. The data is given below in the form of couples (x,y).

(400,32), (380,34), (450,40), (420,36), (370,30),
(390,40), (400,38), (430,42), (380,33), (440,38).

(i) Represent this data on a scatterplot.
(ii) Describe the correlation that exists between X and Y.
(iii) Draw the line of best fit.
(iv) Use the line of best fit to predict the time holding breath of a person with a lung capacity of 410 cm^3.
(v) Find the equation of the line of best fit, by taking two points on the line.
(vi) What does the slope of the line of best fit tell us?
(vii) Use the equation of the line of best fit to estimate the breath holding time for a person with a lung capacity of 520 cm^3.

5. In the scatterplot below, a number of points of the form (x,y) are plotted.

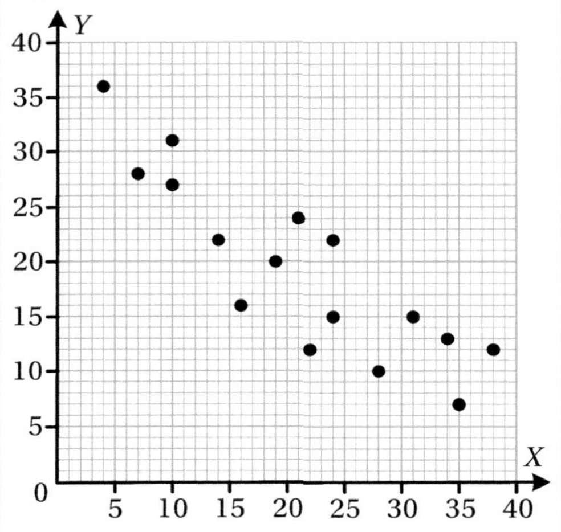

(i) List the points in the form (x,y), e.g. (4,36).
(ii) Is the correlation between X and Y positive or negative? Give a reason.
(iii) Is the correlation between X and Y strong, moderate or weak? Give a reason.
(iv) Calculate the mean of the X values and the mean of the Y values.
(v) Copy the diagram and draw the line of best fit.
(vi) Find the equation of the line of best fit, and use the equation to estimate the value of Y if the value of X is 26.
(vii) What does the slope of the line of best fit tell us?

6. In the scatterplot below, a number of points of the form (x,y) are plotted.

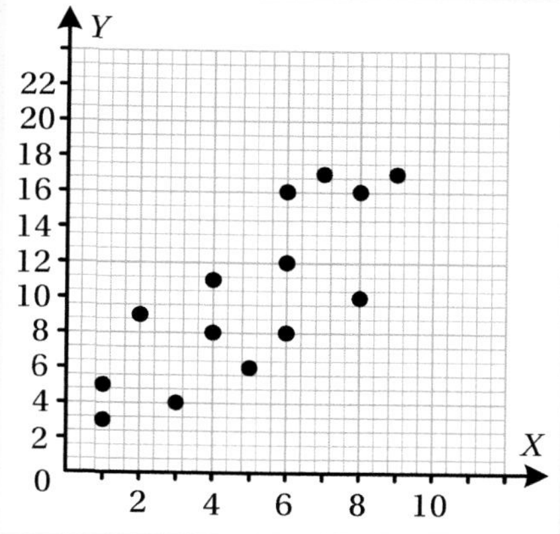

(i) Is the correlation between X and Y positive or negative? Give a reason.
(ii) Is the correlation between X and Y strong, moderate or weak? Give a reason.
(iii) Calculate the mean of the X values and the mean of the Y values.
(iv) Copy the diagram and draw the line of best fit.
(v) Find the equation of the line of best fit, and use the equation to estimate the value of Y if the value of X is 11.
(vi) What does the slope of the line of best fit tell us?

Revision Exercises 38

1. Match the terms in Column A with the description in Column B.

Column A	Column B
interpolation	little connection between the two sets of data
line of best fit	as one set of data increases, the other decreases
positive correlation	the connection between the two sets of data
outlier	estimating a value of Y within the bounds of the X values
weak correlation	the line that most accurately represents the data
correlation	estimating a value of Y outside the bounds of the X values
correlation coefficient	the data points are reasonably close to the line of best fit
extrapolation	both sets of data increase together
negative correlation	a number which expresses the correlation between X and Y
strong correlation	a data pair far removed from the bulk of the data pairs

2. Over a period of two weeks, ten volunteers were monitored for food intake and weight gain. The following table records the results. The average daily food intake is measured in kilocalories (kC) and the weight gain is in kg.

Subject	Average food (kC)	Weight gain (kg)
A	2·2	1·1
B	1·8	0·3
C	3·2	2·1
D	2·7	1·6
E	3·0	0·7
F	1·9	0·5
G	3·8	2·3
H	2·2	0·3
I	2·9	0·6
J	3·4	1·3

(i) Which quantity, average food consumed or weight gain, do you think should be considered as X? Give a reason.
(ii) Draw a scatterplot to represent this data.
(iii) Would you describe the correlation between the two quantities to be positive or negative? Give a reason.
(iv) Would you estimate the correlation to be strong, moderate or weak?
(v) Calculate the correlation coefficient, r, between X and Y. How does the value obtained compare with your estimates from parts (iii) and (iv)?
(vi) Draw the line of best fit.
(vii) Calculate the slope of the line of best fit. What does this tell us?
(viii) Find the equation of the line of best fit. Use it to estimate the weight gain of a person with an average daily food intake of 2·4 kC.
(ix) One extra person, K, is added to the group. This person has an average daily food intake of 3·9 kC for a weight gain of 0·3 kg. How would you describe this last data point? How do you think this extra data point affects the correlation coefficient? Calculate the new value of r, and see if your estimate is confirmed.
(x) Would the presence of this extra person change the position of the line of best fit? Explain your answer.

3. The average daily temperature and the number of lawnmowers sold by a large hardware store over a number of days in July are recorded in the table below.

Temperature (°C)	13	17	15	19	22	25	27
No. of lawnmowers sold	8	15	17	10	6	3	4

(i) Represent the data on a scatterplot.
(ii) Calculate the correlation coefficient, r.
(iii) Draw the line of best fit, and find its slope. What does this slope tell us?
(iv) If one of the data points is considered an outlier, name this point.
(v) If this point is removed, calculate the correlation coefficient of the remaining data. What does this tell us?
(vi) If the outlier is removed, draw the line of best fit of the remaining data, and find its slope. How does this slope compare with the slope of the original line of best fit?

4. A new growth hormone for cattle, free from many of the concerns associated with traditional hormones, is developed. To test its efficiency, it is administered to a number of test herds, in varying doses. The quantity of the dose is measured in cm^3. The weight gains of the cattle are measured in kg. The table below shows the average weight gain per animal in each herd, and the maximum weight gain for an animal in each herd.

(i) Letting X be the dose and Y be the average weight gain, draw a scatterplot showing dose and average weight gain.

(ii) On the same graph, draw a scatterplot of dose and maximum weight gain. (Make sure you can distinguish between the data points for each set. Use different colours or different symbols.)

(iii) Draw the line of best fit for dose against average weight gain. Find the slope of this line of best fit. What does this slope tell us?

(iv) Draw the line of best fit for dose against maximum weight gain. Find the slope of this line of best fit. What does this slope tell us?

(v) What can we conclude from the difference in the slopes of the two lines of best fit?

Dose (cm^3)	Average Gain (kg)	Maximum Gain (kg)
70	16	28
90	15	38
100	12	35
100	22	44
120	14	39
130	30	52
130	21	65
140	34	73
150	19	84
160	38	70
170	28	92
190	34	78

(vi) Calculate the correlation coefficient, r_1, for dose against average weight gain.

(vii) Calculate the correlation coefficient, r_2, for dose against maximum weight gain.

(viii) Which correlation coefficient is greater? Can you give an explanation of why this might be?

5. At the same time on a number of days, the ambient temperature, in degrees C, and the power output of an electricity generating station, in megawatts (MW) were measured. The purpose of the investigation is to see if the ambient temperature has any effect on the output of the power station. The table below shows the measurements obtained.

(i) Which of the two quantities, ambient temperature or power output, should be the variable X? Give a reason.

(ii) Draw a scatterplot to represent this data.

(iii) Would you describe the correlation between the two variables as positive or negative? Give a reason.

(iv) Calculate r, the coefficient of correlation.

(v) Draw the line of best fit.

(vi) Use the line of best fit to estimate the value of the power output if the ambient temperature is 18°.

(vii) Find the equation of the line of best fit, by choosing two points on the line.

(viii) Use the equation of the line of best fit to predict the power output when the ambient temperature is 23°.

Ambient temperature (°C)	Power output (MW)
15	300
13	320
17	300
21	270
10	325
15	260
19	250
14	305
12	310
16	295

6. The scatterplot below represents bivariate data of the form (x,y).

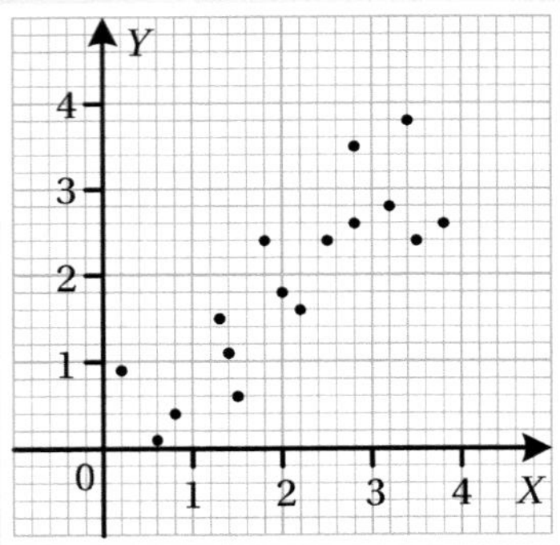

(i) Which of the following values do you think represents r, the correlation coefficient: 0·98, 0·85, 0·63, 0·21, −0·41, −0·81, −0·94? Give a reason.
(ii) Draw the line of best fit.
(iii) Find the equation of the line of best fit. What does the slope of the line of best fit tell us?
(iv) Use the line of best fit to estimate the value of Y if the value of X is 0·24. Is this interpolation or extrapolation?
(v) Use the equation of the line of best fit to predict the value of Y if $X = 4$. Is this interpolation or extrapolation?

7. The scatterplot below represents bivariate data of the form (x,y).

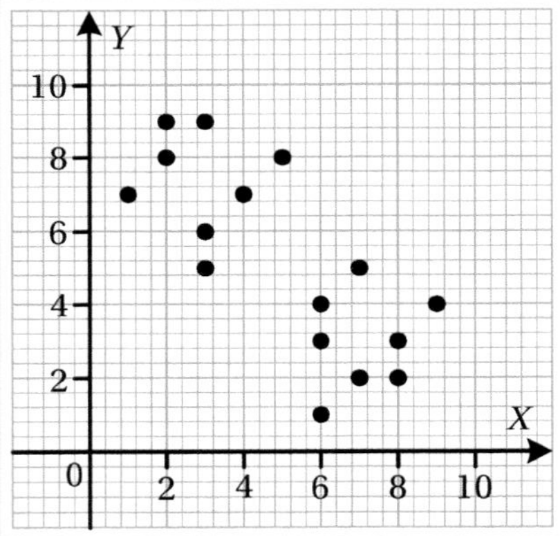

(i) Which of the following values do you think represents r, the correlation coefficient: 0·91, 0·68, 0·34, −0·17, −0·38, −0·75, −0·94? Give a reason.
(ii) Draw the line of best fit.
(iii) Use the line of best fit to estimate the value of Y if the value of X is 3·5. Is this interpolation or extrapolation?
(iv) Find the equation of the line of best fit. What does the slope of the line of best fit tell us?
(v) Use the equation of the line of best fit to predict the value of Y if $X = 10$. Is this interpolation or extrapolation?

In each of the following questions, state whether or not a correlation exists between the quantity (i) and the quantity (ii). If so, state

(a) whether it is a positive or negative correlation,
(b) whether you would expect it to be a weak, moderate or strong correlation,
(c) which quantity should be X and which should be Y,
(d) if you think that X alone causes Y, and if not suggest other factors that may influence the value of Y.

8. **(i)** The average number of hours of sunshine per day over the summer months of a particular year in County Wexford.
(ii) The average yield of silage per hectare in County Wexford in the same year.

9. **(i)** The number of points obtained by a football team in its last four league matches.
(ii) The number of fans attending its next home match.

10. **(i)** The annual income of a person twenty years after sitting their Leaving Cert.
(ii) The number of points obtained by a person in their Leaving Cert exams.

11. **(i)** The number of mistakes made by an actor in reciting his lines in a play.
(ii) The number of hours spent by an actor in learning his lines for a play.

12. **(i)** The length of time spent by a person in prison throughout their life.
(ii) The number of years spent by a person in education.

13. **(i)** The number of people who pay to see a new film in cinemas.
(ii) The number of negative reviews (two stars or less out of five) a film receives in the press.

In each of the following questions consider the statement made. State whether it is true or false, and give an explanation.

14. If the line of best fit has a positive slope, then there is higher correlation than if the line of best fit has a negative slope.

15. If the correlation is positive, then we can have more confidence in estimated values of Y, the closer the correlation coefficient, r, is to 1.

16. If the correlation coefficient, r, is zero, then there is no line of best fit.

17. If we double each of the X values, but leave all the Y values unchanged, then we will double the value of r, the correlation coefficient.

18. If the correlation is positive, then the greater the slope of the line of best fit, the nearer the value of r, the correlation coefficient, is to 1.

19. The presence of an outlier does not always affect the value of r, the correlation coefficient.

20. Consider the two sets, A and B, of bivariate data listed below.

A:

X	Y
1	8
2	7
3	11

B:

X	Y
1	9
2	8
3	12

(i) Calculate r_1, the correlation coefficient of A.
(ii) Calculate r_2, the correlation coefficient of B.
(iii) What do you notice about r_1 and r_2? Can you give an explanation?

39

Normal Distributions

In this chapter we begin to see the interaction of probability theory and statistics. First we see the idea that the probability distribution of a random variable can be treated like a frequency distribution in statistics, and that it has a mean and a standard deviation.

Then, we look at by far the most important distribution of this type, namely the normal probability distribution, better known as the 'bell shaped curve'. This distribution arises surprising often in real life and the theory of statistics. It was first developed by De Moivre in 1733 as an approximation to the binomial distribution. Using the Empirical Rule, we can get a rough estimate of the percentage of the total area under a normal curve that lies within a number of standard deviations of the mean.

The standard normal distribution has a mean of 0 and a standard deviation of 1. Tables of areas under this curve are in the *Formulae and Tables* handbook, and we see how to use transformations, along with the tables, to calculate different areas under any type of normal curve.

39.1 Discrete and Continuous Probability Distributions

1. Discrete Probability Distributions and their Histograms

Let the random variable X represent the number of heads obtained when a fair coin is tossed five times. Then $X = \{0, 1, 2, 3, 4, 5\}$, and so is a discrete random variable. The experiment consists of $n = 5$ repeated Bernoulli trials, with $p = 0{\cdot}5$ and $q = 0{\cdot}5$ for each individual trial.

Using the rules of probability, we can calculate the following probabilities, recalling that, for example, $P(X = 2)$ can be written as $P(2)$. Then

$$P(0) = \frac{1}{32},\quad P(1) = \frac{5}{32},\quad P(2) = \frac{10}{32},$$
$$P(3) = \frac{10}{32},\quad P(4) = \frac{5}{32},\quad P(5) = \frac{1}{32}$$

We can illustrate this so-called **discrete probability distribution** by a histogram, called a **probability histogram**, which is shown below.

On a probability histogram, probability is represented by area. Also, because $P(S) = 1$, the sum of the areas of all the rectangles is 1.

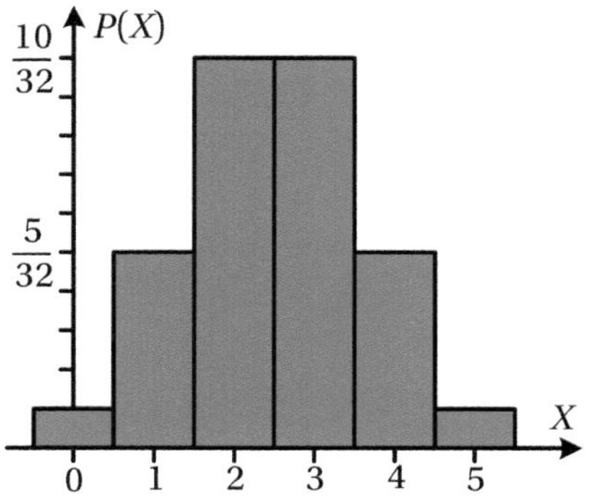

2. Continuous Probability Distributions and their Curves

Suppose X is a continuous random variable, i.e. the values of X are all possible values in an interval e.g. the heights of students in your school or the weights of newborn babies.

The key difference between the probability of a discrete random variable and the probability of a continuous random variable is that for a continuous random variable, we do not talk about the probability of getting one individual $x \in X$. This is because $P(X = x) = 0$, for all $x \in X$.

Instead, we talk about the probability that X lies in an interval, for example $P(a \leq X \leq b)$, which is the probability that X lies somewhere between a and b.

To represent a **continuous probability distribution** graphically, we draw the graph of a function $y = f(X)$, which is called the **probability density function.** It is important to realise that this function is not the probability itself. Rather, if we consider the curve $y = f(X)$, then the probability is the ***area*** between this curve and the X axis. In the diagram below, the shaded area represents $P(a \leq X \leq b)$, i.e. $P(a \leq X \leq b) = \int_a^b f(X)\mathrm{d}X$.

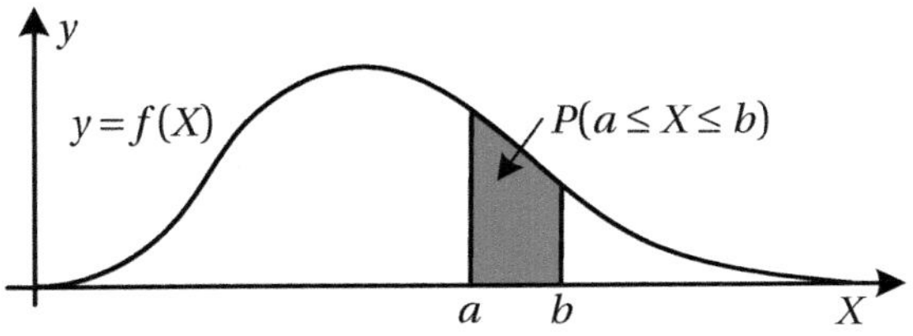

The probability density function, $y = f(X)$, and the corresponding **probability curve** have the following properties.

1. $f(X) \geq 0$ for all values of X. This means that the curve never goes below the X-axis.
2. Because $P(S) = 1$, where S is the sample space, the area under the entire curve is 1.

Exercises 39.1

1. The probability distribution of the random variable X is given in the table below.

x	0	1	2	3	4
P(x)	0·1	0·25	0·35	0·25	k

   (i) Use the fact that $\sum P(x) = 1$ to find the value of k.
   (ii) Draw a probability histogram to represent the distribution.
   (iii) Calculate $E(X)$, the expected value or mean, of the distribution.

2. A bag contains three markers numbered 1, 2 and 3. A marker is drawn at random, its number noted and then returned to the bag. An experiment consists of repeating this trial five times. Let the random variable X be the number of '3's obtained.
   (i) Construct the probability distribution of X.
   (ii) Draw a probability histogram to represent the distribution.
   (iii) Is this histogram symmetric, skewed left or skewed right? Give a reason.

3. X is a continuous random variable such that $0 \le X \le 15$. The graph of the probability density function, $y = f(X)$, is shown below.

If $P(a \le X \le b) = 0{\cdot}34$, $P(0 \le X \le a) = 2k$ and $P(b \le X \le 15) = k$,

(i) calculate k,

(ii) calculate $P(0 \le X \le b)$,

(iii) calculate $P(a \le X \le 15)$.

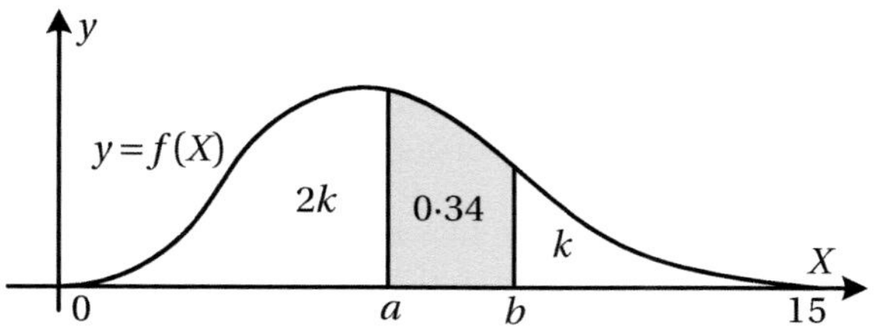

4. X is a continuous random variable such that $0 \le X \le 12$. The graph of the probability density function, $y = f(X)$, is shown below.

If $P(a \le X \le b) = 0{\cdot}48$ and $P(0 \le X \le a) = 3 \times P(b \le X \le 12)$,

(i) calculate $P(b \le X \le 12)$,

(ii) calculate $P(0 \le X \le b)$.

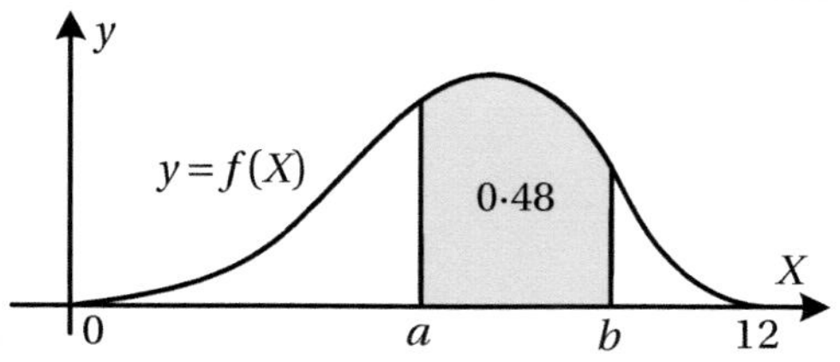

39.2 Normal Distributions and the Empirical Rule

1. Normally distributed datasets

One very important distribution which occurs frequently in real life is the so called **normal distribution**. This continuous distribution is seen in the measurements of heights, blood pressure, exam scores, the weights of items produced by machines, among many other situations.

The frequency curve of the normal distribution, called a **normal curve**, has a distinctive bell-shape, as shown below. Different normal distributions may have different means and different standard deviations, but they all share a number of common properties.

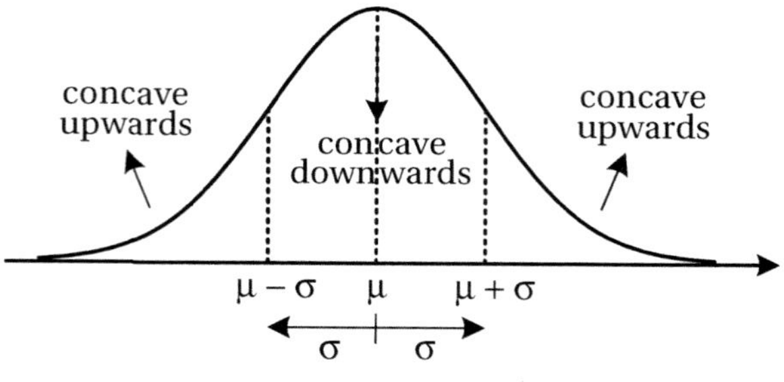

Properties of a Normal Curve

1. The curve is symmetric about the vertical line through the mean, μ. Thus 50% of the data, and hence the area under the curve, lies on each side of this line.
2. The mean, median and mode of the distribution are equal.
3. The percentage of the data that lies within one, two and three standard deviations of the mean is the same for all normal curves.

(i) Within one standard deviation of the mean
Approximately 68% of the data, and hence the area, lies within one standard deviation of the mean, i.e. between $\mu - \sigma$ and $\mu + \sigma$.

(ii) Within two standard deviations of the mean
Approximately 95% of the data, and hence the area, lies within two standard deviations of the mean, i.e. between $\mu - 2\sigma$ and $\mu + 2\sigma$.

(iii) Within three standard deviations of the mean
Approximately 99·7% of the data, and hence the area, lies within three standard deviations of the mean, i.e. between $\mu - 3\sigma$ and $\mu + 3\sigma$.

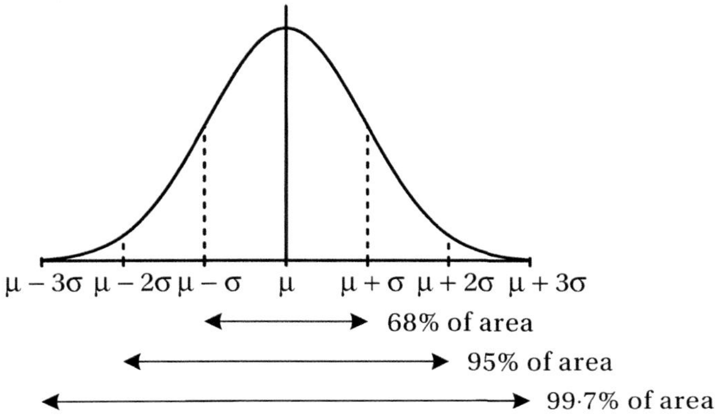

This is known as the **empirical rule**, and can be used to obtain estimates of the number of results in different intervals.

Empirical Rule

If a dataset is normally distributed, then

(i) 68% of the data lies within 1 standard deviation of the mean.

(ii) 95% of the data lies within 2 standard deviations of the mean.

(iii) 99·7% of the data lies within 3 standard deviations of the mean.

Example 1

1000 students take a new design of aptitude test. Their scores are normally distributed with a mean of 65 and a standard deviation of 7. Use the empirical rule to estimate

(i) the percentage of students who scored between 58 and 79 on the test,

(ii) the number of students who scored between 58 and 79 on the test.

Solution

(i) *(We can use the empirical rule to break down the percentages of the data into the regions.*

For example, the percentage of the data between $\mu + \sigma$ and $\mu + 2\sigma$ is a half the difference between 68% and 95%, i.e. 13·5%.)

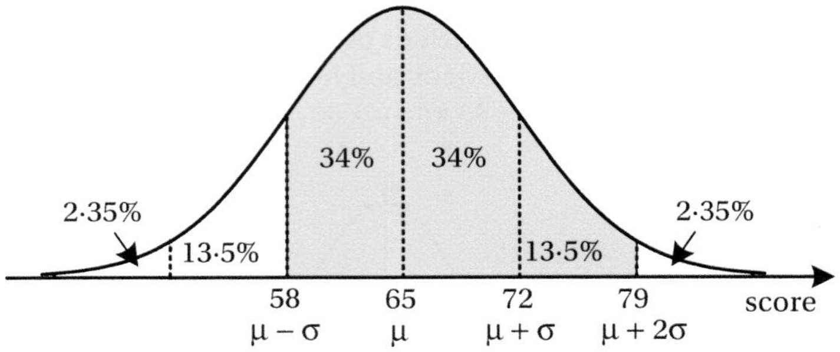

As $\mu - \sigma = 65 - 7 = 58$ and $\mu + 2\sigma = 65 + 2(7) = 79$, the percentage we want is
34% + 34% + 13·5% = 81·5%.

(ii) The expected number of students who scored between 58 and 79 on the test is
81·5% of 1000 = 815.

The empirical rule is useful for

(i) getting a rough idea of the percentage of data in certain intervals;

(ii) providing a test for outliers (an often used definition of an outlier is a result that lies more than three standard deviations from the mean);

(iii) providing a test for normality (if we find that a sizeable percentage, 3% or more, of the probability lies more than three standard deviations from the mean, then the distribution cannot be normal).

2. Normal Probability Distribution

A probability distribution which has the same distinctive bell shape curve as a normal data distribution is called a **normal probability distribution**. This probability distribution occurs very often in practical situations, and is of great importance in the theory of probability and statistics.

All normal probability curves share the properties listed above for normal frequency curves, i.e. symmetry and the empirical rule. They also satisfy one extra property: **the area under the curve is 1**, like the area under all probability curves. The diagram below shows a normal probability curve for the probability distribution of the normal random variable X.

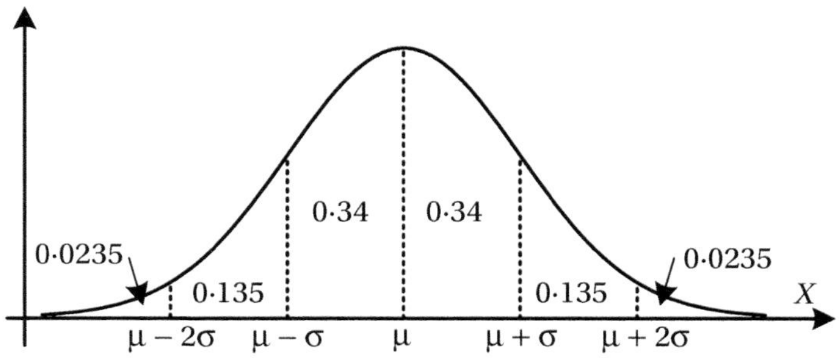

The curve can be used to find the probability that X lies between two given values, although with the empirical rule, we are limited to values which are related to μ and σ. The areas under the different sections of the curve give the probability of that interval.

Example 2

The lifetime of a particular type of battery is normally distributed with a mean of 20 hours and a standard deviation of 2 hours. The random variable X stands for the lifetime of a battery.

(i) Describe in words what is meant by $P(20 \le X \le 24)$.

(ii) Calculate $P(20 \le X \le 24)$.

Solution

(i) $P(20 \le X \le 24)$ stands for the probability that the lifetime of a battery chosen at random lies between 20 hours and 24 hours.

(ii) As $\mu = 20$ and $\sigma = 2$, 24 hours is $\mu + 2\sigma$. From the diagram below, the area under the curve between μ and $\mu + 2\sigma$ is

$$0{\cdot}34 + 0{\cdot}135 = 0{\cdot}475,$$

i.e. $P(20 \le X \le 24) = 0{\cdot}475$.

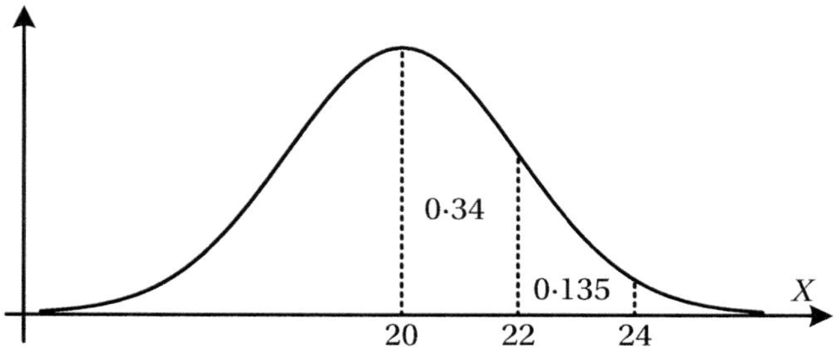

3. The Normal Distribution as an Approximation to many Discrete Distributions

The normal probability curve, which is a continuous curve representing the probability distribution of a continuous random variable, is a very good approximation to many probability histograms which represent the probability distribution of a discrete random variable.

For example, if the random variable X represents the number of heads obtained when a fair coin is tossed ten times, then the probability distribution of X, i.e. $P(X = r)$ for $r = 0, 1, \ldots, 10$, is called a **binomial distribution**.

If we plot the probability histogram for this distribution, we can see that the shape is approximately the same as a normal curve, which is the dashed curve indicated.

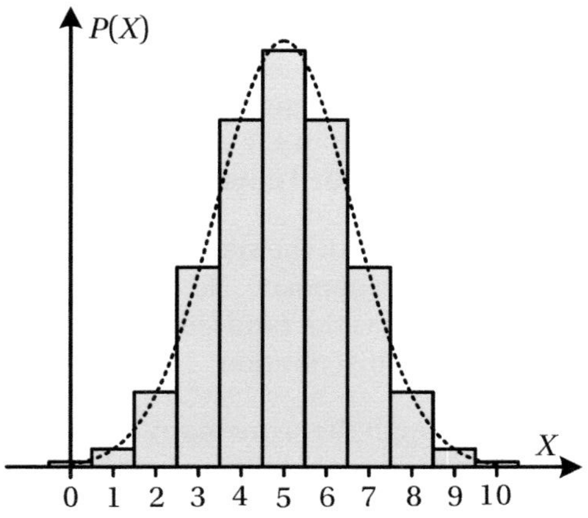

If we toss the coin many more times, e.g. 100 or 1000 times, the shape of the histogram gets closer and closer to a normal curve.

Not all probability histograms are approximated by normal curves, but many of the most important are.

Exercises 39.2

1. The times spent playing computer games per week by 500 students is normally distributed with a mean of 10 hours and a standard deviation of 2 hours. Use the empirical rule to
   (i) find the percentage of students who spent between 8 and 12 hours,
   (ii) estimate the number of students who spend between 6 and 12 hours.

2. In a large corporation, the ages of all new employees is normally distributed with mean 26 years and standard deviation 3 years. Using the empirical rule,
   (i) estimate the percentage of new employees whose age lies between 23 years and 32 years,
   (ii) estimate the number of new employees whose age lies between 26 and 32 years, from a total of 600 new employees.

3. X is a continuous random variable which is normally distributed with mean 5·6 and standard deviation 0·8. Calculate $P(4{\cdot}8 \leq X \leq 7{\cdot}2)$, i.e. the probability that X lies between 4·8 and 7·2, using the empirical rule.

4. X is a continuous random variable which is normally distributed with mean 10·8 and standard deviation 1·2. Calculate $P(8{\cdot}4 \leq X \leq 12)$, i.e. the probability that X lies between 8·4 and 12, using the empirical rule.

5. X is a continuous random variable which is normally distributed with mean 7 and standard deviation 1·5. Calculate $P(4 \leq X \leq 8{\cdot}5)$, i.e. the probability that X lies between 4 and 8·5, using the empirical rule.

6. X is a continuous random variable, with mean 8·5 and standard deviation 0·5. If $P(X \geq 10) = 0{\cdot}06$, do you think that X is normally distributed? Give a reason.

7. X is a continuous random variable, with mean 12 and standard deviation 3. If the probability that X is greater than 22 is 0·06, would you think that X is normally distributed? Give a reason.

39.3 Standard Normal Probability Distribution

The most frequently used normal probability distribution is the **standard normal distribution**. This is a normal distribution with
(i) **mean**: $\mu = 0$
(ii) **standard deviation**: $\sigma = 1$.

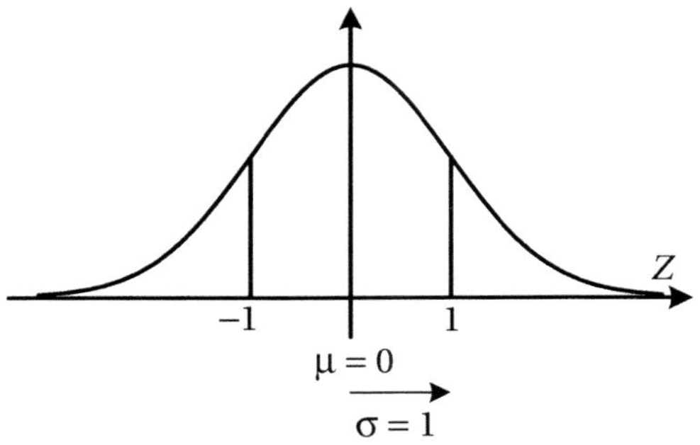

The graph of the standard normal distribution is shown opposite. Note that it is usual practice to use Z as the random variable for the standard normal distribution.

Although there are many normal distributions, tables of probability values for the standard normal distribution can be used to obtain probabilities for any normal probability distribution. This is why it is so important to learn how to calculate probabilities from the standard normal distribution tables.

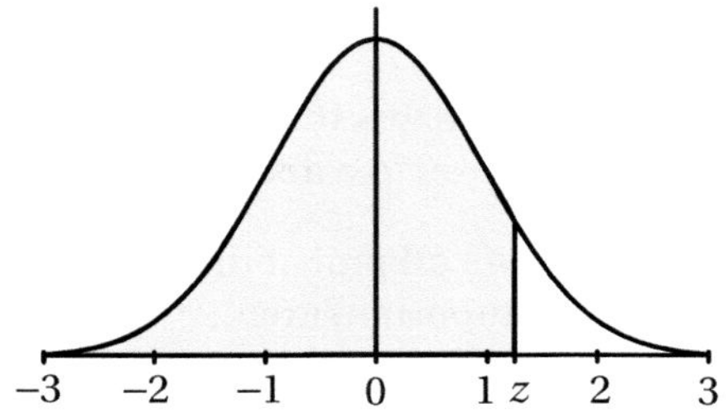

In the *Formulae and Tables*, pages 36 and 37, there are tables of probabilities (areas under the curve) of the form $P(Z \leq z)$, for values of z ranging from 0 to 3·09.

An extract from these tables, which give areas such as that shown previously, is given below.

z	**0.00**	**0.01**	**0.02**	**0.03**	**0.04**	**0.05**	**0.06**	**0.07**	**0.08**	**0.09**
0.0	0.5000	.5040	.5080	.5120	.5160	.5199	.5239	.5279	.5319	.5359
0.1	0.5398	.5438	.5478	.5517	.5557	.5596	.5636	.5675	.5714	.5753

To find $P(Z \le 0{\cdot}16)$, we go to the line '0·1' and then across to under '0·06' and read off the value. Thus $P(Z \le 0{\cdot}16) = 0{\cdot}5636$.

There are different kinds of area that we need to read off the tables. To do so, it is necessary to remember the following properties of the standard normal distribution.

Property 1: The area under the entire curve is 1.
Property 2: The curve is symmetric about the vertical axis through $Z = 0$.

These properties can now be used, along with the tables, to calculate many different kinds of probability connected with the standard normal distribution. We can calculate $P(Z \le z)$ directly from the tables if $z \ge 0$, and below we see how to calculate other areas.

1. **Right Tail with $z > 0$:**

For example, find $P(Z \ge 1{\cdot}75)$. This area can be found by subtracting the area to the left of 1·75 from 1. Thus

$P(Z \ge 1{\cdot}75)$
$= 1 - P(Z \le 1{\cdot}75)$
$= 1 - 0{\cdot}9599$
$= 0{\cdot}0401.$

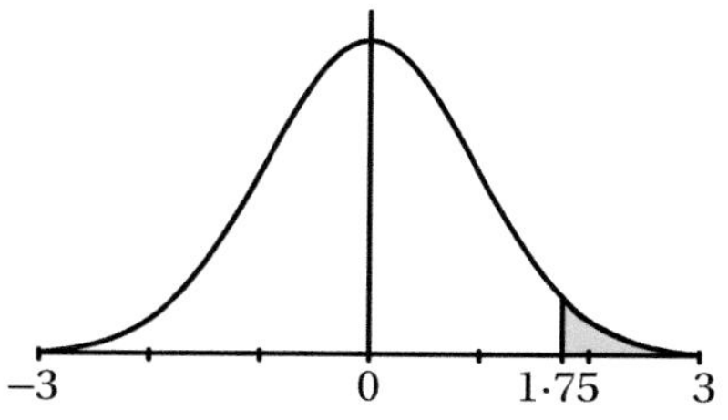

2. **Right Tail with $z < 0$:**

For example, find $P(Z \ge -1{\cdot}25)$. By Property 2, the area to the right of −1·25 is the same as the area to the left of 1·25. Thus

$P(Z \ge -1{\cdot}25)$
$= P(Z \le 1{\cdot}25)$
$= 0{\cdot}8944.$

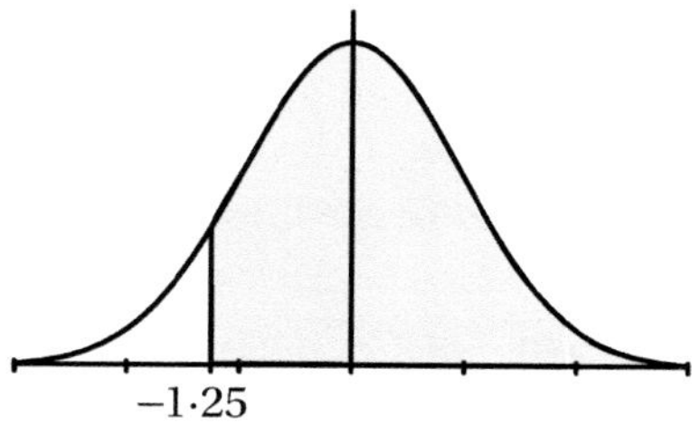

3. **Left Tail with $z < 0$:**

For example, find $P(Z \le -1)$. By Property 2, the area to the left of −1 is the same as the area to the right of 1. Thus

$P(Z \le -1)$
$= P(Z \ge 1)$
$= 1 - P(Z \le 1)$
$= 1 - 0{\cdot}8413$
$= 0{\cdot}1587.$

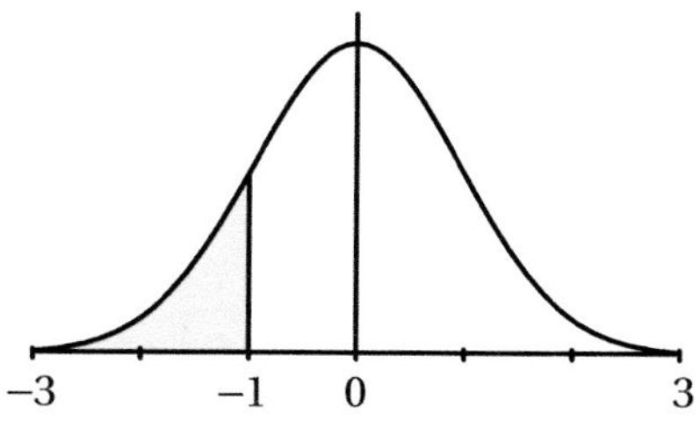

4. **Area between two values of z:**

This is the most awkward type of area (probability) to calculate, and covers a number of cases. We will look at the case where the lower z value is negative and the greater z value is positive. Cases where both z values are negative, or both are positive, are handled slightly differently, but use the techniques seen above.

For example, find
$P(-1{\cdot}5 \le Z \le 0{\cdot}75)$.
This probability is shown as the shaded area in the diagram opposite.

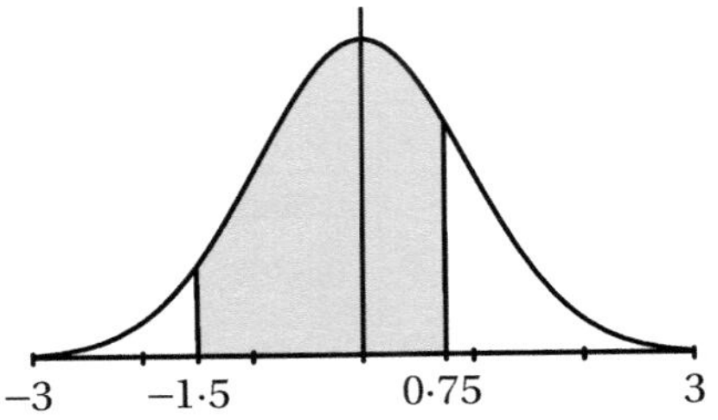

What we do is:

(i) Read directly from the tables the area to the left of 0·75.
$P(Z \le 0{\cdot}75) = 0{\cdot}7734$

(ii) Find the area to the left of –1·5, using the technique seen in Case 3 above.
$P(Z \le -1{\cdot}5) = P(Z \ge 1{\cdot}5)$
$= 1 - P(Z \le 1{\cdot}5) = 1 - 0{\cdot}9332 = 0{\cdot}0668$

(iii) Subtract.
$P(-1{\cdot}5 \le Z \le 0{\cdot}75) = P(Z \le 0{\cdot}75) - P(Z \le -1{\cdot}5)$
$= 0{\cdot}7734 - 0{\cdot}0668 = 0{\cdot}7066.$

There are other possible ways of calculating this probability.

Example 1

By referring to the Standard Normal Tables in your set of Mathematical Tables, answer the following questions. Z is a standard normal variable.

(i) Evaluate $P(Z \ge 1{\cdot}45)$.

(ii) Evaluate $P(Z \le -0{\cdot}84)$.

(iii) Evaluate $P(-1{\cdot}3 \le Z \le 1{\cdot}9)$.

(iv) Find the value of $k \in \mathbb{R}$ for which $P(-k \le Z \le k) = 0{\cdot}95$.

Solution

(i) $P(Z \ge 1{\cdot}45) = 1 - P(Z \le 1{\cdot}45)$
$= 1 - 0{\cdot}9265 = 0{\cdot}0735$

(ii) $P(Z \le -0{\cdot}84) = P(Z \ge 0{\cdot}84)$
$= 1 - P(Z \le 0{\cdot}84)$
$= 1 - 0{\cdot}7995 = 0{\cdot}2005$

(iii) $P(Z \le 1{\cdot}9) = 0{\cdot}9713$

Also

$P(Z \le -1{\cdot}3) = P(Z \ge 1{\cdot}3)$
$= 1 - P(Z \le 1{\cdot}3)$
$= 1 - 0{\cdot}9032 = 0{\cdot}0968$

Then

$P(-1{\cdot}3 \le Z \le 1{\cdot}9) = P(Z \le 1{\cdot}9) - P(Z \le -1{\cdot}3)$
$= 0{\cdot}9713 - 0{\cdot}0968 = 0{\cdot}8745$

(iv) *(The area between –k and k is 1 minus the area in the two tails. Using the Properties, we can come up with an expression for this area.)*

$P(-k \le Z \le k) = P(Z \le k) - P(Z \le -k)$
$= P(Z \le k) - P(Z \ge k)$
$= P(Z \le k) - [1 - P(Z \le k)]$
$= 2 \times P(Z \le k) - 1$

If $P(-k \le Z \le k) = 0{\cdot}95$
then $2 \times P(Z \le k) - 1 = 0{\cdot}95$
$2 \times P(Z \le k) = 1{\cdot}95$
$P(Z \le k) = 0{\cdot}975$

By searching for the value '0·975' in the standard normal tables, we can see that $k = 1{\cdot}96$.

Exercises 39.3

In each of the following questions, Z is a standard normal variable. Answer the following questions by using the Standard Normal Tables in the *Formulae and Tables*.

1. **(i)** What is $P(Z \leq 1)$? **(ii)** What is $P(Z \leq 2{\cdot}3)$?
(iii) What is $P(Z \leq 2{\cdot}87)$?

2. **(i)** What is $P(Z \geq 0{\cdot}69)$? **(ii)** What is $P(Z \geq 1{\cdot}34)$?
(iii) What is $P(Z \geq 2{\cdot}17)$?

3. **(i)** What is $P(Z \geq -0{\cdot}83)$? **(ii)** What is $P(Z \geq -1{\cdot}15)$?
(iii) What is $P(Z \geq -2{\cdot}51)$?

4. **(i)** What is $P(Z \leq -0{\cdot}54)$? **(ii)** What is $P(Z \leq -1{\cdot}28)$?
(iii) What is $P(Z \leq -2{\cdot}07)$?

5. **(i)** What is $P(-0{\cdot}5 \leq Z \leq 0{\cdot}5)$? **(ii)** What is $P(-1{\cdot}3 \leq Z \leq 1{\cdot}3)$?
(iii) What is $P(-1{\cdot}94 \leq Z \leq 1{\cdot}94)$?

6. **(i)** What is $P(-1 \leq Z \leq 1{\cdot}48)$? **(ii)** What is $P(-0{\cdot}74 \leq Z \leq 1{\cdot}93)$?
(iii) What is $P(-1{\cdot}84 \leq Z \leq 0{\cdot}75)$?

7. **(i)** What is $P(Z \leq -1{\cdot}72)$? **(ii)** What is $P(-2 \leq Z \leq -0{\cdot}34)$?
(iii) What is $P(1{\cdot}2 \leq Z \leq 2{\cdot}7)$?

8. **(i)** What is $P(Z \geq -0{\cdot}84)$? **(ii)** What is $P(Z \leq -2{\cdot}17)$?
(iii) What is $P(-1{\cdot}44 \leq Z \leq 2{\cdot}08)$?

9. Determine the value of $k \in \mathbb{R}$ if $P(Z \leq k) = 0{\cdot}8023$.

10. Determine the value of $k \in \mathbb{R}$ if $P(Z \leq k) = 0{\cdot}9292$.

11. Determine the value of $k \in \mathbb{R}$ if $P(Z \geq k) = 0{\cdot}1515$.

12. Determine the value of $k \in \mathbb{R}$ if $P(Z \geq k) = 0{\cdot}2843$.

13. Determine the value of $k \in \mathbb{R}$ if $P(Z \geq k) = 0{\cdot}8577$.

14. Determine the value of $k \in \mathbb{R}$ if $P(Z \geq k) = 0{\cdot}9564$.

15. Determine the value of $k \in \mathbb{R}$ if $P(Z \leq k) = 0{\cdot}0392$.

16. Determine the value of $k \in \mathbb{R}$ if $P(Z \leq k) = 0{\cdot}3228$.

17. Determine the value of $k \in \mathbb{R}$ if $P(-k \leq Z \leq k) = 0{\cdot}8926$.

18. Determine the value of $k \in \mathbb{R}$ if $P(-k \leq Z \leq k) = 0{\cdot}4108$.

39.4 Other Normal Probability Distributions

The diagram below shows a number of normal probability curves, with different means and different standard deviations.

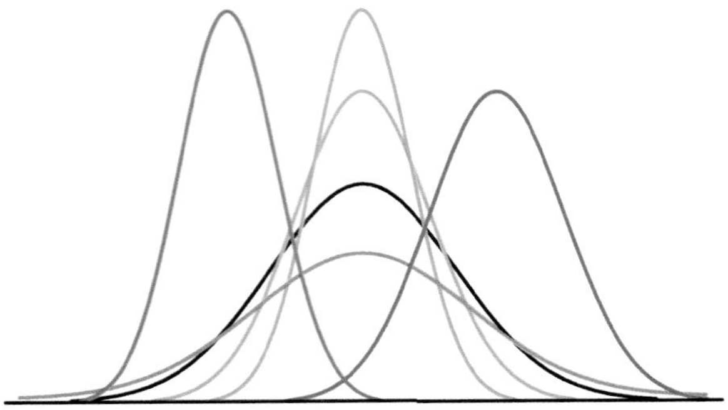

The following explanation shows how we can transform any normal distribution so that the standard normal tables can be used to calculate probabilities for any normal distribution.

1. **Translating**

Suppose X is a normal random variable with mean 3 and standard deviation 1. What is the probability that X is less than or equal to 4·5? First of all, the standard deviation of X is 1, the same as that of the standard normal distribution. So if the X curve is translated 3 units to the left, we will get the standard normal curve.

To achieve this mathematically, we let the new random variable Z be defined by

$Z = X - 3$.

Then Z will be normally distributed with mean 0 and standard deviation 1, the same as that of X. Thus Z is a standard normal variable.

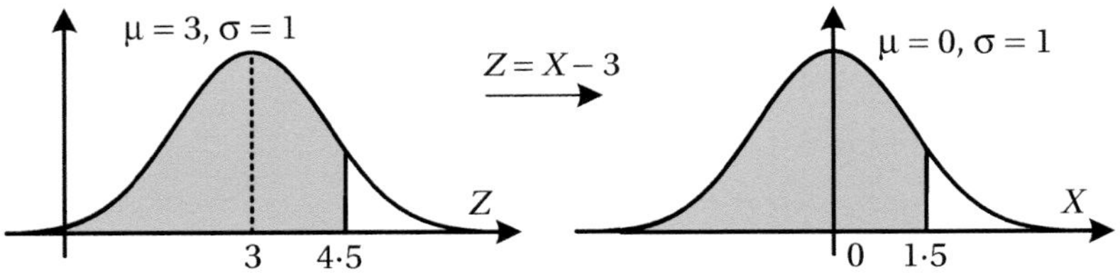

To find the probability that $X \leq 4{\cdot}5$, we need to convert $X = 4{\cdot}5$ to the corresponding value of Z.

$X = 4{\cdot}5$: $Z = X - 3 = 4{\cdot}5 - 3 = 1{\cdot}5$

Thus $P(X \leq 4{\cdot}5) = P(Z \leq 1{\cdot}5) = 0{\cdot}9332$.

2. **Scaling**

Suppose X is a normal random variable with mean 0 and standard deviation 2. What is the probability that X is less than or equal to 4?

X has the same mean (0) as the standard normal distribution. But its standard deviation is 2 rather than 1. So if we divide X by 2 we will scale the graph so that the standard deviation is 1, the same as that of the standard normal distribution.

To achieve this mathematically, we let the new random variable Z be defined by

$$Z = \frac{X}{2}.$$

Then Z will be normally distributed with mean 0, the same as that of X, and standard deviation 1. Hence, Z is a standard normal variable, and the tables of values can be used to calculate probabilities.

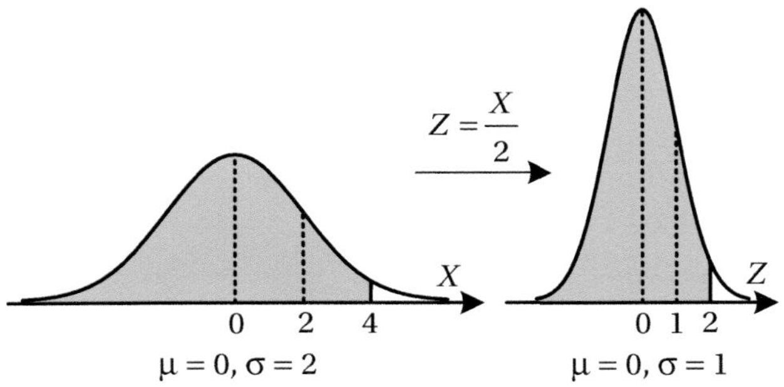

To find the probability that $X \leq 4$, we need to convert 4 to the corresponding value of Z.

$X = 4$: $\quad Z = \frac{X}{2} = \frac{4}{2} = 2$

Thus, $\quad P(X \leq 4) = P(Z \leq 2) = 0{\cdot}9772.$

3. Converting to Standard Units

We can use a combination of translating and scaling to convert any normal probability distribution to a standard normal probability distribution.

Suppose X is a normal variable, with mean μ and standard deviation σ. To convert X to a standard normal variable, we define

$$Z = \frac{X - \mu}{\sigma}.$$

Note that $X - \mu$ translates the variable to a mean of 0. Then dividing by σ scales the variable so that it has a standard deviation of 1.

To calculate, for example, $P(X \leq x_1)$, we start by finding the value of Z that corresponds to $X = x_1$. If z_1 is this value, then $z_1 = \frac{x_1 - \mu}{\sigma}$.

Calculating z_1 is called converting x_1 to **standard units**.

Then $\quad P(X \leq x_1) = P(Z \leq z_1)$,
and this can be determined by consulting the Standard Normal Tables in your set of Maths Tables.

Standard Units

Suppose X is a normal variable with mean μ and standard deviation σ. Then to calculate $P(X \leq x_1)$, we convert x_1 to standard units, using

$$z_1 = \frac{x_1 - \mu}{\sigma}.$$

Then $\quad P(X \leq x_1) = P(Z \leq z_1)$.

Likewise, to calculate $P(x_1 \leq X \leq x_2)$, we convert both x_1 and x_2 to standard units, using $z_1 = \frac{x_1 - \mu}{\sigma}$ and $z_2 = \frac{x_2 - \mu}{\sigma}$. Thus $P(x_1 \leq X \leq x_2) = P(z_1 \leq Z \leq z_2)$.

Example 1

X is a normal variable with mean 10 and standard deviation 2·5. Calculate

(i) $P(X \le 14)$, **(ii)** $P(X \ge 16)$, **(iii)** $P(8 \le X \le 13)$.

Solution

For the distribution of X, $\mu = 10$ and $\sigma = 2{\cdot}5$.

(i) *(We need to start by converting $x_1 = 14$ to standard units.)*

$$x_1 = 14: \quad z_1 = \frac{14 - 10}{2{\cdot}5} = 1{\cdot}6$$

Thus $P(X \le 14) = P(Z \le 1{\cdot}6) = 0{\cdot}9452$

(ii) $x_1 = 16$: $\quad z_1 = \dfrac{16 - 10}{2{\cdot}5} = 2{\cdot}4$

Thus
$$\begin{aligned} P(X \ge 16) &= P(Z \ge 2{\cdot}4) \\ &= 1 - P(Z \le 2{\cdot}4) \\ &= 1 - 0{\cdot}9918 = 0{\cdot}0082 \end{aligned}$$

(iii) $x_1 = 8$: $\quad z_1 = \dfrac{8 - 10}{2{\cdot}5} = -0{\cdot}8$ and $x_2 = 13$: $\quad z_2 = \dfrac{13 - 10}{2{\cdot}5} = 1{\cdot}2$

Thus
$$\begin{aligned} P(8 \le X \le 13) &= P(-0{\cdot}8 \le Z \le 1{\cdot}2) \\ &= P(Z \le 1{\cdot}2) - P(Z \le -0{\cdot}8) \\ &= P(Z \le 1{\cdot}2) - P(Z \ge 0{\cdot}8) \\ &= P(Z \le 1{\cdot}2) - [1 - P(Z \le 0{\cdot}8)] \\ &= P(Z \le 1{\cdot}2) + P(Z \le 0{\cdot}8) - 1 \\ &= 0{\cdot}8849 + 0{\cdot}7881 - 1 = 0{\cdot}673. \end{aligned}$$

Example 2

A machine fills jars with jam so that the mass of jam is normally distributed with mean 500 g and standard deviation 6 g.

(i) Find the probability that the mass of jam in a jar selected at random is less than 490 g.

(ii) If a consignment consists of 1000 jars of jam, how many would we expect to contain less than 490 g, to the nearest whole number?

Solution

(i) For the given distribution, $\mu = 500$ and $\sigma = 6$. Let X be the mass of jam in a jar. We want $P(X \le 490)$. Converting to standard units,

$$x_1 = 490: \quad z_1 = \frac{490 - 500}{6} = -1{\cdot}67$$

Thus
$$\begin{aligned} P(X \le 490) &= P(Z \le -1{\cdot}67) \\ &= P(Z \ge 1{\cdot}67) \\ &= 1 - P(Z \le 1{\cdot}67) \\ &= 1 - 0{\cdot}9525 = 0{\cdot}0475 \end{aligned}$$

(ii) From part (i), we would expect $0{\cdot}0475 = 4{\cdot}75\%$ of the jars in the consignment to contain less than 490 g. Thus the number of jars containing less than 490 g in a consignment of 1000 jars would be expected to be

4·75% of 1000 = 47·5 = 48,

to the nearest whole number.

Exercises 39.4

1. X is a normal variable with mean 20 and standard deviation 4. Calculate
   (i) $P(X \leq 26)$, **(ii)** $P(X \geq 23)$, **(iii)** $P(20 \leq X \leq 25)$.

2. X is a normal variable with mean 40 and standard deviation 8. Calculate
   (i) $P(X \geq 36)$, **(ii)** $P(X \leq 35)$, **(iii)** $P(38 \leq X \leq 42)$.

3. X is a normal variable with mean 22 and standard deviation 2. Calculate
   (i) $P(X \leq 17)$, **(ii)** $P(X \geq 25)$, **(iii)** $P(20 \leq X \leq 26)$.

4. X is a normal variable with mean 48 and standard deviation 5. Calculate
   (i) $P(X \leq 46)$, **(ii)** $P(X \geq 50)$, **(iii)** $P(45 \leq X \leq 52)$.

5. X is a normal variable with mean 36 and standard deviation 4.
   (i) Calculate $P(30 \leq X \leq 42)$.
   (ii) If $W = 2X$, state the mean and the standard deviation of W.
   (iii) Calculate $P(W \geq 80)$.

6. X is a normal variable with mean 16 and standard deviation 2·5.
   (i) If $W = 2X + 4$, what values of X correspond to $W = 32$ and $W = 40$?
   (ii) Hence calculate $P(32 \leq W \leq 40)$.

7. X is a normal variable with mean 60 and standard deviation 10.
   (i) If $Y = 3X - 5$, what values of X correspond to $Y = 160$ and $Y = 205$?
   (ii) Hence calculate $P(160 \leq Y \leq 205)$.

8. X is a normal variable with mean 24 and standard deviation 4.
   If $Y = 5X - 10$, calculate $P(100 \leq Y \leq 140)$.

9. X is a normal variable with mean μ and standard deviation 3. If
   $P(X \geq 15) = 0{\cdot}0668$, find the value of μ.

10. X is a normal variable with mean μ and standard deviation 6. If
    $P(X \geq 31{\cdot}2) = 0{\cdot}1151$, find the value of μ.

11. A certain brand of chocolate bar has weight which is normally distributed with mean 150 g and standard deviation 5 g.
    (i) What is the probability that a bar of chocolate chosen at random has a weight less than 140 g?
    (ii) In a delivery of 2000 of these bars, how many would we expect to weigh less than 140 g?

12. The heights of 800 babies are normally distributed with mean 66 cm and standard deviation 5 cm.
    (i) Calculate the probability that a baby chosen at random will have a height greater than 74 cm.
    (ii) Estimate the number of babies of height greater than 72 cm.
    (iii) Estimate the number of babies of height between 65 cm and 70 cm.

13. The IQs of the 12000 students in a university are normally distributed with mean 120 and standard deviation 10.
    (i) Calculate the probability that a student chosen at random has an IQ of 145 or higher.
    (ii) Estimate the number of students in the university with an IQ less than 105.
    (iii) Estimate the number of students in the university with an IQ between 110 and 135.

14. In a particular year, the marks obtained by students in Leaving Cert maths are normally distributed with mean 70% and standard deviation 12%. 15000 students sat the exam.
    (i) Calculate the probability that a student picked at random scored less than 60%.
    (ii) Estimate the number of students who obtained an 'A' grade, i.e. 85% or higher.
    (iii) Estimate the number of students who obtained a 'D' grade, i.e. between 40% and 55%.

39.5 Measure of Relative Standing: *z* scores

In an earlier chapter, we saw how to use percentiles to determine how one result rates based on the dataset it belongs to. This method is suitable for small datasets.

Another method for determining relative standing is to use ***z* scores**, or **standard scores**. The z score of a result in a distribution tells the number of standard deviations that the result is away from the mean. Thus a z score of 2 says that the result lies two standard deviations above the mean, while a z score of –1 says that the result lies one standard deviation below the mean. z scores work for all distributions, not just those which are normally distributed.

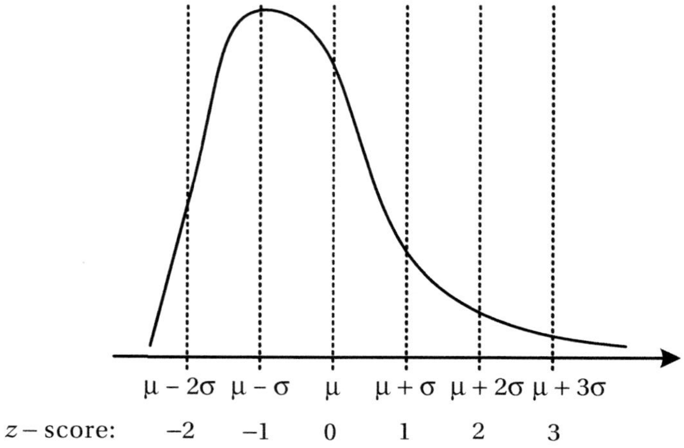

The z-score corresponding to the mean, μ, is 0. If σ is the standard deviation, then the z-scores corresponding to $\mu + \sigma$, $\mu + 2\sigma$, $\mu - \sigma$ are 1, 2 and –1 respectively.

Suppose Mary scores 80% in an English test, and the class mean and standard deviation are 60% and 10% respectively. Then to find her z-score:

$$z = \frac{x - \mu}{\sigma}$$

$$= \frac{80 - 60}{10} = 2$$

Thus her z-score is 2, i.e. she achieved two standard deviations better than the mean.

One of the main uses of z-scores is to compare results from two, or more, completely different sets of data, whether they are normally distributed or not.

Example 1

Peter has two tests in one week at school, maths and physics. In maths he scores 84%, while the mean and the standard deviation for the class are 70% and 12% respectively. In physics he scores 74%, and the mean and standard deviation of the class are 61% and 6% respectively.
By calculating z-scores, determine in which exam Peter did better relative to his classmates.

Solution

(We will call Peter's score x in each case and calculate the corresponding z-score.)

Maths: $\mu = 70, \sigma = 12, x = 84$

$$z = \frac{x - \mu}{\sigma}$$
$$= \frac{84 - 70}{12}$$
$$= 1{\cdot}17, \quad \text{correct to two decimal places.}$$

Physics: $\mu = 61, \sigma = 6, x = 74$

$$z = \frac{x - \mu}{\sigma}$$
$$= \frac{74 - 61}{6}$$
$$= 2{\cdot}17, \quad \text{correct to two decimal places.}$$

As Peter's z-score for physics is higher than his z-score for maths, he performed better in physics, relative to his classmates.

If the data is normally distributed, we can use the z score to determine the percentile of an individual result.

Suppose a large number of students sit an exam, and that the marks are normally distributed with mean 60 and standard deviation 15. If Stephen scores 83 in this exam, in what percentile is he among all the students who sat the exam? Knowing his percentile gives him an idea of his standing relative to his fellow students.

Recall that percentile refers to the percentage of the results that lie below the result in question. Because the marks are normally distributed, we can use the Standard Normal Tables to determine Stephen's percentile.

If we let the normal variable X stand for the mark obtained, to calculate Stephen's percentile, we need to find

$$P(X < 83),$$

and convert this number to a percentage.

As $\mu = 60$ and $\sigma = 15$,

$$z = \frac{83 - 60}{15}$$
$$= 1{\cdot}54$$

Thus $\quad P(X < 83) = P(Z < 1{\cdot}54)$

$$= 0{\cdot}9382$$
$$= 93{\cdot}82\%$$

As 93% (but not 94%) of results are below Stephen's, he has scored in the 93rd percentile.

The same method can be used to determine what result is required to achieve a given percentile.

Example 2

In a university exam, the marks are normally distributed with mean 65% and standard deviation 8%. The university decides to give first class honours to the top 10% of its students. What is the least percentage required to achieve a first class honours in the exam? Give your answer correct to one decimal place.

Solution

(To get a first class honours, a student has to be in the 90th percentile, or higher.)

Let X be the normal variable representing students marks. For X, $\mu = 65$ and $\sigma = 8$.

As $10\% = 0{\cdot}1$, we first want to find z_1 such that

$$P(Z \leq z_1) = 1 - 0{\cdot}1 = 0{\cdot}9.$$

z_1 is the value below which 90% of the area under the standard normal curve lies.

From the Standard Normal Tables,

$$z_1 = 1{\cdot}28.$$

Let x_1 be the mark which corresponds with this value of z. Then

$$z_1 = \frac{x_1 - \mu}{\sigma}$$

$$1{\cdot}28 = \frac{x_1 - 65}{8}$$

$$10{\cdot}24 = x_1 - 65$$

$$x_1 = 75{\cdot}4, \quad \text{correct to one decimal place.}$$

Thus, a student needs a mark of at least 75·4% to be awarded a first class honours.

Exercises 39.5

1. Luke sits two tests on the same day: history and geography. In history, he scores 88%, while the mean and standard deviation for his class were 68% and 12% respectively. In geography, he scores 72%, while the mean and standard deviation for his class are 62% and 5% respectively. In which exam did Luke perform better relative to his classmates?

2. David's height is measured at 163 cm. Doing research, he finds that the mean height of boys of his age is 159 cm, with a standard deviation of 2·3 cm. David's older sister, Susan, has her height measured to be 165 cm. She discovers that the mean height for girls of her age is 161 cm, with a standard deviation of 4·1 cm. Which of the two of them is taller relative to their peers? Give a reason.

3. Paul plays an online game against many other players. On Monday, he scores 21050 and is told that for his group of players the mean and standard deviation are 19550 and 780 respectively. On Tuesday, he plays again against the same group of players. This time he scores 20440, and is informed that the mean and standard deviation are 19400 and 580 respectively. On which day did Paul perform better relative to the other players in his group? Give a reason.

4. Martin and Helen are in different years in school. Both sit a maths test on the same day. Martin scores 88%. The mean and standard deviation in his class are 77% and 8% respectively. Helen score 67%. The mean and standard deviation in her class are 55% and 6% respectively.
   Martin jokes with Helen that he is much better at maths than she is. Helen is not convinced.
   Which of them, Martin or Helen, performed better in the maths exams, relative to their peers? Give a reason.

5. In a maths exam, the marks are normally distributed, with mean 55 and standard deviation 15.
   (i) Sean scores 46. In what percentile is his score?
   (ii) Emer scores 82. In what percentile is her score?

6. The heights of individuals in a large male population is normally distributed with mean 177 cm and standard deviation 8 cm.
   (i) George has a height of 190 cm. In what percentile is his height?
   (ii) James has a height of 165 cm. In what percentile is his height?

7. In the Leaving Cert of one particular year, the marks in higher level English were normally distributed with mean 65% and standard deviation 12%.
   (i) Colm scored 72%. In what percentile is his score?
   (ii) Dermot scored 84%. In what percentile is his score?

8. The weights of individuals in a large female population are normally distributed with mean 69 kg and standard deviation 9 kg.
   (i) Mary has a weight of 56·4 kg. In what percentile is her weight?
   (ii) Chloe has a weight of 74·6 kg. In what percentile is her weight?

9. The marks of all students who sat a particular test are normally distributed with mean 66% and standard deviation 12%. Dylan's Dad has promised him a present if he scores in the top 15% of all the students who sat the test. What is the minimum mark that Dylan must achieve to get the present? Give your answer to the nearest whole number.

10. In a college exam, the scores are normally distributed with mean 62% and standard deviation 14%. The college decides to award an 'A' grade to the top 10% of students, and a 'B' grade to the next 20% of students.
    (i) Calculate, to the nearest whole number, the least score a student must achieve to be awarded an 'A' grade.
    (ii) Calculate, to the nearest whole number, the least score a student must achieve to be awarded a 'B' grade.

Revision Exercises 39

1. For a certain type of machine part, the time to failure is normally distributed with mean 1200 hours and standard deviation 150 hours.
   (i) What is the probability that one such part, chosen at random, has a time to failure greater than 1450 hours?
   (ii) What is the probability that one such part, chosen at random, has a time to failure between 1100 and 1300 hours?
   (iii) One such part fails after 1282 hours. In what percentile is this time to failure?

2. In a university exam, the marks are normally distributed with mean 62 and standard deviation 7.
   (i) What is the probability that a student selected at random obtained a mark less than 50?
   (ii) What is the probability that a student selected at random obtains a mark between 55 and 75?
   (iii) The university decides that the lowest 20% of students must resit the exam. What is the least mark a student must have obtained not to have to resit the exam? Give your answer correct to the nearest whole number.

3. Thirty students in a class attempt a test. The mean mark is 62% and the standard deviation is 10%. It is thought that the marks in the class might be normally distributed.
- **(i)** One of the students, Sean, obtains a mark of 98%. Would you consider his score as an outlier of the data? Give a reason.
- **(ii)** If two other students, Sarah and Aoife, score 97% and 95%, would you conclude that all three of them had cheated, or that the assumption that the data is normally distributed is wrong? Give a reason.

4. The random variable Z has a standard normal distribution.
- **(i)** Find the value of $k > 0$ if $P(-k \le Z \le k) = 0{\cdot}9786$.
- **(ii)** If X is another random variable such that $X = 4Z + 3$, calculate $P(-5 \le X \le 10)$.

5. X is a normal variable with mean 15 and standard deviation 2·4.
- **(i)** If $P(X \le k) = 0{\cdot}2912$, find the value of the real number k.
- **(ii)** If $Y = 3X + 2$, calculate $P(38 \le Y \le 56)$.

6. X is a normal variable with mean 8 and standard deviation 2.
- **(i)** Draw a rough graph of the density function of X.
- **(ii)** Indicate on the graph the regions which are between 1 and 2 standard deviations from the mean.
- **(iii)** Use the empirical rule to estimate the probability that X lies between 1 and 2 standard deviations from the mean.
- **(iv)** Use the Standard Normal Tables to calculate the probability that X lies between 1 and 2 standard deviations from the mean.

7. The IQs of all the students in first year in a university are normally distributed with mean 116 and standard deviation 14.
- **(i)** Find the probability that a first year student picked at random has an IQ greater than 140.
- **(ii)** One first year student, Louise, has an IQ of 135. In what percentile does her IQ lie?
- **(iii)** If there are 3000 students in first year, estimate the number of students with an IQ higher than that of Louise.

8. A machine produces metal discs. The radii of the discs are normally distributed with mean 10 cm and standard deviation 0·05 cm.
- **(i)** Calculate the probability that the radius of a disc selected at random has a radius greater than 10·08 cm.
- **(ii)** A disc is rejected if its radius is less than 9·9 cm or greater than 10·12 cm. Calculate the probability that a disc selected at random is rejected.
- **(iii)** If 1000 good discs are required for a customer, calculate how many discs should be produced to obtain this number of good discs.

9. X is a normal variable with mean 9. If $P(X \ge 12) = 0{\cdot}0062$, calculate σ, the standard deviation of X.

10. Ronan sits an exam in physics and Joseph sits an exam in chemistry. Ronan obtains a score of 78%, and the mean and standard deviation of all physics results are 68% and 5% respectively. In Joseph's chemistry exam, the mean and the standard deviation are 70% and 8% respectively.
- **(i)** What score would Joseph need to obtain in his chemistry exam to perform better relative to his peers than Ronan?
- **(ii)** If the scores in the physics exam are normally distributed, in what percentile is Ronan's score?
- **(iii)** If the scores in chemistry are normally distributed, what score would Joseph need to obtain to be in the top 5% of his fellow students?

Inferential Statistics

40

Inferential statistics is the branch of statistics which uses probability and statistics to draw conclusions from data that are affected by random variation. For example, suppose a candidate in a national election wants to know the percentage of voters who intend to vote for her. She can have a representative random sample of voters taken, and use this to judge her standing. However, the outcome for the sample chosen will probably not match the entire electorate exactly. This leads to the ideas of the 'margin of error' and 'confidence interval', i.e. the interval within which she can be reasonably sure that her true level of support lies.

Another case we study is where we want to estimate the mean of a very large population, which may or may not be normally distributed. So we take a random sample and calculate the mean of this sample. A very famous and important theorem, the Central Limit Theorem, allows us to draw conclusions about the likely mean of the population from the mean of the sample. Yet another question type involves using sample data to test a statement about the mean of a population, by means of what is known as hypothesis testing.

40.1 Population and Sample Proportions: Margin of Error and Confidence Intervals

Suppose there are two candidates in a presidential election, A and B, and that we want to estimate as a percentage, e.g. 45%, or as a decimal, e.g. 0·45, the level of support for candidate A. This measure is called the **proportion** of the population that supports candidate A.

It is common practice to let the population proportion be denoted by the letter p. Notice that there is no standard deviation, as the proportion is just a single number.

Now suppose that we select a simple random sample (SRS) of 200 voters and ask them which candidate they support for the upcoming election. Let the sample proportion who support candidate A be denoted by $\hat{p}$ (called p hat).

It is not reasonable to expect $\hat{p}$ to be exactly the same as p, but it is likely to be not too far away. Common sense tells us that increasing the size of the sample we take will increase the probability that $\hat{p}$ is close to p. So how can we quantify our confidence that the proportion we get from our sample is close to the population proportion?

We do so by introducing quantities such as the standard error of the proportion, the margin of error and confidence intervals.

1. **The Theory**

When we take one sample of size 200 voters and calculate its proportion, $\hat{p}$, we are only finding the proportion from one of many samples of size 200. If we were to consider all such proportions, we would have the **sampling distribution of the proportion**.

The sampling distribution of the proportion i.e. the distribution of all possible sample proportions for samples of the same size, has the following properties:

(i) it is normally distributed,

(ii) its mean, written $\mu_{\hat{p}}$, is p, the true proportion of the population,

(iii) its standard deviation depends on the size of the samples (the larger the sample size, the smaller the standard deviation).

The standard deviation of the sampling distribution of the proportion is called the **standard error (S.E.) of the proportion**, and written $\sigma_{\hat{p}}$. The formula for the S.E. of the proportion is given on page 34 of the *Formulae and Tables* as

$$\sigma_{\hat{p}} = \sqrt{\frac{p(1-p)}{n}},$$

where n is the size of the samples.

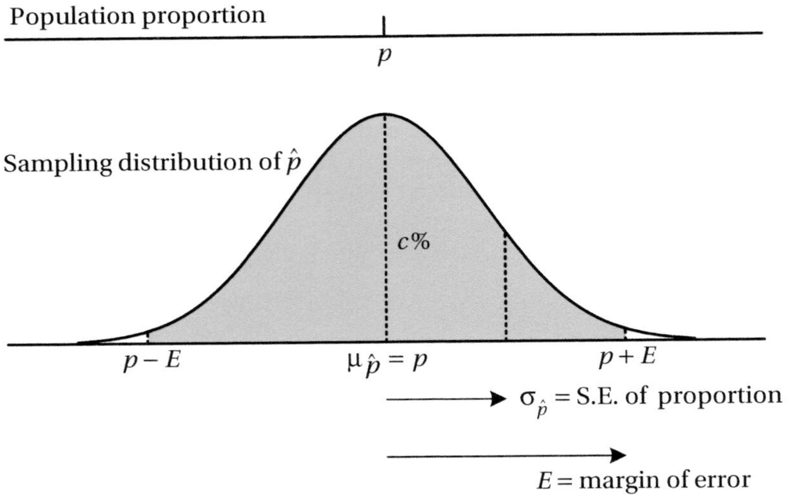

Thus, if we know the true population proportion, p, we can use either the Empirical Rule or the standard normal tables to estimate the probability that a particular sample proportion will lie within a certain distance of the population proportion. The Empirical Rule only gives a rough guide, while the standard normal tables give a more accurate estimate.

The approach used is to form an interval in which we can be c% sure that the true population proportion lies. c% is called the **confidence level**, and from the point of view of calculations, c is written as a decimal. The most commonly used confidence levels is 95% ($c = 0{\cdot}95$), but others you may meet are 90% ($c = 0{\cdot}9$) and 99% ($c = 0{\cdot}99$).

For the confidence level chosen, we can construct the interval in which the probability of a sample proportion lying is c, as a decimal.

This interval is called a c% **confidence interval,** e.g. a 95% confidence interval. This interval is centred on p, the population proportion. The distance from p to an edge of the interval is called the **margin of error**, and denoted by E. The margin of error, E, will depend on c, p and n, and we will see how to calculate it below.

Once E has been calculated, the confidence interval is then $[p - E, p + E]$.

2. The Practice

This is fine in theory, but in most cases we do not know the true population proportion. This is what we are trying to estimate. So we turn the argument on its head. Just as we can say that there is a probability of c that a sample proportion, $\hat{p}$, lies in the interval $[p - E, p + E]$, we can also say that there is a probability of c that p, the population proportion, lies in the interval $[\hat{p} - E, \hat{p} + E]$.

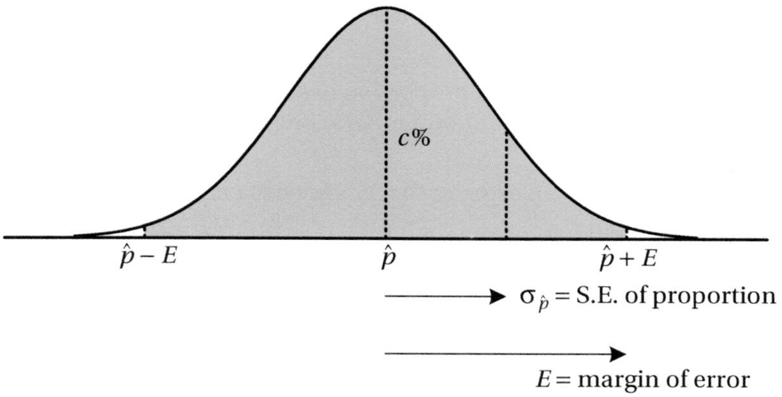

The problem is that because we do not know the value of p, we have to use $\hat{p}$ instead of p if we need to calculate the standard error of the proportion. Thus we use

$$\sigma_{\hat{p}} = \sqrt{\frac{\hat{p}(1-\hat{p})}{n}}$$

for the S.E. of the proportion.

A Margin of Error Approximation for 95% Confidence Interval

The Empirical Rule, which states that approximately 95% of the area (probability) under a normal curve lies within two standard deviations of the mean, can be used to obtain the rough approximation:

$$E = 2\sigma_{\hat{p}}$$

$$E = 2\sqrt{\frac{p(1-p)}{n}} \qquad \text{... or } \hat{p} \text{ instead of } p \text{ if } p \text{ is unknown}$$

To be as safe as possible, we want to allow for the largest possible value of this expression. By calculus, or by completing the square, we can find that the maximum possible value of $p(1-p)$ occurs when $p = \frac{1}{2}$. When $p = \frac{1}{2}$, $p(1-p) = \frac{1}{2} \times \frac{1}{2} = \frac{1}{4}$.

Thus $\quad E = 2\sqrt{\frac{1}{4n}} = 2 \times \frac{1}{2\sqrt{n}} = \frac{1}{\sqrt{n}}$

is a very rough approximation to the margin of error at the 95% confidence level.

Approximate Margin of Error at the 95% Confidence Level

Suppose a sample of size n gives a proportion $\hat{p}$ for a certain characteristic. Then we can be 95% confident that the proportion for the whole population, p lies within the margin of error of $\hat{p}$.

The margin of error is given approximately by:

$$E = \frac{1}{\sqrt{n}}.$$

Thus the 95% confidence interval for p is

$$\hat{p} - \frac{1}{\sqrt{n}} < p < \hat{p} + \frac{1}{\sqrt{n}}.$$

Example 1

A survey is conducted to see what proportion of soup buyers choose Brand A of soup over all other brands. A random sample of 600 shoppers who buy soup is taken and returns a proportion of 33% who choose Brand A.

(i) Calculate the margin of error, at the 95% level of confidence.

(ii) Give the 95% confidence interval for the true proportion of soup buyers who choose Brand A.

(iii) With 95% confidence, what is the highest proportion of soup buyers who could choose Brand A?

(iv) How could the margin of error have been reduced? Are there any implications of taking this action?

Solution

(i) *(We will use the approximate formula, $E = \frac{1}{\sqrt{n}}$, unless asked to be more accurate.)*

Margin of error $= \frac{1}{\sqrt{600}} = 0{\cdot}0408$

(ii) The 95% confidence interval for p, the true proportion of soup buyers who choose Brand A is

$$\hat{p} - \frac{1}{\sqrt{n}} < p < \hat{p} + \frac{1}{\sqrt{n}}$$

$$0{\cdot}33 - 0{\cdot}0408 < p < 0{\cdot}33 + 0{\cdot}0408$$

$$0{\cdot}2892 < p < 0{\cdot}3708$$

(iii) With 95% confidence, the highest proportion who could choose Brand A is

$33\% + 4{\cdot}08\% = 37{\cdot}08\%$.

(iv) The margin of error could have been reduced by increasing the sample size. Increasing the sample size incurs extra costs, which might be considered disproportionate to the reduction in the margin of error.

Example 2

A political party supports candidate A in an election with two candidates. Earlier polls indicate that voters are very evenly split between the two candidates. The political party wishes to conduct a random sample of voters to determine the level of support for their candidate to within 1%, money no object. What sample size should they take at the 95% confidence level?

Solution

(To within 1% means that the margin of error should be 1%.)

Let n be the size of the sample to be taken. The margin of error is $1\% = 0{\cdot}01$.

Then

$$\frac{1}{\sqrt{n}} = 0{\cdot}01$$

$$1 = 0{\cdot}01\sqrt{n}$$

$$\sqrt{n} = \frac{1}{0{\cdot}01}$$

$$\sqrt{n} = 100$$

$$n = 10000.$$

A sample of size 10000 would be required to obtain a margin of error of 1%.

B Confidence Interval for Population Proportion Using the Standard Normal Tables

We revisit Example 1, in which, from a sample of 600 shoppers, 33% choose Brand A. We want to use the standard normal tables to obtain a more accurate expression for the 95% confidence interval for the proportion of shoppers who choose Brand A.

[1] First of all, $\hat{p} = 0{\cdot}33$ and we want to obtain a 95% confidence interval for p. $n = 600$.

[2] Calculate $\sigma_{\hat{p}}$, the S.E. of the proportion.

$$\sigma_{\hat{p}} = \sqrt{\frac{\hat{p}(1-\hat{p})}{n}} \quad \textit{... as p is not available}$$

$$\sigma_{\hat{p}} = \sqrt{\frac{0{\cdot}33(1-0{\cdot}33)}{600}}$$

$$\sigma_{\hat{p}} = 0{\cdot}019196$$

[3] We now need to find the z value for the appropriate value of c, the confidence level, i.e. we want to find the value of z such that $P(-z \le Z \le z) = c$. In this case $c = 0{\cdot}95$.

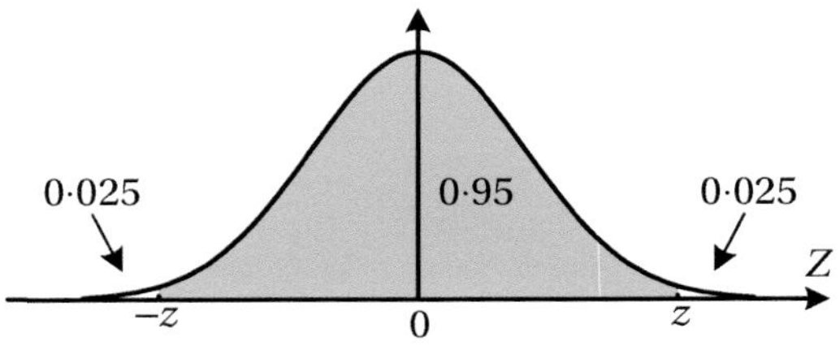

If

$P(-z \le Z \le z) = 0{\cdot}95$

then, from the diagram,

$P(Z \le z) = 0{\cdot}95 + 0{\cdot}025 = 0{\cdot}975$.

From the standard normal tables,

$z = 1{\cdot}96$.

[4] z is the number of standard deviations (S.E.) that the margin of error is from the mean. Thus the margin of error, E, is given by

$E = z \times \sigma_{\hat{p}}$

$E = 1{\cdot}96 \times 0{\cdot}019196$

$E = 0{\cdot}03762$

[5] The 95% confidence interval for the true proportion, p, is then

$\hat{p} - E \le p \le \hat{p} + E$

$0{\cdot}33 - 0{\cdot}03762 \le p \le 0{\cdot}33 + 0{\cdot}03762$

$0{\cdot}29238 \le p \le 0{\cdot}36762$.

i.e. the true proportion, with 95% confidence, lies between 29·238% and 36·762%.

Note that this interval is more restricted than the approximate interval obtained by using the $\frac{1}{\sqrt{n}}$ formula for E, but it is far more accurate.

We can use the same method to find a 99% confidence interval for the proportion of shoppers who choose Brand A. The key difference lies in the calculation of z. We find that

$P(-z \le Z \le z) = 0{\cdot}99$

leads to $P(Z \le z) = 0{\cdot}995$

and to $z = 2{\cdot}575$.

Then the margin of error, E, is $z \times \sigma_{\hat{p}} = 2{\cdot}575 \times 0{\cdot}019196 = 0{\cdot}04943$

Thus the 99% confidence interval is

$\hat{p} - E \le p \le \hat{p} + E$

$0{\cdot}33 - 0{\cdot}04943 \le p \le 0{\cdot}33 + 0{\cdot}04943$

$0{\cdot}28057 \le p \le 0{\cdot}37943$

i.e. the true proportion, with 99% confidence, lies between 28·057% and 37·943%.

You should note that increasing the confidence level from 95% to 99% causes the confidence interval to widen. This is generally true.

Confidence Intervals using Standard Normal Tables

Suppose a sample of size n gives a proportion $\hat{p}$ for a certain characteristic. Then, for the true proportion, p:

(i) Standard Error of the Proportion:

$$\sigma_{\hat{p}} = \sqrt{\frac{\hat{p}(1-\hat{p})}{n}}$$

(ii) Margin of Error (for c% confidence level):

$$E = z.\sigma_{\hat{p}}$$

where the value of z depends on c. For 95% confidence, $z = 1{\cdot}96$.

(iii) Confidence Interval:

$$\hat{p} - E \le p \le \hat{p} + E.$$

Example 3

In a survey of 450 voters, 180 say that they intend to vote yes in a forthcoming referendum.

(i) By using z tables (standard normal tables), determine a 95% confidence interval for the true proportion of voters who intend to vote yes in the referendum.

(ii) Describe how a 98% confidence interval would compare with the interval in part (i).

Solution

(i) Let p be the population proportion. Then $n = 180$ and

$$\hat{p} = \frac{180}{450} = 0{\cdot}4.$$

Also,

$$\sigma_{\hat{p}} = \sqrt{\frac{0{\cdot}4\,(1-0{\cdot}4)}{450}} = 0{\cdot}0231$$

and $E = 1{\cdot}96 \times 0{\cdot}0231 = 0{\cdot}0453$.

Thus the 95% confidence interval for p is

$$0{\cdot}4 - 0{\cdot}0453 \le p \le 0{\cdot}4 + 0{\cdot}0453$$

or $\quad 0{\cdot}3547 \le p \le 0{\cdot}4453$

or, as percentages, we can be 95% confident that the true proportion lies between 35·47% and 44·53%.

(ii) A 98% confidence interval would be centred on $\hat{p} = 0{\cdot}4$ but would be wider (have a greater margin of error) than the 95% confidence interval.

Exercises 40.1

In the following questions, you may use the approximation $E = \frac{1}{\sqrt{n}}$.

1. In a by-election, a random sample of 400 voters suggests that 38% will vote for candidate A.
   (i) What is the margin of error?
   (ii) Give the 95% confidence interval for the true proportion of voters who intend to vote for candidate A.
   (iii) This same sample indicates that the support for candidate B is at 43%. Is there any possibility that the true proportion of voters which favours candidate A is greater than that which favours candidate B? Give a reason.
   (iv) If, in the by-election, candidate A obtains 46% of the vote, suggest reasons why the random sample understated the proportion in favour of candidate A.

2. Prior to the development of a new dairy product, a company conducts a survey to gauge public reaction to the new health features of the product. A random sample of shoppers who buy dairy products were questioned as to their likelihood to prefer the new product over existing brands. The random sample was of size 800, and resulted in a positive response of 27%.
   (i) Calculate the margin of error.
   (ii) Give the 95% confidence interval for the true proportion of people who purchase dairy products in the whole population who are likely to purchase the new product.
   (iii) The company needs a proportion of 30% to justify proceeding with the development of the new product. On the basis of the sample obtained, do you think the company can feel confident about proceeding with the development of the new product? Give a reason.

3. A large air transport company wants to change its pricing structure, but is afraid of losing business to its competitors if it does. It needs to have customer support of at least 70% to introduce its new structure. A sample of its customers is to be taken, but cannot have a margin of error of greater than 2%.
   (i) What size of sample should be taken so that the margin of error is 2%?
   (ii) If the response from the sample is 68% favourable, do you think the company would feel confident implementing the new structure? Give a reason.
   (iii) If the company wants to conduct a new survey with a margin of error of 1%, how much larger would the sample it takes have to be?

4. An engineering company manufactures a sensitive component. To be acceptable to customers, 90% of components have to meet strict standards. A random sample of size n is taken from all the components manufactured in a particular period, and 89% of the components in the sample meet the standards.
   (i) What is the maximum possible value of n for the company to say that the result of the sample is within the margin of error?
   (ii) If a new random sample of 6400 components is taken, what is the least proportion of components that meets the standards for the company to be able to say that the result is within the margin of error?

5. If we require a margin of error of x% for a sample of size n, express n in terms of x.

6. What is the reduction in the margin of error when the sample size is increased from 1000 to 20000?

7. If the margin of error is 4·5%, calculate the size of the sample.

8. If the sample size is multiplied by 100, express as a percentage the reduction in the margin of error.

9. A sample of size x gives a margin of error of n%. Express in terms of n the margin of error of a sample of size $4x$.

In the following questions, the margin of error should be found by using the formula for the standard error of proportion and z tables (standard normal tables).

10. A survey of 800 consumers indicates that 38% of those intend to buy a new brand of dairy spread.
    (i) Find the 95% confidence interval for the true proportion of consumers that intend to use the new brand.
    (ii) Describe how a 99% confidence interval would compare with the interval in part (i).

11. In the run-up to an election, a survey of 250 voters shows that 107 intend to vote for party A.
(i) Find the 95% confidence interval for the true proportion of voters that intends to vote for Party A.
(ii) Describe how a 98% confidence interval would compare with the interval in part (i).

12. In testing, 212 out of 2000 washers produced by a machine failed a quality test.
(i) Find the 95% confidence interval for the true proportion of washers produced by the machine that would fail the quality test.
(ii) Describe how a 90% confidence interval would compare with the interval in part (i).

13. A random sample of 150 shoppers were asked to participate in a coffee tasting test. Of these, 54 said that they preferred Brand Y.
(i) Find the 95% confidence interval for the true proportion of shoppers who prefer Brand Y.
(ii) Describe how a 99% confidence interval would compare with the interval in part (i).

14. A proportion of 30% was obtained from a sample of size n. If the margin of error, at the 95% level of confidence, is to be 2%, calculate the least integer value of n.

15. A proportion of 42% was obtained from a sample of size n. If the margin of error, at the 95% level of confidence, is to be 3%, calculate the least integer value of n.

40.2 Sampling Distribution of the Mean

1. Population

Suppose a fair die is thrown an infinite number of times. Then the population for this experiment is the infinite number of outcomes that would be obtained. In this case, the proportion of the time that each of the numbers 1, 2, 3, 4, 5 and 6 occurs will be equal. This is why we say that the probability of each number is $\frac{1}{6}$.

If the random variable X represents the outcome when the die is thrown, then we can construct the following probability table for X.

X	1	2	3	4	5	6
$P(X)$	$\frac{1}{6}$	$\frac{1}{6}$	$\frac{1}{6}$	$\frac{1}{6}$	$\frac{1}{6}$	$\frac{1}{6}$

Then, the mean, μ, or the expected value, $E(X)$, is given by

$$\mu = 1\left(\frac{1}{6}\right) + 2\left(\frac{1}{6}\right) + 3\left(\frac{1}{6}\right) + 4\left(\frac{1}{6}\right) + 5\left(\frac{1}{6}\right) + 6\left(\frac{1}{6}\right) = 3{\cdot}5.$$

Also, the standard deviation, σ, can be calculated by treating the probabilities as frequencies.

$$\sigma^2 = \frac{\frac{1}{6}(1-3{\cdot}5)^2 + \frac{1}{6}(2-3{\cdot}5)^2 + \frac{1}{6}(3-3{\cdot}5)^2 + \frac{1}{6}(4-3{\cdot}5)^2 + \frac{1}{6}(5-3{\cdot}5)^2 + \frac{1}{6}(6-3{\cdot}5)^2}{\frac{1}{6}+\frac{1}{6}+\frac{1}{6}+\frac{1}{6}+\frac{1}{6}+\frac{1}{6}}$$

$$= \frac{1}{6}(6{\cdot}25 + 2{\cdot}25 + 0{\cdot}25 + 0{\cdot}25 + 2{\cdot}25 + 6{\cdot}25)$$

$$= \frac{35}{12}$$

$$\sigma = \sqrt{\frac{35}{12}} = 1{\cdot}7078.$$

This probability distribution is not normal. In fact, because the probabilities are all equal, it is called a uniform distribution. Its histogram is shown below.

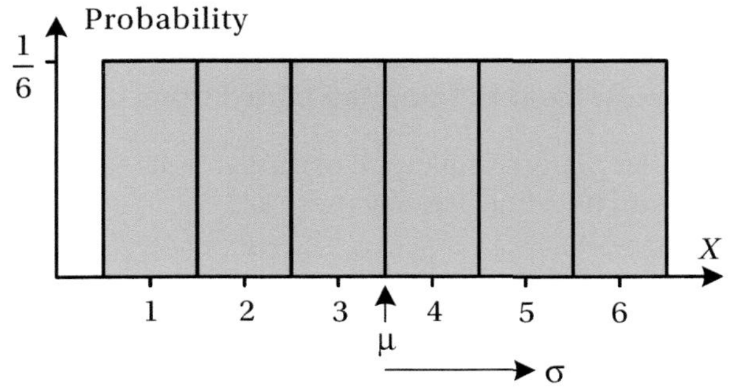

2. Single Sample

Now suppose we take a single sample of reasonable size, say 10, 20 or 100. It is not reasonable to expect the distribution from a relatively small sample like this to be an exact replica of the overall population.

For example, in one experiment, a die is thrown 60 times and the frequencies of each of the numbers is shown in the table below. Also shown is the experimental probability, $P(X)$, obtained by dividing each frequency by 60.

X	1	2	3	4	5	6
Frequency	13	12	7	11	8	9
P(X)	0·217	0·2	0·117	0·183	0·133	0·15

This distribution may be illustrated by a histogram, as shown below.

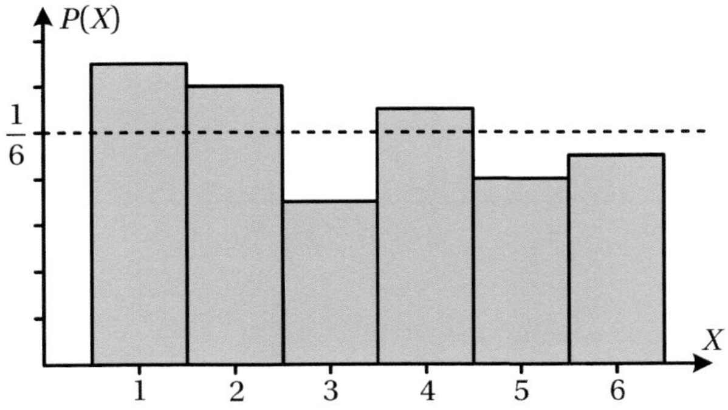

On a point of notation, while the mean and standard deviation of a population are generally written as μ and σ respectively, the mean and standard deviation of a sample are usually denoted by $\bar{x}$ and s, respectively.

For this experimental data, the mean, $\bar{x}$, is 3·27 and the standard deviation, s, is 1·75. These are not exactly the same as for the population, but are not that far away. It is also important to note that if this experiment of throwing a die 60 times is repeated, the outcome is likely to differ from that of the first trial.

If we take larger samples, then the distribution is likely to be closer to that of the population. We can investigate the effect of taking larger samples by using computer programmes such as Excel. Using such a programme to model a large number (21600) of die throws, one set of outcomes is

Number	1	2	3	4	5	6
Frequency	3587	3635	3543	3608	3624	3606
Relative Frequency	0·16606	0·16829	0·16403	0·16704	0·16778	0·16694

giving a mean of 3·523148 and a standard deviation of 1·7086, both very close to the theoretical results obtained previously. Every time the program is run, different but similar results are obtained. Sometimes the mean is slightly above 3·5, and sometimes slightly below. Likewise with the standard deviation: sometimes it is slightly above 1·7078, sometimes slightly below.

3. Distribution of the Sample Means (Sampling Distribution of the Mean)

Now suppose we consider many samples, all of the same size (say size 36). Suppose we just record the mean of each sample, and nothing else. Say these are

$\bar{x}_1, \bar{x}_2, \bar{x}_3, \ldots\ldots$

If we draw a curve to represent the distribution of these sample means, something astonishing happens. This distribution satisfies some interesting and important properties, as long as we take enough samples of the same, sufficiently large, size. The following observations can be made for the distribution of the sample means.

1. The ***distribution of the sample means*** is always approximately ***normal***. The larger the size of the samples, the closer the distribution of the sample means will be to a normal distribution. Most statisticians agree that if the sample size is at least 30, then the distribution of the sample means may be taken to be normal.
2. The ***mean of the distribution of the sample means***, written $\mu_{\bar{x}}$, ***is the same as the mean of the population***, μ, i.e. $\mu_{\bar{x}} = \mu$.
3. If $\sigma_{\bar{x}}$ represents the standard deviation of the sample means, then $\sigma_{\bar{x}} = \frac{\sigma}{\sqrt{n}}$, where n is the size of the samples. $\sigma_{\bar{x}}$ is called the ***standard error*** of the mean and is given on page 34 of the *Formulae and Tables*.

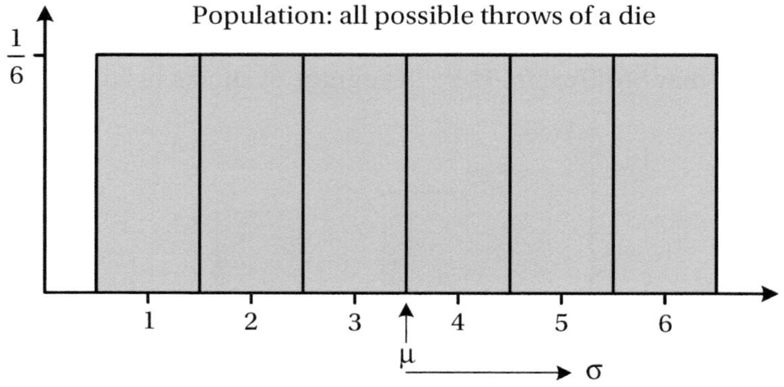

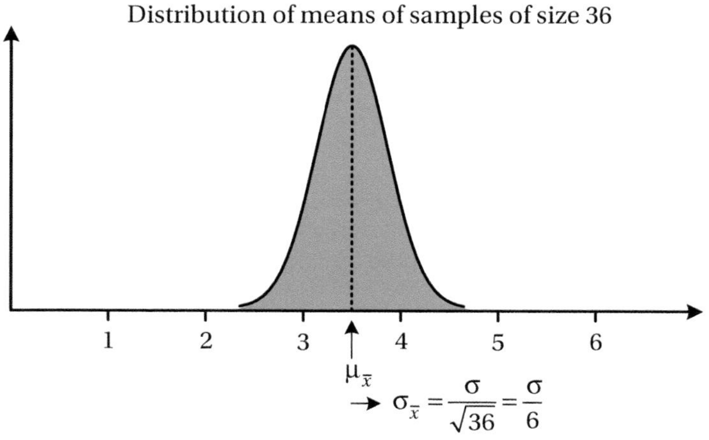

These properties are contained in a theorem, called the **Central Limit Theorem**, which can be mathematically proved. This is a very powerful and far reaching theorem, which has a number of different forms, depending on conditions. The version we use on our course is given below.

Central Limit Theorem

Suppose a population has a mean of μ and a standard deviation of σ. Let $\bar{x}$ be the random variable representing the means of all samples of size n taken from this population. Let this distribution have mean $\mu_{\bar{x}}$ and standard deviation $\sigma_{\bar{x}}$.

(i) $\bar{x}$ is taken to be normally distributed for $n \geq 30$.

(ii) $\mu_{\bar{x}} = \mu$.

(iii) $\sigma_{\bar{x}} = \dfrac{\sigma}{\sqrt{n}}$.

For the example given above of the samples of size 36 throws of a die, the Central Limit Theorem applies. The diagram above shows the relative frequency histogram for the population and the curve representing the distribution of the means of sample size 36. For samples of larger size, e.g. 100, 1000, the distribution of the sample means has even smaller standard deviations.

If the population is itself normally distributed, then the Central Limit Theorem applies even when n is small, i.e. even when $n < 30$.

Because the distribution of the sample means is normal, we can use the Standard Normal Tables to calculate the probability that the mean of a sample of a given size differs from the mean of the population by a certain amount.

Example 1

Bags of flour are known to have a mean weight of 2 kg and standard deviation 50 g.

(i) If a sample of 100 of these bags of flour are chosen at random, what is the probability that their mean weight is less than 1·99 kg?

(ii) At the packing stage, these bags of flour are packed at random into consignments of size 100 bags. If 1200 consignments are produced in a week, how many of these consignments would we expect to have a mean weight per bag of less than 1·99 kg?

Solution

(It is important to recognise that the key distribution we have to deal with is the distribution of the sample means, which is normally distributed. We need to determine its mean and its standard deviation. Then we can convert 1·99 to standard units, and use the Standard Normal Tables to calculate the probability.)

(i) Population (all bags of flour):

$\mu = 2$

$\sigma = 0{\cdot}05$ (50 g = 0·05 kg)

Distribution of the sample means (samples of size 100):

$\mu_{\bar{x}} = \mu = 2$

$$\sigma_{\bar{x}} = \frac{\sigma}{\sqrt{n}}$$
$$= \frac{0{\cdot}05}{\sqrt{100}}$$
$$= 0{\cdot}005$$

This distribution is normal.

$x = 1{\cdot}99$: $\quad z = \dfrac{x - \mu_{\bar{x}}}{\sigma_{\bar{x}}}$
$$= \frac{1{\cdot}99 - 2}{0{\cdot}005}$$
$$= -2$$

Thus

$$P(X \le 1{\cdot}99) = P(Z \le -2)$$
$$= P(Z \ge 2)$$
$$= 1 - P(Z \le 2)$$
$$= 1 - 0{\cdot}9772$$
$$= 0{\cdot}0228.$$

(ii) The expected number of consignments with a mean weight per bag of less than 1·99 kg is

$$np = (1200)(0{\cdot}0228)$$
$$= 27{\cdot}36$$

Thus, we would expect 27 consignments to have a mean weight per bag of less than 1·99 kg.

Exercises 40.2

1. Twenty people each remove the twelve picture cards from a pack of cards. This leaves them with 40 cards each: 4 aces, 4 twos, up to 4 tens. Each person selects a card from their pack, notes the number (with an ace counting as 1), and returns the card to the pack. This procedure of selecting a card is repeated 20 times by each person.

(i) All in all, how many cards are selected? Describe the appearance of a histogram showing the frequency or relative frequency of all cards selected. What should happen to the shape of the histogram if the experiment was expanded to include many more people?

(ii) If it were possible to select cards an infinite number of times, construct a table showing the probabilities, or relative frequencies, of the numbers from 1 to 10. If X is the random variable representing the number obtained, calculate $\mu = E(X)$, the mean and σ, the standard deviation.

(iii) Suppose Sean is one of the twenty people and he picks a card 20 times. Describe how the distribution of his results would compare with the distributions in part (i) and part (ii) above.

(iv) For each person, the mean of their twenty numbers drawn is calculated. Then a distribution is formed of all the means of the samples. Describe the shape of this distribution. If the experiment were expanded to include many more people each selecting a card twenty times, describe what effect this would have on the distribution of the sample means.

(v) If we start the experiment again, and this time ask each of the twenty people to pick a card 100 times, and to calculate the mean of their 100 numbers. How would the distribution of the sample means here compare with the distribution of the sample means in part (iv)? Describe any differences.

(vi) For the experiment in part (v), state the mean of the distribution of the sample means, and calculate its standard deviation. What is the probability that the mean of Sean's 100 selections is less than 5·2?

2. A machine is constructed to select at random a real number between 0 and 10. This means that each point on the number line has an equal chance of being chosen.

(i) Describe the distribution of numbers if the machine makes 20, 100, 1000, 1000000 selections. What happens to the distribution as the number of selections increases?

(ii) The distribution of all possible selections has a mean of 5 and a standard deviation of 2·8868. Suppose samples of size 50 are obtained from the machine and the mean of each sample measured.
Describe the distribution of the sample means, giving its mean and its standard deviation.

(iii) If a single sample of size 50 is chosen, what is the probability that its mean lies between 5·5 and 6?

(iv) What would be the probability that in a single sample of size 100, the mean would lie between 5·5 and 6?

3. The diagram below shows the probability density curve for a population which has mean and standard deviation of 6 and 2·5 respectively.

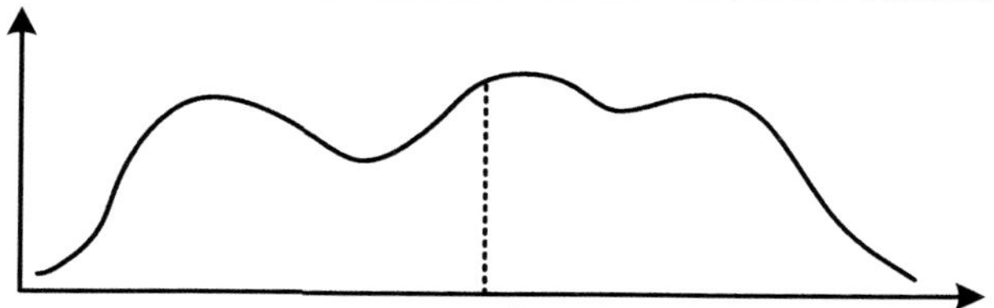

(i) From the graph, is this distribution normal? Give a reason.

(ii) If a single sample of size 64 were drawn from this population, how would you describe the appearance of the distribution of the sample. Comment on what you think its mean and its standard deviation might be.

(iii) Describe the distribution of the means of a large number of samples of size 64. What is its mean? Calculate its standard deviation.

(iv) What is the probability that the mean of a single sample of size 64 is greater than or equal to 6·5?

4. A trial consists of tossing a fair coin 4 times. Let X be the number of heads obtained.

(i) Complete the probability distribution table below.

$x \in X$	0	1	2	3	4
$P(x)$	$\frac{1}{16}$				

(ii) Represent this distribution on a histogram.

(iii) Calculate the expected value, $E(X)$, i.e. the mean μ. Calculate the standard deviation, treating the probabilities as frequencies.

(iv) Suppose one player repeats this trial 36 times and records the number of heads each time. What will this player's distribution look like?

(v) Suppose many people repeat the test 36 times each, and the mean number of heads over the 36 trials is recorded for each person. For the distribution of the sample means, what is the mean and the standard deviation?

(vi) If a single person repeats the trial 36 times, what is the probability that the mean number of heads obtained is greater than 2·3?

40.3 Confidence Intervals for the Population Mean

The Central Limit Theorem may be applied to form a confidence interval for the mean of a population, given the mean of a large enough sample, and a standard deviation.

Suppose a population has a mean of μ and a standard deviation of σ. Also suppose that we have a random sample of size $n \geq 30$ from this population, and that this sample has mean $\bar{x}$. We would like to use this information to form a confidence interval for μ, for example a 95% confidence interval for the population mean.

We may consider $\bar{x}$ to be a single sample mean from the distribution of all sample means of size n. Using the exact same argument as for the population proportion, there is a 95% probability that $\bar{x}$ lies in the interval $[\mu - E, \mu + E]$, i.e. that

$$\mu - E \leq \bar{x} \leq \mu + E$$

where E is the margin of error.

Once again, we reverse the argument. We can equally well say that there is a 95% probability that the population mean, μ, lies in the interval $[\bar{x} - E, \bar{x} + E]$, i.e. that

$$\bar{x} - E \leq \mu \leq \bar{x} + E,$$

where E is the margin of error.

The margin of error, E, is defined in terms of the standard deviation of the distribution of the sample means. This standard deviation is called the **standard error of the mean**, S.E.

From the last section,

$$\text{S.E. of the mean} = \sigma_{\bar{X}} = \frac{\sigma}{\sqrt{n}}.$$

Then, in general, the margin of error is given by

$$E = z \times \sigma_{\bar{X}}$$

where the value of z depends on the confidence level. As we saw in Section 1, for a 95% confidence level, $z = 1{\cdot}96$. Thus the 95% confidence interval for μ is

$$\bar{x} - 1{\cdot}96\sigma_{\bar{X}} \leq \mu \leq \bar{x} + 1{\cdot}96\sigma_{\bar{X}}$$

or $$\bar{x} - 1{\cdot}96\frac{\sigma}{\sqrt{n}} \leq \mu \leq \bar{x} + 1{\cdot}96\frac{\sigma}{\sqrt{n}}.$$

95% Confidence Interval for the Population Mean

A population has a mean of μ and a standard deviation of σ. Suppose a sample of size $n \geq 30$ has a mean of $\bar{x}$. Then the 95% confidence interval for the population mean, μ, is

$$\bar{x} - 1{\cdot}96\frac{\sigma}{\sqrt{n}} \leq \mu \leq \bar{x} + 1{\cdot}96\frac{\sigma}{\sqrt{n}}.$$

In practice, if the standard deviation of the population, σ, is not available, then we use the standard deviation of the sample, s, in its place.

Example 1

A random sample of 64 thirteen-year-old students was taken, and their weekly pocket money was recorded. The mean pocket money of these students was found to be €4·50, and the standard deviation was calculated to be €0·60. Form a 95% confidence interval for the mean pocket money of all thirteen-year-old students in the population.

Solution

Let μ be the mean pocket money of all thirteen-year-old students.

For the sample, $\bar{x} = 4{\cdot}5$, $s = 0{\cdot}6$ and $n = 64$.

As the population standard deviation is not available, we use s instead of σ.

$$\text{S.E. of the mean} = \frac{s}{\sqrt{n}}$$

$$= \frac{0{\cdot}6}{\sqrt{64}} = 0{\cdot}075$$

Then the 95% confidence interval for the mean pocket money of all thirteen-year-old students is

$$4{\cdot}5 - 1{\cdot}96(0{\cdot}075) \le \mu \le 4{\cdot}5 + 1{\cdot}96(0{\cdot}075)$$

$$4{\cdot}353 \le \mu \le 4{\cdot}647$$

Thus, the 95% confidence interval for μ is from €4·36 to €4·64. Note that we round to stay inside the interval from 4·353 to 4·647.

Exercises 40.3

1. The standard deviation of the weight of a certain type of glass bottle produced by a factory is known to be 3·5 g. A random sample of 500 of these bottles has a mean weight of 221·5 g. Obtain a 95% confidence interval for the mean weight of all glass bottles of this type produced by the factory.
2. The standard deviation of the number of vehicles passing through a toll-booth on a working day is known to be 356. In a survey over 80 working days, the mean number of cars passing through the toll-booth is 4683. Obtain a 95% confidence interval for the mean number of cars passing through the toll-booth on working days.
3. The standard deviation of the total number of points scored by both teams in inter-county hurling matches is known to be 6·2. In a survey of 40 matches, the mean number of points scored by both teams is found to be 28·4. Obtain a 95% confidence interval for the mean number of points scored by both teams in inter-county hurling matches.
4. The standard deviation of the running time of films released to cinema is known to be 12·6 minutes. A random sample of 55 films released to cinema have a mean running time of 121 minutes. Obtain a 95% confidence interval for the mean running time for all films released to cinema.
5. The mean length of 200 nails produced by a machine was found to be 7·42 cm. If the standard deviation of nail lengths is known to be 0·53 cm, find the 95% confidence interval for the mean length of all nails produced by the machine.
6. It is known that an examination paper is marked in such a way that the standard deviation is 15·1. In a survey of 80 students who sit the examination, the mean mark is found to be 57·4. Obtain a 95% confidence interval for the mean mark of all the students in the examination.
7. A sample of 120 bags of potatoes produced by a factory was found to have a mean weight of 2·47 kg and a standard deviation of 0·12 kg. Obtain a 95% confidence interval for the mean weight of all bags of potatoes produced by the factory.
8. In a recent marathon race, more than 10000 runners took part. A random sample of 180 of these runners gave a mean finishing time of 174 minutes and a standard deviation of 22 minutes. Obtain a 95% confidence interval for the mean finishing time of all the runners in the race.

9. A random sample of 100 university students shows that their mean weekly spending is €132 with a standard deviation of €13. Obtain a 95% confidence interval for the mean weekly spending of all university students.

10. A random sample of outstanding mortgages of 220 borrowers has a mean of €210000 and a standard deviation of €34000. Obtain a 95% confidence interval for the mean outstanding mortgages of borrowers.

40.4 Hypothesis Testing of the Population Proportion

Hypothesis testing is a technique used in statistics to test whether a claim that is made is consistent with data obtained.

If someone says that 40% of the cars in Ireland are black, common sense tells us that this is wrong. But how do we prove it?

We need to obtain evidence from a sample. For example, we could conduct a survey of a large number of cars, and suppose that we find that 32% of cars are black. This would suggest that the claim is wrong. But does it prove it, or has a very unlikely event just occurred, with the claim still being correct? We need a systematic way of deciding whether or not to reject the claim. This is where hypothesis testing comes in.

The method of hypothesis testing is very precise, and the steps outlined below must be followed. These steps are outlined as they apply to the types of hypothesis testing on our course. At a more advanced level, other options and steps exist.

[1] State the Null Hypothesis, H_0

The null hypothesis, H_0, is that there is nothing wrong (null = nothing) with the claim. For example, if the claim is that the population proportion is 0·4, then we write

H_0: $p = 0{\cdot}4$.

The way hypothesis testing works, unless we have sufficiently convincing evidence to the contrary, we do not reject the null hypothesis, i.e. we do not challenge the claim. It is important to note that this is not the same as saying that we accept the claim.

This is similar to criminal court cases, where a defendant may be found 'not guilty'. This is not the same as saying that he/she is innocent, merely that the charge has not been proved.

[2] Identify the Alternative Hypothesis, H_1

The alternative hypothesis, H_1, also written as H_a, is the hypothesis we accept if we have enough evidence to reject the null hypothesis. On our course, the alternative hypothesis will always be that the null hypothesis is wrong. For example, if

H_0: $p = 0{\cdot}4$

then

H_1: $p \neq 0{\cdot}4$.

On other courses, there are different possible forms of the alternative hypothesis, e.g. that the claim is over-stated or under-stated, rather than just being wrong.

[3] Obtain the Sample Statistic

Identify the sample statistic, i.e. the sample proportion, $\hat{p}$.

One important aspect of hypothesis testing is deciding the **level of significance**, i.e. how unusual a result must be before we say that the claim is wrong. A 5% level of significance means that if the result lies among the 5% of most unlikely results, we will reject the null hypothesis (and accept the alternative hypothesis); otherwise we do not reject the null hypothesis.

In this section, we look only at a special case of hypothesis testing, i.e. where

(i) we are testing a claim about a population proportion,
(ii) the level of significance is 5%,
(iii) we are allowed to use the margin of error approximation, $E = \frac{1}{\sqrt{n}}$, for the margin of error of the distribution of the sample proportions, for samples of size n.

As we know from Section 40.1, approximately 95% of the sample proportions will lie within $E = \frac{1}{\sqrt{n}}$ of the population proportion, i.e. within the interval $[p - E, p + E]$. Hence 5% of the sample proportions will lie outside this interval. We can use this knowledge to make our decision about whether or not to reject the null hypothesis.

[4] Make a Decision

Having calculated E, $p - E$ and $p + E$, we can now make our decision.

(i) If $p - E \leq \hat{p} \leq p + E$, i.e. the sample proportion lies within the margin of error of the population proportion (according to the null hypothesis), then we do not reject the null hypothesis. In this case, we can say that the result is **not significant**.
(ii) If $\hat{p} < p - E$ or if $\hat{p} > p + E$, then we reject the null hypothesis, and accept the alternative hypothesis. In this case, we can say that the result is **significant**. The region of values of $\hat{p}$ for which we reject the null hypothesis is called the **critical region**, and $p - E$, $p + E$ are called critical values.

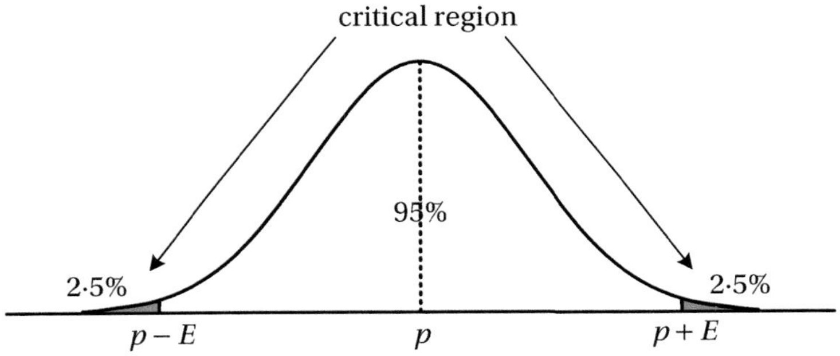

This basis upon which we decide our conclusion is called the **decision rule**. If the value of $\hat{p}$ is very close to either of the critical values, then we tend not to reject the null hypothesis. This is similar to a court case, and the idea of 'beyond reasonable doubt'.

Example 1

An engineering company states in its literature that only 20% of its products experience a problem within the first five years of use. To investigate this claim, you sample 400 of their products and find that 98 of them have experienced a problem within the first five years of use.

(i) What is the hypothesis?
(ii) On what basis will you reject or not reject the hypothesis?
(iii) Calculate the margin of error, using the margin of error approximation.
(iv) Calculate the sample proportion of failures within the first five years.
(v) Can you conclude that company's claim is false? Give a reason.

Solution

(i) *(The 'hypothesis' is assumed to be the null hypothesis.)*

The hypothesis is that the company's claim is true, i.e.

H_0: $p = 20\% = 0{\cdot}2$

(ii) We will reject the hypothesis if the sample proportion lies outside the margin of error of the stated proportion. If it does not lie outside the margin of error, we will not reject the hypothesis.

(iii) To calculate the margin of error:

$$E = \frac{1}{\sqrt{400}} = \frac{1}{20} = 0{\cdot}05 = 5\%$$

(iv) The sample proportion of failures is

$$\hat{p} = \frac{98}{400} = 0{\cdot}245 = 24{\cdot}5\%$$

(v) We will reject the hypothesis if $\hat{p}$ lies outside the interval from

$20\% - 5\% = 15\%$

to $20\% + 5\% = 25\%$

As $\hat{p} = 24{\cdot}5\%$ does not lie outside this interval, we cannot reject the hypothesis, H_0. Thus, we have not got enough evidence to dispute the company's claim.

Exercises 40.4

1. Election workers for a candidate, X, in an election have confidently predicted that she will gain 45% of the first preference votes and so top the poll. To test this claim, the workers for another candidate, Y, take a random sample of 1024 voters. This sample suggest that the support for candidate X is at 42%.

(i) State the null hypothesis and the alternative hypothesis.
(ii) On what basis should the hypothesis be rejected or not rejected?
(iii) Do you think the election workers for candidate Y have evidence to dispute the claim made by the election workers for candidate X? Give a reason.

2. The manufacturers of a new treatment claim that it cures hiccups within 20 seconds for 90% of people. An independent body decides to check this claim. The new treatment is tested on a random sample of 4000 hiccups sufferers, and cures the hiccups of 3540 of these.

(i) State the hypothesis that should be made by the independent body.
(ii) On what basis should the independent body reject or not reject the hypothesis?
(iii) Determine if the independent body should have concern about the claim made by the manufacturers.

3. A lobby group for three-legged aliens states that 60% of the population supports their view that the aliens should be treated as privileged citizens. To test this claim, you conduct a survey. You sample 2000 people at random, and obtain a proportion of 62·4% in support of the claim.

(i) What should your hypothesis be?
(ii) On what basis should you reject or not reject the hypothesis?
(iii) Determine if you have sufficient evidence to reject the claim by the lobby group.

4. A car manufacturer claims in an ad that 70% of company executives prefer its special suspension to the normal one used by all its main competitors. An advertising standards agency decides to check this claim. It chooses a random sample of 600 company executives and queries whether or not they support the car manufacturer's claim.
   (i) State the hypothesis that should be made by the advertising standards agency.
   (ii) What is the margin of error?
   (iii) What is the least number of executives needed to support the claim for the advertising agency not to reject the hypothesis and take issue with the car manufacturer?

5. A cat-food manufacturer claims that 8 out of 10 cats prefer its brand 'Miaow' to all other cat-foods. Some other manufacturers are not convinced. They decide to test the claim. Using rigorous methods, they test n cats to see if they prefer 'Miaow' cat-food.
   (i) State the hypothesis that should be made.
   (ii) If the hypothesis is rejected when the percentage of cats who prefer 'Miaow' is below 78%, calculate n.
   (iii) Find the greatest possible value of n if a result of 76% is not significant.

6. A radio station claims that 55% of all listeners in the 8 am to 9 am slot tune in to their programme, Rise and Shine. To check this claim a competing station commissions a survey of a random sample of listeners in the 8 am to 9 am time slot. The survey indicates that the claim cannot be rejected.
   (i) If the size of the sample taken in the survey is 1000, determine the least and the greatest number of listeners that could have said that they listen to Rise and Shine.
   (ii) If the outcome of the survey was that 52% of the sample said that they listened to Rise and Shine, what is the greatest possible size of the sample?

40.5 Hypothesis Testing of the Population Mean

Hypothesis testing of a population mean is different from the testing of a population proportion, as seen in the last section. The key difference lies in the fact that we have to use the normal distribution to obtain the critical region and the critical values.

Suppose a claim is made that the mean weight of a particular variety of potato after a specified growing time is 375 grams. A random sample of 100 of these potatoes has a mean weight of 368 grams and a standard deviation of 38 grams. Does the data from the sample provide sufficient evidence to dispute the claim that the mean weight of all such potatoes is 375 grams?

The procedure we use to test this claim is as follows.

[1] State the Null Hypothesis, H_0

The null hypothesis is that the mean weight is as claimed, i.e.
H_0: $\mu = 375$

[2] State the Alternative Hypothesis, H_1

The alternative hypothesis is that the true mean weight is not 375 g.
H_1: $\mu \neq 375$

[3] Obtain the Test Statistic, T

The mean of the sample is $\bar{x} = 368$.

The test statistic, T, is the mean of the sample, $\bar{x}$, converted to standard (z) units. This assumes that the sample mean comes from the distribution of all sample means, from samples of size 100. On the basis that the null hypothesis is correct, this distribution has mean

$$\mu_{\bar{X}} = \mu = 375$$

and standard deviation (standard error)

$$\sigma_{\bar{X}} = \frac{s}{\sqrt{n}} = \frac{38}{\sqrt{100}} = 3{\cdot}8$$

using s instead of σ, as the standard deviation of the population is not available.

Then $$T = \frac{\bar{x} - \mu}{\sigma_{\bar{X}}}$$

$$T = \frac{\bar{x} - \mu}{\frac{s}{\sqrt{n}}}$$

$$T = \frac{368 - 375}{3{\cdot}8}$$

$$T = -1{\cdot}8421$$

[4] Use the Significance Level to Determine the Critical Region and Critical Values

A significance level of 5% ($\alpha = 0{\cdot}05$) means that the critical region is the 5% of the most unlikely results. This is the exact opposite of the 95% confidence interval, which refers to the 95% of the most likely results.

As we are dealing with a standard normal distribution, the critical region is given by those values of Z for which

$$P(Z \le -z) + P(Z \ge z) = 0{\cdot}05$$
$$2P(Z \ge z) = 0{\cdot}05$$
$$P(Z \ge z) = 0{\cdot}025$$
$$P(Z \le z) = 1 - 0{\cdot}025 = 0{\cdot}975$$

giving $z = 1{\cdot}96$.

Thus, at the 5% level of significance, the critical region is then to the left of $-1{\cdot}96$ and to the right of $1{\cdot}96$. The values $-1{\cdot}96$ and $1{\cdot}96$ are the critical values.

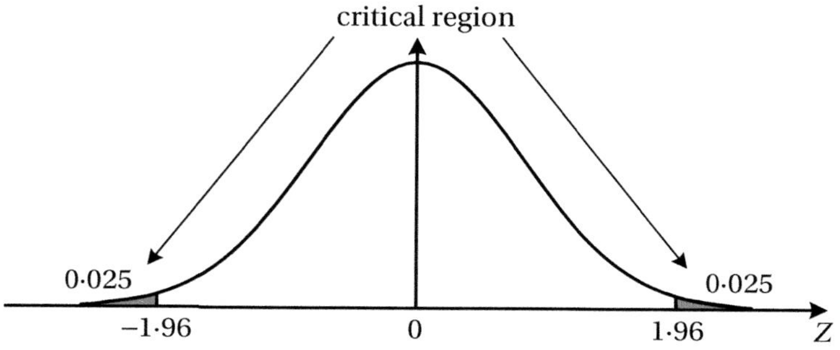

Other levels of significance, e.g. 10%, 1%, can be tackled in similar fashion to obtain the critical region and the critical values.

[5] Make a Decision

Suppose the critical values are $-z_1$ and z_1, where $z_1 > 0$.

(i) If the test statistic, T, lies outside the critical region, i.e.

$$-z_1 \le T \le z_1$$

then we say that the result is **not significant**, and we do **not reject the null hypothesis**.

(ii) If the test statistic, T, lies in the critical region, i.e.

$T < -z_1$ or $T > z_1$

then we say that the result is **significant**, and we **reject the null hypothesis**, and accept the alternative hypothesis.

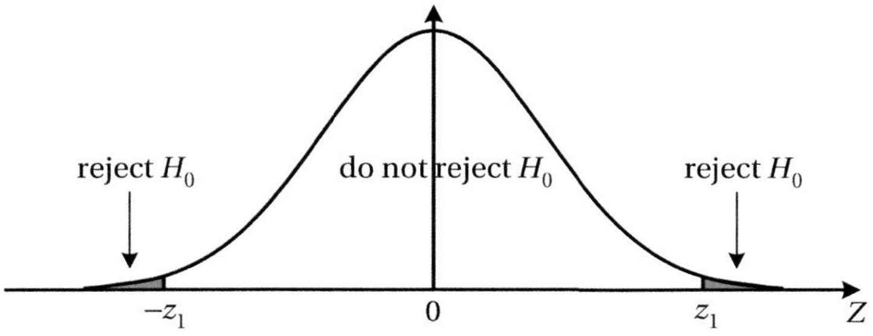

For the example outlined above, at the 5% level of significance,

$-1{\cdot}96 \le -1{\cdot}8421 \le 1{\cdot}96$

i.e. $-z_1 \le T \le z_1$

and so we say that the result is not significant. Thus we do not reject the null hypothesis, i.e. there is not enough evidence to reject the statement that the mean weight of the type of potatoes is 375 g.

Example 1

The mean breaking strength of a certain type of string, manufactured by an old machine, has been established over a long period of time to be 183 g.

A new machine is purchased to manufacture this type of string. A sample of 150 pieces of string obtained from the new machine shows a mean breaking strength of 180 g and a standard deviation of 12 g.

Is there sufficient evidence to say that the new machine produces strings with a different mean breaking strength than the old, at the 5% level of significance?

Solution

Let μ be the mean breaking strength of the strings produced by the new machine.

H_0: $\mu = 183$

H_1: $\mu \ne 183$

Sample mean: $\bar{x} = 180$

Then the test statistic is

$$T = \frac{\bar{x} - \mu}{\frac{s}{\sqrt{n}}}$$

$$T = \frac{180 - 183}{\frac{12}{\sqrt{150}}}$$

$$T = -3{\cdot}06$$

At the 5% level of significance, the critical values are $-1{\cdot}96$ and $1{\cdot}96$.

As $T < -1{\cdot}96$, the result is significant. Thus we reject the null hypothesis, and accept the alternative hypothesis that the mean breaking strength of the string produced by the new machine is different from the mean of the strings produced by the old.

p-Values: An Alternative Approach to Hypothesis Testing

Having stated the null hypothesis and the alternative hypothesis, and calculated the test statistic, we can proceed in an alternative direction to make a decision.

This involves calculating the p-value associated with the test statistic, T. The p-value is the probability of getting a result as extreme, or more extreme, than the actual value of T obtained, assuming that the null hypothesis is correct.

For example, suppose a test statistic $T = 2{\cdot}05$ is obtained. Then the associated p-value is

$$\text{p-value} = P(Z \le -2{\cdot}05) + P(Z \ge 2{\cdot}05).$$

Using the properties of the standard normal distribution, we can rewrite this:

$$\begin{aligned}\text{p-value} &= 2P(Z \ge 2{\cdot}05) && \text{... by symmetry}\\ &= 2\big(1 - P(Z \le 2{\cdot}05)\big) && \text{... as the total area is 1}\end{aligned}$$

We can now look up $P(Z \le 2{\cdot}05)$ in the *Formulae and Tables*, and finish calculating the p-value.

$$\begin{aligned}\text{p-value} &= 2(1 - 0{\cdot}9798)\\ &= 0{\cdot}0404.\end{aligned}$$

In general, because the test statistic, T, can be negative, we can write

$$\text{p-value} = 2\big(1 - P(Z \le |T|)\big)$$

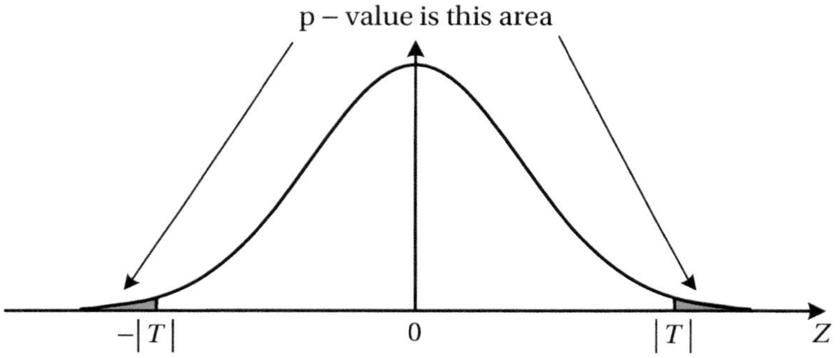

p-Value for a Test Statistic

The p-value for a test statistic, T, is the probability of getting a result as extreme, or more extreme, than the value of T obtained, assuming that the null hypothesis is correct. The p-value for T may be calculated using

$$\text{p-value} = 2\big(1 - P(Z \le |T|)\big).$$

The decision to reject, or not reject, the null hypothesis is based on a comparison of the p-value with the level of significance, α.

(i) If p-value $\ge \alpha$
then the result is **not significant**, and we do not reject the null hypothesis.

(ii) If p-value $< \alpha$
then the result is **significant**, and we reject the null hypothesis in favour of the alternative hypothesis.

Example 2

A food company claims that the mean weight of the packets of muesli it produces is 500 g, with a standard deviation of 15 g. A random sample of 64 of these shows a mean weight of 496 g.

(i) Calculate the test statistic obtained from the sample mean.

(ii) Calculate the p-value for the test statistic.

(iii) Is this result significant at the 5% level of significance? Give a reason.

(iv) Is this result significant at the 1% level of significance? Give a reason.

Solution

(i) Let μ be the mean weight of all packets of muesli produced.

H_0: $\mu = 500$

H_1: $\mu \neq 500$

For the sample: $\bar{x} = 496$

The test statistic is then

$$T = \frac{\bar{x} - \mu}{\frac{\sigma}{\sqrt{n}}}$$

$$T = \frac{496 - 500}{\frac{15}{\sqrt{64}}}$$

$$T = -2{\cdot}13$$

(ii) The associated p-value is then

$$\begin{aligned} \text{p-value} &= 2(1 - P(Z \leq |T|)) \\ &= 2(1 - P(Z \leq |-2{\cdot}13|)) \\ &= 2(1 - P(Z \leq 2{\cdot}13)) \\ &= 2(1 - 0{\cdot}9834) \\ &= 0{\cdot}0332 \end{aligned}$$

(iii) At a 5% level of significance, $\alpha = 0{\cdot}05$. As the p-value is less than α, the result is significant, and we reject the null hypothesis.

(iv) At the 1% level of significance, $\alpha = 0{\cdot}01$. As the p-value is greater than α, the result is not significant, and we do not reject the null hypothesis.

An alternative definition of the p-value is that it is the smallest level of significance at which the null hypothesis is rejected. For example, a p-value of 0·05 will result in rejection of the null hypothesis only if the level of significance is 5% = 0·05 or more.

p-values are very frequently used in hypothesis testing, as they make it easier to decide whether to reject, or not reject, the null hypothesis at different levels of confidence.

p-values are used extensively in academic and professional work. When publishing the results of a statistical hypothesis test in journals, many researchers report the p-value. It is then left to the reader of the report to judge the significance of the result, i.e. the reader must determine, on the basis of the reported p-value, whether or not to reject the null hypothesis. Some readers might want to use a 5% level of significance, others might insist on a more demanding level such as 1%.

Exercises 40.5

1. A coal merchant who sells his coal in bags marked '50 kg' claims that the bags have a mean weight of 50 kg and a standard deviation of 1 kg. A trade inspector decides to test the claim about the mean weight. A random selection of 60 of these bags are weighed and are found to have a mean weight of 49·6 kg.
   (i) What is the null hypothesis?
   (ii) What is the alternative hypothesis?
   (iii) What is the test statistic for the sample mean?
   (iv) At the 5% level of significance, is there evidence to show that the mean weight of the bags of coal is not 50 kg? Explain your reasoning.

2. An insurance company estimated a number of years ago that the average payout on claims is €3400. It is decided to conduct a review of this estimate. A random sample of 200 claims is found to have an average payout of €3450 with a standard deviation of €350.
   (i) What is the null hypothesis?
   (ii) What is the alternative hypothesis?
   (iii) What is the test statistic for the sample mean?
   (iv) At the 5% level of significance, is there evidence to show that the average payout on claims is no longer €3400? Explain your reasoning.

3. A consumer agency claims that the average weekly shopping bill for families is €220. You decide to test this claim. You take a random sample of 80 families and determine that, for these families, the average weekly shopping bill is €228 with a standard deviation of €41. Determine if there is enough evidence to conclude that the claim made by the consumer agency is not true, at the 5% level of significance.

4. A car battery manufacturer claims that the average life of the batteries they produce is 4·6 years, with a standard deviation of 0·8 years. To test this claim, a random sample of 120 batteries was tested, and their average life was found to be 4·8 years. Determine if there is enough evidence to conclude that the claim made by the car battery manufacturer is not true, at the 5% level of significance.

In each of the following questions, you are given μ, the claimed mean of a population, $\bar{x}$, the mean of a random sample, n, the size of sample and either σ, the population standard deviation, or s, the sample standard deviation. In each case, calculate
(i) the sample statistic, T,
(ii) the p-value for the sample.

5. $\mu = 12{\cdot}5, \bar{x} = 12{\cdot}9, n = 50, \sigma = 1{\cdot}5$
6. $\mu = 420, \bar{x} = 411, n = 80, s = 42$
7. $\mu = 12500, \bar{x} = 12734, n = 180, \sigma = 1520$
8. $\mu = 7{\cdot}35, \bar{x} = 7{\cdot}24, n = 120, s = 0{\cdot}66$

9. An internet provider claims that the mean speed of its internet connection is 45 MB/s, with a standard deviation of 4 MB/s. A random sample of 80 users of this internet provider shows a mean speed of 44 MB/s.
   (i) Calculate the sample statistic for this sample.
   (ii) Determine the p-value for this sample statistic.
   (iii) Is this result significant at the 5% level of significance? Give a reason.
   (iv) Is this result significant at the 1% level of significance? Give a reason.

10. A fashion magazine claims that the average adult male waistline is 89 cm, with a standard deviation of 6 cm. A sample of 240 adult males is taken and their waistlines are measured. This shows an average of 90·1 cm.
   (i) Calculate the sample statistic for this sample.
   (ii) Determine the p-value for this sample statistic.

(iii) Is this result significant at the 5% level of significance? Give a reason.
(iv) Is this result significant at the 1% level of significance? Give a reason.

11. A newspaper advertises that the average annual income of its regular readers is €75000. A random sample of 200 of the regular readers of the newspaper shows that their average annual income is €73400 with a standard deviation of €10350.
(i) Calculate the sample statistic for this sample.
(ii) Determine the p-value for this sample statistic.
(iii) Is this result significant at the 5% level of significance? Give a reason.
(iv) Is this result significant at the 1% level of significance? Give a reason.

12. An aptitude test for children of a certain age was standardised some time ago to have a mean of 100 and a standard deviation of 15. Recently this test was given to a randomly selected group of children and the mean score was recorded as 101·6.
No record was kept of the number of children tested.
What is the least number of children tested if the result shows, at the 5% level of significance, that the population mean is unlikely to be still 100?

Revision Exercises 40

1. A company wants to determine the level of satisfaction among its customers for its after-sales service. It conducts a survey of 360 of its customers chosen at random, and finds that 278 express satisfaction with the company's after-sales service.
(i) Calculate the margin of error.
(ii) Give the 95% confidence interval for the true proportion of customers who are satisfied with the company's after-sales service.
(iii) The company decides to claim that 80% of customers are satisfied with the after-sales service they provide. Do you think there is evidence to dispute the company's claim? Give a reason.

2. (i) What sample size would be required to have a margin of error of 1%?
(ii) Are there any problems associated with acquiring a sample of this size? Explain.

3. Zoe wants to determine the proportion of adults in her area who attend the local cinema at least once a month. She conducts a survey by selecting a sample from the adults in her area.
(i) If she gets a 95% confidence interval of between 32% and 38%, what sample size did she take?
(ii) If she were to double the size of her sample and achieve the same sample proportion, what would be the confidence interval now?

4. A claim that 40% of people eat fruit at least once a day is rejected on the basis of a sample proportion of 37%. What is the least number of people that could have been surveyed to justify the rejection?

5. A political party wants to gauge the support for its candidate in an upcoming bi-election. So it commissions a survey which predicts, with 95% confidence, that the party's candidate will receive between 28% and 36% of the first preference vote. Calculate the size of the sample of voters taken.

6. A property development company is considering building a new retail outlet in a country town. To be viable, it would need 40% of the people in the town and its surrounding area to indicate their willingness to switch to their new store, should it be built. A random sample of local shoppers is obtained, and 37% of these indicate that they will switch.
(i) If the sample is of size 100, on the basis of the outcome, should the company go ahead with the development, not go ahead, or take a larger sample? Give a reason.
(ii) The company decides not to go ahead with its plans, as the result is outside the margin of error. Find the least possible size of the sample.

7. A manufacturer of light bulbs states that 80% of its light bulbs work for more than 1000 hours. After some complaints, a consumer body decides to investigate the claim.

(i) What should the hypothesis be?

(ii) On what basis should the body reject or not reject the hypothesis?

(iii) If a sample of 400 bulbs is selected at random and 76% are found to last for more than 1000 hours, should the hypothesis be rejected? Give a reason.

(iv) A sample of size n bulbs is selected at random and 83% are found to last more than 1000 hours. If the hypothesis is rejected, find the least possible value of n.

8. There is doubt as to whether a coin is fair or not. The coin is tossed 1000 times, and the number of heads obtained is recorded.

(i) If the coin is fair, what should the proportion of heads be if it is tossed a very large number of times? Give a reason.

(ii) In testing to see if the coin is fair, what should the hypothesis be?

(iii) On what basis should we reject or not reject the hypothesis?

(iv) What is the least number of heads that we could obtain that would not cause us to reject the hypothesis?

(v) What is the greatest number of heads that we could obtain that would not cause us to reject the hypothesis?

9. A newspaper, the Globe, claims that 77% of those in the AB social class (managerial and professional) read its newspaper every day. This claim is contested by other newspapers. A sample of 2000 people in the AB social class, chosen at random, is queried as to whether or not they read the Globe each day.

(i) What should the hypothesis be?

(ii) On what basis should the hypothesis be rejected or not rejected?

(iii) If 72% of those surveyed indicate that they do read the Globe each day, should the hypothesis be rejected? Give a reason.

(iv) If, in an additional question, 75% of those surveyed said that they read the Globe at least four times a week, do you think that the Globe would be entitled to change it's advertising to say that 77% of those in the AB social class read the Globe at least four times a week? Give a reason.

10. A well-known media commentator, Lance Boyle, claims that over 80% of 'ordinary' people consider that personal crime has got worse in the last five years, citing a large number of friends and acquaintances he has asked. He proposes draconian action be taken against anyone convicted of a personal crime. In order to test his claim, a civil rights group obtains a random sample of size 600, and finds that 453 support Mr Boyle's claim.

(i) What should the hypothesis be?

(ii) On what basis should the hypothesis be rejected or not rejected?

(iii) Based on the outcome of the survey, should the civil rights group take issue with Mr Boyle's claim?

(iv) Is it possible that Mr Boyle has reason to believe his claim is true, based on the survey he conducted informally? Give a reason.

11. The diagram below shows the probability density function for a population that has a mean of 15 and a standard deviation of 6.

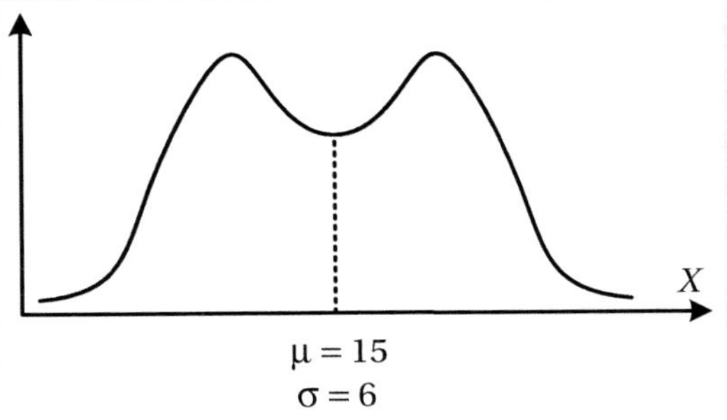

(i) From the graph, is this distribution normal? Give a reason.
How would you describe the distribution?
(ii) If a single sample of size 100 was taken, what would you expect the appearance of its distribution to be? Comment on what you think its mean and its standard deviation might be.
(iii) Describe the distribution of the means of a large number of samples of size 100.
What is its mean and what is its standard deviation?
(iv) A single sample of size 100 is taken. What is the probability that its mean is greater than 16?

12. The marks obtained in a mathematics examination have mean 54 and standard deviation 13.
(i) Why is it not possible from the information supplied to determine the probability that a single result is greater than 70?
(ii) What is the probability that from a random sample of 40 marks, the mean mark is greater than 58?

13. In a particular industry, the daily wages of a certain type of worker are normally distributed with a mean of €16·50 and a standard deviation of €1·50. 25 such workers are chosen at random.
(i) Explain why we can consider the distribution of the sample means of all samples of size 25 to be normally distributed.
(ii) What is the probability that the mean wage of the 25 workers chosen is less than €15·75?

14. In a company savings bank, the average savings is €159·32 with a standard deviation of €18. What is the probability that a group of 400 accounts chosen at random have a mean savings of €160 or more?

15. In a certain constituency in the last election, 62·5% of voters supported the Good Time Party. In a sample of 200 voters, it is now found that 107 support the Good Time Party.
(i) Estimate the margin of error for the distribution of the sample proportion.
(ii) Determine if there is evidence, at the 5% level of significance, that the support for the Good Time Party has changed since the last election.

16. A producer of electric light bulbs claims that its bulbs have a mean life of 1600 hours and a standard deviation of 250 hours. A random sample of 300 of these bulbs is found to have a mean life of 1571 hours.
(i) Obtain the test statistic for the sample mean.
(ii) Calculate the p-value for the sample statistic.
(iii) Is this result significant at the 5% level of significance? Give a reason.
(iv) Is this result significant at the 1% level of significance? Give a reason.

17. In a far-off country, the government claims that the mean hourly rate earned by workers is €23·42. The political opposition decide to test this claim. A random sample of 800 workers is chosen, and found to have a mean hourly rate of €22·92, with a standard deviation of €8·56.
(i) Obtain the test statistic for the sample mean.
(ii) Calculate the p-value for the sample statistic.
(iii) Is this result significant at the 5% level of significance? Give a reason.
(iv) Is this result significant at the 1% level of significance? Give a reason.

18. The average cholesterol level in a population is known to be 5·7. A study is conducted of the sufferers of a particular disease to see if they have a different average cholesterol level from the population. A random sample of 80 sufferers of the disease have their cholesterol level measured. They are found to have a mean of 5·87 and a standard deviation of 0·78.
(i) Obtain the test statistic for the sample mean.
(ii) Calculate the p-value for the sample statistic.
(iii) Is this result significant at the 5% level of significance? Give a reason.
(iv) Is this result significant at the 1% level of significance? Give a reason.

Answers

Chapter 21

Exercises 21.1, Pages 1–2

1. (i) Because the possible outcomes are not well defined, this is not a valid experiment. **(ii)** Because the possible outcomes are now clear, this is a valid experiment. **2. (i)** Yes, as the outcome will be a number. **(ii)** No, as 'attitude' is not well-defined.
3. (i) Yes, this is a valid experiment, with 20 possible outcomes. **(ii)** Yes, as the outcome is a number. The number of possible outcomes is very large, with many numbers from $1 \times 2 \times 3 \times 4 \times 5 = 120$ to $16 \times 17 \times 18 \times 19 \times 20 = 1860480$. There are too many to make listing them all a practical proposition.
4. (i) Yes. **(ii)** Monday, Tuesday, Wednesday, Thursday, Friday, Saturday and Sunday. **(iii)** There are 7 possible outcomes.
5. (i) Yes. There are 52 possible outcomes. **(ii)** If the card is red, then there are 26 possible outcomes. **(iii)** If the card is not a diamond, then the number of possible outcomes is 52 – 13 = 39.

Exercises 21.2, Pages 4–5

1. (i) 15 **2.** 12 **3. (i)** 45 **(ii)** 24 **4. (i)** 39 **(ii)** 12 **5. (i)** 2025 **(ii)** 720 **6. (i)** 18 **(ii)** 21 **7. (i)** 48 **(ii)** 250 **8. (i)** 15 **(ii)** 6 **9. (i)** 26000 **(ii)** 2600 **(iii)** 13000 **10. (i)** 58500 **(ii)** 5100 **11. (i)** 81 **(ii)** 648 **12. (i)** 100000 **(ii)** 5000

Exercises 21.3, Pages 8–9

1. (i) 5040 **(ii)** 720 **2. (i)** 720 **(ii)** 120 **3. (i)** 120 **(ii)** 24 **4. (i)** 40320 **(ii)** 5040 **(iii)** 720 **5. (i)** 72 **(ii)** 12 **6. (i)** 720 **(ii)** 48 **7. (i)** 5040 **(ii)** 1440 **8. (i)** 40320 **(ii)** 4320 **9. (i)** 720 **(ii)** 120 **(iii)** 240 **10. (i)** 120 **(ii)** 48 **(iii)** 36 **11.** 240 **12. (i)** 40320 **(ii)** 80640 **(iii)** 30240 **13. (i)** 3,628,800 **(ii)** 14400 **14.** 5040 **15.** 2,193,360 **16.** 1008

Exercises 21.4, Pages 12–13

1. 1287 **2.** 165 **3.** 136 **4.** 8 **5.** 3003 **6.** 1771 **7.** 120 **8.** 2,598,960 **9.** 28 **10. (i)** 126 **(ii)** 56 **11. (i)** 5,245,786 **(ii)** 91390 **12.** 20 **13. (i)** 3003 **(ii)** 1287 **(iii)** 1716 **(iv)** 1419 **14. (i)** 126 **(ii)** 60 **(iii)** 45 **(iv)** 121 **15.** 56 **16. (i)** 924 **(ii)** 350 **17. (i)** 126 **(ii)** 40 **18. (i)** 45 **(ii)** 21 **19. (i)** 103776 **(ii)** 886656 **(iii)** 3744 **20. (i)** 364 **(ii)** 78 **(iii)** 344 **(iv)** 224 **21.** 14 **22.** 17 **23.** 19

Revision Exercises 21, Pages 13–14

1. (i) 126 **(ii)** 35 **2. (i)** 720 **(ii)** 240 **3. (i)** 840 **(ii)** 816 **4. (i)** 100000 **(ii)** 5000 **5. (i)** 60 **(ii)** 5 **6. (i)** 330 **(ii)** 150 **7. (i)** 126 **(ii)** 60 **8. (i)** 40320 **(ii)** 6720 **9.** 3600 **10. (i)** 64 **(ii)** 49 **11. (i)** 648 **(ii)** 5184 **12.** 3528 **13. (i)** 24 **(ii)** 2880 **14.** 238

Chapter 22

Exercises 22.1, Pages 18–20

1. (i) all cards in pack of cards **(ii)** list all the diamonds **(iii)** yes **(iv)** diamond **2. (i)** 1, 2, 3, 4, 5, 6 **(ii)** even number: 2, 4, 6 **(iii)** $\frac{13}{24}$ **(iv)** 140 **3. (i)** 250 **(ii)** $\frac{36}{125}$ **(iii)** $\frac{119}{250}$ **(iv)** 36 **(v)** $\frac{117}{250}$ **4. (i)** 3, 4, 5, 6, 7, 8, 9, no **(ii)** no **(iii)** $\frac{7}{25}$ **5. (i)** 0, 1, 2, 3, 4 **(ii)** no **6.** no **7.** 21 **8.** 3·5, no

Exercises 22.2, Pages 23–24

1. (i) choose one student, all students, 22 **(ii)** boy, 10 **(iii)** $\frac{5}{11}$
2. (i) pick a marker, 12 **(ii)** green marker, 5 **(iii)** $\frac{5}{12}$
3. (i) throw die, 1, 2, 3, 4, 5, 6, $\#(S) = 6$ **(ii)** yes **(iii)** '3' or '4', 2 **(iv)** $\frac{1}{3}$ **4. (i)** 45 **(ii)** (1,4), (2,3) **(iii)** $\frac{2}{45}$ **5. (i)** 120 **(ii)** 63 **(iii)** $\frac{21}{40}$ **6. (i)** $\frac{3}{8}$ **(ii)** $\frac{3}{4}$ **(iii)** $\frac{3}{4}$ **7. (i)** $\frac{35}{66}$ **(ii)** $\frac{7}{22}$ **8.** $\frac{146}{4845}$ **9.** $\frac{55}{78}$ **10.** $\frac{4}{17}$ **11. (i)** 120 **(ii)** 48 **(iii)** $\frac{2}{5}$ **12. (i)** $\frac{5}{18}$ **(ii)** $\frac{11}{36}$ **13. (i)** $\frac{1}{6}$ **(ii)** $\frac{19}{36}$

Exercises 22.3, Pages 26–27

1. (i), (iv), (v) **2. (i)** A **(ii)** no **3.** $\frac{141}{175}$ **4. (i)** no **(ii)** $\frac{31}{35}$ **5.** $\frac{2}{5}$ **6.** $\frac{4}{9}$ **7. (i)** yes **(ii)** $\frac{3}{10}$ **8. (i)** yes **(ii)** $\frac{7}{16}$ **9. (i)** $\frac{2}{5}$ **(ii)** $\frac{3}{5}$ **(iii)** no **(iv)** 1 **(v)** no **10. (i)** $\frac{3}{44}$ **(ii)** $\frac{3}{11}$ **(iii)** yes **(iv)** $\frac{15}{44}$

Exercises 22.4, Page 29

1. $\frac{11}{36}$ **2.** $\frac{25}{26}$ **3.** $\frac{5}{6}$ **4.** $\frac{32}{33}$ **5. (i)** $\frac{7}{8}$ **(ii)** $\frac{1}{2}$ **6. (i)** $\frac{10}{13}$ **(ii)** $\frac{66}{91}$ **7.** $\frac{1343}{1728}$ **8.** $\frac{1111}{3750}$

Revision Exercises 22, Pages 29–30

1. (i) $\frac{1}{270725}$ **(ii)** $\frac{468}{20825}$ **2. (i)** $\frac{2}{3}$ **(ii)** $\frac{5}{42}$ **(iii)** $\frac{37}{42}$ **3. (i)** $\frac{1}{364}$ **(ii)** $\frac{9}{91}$ **(iii)** $\frac{55}{182}$ **(iv)** $\frac{149}{182}$ **4. (i)** $\frac{3}{10}$ **(ii)** $\frac{1}{12}$ **(iii)** $\frac{11}{12}$ **5. (i)** $\frac{11}{850}$ **(ii)** $\frac{13}{68}$ **(iii)** $\frac{997}{1700}$ **6. (i)** yes **(ii)** $\frac{1}{7}$ **(iii)** $\frac{4}{7}$ **(iv)** $\frac{5}{7}$ **7.** no **8. (i)** no **(ii)** no **9. (i)** $\frac{1}{12}$ **(ii)** $\frac{5}{12}$ **(iii)** $\frac{7}{12}$ **10. (i)** $\frac{50}{143}$ **(ii)** $\frac{3002}{3003}$ **(iii)** $\frac{7}{429}$ **11. (i)** 720 **(ii)** 240 **(iii)** $\frac{1}{3}$ **12. (i)** 40320 **(ii)** $\frac{3}{28}$ **13. (i)** 6 **(ii)** $\frac{1}{2}$ **14.** 8 **15. (i)** $\frac{30x}{(x+6)(x+5)(x+4)}$ **(ii)** 7

Chapter 23

Exercises 23.1, Pages 33–34

1. 0·68 **2.** $\frac{11}{12}$ **3.** $\frac{3}{4}$ **4.** 0·05 **5.** 0·27 **6.** 0·55 **7. (i)** 0·39, $E \subset F$ **(ii)** 0·81, 0·42 **8. (i)** $\frac{1}{2}, \frac{1}{13}$ **(ii)** $\frac{1}{26}$ **(iii)** $\frac{7}{13}$ **9. (i)** $\frac{1}{6}$ **(ii)** $\frac{5}{36}$ **(iii)** $\frac{1}{36}$ **(iv)** $\frac{5}{18}$ **10. (i)** $\frac{13}{110}$ **(ii)** $\frac{17}{693}$ **(iii)** $\frac{1}{231}$ **(iv)** $\frac{137}{990}$ **11.** $\frac{85}{231}$

Exercises 23.2, Page 39

1. $\frac{1}{2}$ **2.** $\frac{2}{5}$ **3.** $\frac{2}{3}$ **4. (i)** $\frac{3}{8}$ **(ii)** $\frac{3}{5}$ **5. (i)** $\frac{1}{2}$ **(ii)** $\frac{1}{4}$ **6.** $\frac{10}{11}$ **7. (i)** $\frac{1}{12}$ **(ii)** $\frac{1}{4}$ **(iii)** $\frac{1}{3}$ **8.** $\frac{4}{7}$ **9.** $\frac{90}{589}$ **10.** $\frac{45}{173}$ **11.** $\frac{15}{37}$ **12.** $\frac{3}{11}$ **13.** $\frac{16}{31}$ **14.** $\frac{5}{11}$

Exercises 23.3, Pages 41–42

1. (i) $\frac{1}{2}$ (ii) $\frac{1}{2}$ (iii) $\frac{1}{4}, \frac{1}{2}$, yes 2. (i) $\frac{1}{2}, \frac{3}{4}$ (ii) yes 3. (i) $\frac{1}{5525}, \frac{741}{1700}$ (ii) no 4. $\frac{1}{9}$ 5. $\frac{1}{3}$ 7. no 8. (i) no (ii) no

Exercises 23.4, Pages 45–46

1. (i) $\frac{1}{17}$ (ii) $\frac{13}{204}$ (iii) $\frac{1}{221}$ (iv) $\frac{4}{663}$ 2. (i) $\frac{5}{32}$ (ii) $\frac{7}{16}$ (iii) $\frac{23}{32}$ 3. (i) $\frac{2}{51}$ (ii) $\frac{5}{34}$ (iii) $\frac{57}{68}$ 4. (i) $\frac{1}{10}$ (ii) $\frac{1}{5}$ 5. (i) $\frac{51888}{1812175}$ (ii) $\frac{188}{221}$ 6. (i) $\frac{15}{91}$ (ii) $\frac{15}{91}$ (iii) $\frac{5}{21}$ 7. (i) $\frac{2}{15}$ (ii) $\frac{1}{3}$ 8. $\frac{7}{11}$ 9. $\frac{16}{33}$ 10. (i) $\frac{15}{91}$ (ii) $\frac{48}{91}$ 11. (i) $\frac{1}{16}$ (ii) $\frac{7}{80}$ (iii) $\frac{3}{16}$ (iv) $\frac{1}{4}$ 12. (i) $\frac{169}{1700}$ (ii) $\frac{39}{850}$ 13. $\frac{468}{20825}$ 14. (i) $\frac{2}{35}$ (ii) $\frac{18}{35}$

Exercises 23.5, Pages 50–51

1. (i) $\frac{1}{4}$ (ii) $\frac{1}{32}$ (iii) $\frac{1}{1024}$ 2. (i) 0·6 (ii) 0·24 (iii) 0·00393 3. (i) $\frac{4}{27}$ (ii) $\frac{16}{243}$ (iii) $\frac{128}{6561}$ 4. (i) $\frac{1}{4}$ (ii) $\frac{1}{16}$ (iii) $\frac{1}{64}$ 5. (i) $\frac{3}{16}$ (ii) $\frac{81}{1024}$ (iii) $\frac{729}{16384}$ 6. (i) $\frac{1}{64}$ (ii) $\frac{15}{64}$ (iii) $\frac{11}{32}$ 7. (i) $\frac{3125}{7776}$ (ii) $\frac{3125}{7776}$ (iii) $\frac{13}{3888}$ 8. (i) $\frac{1120}{6561}$ (ii) $\frac{2560}{6561}$ (iii) $\frac{43}{2187}$ 9. (i) $\frac{1215}{4096}$ (ii) $\frac{135}{512}$ 10. (i) 0·2575 (ii) 0·1159 (iii) 0·404 11. $\frac{5}{32}$ 12. $\frac{125}{1944}$ 13. $\frac{567}{262144}$ 14. 0·0911 15. (i) $\frac{75}{256}$ (ii) $\frac{35}{512}$

Revision Exercises 23, Pages 51–53

1. (i) $\frac{1}{13}, \frac{3}{4}, \frac{3}{52}$ (ii) no (iii) yes (iv) $\frac{10}{13}$ 2. $\frac{45}{101}$ 3. (i) $\frac{1}{5}$ (ii) $\frac{48}{125}$ (iii) $\frac{369}{625}$ 4. $\frac{5}{8}$ 6. $\frac{7}{11}$ 7. $\frac{1256}{5525}$ 8. (i) $\frac{25}{216}$ (ii) $\frac{2821}{7776}$ 9. (i) $\frac{5}{16}$ (ii) 0·149 10. (i) $\frac{1}{3}$ (ii) $\frac{37}{45}$ (iii) yes (iv) no 11. (i) $\frac{1}{4096}$ (ii) $\frac{81}{4096}$ (iii) $\frac{9}{2048}$ (iv) $\frac{4077}{4096}$ 12. $\frac{55}{56}$ 13. $\frac{88}{16575}$ 14. $\frac{2000}{16807}$ 15. $\frac{193}{512}$ 16. (i) $\frac{3087}{100000}$ (ii) $\frac{3087}{10000}$ (iii) $\frac{52822}{100000}$ 17. (i) $\frac{125}{729}$ (ii) $\frac{100}{243}$ (iii) $\frac{40}{81}$ 18. $\frac{2}{3}$ 19. (i) $\frac{1}{3}$ (ii) $\frac{2}{3}$ (iii) no (iv) $\frac{1}{12}$ 20. (i) $\frac{4}{13}$ (ii) $\frac{2}{9}$ (iii) $\frac{62}{117}$

Chapter 24

Exercises 24.1, Pages 56–57

1. $\frac{47}{20}$ 2. $\frac{13}{5}$ 3. (i) $\frac{1}{9}, \frac{2}{9}$ (ii) $\frac{11}{3}$ 4. (i) 0, 1, 2, 3, 4 (ii) 1·68 (iii) no 5. (i) 1, 2, 3, 4, 5, 6, 7, 8, 9, 10 (iii) $\frac{85}{13}$ 6. (ii) $\frac{5}{2}$ 7. 1·75 8. (i) 0, 1, 2, 3, 4 (ii) 2 9. (i) $\frac{11}{84}$ (ii) $\frac{113}{84}$ 10. $k = \frac{1}{12}, m = \frac{1}{12}$

Exercises 24.2, Pages 61–62

1. (i) $\frac{1}{2}$ (ii) $\frac{1}{2}$ (iii) fair 2. (i) $\frac{1}{3}$ (ii) $\frac{2}{3}$ (iii) no 3. no 4. (i) 0·55 (ii) 0·45 (iii) no, Aoife (iv) no, Aoife 5. (i) −€0·17 (ii) €0·17 (iii) no 6. (i) −€0·17 (ii) €10 (iii) €10 7. (ii) down €20 (iii) €$\frac{7}{3}$ 8. (ii) down €15 9. €3·50 10. no 11. (i) 3, 1, −1 (ii) no 12. (i) $\frac{8}{15}$ (ii) no 13. (i) −3, 0, 1, 2, 3 (ii) −€0·25 (iii) no (iv) €2·75 14. (i) no (ii) €0·83 15. (i) −1, 1000, 2000, 5000 (ii) no

Revision Exercises 24, Pages 63–64

1. 1·72 2. 8 3. $\frac{31}{16}$ 4. $\frac{65}{27}$ 5. €3 6. €8·50 7. $\frac{13}{11}$ 8. $\frac{15}{8}$ 9. €300 10. (i) €0·25 (ii) −€0·75 11. €20 12. €4·26 13. (i) −€0·25 (ii) no 14. no 15. no 16. (i) $\frac{1}{2}$ (ii) $\frac{1}{2}$ (iii) yes

Chapter 25

Exercises 25.1, Page 69

1. 9 2. $\frac{15}{7}$ 3. 2 4. 33 5. does not exist 6. does not exist 7. does not exist 8. does not exist 9. $\frac{1}{10}$ 10. $\frac{7}{2}$ 11. 5 12. 3 13. $\frac{1}{4}$ 14. $\frac{1}{2}$ 15. $\frac{1}{2}$ 16. $\frac{1}{6}$

Exercises 25.2, Page 71

1. $\frac{2}{3}$ 2. $\frac{1}{2}$ 3. 2 4. 10 5. $\frac{6}{5}$ 6. $\frac{1}{2}$ 7. $\frac{7}{3}$ 8. 3 9. $\frac{2}{5}$ 10. 6 11. $\frac{4}{3}$ 12. $\frac{5}{3}$ 13. 1 14. 2 15. $\frac{3}{4}$ 16. $\frac{5}{16}$

Exercises 25.3, Pages 74–75

3. yes 4. yes 5. (i) yes 6. (i) no 7. −7 8. −2 9. (i) yes, 3 (ii) no 10. (i) no (ii) no 11. (i) yes, 1 (ii) no 12. (i) no (ii) no

Exercises 25.5, Pages 81–82

1. (i) 2 (ii) same (iii) same 2. (i) −4 (ii) same (iii) same 3. (i) $2x - 2$ (iii) 4 (iv) 5 4. (i) $2x + 4$ (iii) 6 (iv) 7 5. 7 6. −2 7. $\frac{1}{2}$ 8. $-\frac{3}{2}$ 9. $2x - 6$ 10. $6x + 5$ 11. $-2x + 3$ 12. $-4x + 3$ 13. $x - 2$ 14. $\frac{4}{3}x + \frac{1}{2}$

Revision Exercises 25, Pages 82–83

1. (i) $2\cos\left(\frac{2x+h}{2}\right)\sin\left(\frac{h}{2}\right)$ (ii) $\cos x$ (iii) $\cos x$ 2. (i) $-2\sin\left(\frac{2x+h}{2}\right)\sin\left(\frac{h}{2}\right)$ (ii) $-\sin x$ (iii) $-\sin x$ 3. (i) no (iii) no (iv) $2x$ 4. (i) no (iii) no (iv) $-4x$ 5. (i) $f: x \to \begin{cases} x-1, & \text{for } x \geq 1 \\ -(x-1), & \text{for } x < 1 \end{cases}$ (iii) −1 (iv) 1 6. (i) $2ax + b$ (ii) $2ak + b$ (iii) $2ak + b$ 7. 7 8. 3 9. $\frac{1}{6}$ 10. $\frac{1}{30}$

Chapter 26

Exercises 26.1, Pages 88–89

1. $6x^5$ 2. $10x^9$ 3. $24x^{23}$ 4. $18x^{17}$ 5. $\frac{-1}{x^2}$ 6. $\frac{-2}{x^3}$ 7. $\frac{-3}{x^4}$ 8. $\frac{-4}{x^5}$ 9. $15x^2$ 10. $42x^6$ 11. $12\cos x$ 12. $-8\sin x$ 13. $-2\sec^2 x$ 14. $3\sin x$ 15. 0 16. 0 17. 4 18. 5 19. $2x - 4$ 20. $6x - 7$ 21. $3x^2 + 8x - 8$ 22. $12x^2 - 10x + 7$ 23. $8x - \frac{3}{x^2}$ 24. $6 - 6x^{-3} + 2x^{-\frac{1}{2}}$ 25. $3\cos x - 5\sin x$ 26. $2\sin x + 7\cos x$ 27. $5\cos x + 2\sec^2 x$ 28. $-6\sin x + 4x^{-3}$ 29. (i) $6x - 4$ (ii) 8 (iii) 2 30. (i) $8x + 12$ (ii) 4 (iii) 28 31. $\frac{9}{4}$ 32. −2

Exercises 26.2, Page 90

1. $12x^3 + 10x$ 2. $12x^2 + 4x + 18$ 3. $15x^2 + 14x - 26$ 4. $4x^3 + 3x^2 - 4x - 1$ 5. $4x + \frac{3}{2}\sqrt{x}$ 6. $3\sqrt{x} - \frac{1}{2\sqrt{x}}$ 7. $x^2\cos x + 2x\sin x$ 8. $(-3x + 1)\sin x + 3\cos x$

9. $\sin x + \sin^2 x + 2\cos x - \cos^2 x$ **10.** $(x^2+1)\sec^2 x + 2x\tan x$
11. $(1+x)\cos x + (1-x)\sin x$ **12.** $(2x^2-3)\cos x + 4x\sin x$

Exercises 26.3, Page 91

1. $\frac{2}{(x+1)^2}$ **2.** $\frac{-7}{(2x-1)^2}$ **3.** $\frac{10}{(2x+1)^2}$ **4.** $\frac{-29}{(3x-4)^2}$ **5.** $\frac{6x}{(x^2+2)^2}$
6. $\frac{-22x}{(2x^2-1)^2}$ **7.** $\frac{2x^2-6x-5}{(2x-3)^2}$ **8.** $\frac{-2x^2-2x+8}{(x^2-2x+3)^3}$ **9.** $\frac{2\cos x+1}{(2+\cos x)^2}$
10. $\frac{\cos x-\sin x-1}{(1-\cos x)^2}$ **11.** $\frac{1+\sin x-x\cos x}{(1+\sin x)^2}$ **12.** $\frac{3\cos x+2\sin x+1}{(3+\cos x)^2}$
13. $\frac{9}{(x+2)^2}$ **14.** $\frac{14}{(x+4)^2}$ **15.** 1 **16.** 2

Exercises 26.4, Page 95

1. $16x(2x^2-1)^3$ **2.** $3(x^2-x+5)^2(2x-1)$ **3.** $64x(8x^2-5)^3$
4. $5(2\sin x+\cos x)^4(2\cos x-\sin x)$ **5.** $\frac{5}{2\sqrt{5x+2}}$ **6.** $\frac{x}{\sqrt{x^2+3}}$
7. $\frac{\cos x}{\sqrt{3+2\sin x}}$ **8.** $\frac{\sin x}{2\sqrt{4-\cos x}}$ **9.** $\frac{-3}{(3x+2)^2}$ **10.** $\frac{-4}{(4x-5)^2}$
11. $\frac{-4x}{(x^2-1)^3}$ **12.** $\frac{-12}{(4x+3)^4}$ **13.** $2\sin x\cos x$ **14.** $-4\cos^3 x\sin x$
15. $6\sin^5 x\cos x$ **16.** $2\tan x\sec^2 x$ **17.** $3\tan^2 x\sec^2 x$
18. $7\sin^6 x\cos x$ **19.** $7\cos 7x$ **20.** $9\cos 9x$ **21.** $-3\sin 3x$
22. $-5\sin 5x$ **23.** $4\sec^2 4x$ **24.** $8\sec^2 8x$ **25.** $5\cos(5x-3)$
26. $-4x\sin(2x^2+3)$ **27.** $2x\sec^2(x^2-6)$ **28.** $-2x\cos(3-x^2)$
29. $(8x+2)\cos(4x^2+2x-1)$ **30.** $(3-2x)\sin(x^2-3x+2)$
31. $\frac{-\cos\left(\frac{1}{x}\right)}{x^2}$ **32.** $\frac{\sin\left(1+\frac{1}{x}\right)}{x^2}$ **33.** **(i)** $2\sin x\cos x$ **(ii)** $2x\cos x^2$
34. **(i)** $-2x\sin(1+x^2)$ **(ii)** $-2\cos x\sin x$ **35.** **(i)** $\frac{\cos x}{\sqrt{2\sin x}}$ **(ii)** $\frac{\cos\sqrt{x}}{\sqrt{x}}$
36. **(i)** $-32\cos x\sin x$ **(ii)** $-8x\sin(x^2+1)$

Exercises 26.5, Pages 97–98

1. $-4\sin 2x(3+\cos 2x)$ **2.** $36\cos 3x(2+3\sin 3x)^3$
3. $6\sin 3x\cos 3x$ **4.** $-12\sin 4x\cos^2 4x$ **5.** $9\cos(3x-1)\sin^2(3x-1)$
6. $\frac{\cos 2x}{\sqrt{1+\sin 2x}}$ **7.** $\frac{-6\sin 3x}{\sqrt{4\cos 3x-1}}$ **8.** $18x^2(1+3x^2)^2+(1+3x^2)^3$
9. $\frac{5x}{2\sqrt{5x+1}}+\sqrt{5x+1}$ **10.** $\frac{x^2+x}{\sqrt{x^2+3}}+\sqrt{x^2+3}$
11. $3\cos 2x\cos 3x - 2\sin 3x\sin 2x$
12. $3\cos^2 x(1+\sin x)^2 - \sin x(1+\sin x)^3$ **13.** $\frac{3}{2}$
14. $\frac{1}{(1-4x^2)^{\frac{3}{2}}}$ **15.** -4 **16.** 2 **18.** $\frac{1}{4\sqrt{2}}$ **19.** $3\cos 3x - 2\sin 2x$
20. $4\sin^2 x$

Exercises 26.6, Pages 99–100

3. $\frac{2-x}{y-4}, 2$ **4.** $\frac{x+4}{-y+1}, -\frac{3}{2}$

Exercises 26.7, Page 103

3. $2x+\frac{3}{\sqrt{1-x^2}}$ **4.** $9x^2+2+\frac{1}{1+x^2}$ **5.** $\frac{x^2}{\sqrt{1-x^2}}+2x\sin^{-1}x$
6. $\frac{2x+1}{\sqrt{1-x^2}}+2\sin^{-1}x$ **7.** $\frac{1+x^3}{1+x^2}+3x^2\tan^{-1}x$ **8.** $\frac{2}{\sqrt{1-x^2}}+\frac{3}{1+x^2}$
9. $\frac{2}{\sqrt{1-4x^2}}$ **10.** $\frac{5}{\sqrt{1-25x^2}}$ **11.** $\frac{4}{1+16x^2}$ **12.** $\frac{7}{1+49x^2}$
13. $\frac{1}{\sqrt{1-(x+2)^2}}$ **14.** $\frac{1}{1+(x-1)^2}$ **15.** $\frac{2}{\sqrt{1-(2x-3)^2}}$
16. $\frac{4}{1+(4x-2)^2}$ **17.** $\frac{2x}{1+x^4}$ **18.** $\frac{2x}{\sqrt{1-(x^2-1)^2}}$
19. $\frac{2\sin^{-1}x}{\sqrt{1-x^2}}$ **20.** $\frac{-\sin x}{1+\cos^2 x}$ **21.** -1 **22.** $\frac{-1}{x^2+1}$

Exercises 26.8, Page 105

1. $3x^2+2e^x$ **2.** $2\cos x - e^x$ **3.** $\frac{1}{1+x^2}+3e^x$ **4.** $(x+1)e^x$
5. $(x^2+3+2x)e^x$ **6.** $3xe^x+3e^x-1$ **7.** $\frac{(x-1)e^x}{x^2}$ **8.** $\frac{-1-2x}{e^x}$
9. $\frac{-2e^x}{(e^x-1)^2}$ **10.** $-e^{-x}$ **11.** $4e^{4x+2}$ **12.** $-e^{\cos x}\sin x$
13. $(4x-3)e^{2x^2-3x+1}$ **14.** $2e^{2\sin x+3}.\cos x$ **15.** $\frac{e^{\sqrt{x+1}}}{2\sqrt{x+1}}$
16. $2(x^2+x+1)e^{2x}$ **17.** $e^{3x}(-\sin x+3\cos x)$
18. $e^{-x}(2\cos 2x-\sin 2x)$ **19.** $e^{-2x}(3\cos 3x-2\sin 3x)$ **20.** $\frac{e^{2x}-1}{e^x}$
21. $\frac{-6e^{3x}}{(e^{3x}-1)^2}$ **22.** $\frac{e^x}{\sqrt{1-e^{2x}}}$ **23.** $e^{2-2x}(-2x^2+2x)$ **24.** $\frac{4}{(e^x+e^{-x})^2}$

Exercises 26.9, Page 108

1. $2x+\frac{1}{x}$ **2.** $\frac{3}{x}-12x^2$ **3.** $3\cos x-\frac{2}{x}$ **4.** $x^2+3x^2\ln x$
5. $\frac{2x-1}{x}+2\ln x$ **6.** $\frac{\sin x+2}{x}+\cos x\ln x$ **7.** $\frac{2x}{1+x^2}$ **8.** $\frac{6x}{3x^2-2}$
9. $\frac{2x^2}{2x+1}+2x\ln(2x+1)$ **10.** $\frac{2}{x}+\cot x$ **11.** $\frac{3}{x}+\frac{1}{2(x+1)}$
12. $\frac{2}{x}-\frac{x}{x^2+1}$ **13.** $\frac{1}{x}+2\cot x$ **14.** $-\tan x-\frac{1}{2x}$ **15.** $\frac{1-2\ln x}{x^3}$
16. $3^x\ln 3$ **17.** $8^x\ln 8$ **18.** $10^x\ln 10$ **19.** $[2^{x^2+3x}\ln 2](2x+3)$
20. $[4^{\sin x+\cos x}\ln 4](\cos x-\sin x)$ **21.** $[6^{2x^2+\sqrt{x}}\ln 6]\left(4x+\frac{1}{2\sqrt{x}}\right)$
22. $x^x(1+\ln x)$

Revision Exercises 26, Pages 109–110

4. $\sqrt{\frac{3}{32}}$ **5.** $-\frac{1}{2}$ **8.** $-\frac{3}{2}$ **9.** $k=2, p=\frac{1}{2}, q=\frac{3}{2}$ **11.** $\frac{\tan^{-1}\sqrt{x}}{(1+x)\sqrt{x}}$
15. $\frac{3}{9-x^2}$ **16.** **(i)** $\frac{-2}{x^2+4}$ **(iii)** $\frac{\pi}{2}$ **17.** $\frac{4x}{1-x^4}$ **18.** $a=3, b=1$

Chapter 27

Exercises 27.1, Page 113

1. $y=3x-12$ **2.** $y=6x-2$ **3.** $4y=3x+7$ **4.** $y=x$ **5.** $y=2x$
6. $y=-7x+30$ **7.** (6,23) **8.** (–1,6) **9.** $\left(\frac{5}{2},\frac{25}{4}\right)$ **10.** (–1,–6)
11. (–2,27), (4,–63) **12.** (1,6), (3,14)

Exercises 27.2, Page 115

3. **(i)** $x>\frac{3}{2}$ **(ii)** $x<\frac{3}{2}$, $\left(\frac{3}{2},-\frac{3}{2}\right)$ **4.** **(i)** $x>2$ **(ii)** $x<2$, (2,–4)
11. $-1<x<3$ **12.** $x<1$ or $x>5$

Exercises 27.3, Pages 117–118

1. (0,0), (2,4) **2.** (0,–6), (1,–7) **3.** (–2,20), (1,–7) **4.** (2,12) **5.** (0,0)
6. (1,2) max, (3,–2) min **7.** (–1,0), (1,0) saddle points, (0,–1) min
8. (1,0) max, $\left(\frac{9}{5},-\frac{3456}{3125}\right)$ min, (3,0) saddle point

Exercises 27.4, Pages 120–121

1. $-\sin x$ 2. $18x + 10$ 3. $168(2x - 1)^5$ 4. $-4\cos(2x + 3)$
5. $216x^2(3x^2 + 1) + 18(3x^2 + 1)^2$ 6. $3\sin x(2\cos^2 x - \sin^2 x)$
10. $x > -\dfrac{b}{2a}$ 12. $x > -2$

Exercises 27.5, Pages 123–124

1. (0,0) max, (–2,–32) min, (1,–5) min
2. (0,2) max, (2,–30) min, (–1,–3) min
3. (0,2) min, (–4,–6) max 4. (2,1) max, $\left(-\frac{1}{2},-4\right)$ min 5. (2,3) min
6. $a = 2$, $b = -8$ 7. $a = -3$, $b = 6$, (3, – 21) 9. $\left(1,\frac{1}{e}\right)$ max
10. $\left(\frac{1}{\sqrt{2}},\frac{1}{\sqrt{2e}}\right)$ max, $\left(\frac{-1}{\sqrt{2}},\frac{-1}{\sqrt{2e}}\right)$ min 11. (0,0) min, $\left(2,\frac{4}{e^2}\right)$ max
12. (0,0) min 13. $\left(\frac{1}{e},-\frac{1}{e}\right)$ min 14. $\left(e,\frac{1}{e}\right)$ max
15. $(a,0)$ min, $\left(\frac{a+2b}{3},\frac{4(b-a)^3}{27}\right)$ max 16. –1

Exercises 27.6, Page 127

1. (0,8) 2. (3,–83) 3. (1,–1), (2,0) 4. (1,8), (3,10)
5. (0,0), (1, –7), (–1,7) 6. $\left(-\frac{1}{\sqrt{2}},\frac{1}{\sqrt{e}}\right),\left(\frac{1}{\sqrt{2}},\frac{1}{\sqrt{e}}\right)$ 7. $\left(-1,\frac{-1}{e^2}\right)$

Exercises 27.7, Page 131

1. $x = 3$ 2. $x = -2$ 3. $x = 1, x = -1$ 4. $x = 0$ 5. 4 6. $\frac{1}{2}$ 7. $\frac{-1}{3}$
8. 0 9. (i) $\frac{1}{3}$ (ii) 2 (iii) $\frac{5}{2}$ 10. (i) $\frac{3}{4}$ 12. (i) $\frac{3}{2}$ 13. $y = 1$
14. $y = \frac{2}{3}$ 15. $y = \frac{3}{2}$ 16. $y = \frac{1}{2}$ on right, $y = \frac{3}{7}$ on left
17. $x = 5, y = 1$ 18. $x = -3, y = 2$
19. $x = \ln 2$, $y = \frac{5}{2}$ on right, $y = -\frac{1}{4}$ on left 20. $y = 0$

Exercises 27.8, Pages 135–136

1. (i) (1,0) max, (5,–22) min (ii) (3,–6)
2. (i) (–2,64) max, (4,–44) min (ii) (1,10) 3. (ii) (1,0), (5,0)
4. (ii) (0,0), (2,0) 5. (ii) (0, –5), (5,–130) 6. (i) $a = -45$, $b = 10$
(ii) (–5,185) 7. (i) $x = -2, y = 1$ 8. (i) $x = 1, y = 1$ (iii) (3,0), (0,3)
(v) (0,3), (2,–1) 9. (i) $x = -1, y = 1$ (iii) (–4,0), (0,4)
(v) $\left(-3,-\frac{1}{2}\right),\left(1,\frac{5}{2}\right)$ 10. (i) $y = 1$ on right, $y = 0$ on left (ii) $\left(0,\frac{1}{2}\right)$

Exercises 27.9, Pages 137–139

7. (i) $C: y = f(x)$, $B: \frac{dy}{dx} = f'(x)$, $A: \frac{d^2y}{dx^2} = f''(x)$
8. (i) $B: y = f(x)$, $A: \frac{dy}{dx} = f'(x)$, $C: \frac{d^2y}{dx^2} = f''(x)$

Revision Exercises 27, Pages 139–140

1. least = –1, greatest = 0 3. $\left(\frac{1}{2}, \tan^{-1}\frac{1}{2} - \ln\frac{5}{4}\right)$
4. $(-1, -e^2)$ min, $\left(2,\frac{2}{e^4}\right)$ max
8. (i) $A: y = f(x)$, $C: \frac{dy}{dx} = f'(x)$, $B: \frac{d^2y}{dx^2} = f''(x)$

Chapter 28

Exercises 28.1, Pages 146–147

1. 9 2. $\frac{4000}{27}$ 3. 216π 4. 12 m² 5. $6\sqrt[3]{160000\pi}$ cm²
7. $\frac{2000\pi}{9\sqrt{3}}$ cm³ 8. 2·66 cm 9. $2r^2$ 10. $\frac{704\pi}{27}$ cm³ 12. $\frac{32\pi r^3}{81}$
14. 4 15. $\frac{1}{20}(24y - 9y^2), \frac{4}{5}$ 16. (i) $-2q^3 + 6q^2 + 18q - 4$ (ii) 3
(iii) €50 17. (i) 50 (ii) 1839 18. (i) 18 (ii) 750540

Exercises 28.2, Pages 150–151

1. 52 m³ 2. 160 3. $\frac{\pi^2 + 8\pi}{16\sqrt{2}}$ 4. (i) $-\frac{3}{4}$ ms⁻¹, 1 ms⁻² (ii) 3
(iii) $\frac{1}{16}$ ms⁻² 5. (i) 6 ms⁻¹, –8 ms⁻² (ii) 42·25 ms⁻¹, 37 ms⁻²
6. (i) 100 ms⁻¹ (ii) 4 s (iii) 200 m (iv) –100 ms⁻¹ 7. $\frac{60\pi}{e^4}$ cms⁻¹
8. $\frac{16\pi}{e^4}$ cms⁻¹

Exercises 28.3, Pages 154–155

1. (i) 160π (ii) $\frac{3}{7\pi}$ 2. (i) $\frac{200}{3}$ (ii) $\frac{4}{5}$ 3. $5\sqrt{2}$ 4. 0·012 cm²s⁻¹
5. $\frac{1}{150\pi}$ cms⁻¹ 6. (i) $\frac{3}{4\pi r^2}$ (ii) $\frac{1}{2}$ cm²s⁻¹ 7. $\frac{25}{192\pi}$ cms⁻¹
8. $\frac{1}{10}$ cms⁻¹ 9. 24 ms⁻¹ 10. 0·01 ms⁻¹

Revision Exercises 28, Pages 155–156

1. (ii) 3 2. (i) $h = \frac{K}{\pi r^2}$ (ii) 1 : 2 3. 108 cm³ 4. (i) $-x^2 + 5x - 4$
(ii) 2500, €2250000 (iii) $x < 2·5$ (iv) $1 < x < 4$ 5. (i) 20 (ii) 3679
6. (i) 50 (ii) €42·94 7. (i) $4000000 - 4000000e^{-0·02x} - 1000x$
(ii) 104 (iii) €2460279 8. –2 9. (i) 6π cm³s⁻¹ (ii) 2π cm²s⁻¹
10. $\frac{-1}{10\sqrt{3}}$ rad h⁻¹.

Chapter 29

Exercises 29.1, Pages 160–161

1. (ii) $u_{n+1} = u_n + 1, u_n = n$ (iii) $u_{n+1} + 3, u_n = 3n + 1, u_{100} = 301$
(iv) $u_{n+1} = u_n + 2$ 2. (ii) $u_{n+1} = u_n + 2, u_n = 2n - 1$
(iii) $u_{n+1} = u_n + 4, u_n = 4n - 1$ 3. (i) 21, 26 (ii) $u_{n+1} = u_n + 5$
(iii) $u_n = 5n - 4$ 4. (i) $\frac{1}{2}, \frac{1}{4}$ (ii) $u_{n+1} = u_n \times \frac{1}{2}$ (iii) $u_n = 8 \times \left(\frac{1}{2}\right)^{n-1}$
5. (i) $\frac{1}{5}, \frac{1}{6}$ (iii) $u_n = \frac{1}{n}$ 6. (i) –4, –8 (ii) $u_{n+1} = u_n - 4$
(iii) $u_n = -4n + 16$ 7. (i) 50, 72 (iii) $u_n = 2n^2$ 8. (i) $\frac{5}{6}, \frac{6}{7}$
(iii) $u_n = \frac{n}{n+1}$ 9. $\frac{1}{2}, 1, \frac{5}{4}, \frac{15}{8}$ 10. 6, 2, 0, $n = 3$ and $n = 4$
11. 3, 6, 12, $n = 13$ 12. $\frac{3}{4}, \frac{8}{5}, \frac{5}{2}, n = 9$

Exercises 29.2, Page 164

1. $\frac{1}{3}$ 2. $\frac{5}{2}$ 3. $\frac{7}{2}$ 4. $-\frac{3}{5}$ 5. $\frac{1}{2}$ 6. $\frac{2}{5}$ 7. $\frac{1}{3}$ 8. 2 9. 0 10. 0
11. ±∞ (or doesn't exist) 12. ±∞ (or doesn't exist) 13. 1 14. 0
15. 1 16. $\frac{3}{5}$ 17. $\frac{1}{3}$ 18. 2 19. $\sqrt{\frac{3}{2}}$ 20. $\frac{1}{\sqrt{3}}$ 21. $\frac{1}{\sqrt{2}}$ 22. $\frac{1}{\sqrt{3}}$

Exercises 29.3, Pages 169–170

1. yes **2.** yes **3.** yes **4.** no **5. (i)** $5n-1$ **(ii)** 120 **6.** $3n+1$, 61 **7.** $8n-11$, 317 **8.** 15 **9.** 31 **10.** −15, 5, 130 **11.** 4, 3, 70 **12.** $238-5n$, 38 **13.** 59 **14.** $-\frac{1}{3}$ **15.** $3n^2-n$, 29900 **16.** $\frac{n}{2}(27-3n)$, −3075 **17.** 83667 **18.** 6375 **19.** 367·5 **20.** 4 **21.** 24 **22.** −17, 3 **24.** $-\frac{5}{2}, \frac{1}{2}$ **25.** 3, 5 **26.** 7 **27.** $3n$ **28. (iii)** n^2+2n+5 **29. (ii)** 15, 22, 31 **(iii)** $n^2-4n+10$ **30. (ii)** 50, 73, 100 **(iii)** $2n^2+n-5$

Exercises 29.4, Pages 176–177

4. $3(2^{n-1})$, 96 **5.** $3^{n-1}x^{n-1}$, $729x^6$ **6.** 324 **7.** $\frac{375}{16}$ **8.** $\pm\frac{3}{2}$ **9.** ±16 **10.** $\frac{1-(3a)^n}{1-3a}, \frac{1-(3a)^{10}}{1-3a}$ **11.** $1-\frac{1}{2^n}, \frac{1023}{1024}$ **12.** 5 **13.** 8 **14.** $\frac{1875}{32}, \frac{15561}{160}$ **15.** 2 **16.** 2 **17.** $\frac{3280}{9}$ **18. (i)** 3 **(ii)** $1+x$ **19.** $\frac{2x+1}{2x-2}$ **20.** $\frac{\sqrt{2}}{\sqrt{2}-1}$ **21.** $\frac{1}{2}<x<\frac{3}{2}, \frac{x}{2x-1}$ **22.** $-1<x<0, \frac{-1}{2x^2}$ **23.** 25·6 **24.** $\frac{1}{2}$

Exercises 29.5, Pages 178–179

1. $\frac{127}{30}$ **2.** $\frac{5}{3}$ **3.** $\frac{43}{9}$ **4.** $\frac{83}{33}$ **5.** $\frac{14}{11}$ **6. (i)** $(0{\cdot}05P)+(0{\cdot}05P)\times 0{\cdot}95$ **(ii)** $P(1-0{\cdot}95^n)$ **(iii)** 32 **7. (i)** 2·4 m **(ii)** 15·07 m **(iii)** 16 m **(iv)** no **8. (i)** 75·496 m **(ii)** 80 m **9. (i)** $\frac{2}{3}$ km **(ii)** $\frac{320}{81}$ km **(iii)** 4 km

Revision Exercises 29, Pages 179–181

1. (ii) n^2 **(iii)** 40000 **2.** $\frac{1}{2}$ **3.** 2 **4. (i)** $\frac{n(n+1)}{2}$ **(ii)** $\frac{1}{\sqrt{2}}$ **6. (i)** 12, 24, 48 **(ii)** geometric **(iii)** $6\times 2^{n-1}$ **(iv)** 6138 **7. (i)** $\frac{4}{3}, \frac{8}{9}, \frac{16}{27}$ **(ii)** geometric **(iii)** $2\left(\frac{2}{3}\right)^n$ **(iv)** $6\left(1-\left(\frac{2}{3}\right)^n\right)$ **(v)** 6 **8. (i)** $2\left(-\frac{1}{2}\right)^{n+1}-2, 2\left(-\frac{1}{2}\right)^{n+2}-2$ **9.** 2, 1, 4, −1, 2, 1 **10.** 31570 **12.** $-\frac{1}{2}$ **13.** $a+3b$ **14. (ii)** $5(2^n-1)$ **(iv)** $\frac{n[2\log_2 5+n-1]}{2}$ **15.** $-\frac{1}{3}$ **16.** $\frac{16}{3}, \frac{3}{2}$ **17. (i)** ar^{2m} **(ii)** ar^m **18. (i)** €3689·28 **(ii)** €5000 **19. (i)** 2^{n-1} **(ii)** 13 **(iii)** 8.56 am **20. (i)** 2·16 m **(ii)** 36·112 m **(iii)** 40 m

Chapter 30

Exercises 30.1, Page 185

1. (i) 3·217 km **(ii)** 24·87 **(iii)** 5·29 ms^{-1}, 19·05 kmh^{-1} **2. (i)** 31 mph **(ii)** 96·54 kmh^{-1} **3. (i)** 9·42 litres per 100 km **(ii)** 53·31 miles per gallon **4. (i)** 60000 square yards **(ii)** 63434 square yards **(iii)** 13·11 acres **(iv)** 8 hours 5 minutes **5. (i)** 28800 **(ii)** 14025600 **6. (i)** 5 hours **(ii)** 24 kmh^{-1} **7.** 108 **8.** 36651·11 kg

Exercises 30.2, Pages 189–191

1. (i) 35% **(ii)** 37·5% **(iii)** 73·33% **(iv)** 75·76% **(v)** 38·10% **2. (i)** 82·7% **(ii)** 134% **(iii)** 0·32% **(iv)** 217% **(v)** 0·02% **3. (i)** 0·24 **(ii)** 0·15 **(iii)** 0·375 **(iv)** 0·0225 **4.** 351 **5.** 98 **6.** €175 **7.** €736 **8.** 15% **9.** 12% **10.** 24% **11.** 21% **12.** Stephen: €150, Louise: €90 **13.** Mark: €280, Conor: €160 **14.** Paul: €180, Luke: €120, Daniel: €420 **15.** Maeve: €300, Tom: €480, Greg: €420 **16. (i)** €560 **(ii)** Brona €280, Charlie: €160 **17. (i)** €440 **(ii)** Therese: €80, Mary: €160 **18. (i)** 720 g **(ii)** 350 g **19. (i)** 9 : 3 **(ii)** €60 : €270 : €90 **20. (i)** 2 : 9 : 3 **(ii)** €180, €120, €480 **21.** 64·86% **22. (i)** 25%, 43·75%, 31·25% **(ii)** increases by 0·75% **23. (i)** 56% **(ii)** 48·28% **24.** 76·7% **25.** 62·5% **26.** €14500 **27.** €56 **28.** profit of 6·7% **29. (i)** €120, €139·80 **(ii)** profit of 16·5% **30. (i)** 66% **(ii)** 40% **31. (i)** 45% **(ii)** 31% **32. (i)** €1·11 **(ii)** €1·04 **33.** 75% **34.** 26% **35.** 60%

Exercises 30.3, Pages 195–197

1. $\frac{27}{1173}$, 2·30% **2. (i)** 1·59% **(ii)** 2·49% **3.** 8·48% **4.** 2·10% **5.** 0·6% **6.** 6·75% **7. (i)** $\frac{1}{16}$ inch **(ii)** $\left[10\frac{7}{16}, 10\frac{9}{16}\right]$ **8. (i)** 1 mm **(ii)** [10·3,10·5] **9. (i)** (765 ± 2·5) g **(ii)** 0·39% **10. (i)** [760,840] **(ii)** 3·85% **11. (i)** [11·5,12] **(ii)** 1·28% **12. (i)** 0·2 V **(ii)** 0·005 V **13. (i)** 0·02 m **(ii)** 0·0005 m **14.** 1·2% **15.** 1·6% **16.** 2·7% **17.** 4·0% **18.** 2·1% **19. (i)** 5·25% **(ii)** 13·22% **20. (i)** 1·08% **(ii)** 11·36% **21. (i)** 0·61% **(ii)** 4·76% **22. (i)** 0·03% **(ii)** 0·31% **23. (i)** 0·32% **(ii)** 3·13% **24. (i)** 0·65% **(ii)** 0·1 cm **(iii)** 1·06% **(iv)** 98·57° **(v)** 104·33° **25. (i)** [65°,67°] **(ii)** 13·55 **(iii)** 13·29

Exercises 30.4, Pages 199–200

1. 10 **2.** 12 **3.** 12 **4.** 5 **5.** 5 **6.** 12 **7. (i)** 6 **(ii)** 10 **8.** 3 **9.** 32250000 **10. (i)** 483000 **(ii)** $3{\cdot}2844\times 10^{16}$ **11.** 17472 **12.** 146667

Exercises 30.5, Pages 202–203

1. (i) €10204 **(ii)** €10189 **2.** €3155 **3. (i)** 125440 rupees **(ii)** 44556·61 rupees **(iii)** 143·87 dinar **4. (i)** €30 **(ii)** €241 **5.** €56·50 **6.** €544·50 **7.** €950 **8.** €720 **9.** €908 **10.** €105·10 **11. (i)** 850 **(ii)** €119·85 **(iii)** 13·5% **12.** 4175 **13. (i)** €39 **(ii)** €47·19 **14.** €2315·38

Exercises 30.6, Pages 206–207

1. (i) €7336 **(ii)** €2888·67 **2. (i)** €20446 **(ii)** €4233·67 **3. (i)** €1783·10 **(ii)** €4316·90 **4. (i)** €1938·90 **(ii)** €4579·10 **5. (i)** €21855 **(ii)** €3150 **6. (i)** €26628 **(ii)** €2840 **7.** €6250 **8.** €7150 **9.** €4138·86 **10.** €3195·58 **11.** €747·75 **12.** €2387·93

Revision Exercises 30, Pages 208–209

1. (i) 195 min **(ii)** 2·5 kg **2. (i)** 4 h 52 m **(ii)** 13:37 **3. (i)** 1 h 16 m **(ii)** 73 kmh^{-1} **4.** 45·15 kmh^{-1} **5.** 102 : 51 : 204 **6. (i)** 86 kmh^{-1} **(ii)** 67·35 **(iii)** 15·92 litres **7.** 7·4% **8. (i)** 7·2% **(ii)** 0·8% **9.** 75 kmh^{-1} **10.** 4·1% **11. (i)** 8 **(ii)** 5×10^7 **(iii)** 1·08% **12. (i)** 324 **(ii)** 4·71% **13. (i)** 42·5 **(ii)** 35·49, 19·75% **14. (i)** [28,28·8] **(ii)** 1·41% **15. (i)** 8640 **(ii)** 3·13% **16.** 57 **17. (i)** €4305 **(ii)** 21% **18. (i)** 15% **(ii)** reduced by 2·3% **19. (i)** €275·20 **(ii)** €35 **20. (i)** €40612·36

Chapter 31

Exercises 31.1, Pages 214–215

1. (i) €2704 **(ii)** €2839·20 **2. (i)** €6090 **(ii)** €6455·40 **3.** €3500 **4.** €4800 **5. (i)** €2650 **(ii)** 5% **6. (i)** €3990 **(ii)** 4% **7.** €1492·22 **8.** €3406·63 **9.** €7236·52, €1836·52 **10.** €4891·02, €1181·02 **11.** €4000 **12.** €7200 **13.** €24000, €19200, €15360, €12288 **14.** €4134·38 **15.** €60000 **16.** €28000 **17.** 14·866% **18.** 37·07% **19.** 12%

Exercises 31.2, Pages 218–219

1. (i) €4807·69 **(ii)** €4444·98 **(iii)** €4902·90 **2. (i)** €1803·89 **(ii)** €5964·34 **(iii)** €3898·11 **3. (i)** €1119·32 **(ii)** €1941·95 **(iii)** €4552·88 **4. (i)** €3759·08 **(ii)** €4184·65 **(iii)** €4934·72 **5. (i)** €3125·42 **(ii)** €5878·63 **(iii)** €14310·22 **6. (i)** €11368·87 **(ii)** €3946·93 **(iii)** €4933·67 **7. (i)** €574·83 **(ii)** €71640·84 **8. (i)** €16854 **(ii)** €47113·08 **9.** no **10. (i)** €1048733·27 **(ii)** yes **11.** yes

Exercises 31.3, Page 224

1. 0·80% **2.** 0·55% **3.** 16·77% **4.** 8·73% **5. (i)** 3·66% **(ii)** 5·0625% **(iii)** 6·975% **6. (i)** 7·9% **(ii)** 6·93% **(iii)** 8% **7.** 0·565% **8.** 1·467% **9.** 9·38% **10.** 12·55% **11. (i)** 15·5625% **(ii)** 15·865% **(iii)** 16·075% **(iv)** 16·158% **12.** B **13. (i)** €259122·50 **(ii)** €23100 **14.** 4·81%

Exercises 31.4, Pages 230–231

1. (i) 0·0036748 **(ii)** €1130·02 **(iii)** €991·30 **2. (i)** €6692·58 **(ii)** €542·94 **3. (i)** €1806·66 **(ii)** €1419·91 **(iii)** €1883·37 **4. (i)** 0·004074 **(ii)** €980·75 **(iii)** €40·76 **5. (i)** €602·22 **(ii)** €614·94 **(iii)** €627·79, no **6. (i)** €18067·44 **7. (i)** €14017·24 **(iii)** €1127·34 **8. (i)** €2280·83 **(ii)** €59040·83 **9. (i)** €13910·47 **(ii)** €57807·45 **(iii)** €18054·27 **(v)** €32642·45 **10. (v)** $P_n = P\dfrac{1 - v^{t-n}}{1 - v^t}$ **(vi)** €103724·98

Exercises 31.5, Pages 236–238

1. €415·98 **2.** €29078·19 **3. (i)** €1562·68 **(ii)** €2026·17 **4. (i)** 7314·95 **(ii)** 7511·88 **(iii)** 3487·89 **5.** 18435·14 **6. (i)** €443959·25 **(ii)** 629·8494967A **(iii)** 704·87 **7. (i)** €702724·45 **(ii)** 687·5139625A **(iii)** 1022·12 **8. (i)** €478755·91 **(ii)** €434184·31 **9. (i)** €271865·87 **(ii)** €349878·36 **10. (i)** €3584·46 **(ii)** €3569·91 **11.** €23459·72 **12.** €31080 **13.** €15136·77 **14.** €4966·78 **15.** €14847·94 **16.** €46928

Exercises 31.6, Page 240

1. (i) 8·3287% **(ii)** 0·6689% **2. (i)** 5·6541% **(ii)** 0·4599% **3.** 0·058269 **4.** 0·0953101798 **5.** 7·9735% **6.** 9·9586%

Revision Exercises 31, Pages 240–242

1. (i) 5·5% **(ii)** 7% **2.** €24·75 **3.** 1000 **4. (i)** €72900 **(ii)** €243900 **5. (i)** €2678 **(ii)** 2·5% **6. (i)** 0·007592 **(ii)** €477·76 **(iii)** €477·76 **7.** €21·1388 million **8. (i)** €1966·91 **(ii)** 39·12 **9. (i)** €137615·11 **(ii)** €26935·19 **10. (i)** €9613 **(ii)** €8861 **11.** 12 **13.** 6·168% **14. (i)** 0·000708 **(ii)** €15721·26 **15.** €121515·75 **16.** 0·159

Chapter 32

Exercises 32.1, Page 245

1. (i) $\frac{5}{2}, \frac{5}{3}, \frac{5}{4}$ **(ii)** $u_n = \frac{5}{n}$ **2. (ii)** $\frac{2}{3}, \left(\frac{2}{3}\right)^2, \left(\frac{2}{3}\right)^3$ **(iii)** $u_n = \left(\frac{2}{3}\right)^{n-1}$

Exercises 32.2, Pages 247–248

1. (i) 1620 **(ii)** 250500 **2. (i)** 1275 **(ii)** 1743

Chapter 33

Exercises 33.1, Pages 258–259

1. (i) 7, −5 **(ii)** 8, 2 **(iii)** −2, −1 **(iv)** 0, 11 **2. (i)** −3, −2 **(ii)** 5, −4 **(iii)** 8, 0 **(iv)** 0, −6 **3. (i)** −1 **(ii)** i **(iii)** −1 **4. (i)** $-i$ **(ii)** $-i$ **(iii)** $-i$ **5. (i)** (5,2) **(ii)** (−2,1) **(iii)** (0,6) **(iv)** (−4,0) **6. (i)** (−3,4) **(ii)** (6,−1) **(iii)** (0,−4) **(iv)** (6,0) **7. (ii)** z_2 **8. (ii)** z_3

Exercises 33.2, Pages 264–266

1. $x = 3, y = -2$ **2.** $p = -1, q = 2$ **3.** $x = 1, y = 3$ **4.** $x = 2, y = 3$ **7. (i)** $-7 + 4i$ **(ii)** $-1 + 3i$ **(iii)** $-5 + 5i$ **8. (i)** $3 - 5i$ **(ii)** $1 - 3i$ **(iii)** $-2 - 5i$ **9. (i)** $7 + i$ **(ii)** $5 - 4i$ **(iii)** $14 + 5i$ **(iv)** $15 - 8i$ **10. (i)** $-5 + 5i$ **(ii)** $-5i$ **(iii)** $-2 + 11i$ **(iv)** $-1 - 2i$ **11. (i)** $4 + 7i$ **(ii)** $14 + 23i$ **(iii)** $9 - 19i$ **(iv)** $-6 - 10i$ **12. (i)** $-13 + 19i$ **(ii)** $10 - 7i$ **(iii)** $16 + 21i$ **(iv)** $-6 + 32i$ **13.** −26 **14.** −44 **15.** $k = 2, t = 5$ **16.** $t = -5, k = 9$ **22. (i)** $\sqrt{20}$ **(ii)** $\sqrt{10}$ **(iii)** $\sqrt{10}$, no **23. (i)** $\sqrt{13}$ **(ii)** $\sqrt{10}$ **(iii)** $\sqrt{98}$, no **24.** $\sqrt{50}$ **25.** $\sqrt{34}$

Exercises 33.3, Pages 269–270

1. (i) 8 **(ii)** $-4i$ **(iii)** 20 **2. (i)** −6 **(ii)** $-10i$ **(iii)** 34 **3.** 61 **4.** 1 **5.** $3 + 2i$ **6.** $4 + i$ **7.** $\frac{13}{2} - \frac{5}{2}i$ **8.** $-\frac{1}{13} - \frac{31}{13}i$ **9.** $\frac{34}{13} - \frac{3\sqrt{3}}{13}i$ **10.** $\frac{13}{11} + \frac{8\sqrt{2}}{11}i$ **11.** $\frac{3}{2} + \frac{1}{2}i$ **12.** $0 + \frac{8}{5}i$ **13.** −2 **14.** 1 **15.** $24 + 10i$ **16.** −1

Exercises 33.4, Page 271

1. $p = 5, q = 1$ or $p = -5, q = -1$ **2.** $s = 1, t = -3$ or $s = -1, t = 3$ **3.** $a = 6, b = 1$ or $a = -6, b = -1$ **4.** $\pm(2 - 3i)$ **5.** $\pm(7 + i)$ **6.** $\pm(3 - 5i)$

Exercises 33.5, Page 274

1. $1 - 4i$ **2.** $2 + 3i$ **3.** $4 - i$ **4.** $3 + 2i$ **5.** $\frac{1}{2} + \frac{3}{2}i$ **6.** $-1 + \frac{1}{2}i$ **7.** $3 \pm 5i$ **8.** $4 \pm 2i$ **9.** $-5 \pm 4i$ **10.** $6 \pm 3i$ **11.** $1, 1 - i$ **12.** $1 + i, 1 - 2i$ **13. (i)** $\pm(2 - 2i)$ **(ii)** $3, 1 + 2i$ **14. (i)** $\pm(2 - i)$ **(ii)** $3 - 2i, 1 - i$ **15.** $2 - i, 1 + 3i$ **16.** $4 - i, 1 + 2i$ **17.** $4 + 3i$ **18.** $3 - 2i$ **19.** $2 + i$ **20.** $3 + 4i, -3 + 4i$ **21.** $2 + i, -1 + i$ **22.** $-5, 1 - 3i$

Exercises 33.6, Page 277

1. (ii) $2i, 5, -3$ **2.** $1 + 2i, 1 - 2i$ **3.** 2, 4 **4. (ii)** $1 + i, 2, -2$ **5.** −3, 2 **6.** $2 + 3i, -2$ **7.** $1 + 5i, 3$ **8.** $1 - i, 5$ **9.** $1 - 3i, 3$ **10.** $2 - i, 4$

Revision Exercises 33, Pages 278–279

3. no **4.** **(i)** no **(ii)** the real parts must be equal **(iii)** z and w are conjugates **6.** $1 + 2i$ **7.** $\frac{1}{10} + \frac{33}{10}i$ **9.** $x = \frac{3}{10}, y = \frac{9}{10}$ **10.** ± 2 **11.** $a = 2 - i, b = 4 - i$ **12.** $\pm 2, \frac{1}{3}$ **13.** $a = -8, b = 27, c = -38, d = 26$ **14.** **(i)** $\pm(4 + i)$ **(ii)** $2 - i, 1 + 3i$ **15.** $\frac{1 + 3i}{2}, \frac{-3 + 3i}{2}$ **16.** $2 - 3i, 2 + i$ **17.** $4, -4, -1 - i$

Chapter 34

Exercises 34.1, Page 284

1. $\sqrt{2}\,(\cos 45° + i \sin 45°)$ **2.** $4\,(\cos 30° + i \sin 30°)$
3. $6\,(\cos 45° + i \sin 45°)$ **4.** $8\,(\cos 60° + i \sin 60°)$
5. $\sqrt{2}\,(\cos 135° + i \sin 135°)$ **6.** $2\,(\cos 150° + i \sin 150°)$
7. $1\,(\cos 120° + i \sin 120°)$ **8.** $2\,(\cos 135° + i \sin 135°)$
9. $\sqrt{2}\,((\cos(-45°) + i \sin(-45°))$ **10.** $2(\cos(-30°) + i \sin(-30°))$
11. $8(\cos(-135°) + i \sin(-135°))$ **12.** $4(\cos(-120°) + i \sin(-120°))$
13. $4\,(\cos 0° + i \sin 0°)$ **14.** $\frac{1}{2}(\cos 90° + i \sin 90°)$
15. $6\,(\cos 180° + i \sin 180°)$ **16.** $3(\cos(-90°) + i \sin(-90°))$
17. $-2 + 2\sqrt{3}i$ **18.** $3 - 3\sqrt{3}i$ **19.** $-\sqrt{2} - \sqrt{2}i$ **20.** $-4\sqrt{3} - 4i$
21. $\frac{3}{\sqrt{2}} + \frac{3}{\sqrt{2}}i$ **22.** $-5\sqrt{3} + 5i$ **23.** **(i)** $7(\cos(-123°) + i \sin(-123°))$
(ii) $-3{\cdot}81 - 5{\cdot}87i$ **24.** **(i)** $19\,(\cos 142° + i \sin 142°)$
(ii) $-14{\cdot}97 + 11{\cdot}70i$

Exercises 34.2, Pages 289–290

1. $-\frac{1}{2} + \frac{\sqrt{3}}{2}i$ **2.** $-\frac{1}{\sqrt{2}} - \frac{1}{\sqrt{2}}i$ **3.** $\cos 7\theta + i \sin 7\theta$
4. $\cos 10A + i \sin 10A$ **5.** $\frac{1}{2} - \frac{\sqrt{3}}{2}i$ **6.** $-\frac{\sqrt{3}}{2} - \frac{1}{2}i$ **7.** $\frac{\sqrt{3}}{2} + \frac{1}{2}i$
8. $-\frac{\sqrt{3}}{2} + \frac{1}{2}i$ **9.** $\frac{1}{2} + \frac{\sqrt{3}}{2}i$ **10.** $\frac{\sqrt{3}}{2} + \frac{1}{2}i$ **11.** $\cos 3A + i \sin 3A$
12. $\cos 9X + i \sin 9X$ **13.** $2\left(\cos \frac{13B}{12} + i \sin \frac{13B}{12}\right)$
14. $8\left(\cos \frac{11\pi}{12} + i \sin \frac{11\pi}{12}\right)$ **15.** $0 + 6i$ **17.** **(i)** $1\,(\cos 90° + i \sin 90°)$
18. **(i)** $4\,(\cos 60° + i \sin 60°)$ **(ii)** $2(\cos(-90°) + i \sin(-90°))$
(iii) $\frac{1}{2}(\cos(-150°) + i \sin(-150°))$ **19.** **(i)** $|w| = 1$
(ii) $\cos(-150°) + i \sin(-150°)$
20. **(i)** $6\,(\cos 120° + i \sin 120°), 3(\cos(-30°) + i \sin(-30°))$
(ii) $2(\cos 150° + i \sin 150°)$

Exercises 34.3, Page 292

1. i **2.** $-\frac{\sqrt{3}}{2} + \frac{1}{2}i$ **3.** $-\frac{\sqrt{3}}{2} - \frac{1}{2}i$ **4.** $\frac{1}{2} + \frac{\sqrt{3}}{2}i$ **5.** $-\frac{1}{2} + \frac{\sqrt{3}}{2}i$
6. $-\frac{1}{\sqrt{2}} - \frac{1}{\sqrt{2}}i$ **7.** $-i$ **8.** $-\frac{1}{2} - \frac{\sqrt{3}}{2}i$ **9.** $\cos 10A + i \sin 10A$
10. $\cos 21\theta + i \sin 21\theta$ **11.** $\cos 4X + i \sin 4X$ **12.** **(ii)** $120°$
(iii) $\frac{3}{2}(\cos 120° + i \sin 120°)$ **13.** **(ii)** $-150°$
(iii) $\frac{1}{2}(\cos(-150°) + i \sin(-150°))$ **14.** $-120°, 120°$

Exercises 34.4, Pages 293–294

1. **(i)** $\sqrt{2}\,(\cos(-45°) + i \sin(-45°))$ **(ii)** $8 + 8i$
2. **(i)** $2\,(\cos 150° + i \sin 150°)$ **(ii)** $16\sqrt{3} + 16i$
3. **(i)** $2\sqrt{2}\,(\cos(-135°) + i \sin(-135°))$ **(ii)** $-512i$ **4.** $32i$
5. -1 **6.** $\sqrt{2}\,(\cos 45° + i \sin 45°), -32 + 32i$ **7.** $4 - 4i$ **8.** $-8 - 8\sqrt{3}i$

Exercises 34.5, Pages 298–299

1. $2(\cos(120° + n(360°)) + i \sin(120° + n(120°)))$
2. $2\sqrt{2}\,(\cos(-135° + n(360°)) + i \sin(-135° + n(360°)))$
3. $8(\cos(-90° + n(360°)) + i \sin(-90° + n(360°)))$
4. $4\sqrt{2}\,(\cos(-45° + n(360°)) + i \sin(-45° + n(360°)))$
5. $\frac{3}{2} + \frac{3\sqrt{3}}{2}i, -3, \frac{3}{2} - \frac{3\sqrt{3}}{2}i$
6. $\frac{3}{\sqrt{2}} + \frac{3}{\sqrt{2}}i, -\frac{3}{\sqrt{2}} + \frac{3}{\sqrt{2}}i, -\frac{3}{\sqrt{2}} - \frac{3}{\sqrt{2}}i, \frac{3}{\sqrt{2}} - \frac{3}{\sqrt{2}}i$
7. $\frac{1}{\sqrt{2}} - \frac{\sqrt{3}}{\sqrt{2}}i, -\frac{1}{\sqrt{2}} + \frac{\sqrt{3}}{\sqrt{2}}i$ **8.** $2, 1 + \sqrt{3}i, -1 + \sqrt{3}i, -2, -1 - \sqrt{3}i, 1 - \sqrt{3}i$
9. $\frac{1}{2} + \frac{\sqrt{3}}{2}i, i, -\frac{\sqrt{3}}{2} + \frac{1}{2}i, -\frac{\sqrt{3}}{2} - \frac{1}{2}i, -i, \frac{1}{2} - \frac{\sqrt{3}}{2}i$
10. **(i)** $\frac{1}{2} + \frac{\sqrt{3}}{2}i, -\frac{1}{2} + \frac{\sqrt{3}}{2}i, -1, -\frac{1}{2} - \frac{\sqrt{3}}{2}i, \frac{1}{2} - \frac{\sqrt{3}}{2}i$
11. **(i)** $\cos 0° + i \sin 0° = 1, \cos 72° + i \sin 72°, \cos 144° + i \sin 144°, \cos 216° + i \sin 216°, \cos 288° + i \sin 288°$
12. **(i)** 9 **(ii)** $a = \cos 80° + i \sin 80°, b = \cos 160° + i \sin 160°, c = \cos 200° + i \sin 200°, d = \cos 320° + i \sin 320°$ **(iii)** $\bar{z}, \frac{1}{z}$

Revision Exercises 34, Pages 300–301

1. **(i)** $\sqrt{2}\,(\cos 45° + i \sin 45°), 2(\cos(-30°) + i \sin(-30°))$
(ii) $\frac{1}{\sqrt{2}}(\cos 75° + i \sin 75°)$ **(iii)** $12, -\frac{1}{64}$ **2.** **(i)** $r = 1, \theta = 90°$ and $r = 1, \theta = 45°$ **3.** $\cos 2\theta + i \sin 2\theta$ **4.** $1 - i \tan \frac{\theta}{2}$ **5.** 1 **6.** 1
7. $-\frac{1}{2} + \frac{\sqrt{3}}{2}i$ **8.** $1 + i, -1 + i, -1 - i, 1 - i, (z^2 - 2z + 2)(z^2 + 2z + 2)$
9. **(i)** $16(\cos(-120°) + i \sin(-120°))$ **(ii)** 4096
(iii) $\sqrt{3} - i, 1 + \sqrt{3}i, -\sqrt{3} + i, -1 - \sqrt{3}i$ **10.** **(ii)** 32 **11.** $5, \tan^{-1}\frac{3}{4}$

Chapter 35

Exercises 35.1, Page 305

1. **(i)** $\frac{1}{2}x^2, \frac{1}{2}x^2 + 1, \frac{1}{2}x^2 - 1$ **(ii)** $\frac{1}{2}x^2 + c$ **2.** **(i)** $\frac{1}{6}x^6, \frac{1}{6}x^6 + 1, \frac{1}{6}x^6 - 1$
(ii) $\frac{1}{6}x^6 + c$ **3.** **(i)** $\frac{1}{3}x^3 + x^2, \frac{1}{3}x^3 + x^2 + 1, \frac{1}{3}x^3 + x^2 - 1$ **(ii)** $\frac{1}{3}x^3 + x^2 + c$
4. **(i)** $\frac{1}{4}x^4 + \ln|x|, \frac{1}{4}x^4 + \ln|x| + 1, \frac{1}{4}x^4 + \ln|x| - 1$ **(ii)** $\frac{1}{4}x^4 + \ln|x| + c$
5. $\frac{1}{6}x^6 + c$ **6.** $\frac{1}{9}x^9 + c$ **7.** $x^4 + c$ **8.** $\frac{5}{9}x^9 + c$ **9.** $\frac{2}{3}x^3 + \frac{3}{2}x^2 - x + c$
10. $2x^4 + \frac{2}{3}x^3 - \frac{5}{2}x^2 + x + c$ **11.** $\frac{2}{3}x^6 - \frac{3}{4}x^4 + x^2 + 7x + c$
12. $\ln|x| + \frac{3}{2}x^2 - 2x + c$ **13.** $-\frac{2}{x} + c$ **14.** $-\frac{1}{2}x^{-2} - \frac{1}{3}x^{-3} + c$
15. $\frac{1}{3}x^3 + 3x^2 + 9x + c$ **16.** $\frac{4}{3}x^3 - 2x^2 + x + c$
17. $\frac{1}{3}x^3 + \frac{7}{2}x^2 + 12x + c$ **18.** $\frac{4}{3}x^3 - x + c$ **19.** $\frac{1}{3}x^3 - 2x - \frac{1}{x} + c$
20. $\frac{1}{2}x^2 - 2x + \ln|x| + c$

Exercises 35.2, Page 307

1. $\frac{7}{3}$ **2.** 32 **3.** $\frac{17}{4}$ **4.** $\frac{1012}{5}$ **5.** $\frac{40}{3}$ **6.** $-\frac{256}{3}$ **7.** $\frac{4\sqrt{2}}{3} - \frac{2}{3}$
8. $\frac{9}{2} - 2\sqrt{3}$ **9.** 76 **10.** 10 **11.** $2 \ln 2 + 6$ **12.** $\frac{2}{3} - \ln 3$ **13.** 1

Exercises 35.3, Pages 312–313

1. $e^2 - 1$ **2.** $e^{\sqrt{3}} - e$ **3.** $\frac{1}{2}e^3 - \frac{1}{2}e$ **4.** $\frac{1}{4}e^8 - \frac{1}{4}e^{-4}$ **5.** $1 - e^{-4}$

6. $\frac{1}{7}e^{5\cdot6} - \frac{1}{7}e^{0\cdot7}$ **7.** $e^3 - e + 4$ **8.** $\frac{1}{2}e^4 + 2e^2 - \frac{1}{2}$ **9.** $\frac{1}{2}e^8 + e^4 - \frac{1}{2}e^2 - e$

10. $\frac{1}{2}e^6 + \frac{59}{2}$ **11.** $\ln 3 + \frac{1}{2}e^6 - \frac{1}{2}e^2$ **12.** $\frac{1}{3}e^6 - \frac{1}{3}e^3 - \frac{31}{6} - 2\ln 4$

13. $\frac{1}{\ln 2}$ **14.** $\frac{1}{\ln 5}(5^{0\cdot7} - 5^{0\cdot2})$ **15.** $\frac{3}{\ln 4}(4^{1\cdot3} - 4^{0\cdot1})$ **16.** $\frac{2}{\ln 1\cdot5} + 1$

17. $\frac{5}{\ln 1\cdot2}((1\cdot2)^{1\cdot8} - (1\cdot2)^{1\cdot2})$

18. $\frac{3}{\ln 2\cdot1}((2\cdot1)^2 - 1) - \frac{2}{\ln 1\cdot8}((1\cdot8)^2 - 1)$ **19. (i)** 4^x **(ii)** $\frac{3}{\ln 4}$

20. (i) 81^x **(ii)** $\frac{80}{\ln 81}$ **21.** 0 **22.** $\frac{3}{4}$ **23.** 0 **24.** $\frac{1}{3}$ **25.** $\frac{\pi}{4} - \frac{1}{2}$

26. $\frac{\pi}{8} + \frac{1}{4}$ **27.** $\frac{\sqrt{3}}{16}$ **28.** 0 **29.** $\frac{7}{12}$ **30.** $\frac{3\sqrt{3}}{16}$ **31.** $\frac{\pi}{8} + \frac{1}{4}$

32. $\frac{\pi}{6} - \frac{\sqrt{3}}{8}$ **33.** $\frac{\pi}{6}$ **34.** $\frac{\pi}{4}$

Exercises 35.4, Pages 317–318

1. $\frac{74}{3}$ **2.** $\frac{32}{3}$ **3.** $\frac{53}{3}$ **4.** $\frac{34}{3}$ **5.** 8 **6.** $\frac{81}{2}$ **7.** 4 **8.** $\frac{81}{2}$ **9.** $\frac{14}{\ln 2}$

10. $\frac{26}{\ln 3}$

Exercises 35.5, Page 319

1. $\frac{32}{3}$ **2.** $\frac{32}{3}$ **3.** 8 **4.** $\frac{32}{3}$ **5.** $\frac{8}{3}$ **6.** $\frac{3}{2} + \frac{1}{2}e^4$

Exercises 35.6, Pages 324–325

1. $\frac{32}{3}$ **2.** 36 **3.** 32 **4.** $\frac{32}{3}$ **5.** 9 **6.** 9 **7.** $\frac{32}{3}$ **8.** $\frac{7}{12}$ **9.** 9

10. $\frac{9}{2}$ **11.** 20·41 **12.** 162·30

Exercises 35.7, Page 328

1. 12 **2.** 1 **3.** $9 + \frac{1}{2}\ln 5$ **4.** 6 **5.** 7 **6.** $\frac{1}{3}(e^6 - 1)$ **7.** $\frac{3}{4}(e^4 - 1)$

8. $\frac{30}{\ln 4}$ **9.** 4 **10.** $\frac{259\pi}{6}$ **11.** 3·2436 million **12.** 21 ms^{-1}

13. $\frac{26}{3}$ ms^{-1} **14. (i)** 7·03 m **(ii)** 3·52 ms^{-1}

Revision Exercises 35, Page 329

1. $\frac{59}{6}$ **2.** $6x + \cos x - \frac{1}{2}$ **3.** $e^2 - e$ **4.** $\frac{63}{\ln 8} + \frac{3}{\ln 2}$ **5.** $-\frac{1}{6}$ **6.** $\frac{\sqrt{3}}{4}$

. $3 + 4\ln 2 - 2\ln 5$ **9. (ii)** $\frac{h}{3}[y_1 + 4y_2 + y_3]$ **10.** $\frac{32}{3}$ **14.** 6

hapter 36

rcises 36.1, Pages 332–333

discrete numeric **(ii)** €0 to €100, etc **2. (i)** continuous
ric **(ii)** discrete numeric **(iii)** grouped numeric
ontinuous numeric **(ii)** discrete numeric **(iii)** 70 to
, etc **4. (i)** nominal categorical **(ii)** discrete numeric
gorical and discrete paired **5. (i)** nominal categorical
orical and continuous paired **6. (i)** discrete numeric
e paired **7. (i)** discrete (or continuous) **(ii)** discrete/
categorical paired **8. (i)** nominal categorical
cal paired **9. (i)** he collects the data
ected by others **(iii)** the secondary data
lects the data **(ii)** data collected by others
ata **(iv)** survey shop owners

Exercises 36.2, Pages 335–336

1. (i) all passengers on Cork Dublin train **(ii)** take average age of all passengers **(iii)** take average of those in sample **(iv)** inferential **2. (i)** all people in Ireland with mobile phones, the average spend **(ii)** the average spend by those in her sample **(iii)** inferential **3. (i)** all cars passing school gate, average speed of all such cars **(ii)** no, not without equipment **(iii)** sample, sample statistic **4. (i)** {3, 4, 5, ...} **(ii)** average number of throws required **(iii)** sample statistic **5. (i)** no **(ii)** yes **6.** conclusion false **7.** conclusion not justified **8. (i)** people trying to get a long weekend **(ii)** same average as other days

Exercises 36.3, Pages 340–341

1. (i) SRS **(ii)** any random method **(iii)** students not in yard cannot be chosen **(iv)** cluster sample **(v)** random selection **(vi)** stratified sample **2. (i)** stratified sample **(ii)** 12, 18 **(iii)** random selection **(iv)** no expected difference in response **(v)** $x = 2, y = 3$ **3. (i)** stratified sampling **(ii)** 10, 20 **(iii)** random selection **4. (i)** some years could be over-represented **(ii)** strata should be the year groups, 5 **(iii)** 5 **5.** cluster sampling **6.** stratified sampling **7.** cluster sampling **8.** quota sampling **9.** respondent driven sampling **10.** convenience sampling

Exercises 36.4, Pages 345–346

1. person may never have eaten chocolate **2.** does not cover all possibilities **3.** more options should be included **4.** too vague **5.** leading question **6.** embarrassing question **7.** options not balanced **8.** too vague **11. (i)** define neighbourhood **12. (i)** define neighbourhood

Exercises 36.5, Pages 350–351

1. (i) observing **(ii)** more reliable responses **(iii)** poor response rates, unreliable responses **(iv)** no treatment **(v)** not investigating causality **2. (i)** observing **(ii)** more reliable, expensive **(iii)** cheaper, unreliable **(iv)** no treatment **(v)** not investigating causality **3. (i)** investigating causality **(ii)** yes/no with reason **(iii)** most reliable for investigating causality **(iv)** avoid unmatched groups **4. (i)** cannot justify denying new medicine to control group **(iii)** investigating causality **(iv)** investigating causality **5. (i)** investigating causality **(ii)** choosing who had to undergo the procedure **(iv)** no **6. (i)** investigating causality **(ii)** cannot justify exposing people to wood shavings **7. (i)** investigating causality **8. (i)** controlled experiment **(ii)** observational study

Revision Exercises 36, Pages 351–353

1. too vague **2.** too personal **3.** options do not cover all possibilities **4.** leading question **5.** leading question **6.** leading question **7.** ambiguous **8.** leading question **13. (ii)** those who buy or are likely to buy new bikes **(iii)** survey **14. (ii)** the population at large **(iii)** unethical to ask people to eat fast food **(iv)** observational study **(v)** interview to determine eating habits **15. (i)** people between 20 and 40 with back pain

(ii) obtain a way to measure back pain **(iii)** controlled experiment **16. (i)** stratify according to party support **(ii)** voting intentions before and after **(iii)** have all subjects watch in silence in a controlled environment **(iv)** give overall changes and changes in each stratum **(v)** pick the most radical change **17. (i)** components in batch **(ii)** stratified sample **(iii)** data available for each machine **18. (ii)** 60 male, 40 female **(iii)** quota sampling **19. (i)** observational study **(ii)** yes **20. (i)** clarify bully and stepfamily **(ii)** can't force children to belong to a stepfamily **(iii)** observational study

Chapter 37

Exercises 37.1, Pages 359–361

1. (i) 30 **(iv)** bar chart **2. (iii)** pie chart **3. (iii)** because the owners are categorical data **4. (i)** 60 **(ii)** 15 **(iii)** Dermot, 24 **5. (i)** 54 **6.** 4 **7.** 5 **8. (iii)** by number of sick days **10. (i)** data given in intervals **(ii)** 28 **11. (i)** 34 **(ii)** data given in intervals **12. (i)** data given in intervals **(iii)** 28 **13. (ii)** 24, 36, 20, 12, 8 **(iii)** 12, 18, 10, 6, 4

Exercises 37.2, Pages 364–365

6. (iv) perhaps a mixed class of buys and girls **8. (ii)** average of Team B is higher **9. (ii)** 2009, higher average **10. (ii)** A: county town, B: big city **11. (ii)** maths **12. (ii)** A, sells higher value cars

Exercises 37.3, Pages 370–372

1. (i) 7·2 **(ii)** 4 **(iii)** 16 **2. (i)** 11 **3. (i)** 9 **(ii)** 3 **(iii)** 15 **4. (i)** $2\overline{x}$ **(ii)** $5-\overline{x}$ **(iii)** $4+3\overline{x}$ **5.** 3 **6.** 8 **7.** €23214 **8.** 5 **9. (i)** 5 **(ii)** $x \le 4$ **(iii)** $x \ge 6$ **10. (i)** $x \le 8, y \ge 9$ **(ii)** $x = 11, y \ge 11$ **(iii)** 10·5 **11. (i)** 4 **(ii)** 5 **(iii)** 3·34 **(iv)** mode < median < mean **12. (i)** 2 **(ii)** 1 **(iii)** 2·45 **(iv)** mode < median < mean **13. (i)** 23 **(ii)** median **14. (i)** median **(ii)** mean **15.** weight of teacher is an outlier **16.** mode **17. (i)** median = 5 **(ii)** mode = 5 **(iii)** a little less than 5 **18.** mode

Exercises 37.4, Pages 374–376

1. (i) 19 **(ii)** no **(iii)** 2 or 25 **2. (i)** 24 **(ii)** 49 **(iii)** 48 **3. (i)** 24 **(ii)** e.g. 5, 8, 8, 9, 16 **(iii)** no **4. (i)** 13 **(ii)** lie between 2 and 15 **(iii)** by 6 to 7 **5. (i)** 37th **(ii)** 5 **(iii)** 10 **6. (ii)** 11th **(iii)** 9 **7. (ii)** 24·5, median **(iii)** 19, lower quartile **(iv)** 32, upper quartile **8. (ii)** 38 **(iii)** 41 kg **(iv)** yes **9. (ii)** 31 **(iii)** 78% **10. (i)** no **(ii)** 25% **(iii)** no **11. (i)** above 54th percentile **(ii)** yes **12. (ii)** 56, 64 **(iii)** 8 **13. (ii)** 27, 44·5 **(iii)** 17·5 **(iv)** lower, more closely bunched at the upper end

Exercises 37.5, Pages 378–379

1. 3, $\sqrt{2}$ **2.** 10, 3·29 **3.** 14, 4·43 **4.** 40, 13·81 **5.** 13, 3·69 **6.** 9, 7·80 **7.** 2, 1·16 **8.** 6, 1·21 **9.** 4, 1·31 **10.** 3, 1·43 **11.** 2, 1·37 **12.** 3, 1·33 **13.** 5, 2·31 **14.** 40, 9·51 **15.** 45, 13 **16.** 3·03, 1·12

Exercises 37.6, Pages 384–385

1. (i) 6 **(ii)** symmetric **2. (i)** no **(ii)** skewed left **(iii)** about 9 **3. (i)** about 8·5 **(ii)** skewed right **4. (i)** about 11 **(ii)** skewed left **5. (ii)** skewed right **(iii)** 2 outliers **6. (i)** skewed right **(ii)** skewed right **(iii)** skewed left **(iv)** roughly symmetric **7. (i)** 3 **(ii)** B **(iii)** 3 **(iv)** B **8. (i)** mean of A slightly greater than 3, mean of B is 3 **(ii)** roughly the same **(iii)** mean of A is 3·17, mean of B is 3 **(iv)** for A, σ = 1·70, for B, σ = 1·78 **9. (i)** both means are 3 **(ii)** standard deviation of A greater than the standard deviation of B **(iii)** means are both 3 **(iv)** for A, σ = 1·87, for B, σ = 1·5 **10. (i)** mean a little to the right of 24, the mode further to the right **(ii)** the median and the mode will be further to the right

Revision Exercises 37, Pages 386–387

1. (i) 5 **(ii)** nominal categorical **(v)** 3·2° **2. (i)** no **(ii)** skewed left **(iii)** modal class is '70 – 80', median is about 75, mean is 68·5 **(iv)** 22 **(v)** no **4. (i)** B **(ii)** B **(iii)** median for A is 27, median for B is 24 **(iv)** mean for A is 27·2, mean for B is 28·2 **(v)** IQR for A is 10·5, IQR for B is 17·5, B is more widely spread than A **(vi)** for A, σ = 7·7, for B, σ = 10·6 **5. (i)** 3·5 **(ii)** A **(iii)** 3·5 **(iv)** for A, σ = 1·95, for B, σ = 1·76 **(v)** B, unimodal **6. (i)** 2σ **(ii)** 3σ

Chapter 38

Exercises 38.1, Page 390

1. (i) height: start at 1·50 m, weight: start from 50 kg **3. (i)** *X* is IC
4. (i) *X* is number of hours TV

Exercises 38.2, Pages 393–395

1. (i) negative **(ii)** moderate **(iii)** –0·53 **2. (i)** positive **(ii)** moderate **(iii)** 0·34 **(iv)** D **(v)** B and F **3. (ii)** posit
(iii) moderate **(iv)** 0·66 **(v)** F **(vi)** no change **4. (ii)** r
(iii) strong **(iv)** –0·76 **(v)** K **(vi)** no change
5. (i) *A*: 0, *B*: 0·32, *C*: – 0·39 **(ii)** A **(iii)** for B and C th
is moderate **6. (i)** *A*: – 0·58, *B*: 0·54, *C*: 0 **(ii)** C
(iii) for A and B the correlation is moderate **7.** r
weak to moderate **8.** positive, strong **9.** neg
10. positive, moderate **11.** no correlation
moderate **13.** positive, strong **14.** negati
15. positive, weak **16.** negative, moderat
18. (i) –0·85 **(ii)** 0·23

Exercises 38.3, Pages 397–39

1. (i) 0·33 **(ii)** moderate **2. (i)** 0·7
(iv) no change **3. (i)** 0·21 **(ii)**
(iv) –0·47 **(v)** no **4. (ii)** abou
7. no **8.** no **9.** no

Exercises 38.4, Pag

1. (ii) 0·79, strong pos
(vi) $y = 9600x - 1000$
education, expect
2. (ii) strong pos
(vi) $y = 27 + \frac{1}{4}$
distance in
3. (ii) strong

(v) e.g. $y = 235 - 1{\cdot}8x$ **(vi)** for every extra km run on average, the finishing time is reduced by 1·8 min **(vii)** $y = 235{\cdot}74 - 1{\cdot}8065x$ **(viii)** 127·35 min **4. (i)** moderate to strong positive **(iv)** about 37 s **(vii)** about 48 s **5. (ii)** negative **(iii)** strong **(iv)** 21·0625, 19·375 **(vi)** $y = 33{\cdot}892 - 0{\cdot}6893x$, 15·97 **(vii)** for each unit increase in X, Y decreases by 0·6893 units **6. (i)** positive **(ii)** strong, $r = 0{\cdot}79$ **(iii)** 5, 10·14286 **(v)** $y = 2{\cdot}7565 + 1{\cdot}4773x$, 19 **(vi)** for each unit increase in X, Y increases by 1·4773 units

Revision Exercises 38, Pages 405–409

1. interpolation	estimating a value of Y within the bounds of the X values
line of best fit	the line that most accurately represents the data
positive correlation	both sets of data increase together
outlier	a data pair far removed from the bulk of the data pairs
weak correlation	little connection between the two sets of data
correlation	the connection between the two sets of data
correlation coefficient	a number which expresses the correlation between X and Y
extrapolation	estimating a value of Y outside the bounds of the X values
negative correlation	as one set of data increases, the other decreases
strong correlation	the data points are reasonably close to the line of best fit

2. (i) food intake **(iii)** positive **(iv)** strong **(v)** 0·76 **(vii)** 0·8295 **(viii)** $y = -1{\cdot}1679 + 0{\cdot}8295x$, 0·82 kg **(ix)** 0·47 **(x)** yes **3. (ii)** −0·74 **(iii)** −0·7619, for every 1° rise in temperature, the number of lawnmowers sold decreases by 0·7619 **(iv)** (13,8) **(v)** −0·96 **(vi)** −1·2021, for every 1° rise in temperature, the number of lawnmowers sold decreases by 1·2021 **4. (iii)** 0·1852, for every 1 cm^3 in dose, the average weight gain increases by 0·1852 kg **(iv)** 0·5472, for every 1 cm^3 in dose, the maximum weight gain increases by 0·5472 kg **(vi)** 0·73 **(vii)** 0·90 **(viii)** r_2 **5. (i)** ambient temperature **(iii)** negative **(iv)** −0·77 **(vi)** 275 **(viii)** 247 MW **6. (i)** 0·85 **(iii)** $y = 0{\cdot}1262 + 0{\cdot}8426x$, for each 1 unit increase in x, y increases by 0.8426 units **(iv)** 0.33, interpolation **(v)** 3·5, extrapolation **7. (i)** −0·75 **(iii)** 6·4, interpolation **(iv)** $y = 9{\cdot}1549 - 0{\cdot}7935x$, for each 1 unit rise in X, Y decreases by 0·7935 units **(v)** 1·22, extrapolation **8. (a)** positive **(b)** moderate to strong **(c)** X is no of hours of sunshine **(d)** other factors: rainfall, storms **9. (a)** positive **(b)** moderate **(c)** X is average no of hours sunshine **(d)** other factors: fans allegiance, weather **10. (a)** positive **(b)** moderate to strong **(c)** X is points obtained **(d)** other factors: personality, entrepreneurship **11. (a)** negative **(b)** moderate to strong **(c)** X is the no of hours spent learning lines **(d)** other factors: ability to learn lines, personal circumstances **12. (a)** negative **(b)** strong **(c)** X is the number of years in education **(d)** other factors: character of the individual **13. (a)** negative **(b)** moderate **(c)** X should be the no of negative reviews **(d)** other factors: genre, word of mouth **14.** not true **15.** true **16.** true **17.** not true **18.** not true **19.** true **20. (i)** 0·720577 **(ii)** 0·720577 **(iii)** the same

Chapter 39

Exercises 39.1, Pages 411–412

1. (i) 0·05 **(ii)** 1·9 **2. (iii)** skewed right **3. (i)** 0·22 **(ii)** 0·78 **(iii)** 0·56 **4. (i)** 0·13 **(ii)** 0·87

Exercises 39.2, Page 416

1. (i) 68% **(ii)** 408 **2. (i)** 81·5% **(ii)** 285 **3.** 0·815 **4.** 0·815 **5.** 0·815 **6.** no **7.** no

Exercises 39.3, Page 419

1. (i) 0·8413 **(ii)** 0·9893 **(iii)** 0·9979 **2. (i)** 0·2451 **(ii)** 0·0901 **(iii)** 0·015 **3. (i)** 0·7967 **(ii)** 0·8749 **(iii)** 0·9940 **4. (i)** 0·2946 **(ii)** 0·1003 **(iii)** 0·0192 **5. (i)** 0·383 **(ii)** 0·8064 **(iii)** 0·9476 **6. (i)** 0·7719 **(ii)** 0·7436 **(iii)** 0·7405 **7. (i)** 0·0427 **(ii)** 0·3441 **(iii)** 0·1116 **8. (i)** 0·7995 **(ii)** 0·0150 **(iii)** 0·9063 **9.** 0·85 **10.** 1·47 **11.** 1·03 **12.** 0·57 **13.** −1·07 **14.** −1·71 **15.** −1·76 **16.** −0·46 **17.** 1·61 **18.** 0·54

Exercises 39.4, Page 423

1. (i) 0·9332 **(ii)** 0·2266 **(iii)** 0·3944 **2. (i)** 0·6915 **(ii)** 0·2659 **(iii)** 0·1974 **3. (i)** 0·0062 **(ii)** 0·0668 **(iii)** 0·8185 **4. (i)** 0·3446 **(ii)** 0·3446 **(iii)** 0·5138 **5. (i)** 0·8664 **(ii)** mean is 72, standard deviation is 8 **(iii)** 0·1587 **6. (i)** 14, 18 **(ii)** 0·5762 **7. (i)** 55, 70 **(ii)** 0·5328 **8.** 0·6247 **9.** 11·5 **10.** 24 **11. (i)** 0·0228 **(ii)** 46 **12. (i)** 0·0548 **(ii)** 92 **(iii)** 294 **13. (i)** 0·0062 **(ii)** 0·0668 **(iii)** 0·7745 **14. (i)** 0·2033 **(ii)** 1584 **(iii)** 1491

Exercises 39.5, Pages 426–427

1. geography **2.** David **3.** Monday **4.** Helen **5. (i)** 27th **(ii)** 96th **6. (i)** 94th **(ii)** 6th **7. (i)** 71st **(ii)** 94th **8. (i)** 8th **(ii)** 73rd **9.** 78% **10. (i)** 80% **(ii)** 69%

Revision Exercises 39, Page 427–428

1. (i) 0·0475 **(ii)** 0·4972 **2. (i)** 0·0436 **(ii)** 0·8099 **(iii)** 56% **3. (i)** yes **(ii)** not normally distributed **4. (i)** 2·3 **(ii)** 0·9371 **5. (i)** 13·68 **(ii)** 0·7888 **6. (iii)** 0·27 **(iv)** 0·2718 **7. (i)** 0·0436 **(ii)** 91st **(iii)** 261 **8. (i)** 0·0548 **(ii)** 0·969 **(iii)** 1032 **9.** 1·2 **10. (i)** 86% **(ii)** 97th **(iii)** 83·16

Chapter 40

Exercises 40.1, Pages 435–436

1. (i) 0·05 **(ii)** $0{\cdot}33 < p < 0{\cdot}43$ **(iii)** yes **(iv)** last minute change of mind, dishonesty **2. (i)** 0·035 **(ii)** $0{\cdot}235 < p < 0{\cdot}305$ **(iii)** no **3. (i)** 2500 **(iii)** no **(iii)** 7500 **4. (i)** 10000 **(ii)** 88·75%

5. $\frac{10000}{x^2}$ **6.** 2·39% **7.** 494 **8.** 90% **9.** $\frac{n}{2}$%

10. (i) $0{\cdot}3464 \le p \le 0{\cdot}4136$ **(ii)** same centre but wider **11. (i)** $0{\cdot}3667 \le p \le 0{\cdot}4893$ **(ii)** same centre but wider **12. (i)** $0{\cdot}0925 \le p \le 0{\cdot}1195$ **(ii)** same centre but shorter

13. (i) $0{\cdot}2832 \le p \le 0{\cdot}4368$ **(ii)** same centre but wider
14. 2017 **15.** 1040

Exercises 40.2, Pages 440–441

1. (i) 400, close to uniform, closer to uniform **(ii)** 5·5, 2·87 **(iii)** very different **(iv)** roughly normal **(v)** much closer to normal **(vi)** 5·5, 0·287, 0·1469 **2. (i)** the larger the sample, the closer it is to uniform **(ii)** 5, 0·4083 **(iii)** 0·1041 **(iv)** 0·0418 **3. (i)** not normal **(ii)** similar to population **(iii)** normal, with $\mu_{\bar{x}} = 6$, $\sigma_{\bar{x}} = 0{\cdot}3125$ **(iv)** 0·0548 **4. (iii)** 2, 1 **(iv)** roughly like the population **(v)** 2, 0·167 **(vi)** 0·0359

Exercises 40.3, Pages 443–444

1. $221{\cdot}19 \le \mu \le 221{\cdot}81$ **2.** $4605 \le \mu \le 4761$ **3.** $26{\cdot}48 \le \mu \le 30{\cdot}32$ **4.** $117{\cdot}67 \le \mu \le 124{\cdot}33$ **5.** $7{\cdot}347 \le \mu \le 7{\cdot}493$ **6.** $54{\cdot}09 \le \mu \le 60{\cdot}71$ **7.** $2{\cdot}4485 \le \mu \le 2{\cdot}4915$ **8.** $170{\cdot}79 \le \mu \le 177{\cdot}21$ **9.** $129{\cdot}45 \le \mu \le 134{\cdot}55$ **10.** $205507 \le \mu \le 214493$

Exercises 40.4, Page 446–447

1. (i) $H_0: p = 0{\cdot}45$, $H_1: p \ne 0{\cdot}45$ **(iii)** no **2. (i)** $H_0: p = 0{\cdot}9$ **(iii)** no **3. (i)** $H_0: p = 0{\cdot}6$ **(iii)** yes **4. (i)** $H_0: p = 0{\cdot}7$ **(ii)** 0·0408 **(iii)** 396 **5. (i)** $H_0: p = 0{\cdot}8$ **(ii)** 2500 **(iii)** 624 **6. (i)** 519, 581 **(ii)** 1111

Exercises 40.5, Page 452–453

1. (i) $H_0: \mu = 50$ **(ii)** $H_1: \mu \ne 50$ **(iii)** –3·098 **(iv)** yes **2. (i)** $H_0: \mu = 3400$ **(ii)** $H_1: \mu \ne 3400$ **(iii)** 2·02 **(iv)** no **3.** no **4.** yes **5. (i)** 1·89 **(ii)** 0·0588 **6. (i)** –1·92 **(ii)** 0·0548 **7. (i)** 2·07 **(ii)** 0·0384 **8. (i)** –1·83 **(ii)** 0·0672 **9. (i)** –2·24 **(ii)** 0·025 **(iii)** yes **(iv)** no **10. (i)** 2·84 **(ii)** 0·0046 **(iii)** yes **(iv)** yes **11. (i)** –2·19 **(ii)** 0·0286 **(iii)** yes **(iv)** no **12.** 338

Revision Exercises 40, Page 453–455

1. (i) 0·0527 **(ii)** $0{\cdot}7195 < p < 0{\cdot}8249$ **(iii)** no **2. (i)** 10000 **(ii)** large costs and efforts **3. (i)** 1111 **(ii)** from 32·88% to 37·12% **4.** 1112 **5.** 625 **6. (i)** no **(ii)** 1112 **7. (i)** $H_0: p = 0{\cdot}8$ **(iii)** no **(iv)** 1112 **8. (i)** $\frac{1}{2}$ **(ii)** $H_0: p = 0{\cdot}5$ **(iv)** 469 **(v)** 531 **9. (i)** $H_0: p = 0{\cdot}77$ **(iii)** yes **(iv)** yes **10. (i)** $H_0: p = 0{\cdot}8$ **(iii)** yes **11. (i)** no **(ii)** similar to population **(iii)** normal, mean of 15 and standard deviation of 0·6 **(iv)** 0·0475 **12. (i)** type of distribution is unknown **(ii)** 0·0256 **13. (i)** not normal **(ii)** 0·0062 **14.** 0·2236 **15. (i)** 0·0707 **(ii)** yes **16. (i)** –2·01 **(ii)** 0·0444 **(iii)** yes **(iv)** no **17. (i)** –1·65 **(ii)** 0·099 **(iii)** no **(iv)** no **18. (i)** 1·95 **(ii)** 0·0512 **(iii)** no **(iv)** no

Notes

Notes